248 W. Fulton

825

W9-CHP-445

PHYSICAL CHEMISTRY

JOHN WILEY & SONS, INC., NEW YORK · LONDON

PHYSICAL CHEMISTRY

FARRINGTON DANIELS

Professor Emeritus of Chemistry
University of Wisconsin

ROBERT A. ALBERTY

Professor of Chemistry
University of Wisconsin

2ND EDITION

COPYRIGHT, 1955 © 1961 BY JOHN WILEY & SONS, INC.

All rights reserved. This book or any part thereof must not be reproduced in any form without the written permission of the publisher.

LIBRARY OF CONGRESS CATALOG CARD NUMBER: 61-6769

Printed in the United States of America

PREFACE

This book is intended for a comprehensive first course in physical chemistry. In this edition we have raised the level of presentation and placed more emphasis on the mathematical approach in keeping with the better preparation which students are now bringing to the study of physical chemistry. In order to include additional new material it has been necessary to eliminate some of the older and more elementary sections in earlier editions.

Since there is a variation in the number of credits in physical chemistry courses at different universities and therefore in the need for more advanced material, more topics have been included in this edition than can be covered in some courses.

In this edition there has been some rearrangement of material in order to give early grounding in fundamental thermodynamics, which forms a foundation for applications throughout the book.

Several new chapters have been written; the titles of three chapters containing mostly new material are Kinetic Theory, Spectroscopy, and Statistical Mechanics. Some more specialized derivations have been given in the Appendix.

Many new problems have been substituted for old ones. Different types are offered at the end of each chapter to meet the needs of students with varying backgrounds and interests. There are three parallel sets to give ample choice. The answers are given for the first set of problems, and then the student is "on his own." In each chapter several typical problems are worked out as *Examples*.

Outlines of Theoretical Chemistry, as it was then entitled, was first written in 1913 by Dr. Frederick H. Getman, who carried it through 1927 in four editions. The next four editions were written by the senior author of this book. In 1955 Dr. Alberty joined Dr. Daniels in the first edition of the present book. The edition of 1961 thus has had the benefit of experience with nearly half a century of classes and has profited greatly from the advice of many colleagues at the University of Wisconsin and from a wealth of helpful suggestions that have come for decades from teachers all over the world. We greatly appreciate these suggestions and welcome further comments and criticisms for improving the book in the future.

Previous editions have been improved by careful criticisms and help from Professors Paul Bender, C. Daniel Cornwell, Paul C. Cross, George W. Murphy, Darrell W. Osborne, T. Fraser Young, and many others. In the preparation of the present edition, we are particularly indebted to Professors L. S. Bartell, Paul Bender, R. B. Bird, C. Daniel Cornwell, Charles F. Curtiss, L. Dahl, J. D. Ferry, J. de Heer, J. O. Hirschfelder, W. Kauzmann, Edward L. King, John L. Margrave, L. M. Peller, R. Scott, E. O. Stejskal, John E. Willard, J. W. Williams, and others. Valuable help in checking calculations and problems has been contributed by Dr. L. E. Erickson, Dr. L. Barnett, Mr. V. Bloomfield, Mr. G. Fleck, Mr. G. Blytas, and Mr. P. Kokoropoulos.

FARRINGTON DANIELS
ROBERT A. ALBERTY

Madison, Wisconsin
January, 1961

CONTENTS

TABLE OF IMPORTANT CONSTANTS

The following approximate values will be used for problems. Most of them are sufficiently important to memorize during the course of the work.

Acceleration of gravity	**980.7**	cm sec^{-2}
Molar volume (0°, 1 atm)	**22.41**	l mole^{-1}
Ice point (0°)	**273.1°**	K
One calorie (defined)	**4.184**	joules
R	**8.314**	joules deg^{-1} mole^{-1}
	1.987	cal deg^{-1} mole^{-1}
	0.08205	l-atm deg^{-1} mole^{-1}
Faraday	**96,500**	coulombs equiv^{-1}
	23,060	cal (volt equiv)$^{-1}$
Avogadro number	**6.02 $\times$ 10^{23}**	mole^{-1}
Planck's constant	**6.62 $\times$ 10^{-27}**	erg sec
Velocity of light	**3 $\times$ 10^{10}**	cm sec^{-1}
Conversion log$_{10}$ to log$_e$	**2.303**	

These and other constants are given with the highest precision now warranted on page 727.

SYMBOLS AND ABBREVIATIONS

A_s absorbancy

A Helmholtz free energy

A angstrom unit

C heat capacity, concentration in equivalents per liter

$\bar{C}$ molar heat capacity

D diffusion coefficient

E internal energy

E_a activation energy

$\boldsymbol{E}$ potential difference

F faraday (96,493 coulombs equiv^{-1})

G Gibbs free energy

$\bar{G}$ molar and partial molal Gibbs free energy

H enthalpy

I ionic strength, moment of inertia, intensity of light, current

K equilibrium constant or quotient

K   Kelvin scale

K_b boiling-point constant

K_f freezing-point constant

M molecular weight

M   molar scale

N number of molecules, number of states

N_0 Avogadro's number

P total pressure, polarization

Q partition function for a molecule

R ideal gas constant

$\boldsymbol{R}$ Rydberg constant

S entropy

$\bar{S}$ molar entropy

T absolute temperature

$\left.\begin{array}{l} T_+ \\ T_- \end{array}\right\}$ transference numbers

V volume, potential energy

$\bar{V}$ molar volume

W number of states in a class of states

X mole fraction

Z number of collisions per unit time per unit volume, partition function for a system

a_s absorbancy index

a activity

c concentration in moles per liter, number of components in phase rule, velocity of light

e electronic charge, electron

ev   electron volts

f frictional coefficient

g acceleration of gravity (980 cm sec^{-2})

h Planck's constant

i current density

k Boltzmann constant (R/N_0), reaction-rate constant

l mean free path

m mass

m molal scale

m molal concentration (moles per 1000 grams of solvent)

n number of moles, number of molecules per cubic centimeter, refractive index

p partial pressure, number of phases in phase rule, momentum

pH measure of hydrogen-ion activity

q quantity of heat absorbed

r internuclear distance

t centigrade temperature, time

v velocity, variance

w work done, weight

z number of collisions per second per molecule, number of electrical charges

α degree of reaction, angle of optical rotation

β beta particle

γ activity coefficient, gamma ray, surface tension

δ small increment, inexact differential

ϵ dielectric constant, quantum

η viscosity

κ specific conductance

λ wavelength, coefficient of thermal conductivity

Λ equivalent conductance

μ dipole moment, chemical potential, micron

ν frequency, number of collisions per square centimeter per second, neutrino

$\tilde{\nu}$ wave number

π osmotic pressure

ρ density

Σ summation

σ symmetry number

ψ wave function

Φ quantum yield

ω angular velocity

A superscript zero, as in S°, on a thermodynamic function means that the substance is in its standard state.

A Δ in front of a thermodynamic function, as in ΔG, means that the change (final minus initial) is referred to.

A bar over a thermodynamic function designates the molal or partial molal quantity.

INTRODUCTION

1

Survey of Physical Chemistry. The purposes of the study of physical chemistry are to understand the laws of chemistry and physics and to predict and control chemical phenomena. Physical chemistry emerged about seventy-five years ago as a branch of chemistry closely related to physics and making considerable use of mathematical techniques. It involves many different approaches, as indicated in the following chart:

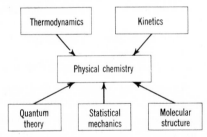

Thermodynamics is one of the most powerful tools of physical chemistry. It provides exact relations between energy and properties of systems without any information about molecules or mechanisms of processes. Thermodynamics applies to systems at equilibrium and is concerned only with initial and final states. It has nothing to do with time. Thermodynamics provides an answer to the question, "How far will this particular reaction go before equilibrium is reached?" Because of the importance of thermodynamics in physical chemistry the first part of the book is largely devoted to this subject.

Kinetics involves the time factor and is concerned with molecules and mechanisms. In many reactions in organic chemistry, inorganic chemistry, biochemistry, and many industrial processes, the products

1

are not in a state of equilibrium, and the yields are controlled more by the relative rates of reaction than by thermodynamics. Chemical kinetics is based on almost all of physical chemistry, and its study might be postponed to the end of the book. However, kinetics is so important that the first discussion of the subject is given near the middle of the book. The theoretical basis of kinetics is discussed in Chapter 23.

The alert physical chemist analyzes his problem and determines whether the limiting factors belong primarily to thermodynamics or to kinetics; then he may use information on molecular structure and mechanisms in making predictions and controlling conditions.

Kinetic theory is based upon certain assumptions about molecules. The results of kinetic theory based upon classical physics have been very useful but come into direct contradiction with certain experimental results, such as the dependence of heat capacity upon temperature. However, classical kinetic theory is very helpful in understanding the results of both thermodynamics and chemical kinetics. It is necessary to utilize quantum theory to obtain a completely satisfactory theory.

Quantum theory, which revolutionized physics in the early part of this century, is required for an understanding of chemistry. The spectra of atoms and molecules are explained by quantum mechanics, and their theoretical treatment yields quantities of importance in various areas of physical chemistry. The nature of chemical bonding is explained by quantum theory.

Molecular structure can be determined from X-ray diffraction, electron diffraction, and molecular spectra. Information on molecular structure is of importance for understanding chemical reactions and for calculating thermodynamic and kinetic behavior. Certain types of chemical behavior can be predicted when the molecular structure is known.

Statistical mechanics has been developed to provide an interpretation of the properties of matter in terms of the properties of molecules, atoms, ions, and electrons. Both thermodynamic properties and kinetic properties of matter may be calculated using statistical mechanics, provided that certain information about molecules is known from spectroscopic or other measurements.

All these areas of physical chemistry are based upon experimental measurements. Experimental physical chemistry is a large, specialized field; and, since it is covered in another book from this laboratory,*

* F. Daniels, J. H. Mathews, J. W. Williams, P. Bender, and R. A. Alberty, *Experimental Physical Chemistry*, McGraw-Hill Book Co., New York, 1956.

the laboratory techniques are discussed in this book only in general terms.

A characteristic of physical chemistry is its frequent use of mathematics. Mathematics has added much to our understanding of nature and provides the most precise way of stating relationships. During the course in physical chemistry the student will become more and more convinced of the usefulness of mathematics. As an aid to reviewing the mathematics that will be used in this book and in order to make some of the more important equations available for ready reference, a section on mathematics has been included in the Appendix, pp. 713–718. Everyone starting the study of this book is urged to review his mathematical background by reference to this summary and to consult the mathematics books he has previously used when he is not clear about a mathematical operation.*

Physical chemistry is in a process of continual change and development. Ideas held at present may fade in importance as progress continues, but the methods will continue to be useful. Thus in studying physical chemistry the methods should be studied as well as the results.

Fundamental Units. As far as possible, measurements are expressed in terms of centimeters, grams, and seconds, and their derived units; that is, the measurements are expressed in the cgs system. The centimeter is defined in terms of a standard meter bar, and the gram in terms of a standard kilogram weight; both bar and weight are very exact standards kept in government laboratories for reference. The unit of time, the second, is defined by means of astronomical observations.

In making calculations it is necessary that the units of the quantities in an equation be consistent or that conversion factors be introduced. Two tables of energy-conversion factors are given in the Appendix, p. 728. In order to avoid errors that result from inadequate attention to units, it is convenient to indicate the units of the quantities in an equation and to check the equation to see that these units cancel in such a way as to give the proper units in the final result.

* An elementary treatment of the mathematics needed for the study of elementary physical chemistry is given in F. Daniels, *Mathematical Preparation for Physical Chemistry*, McGraw-Hill Book Co., New York, 1928. Mathematical techniques are so important in physical chemistry that those who specialize in the subject must take more advanced mathematics. Two more advanced books on the mathematics of physical chemistry are the following: H. Margenau and G. M. Murphy, *The Mathematics of Physics and Chemistry*, D. Van Nostrand Co., Princeton, N. J., 1956, and G. J. Kynch, *Mathematics for the Chemist*, Academic Press, New York, 1955.

A number of problems concerned with notation and units are discussed by Guggenheim and Prue.* They point out that a symbol should denote a physical quantity and not its measure in some particular units. For example, P may denote pressure in atmospheres, dynes per square centimeter, or millimeters of mercury, and so it is necessary always to give the units used.

The values and units of important physical quantities used in physical chemistry are given on p. viii and in more complete form on p. 727. A list of symbols used in this book will be found on p. ix. We have attempted to follow the recommendations of the International Union of Pure and Applied Chemistry, 1959.†

Scientific Research. Chemistry and all other sciences are based on experimentally established facts. When a number of facts have been collected and classified, we may draw inferences as to the probable behavior of systems under conditions that have not been investigated. When a number of phenomena have been observed and studied with exact measurements, we can often develop a *law* that will predict the behavior of similar systems under different conditions. The law is a condensed statement of facts that have been discovered by experiment. It enables us to obtain needed information without continued recourse to experiment.

Natural laws may be discovered either by the correlation of experimentally determined facts, as we have just shown, or by means of a speculation as to the probable cause of the phenomenon in question. Such a speculation regarding the cause of a phenomenon is called a *hypothesis*. After a hypothesis has been subjected to the test of experiment and has been shown to apply to a large number of phenomena, it is termed a *theory*.

Many hypotheses are destined to be discarded when new facts and more precise data are obtained, but they fulfill a very vital function in the development of science. A successful hypothesis is not necessarily a permanent hypothesis, but it is one that stimulates additional research, opens up new fields, or explains and coordinates previously unrelated facts. The scientist needs imagination in creating new hypotheses, but he needs also ingenuity and skill in devising experiments to test them and critical judgment in evaluating the results. Physical chemistry has many unsolved problems and opportunities for pioneering in frontier fields.

* E. A. Guggenheim and J. E. Prue, *Physicochemical Calculations*, Interscience Publishers, New York, 1955, pp. 1–8.

† J. A. Christiansen, *J. Am. Chem. Soc.*, *82*, 5517 (1960).

Science is based on truth, and the scientist cannot allow himself to be influenced by any prejudice. Science has become such a potent factor in our national and international affairs that the scientist now faces a social responsibility extending far beyond the laboratory.

REFERENCES

F. Daniels, "History of Physical Chemistry," *Ind. Eng. Chem.*, *43*, 278–288 (1951).

E. Bright Wilson, *Introduction to Scientific Research*, McGraw-Hill Book Co., New York, 1952.

GASES

2

Matter may be described from both macroscopic and microscopic points of view. When the macroscopic view is employed, matter is described by properties which are suggested by sense perceptions, such as pressure, temperature, volume, and mass. It is found that in order to describe completely a piece of matter so that it can be recognized when it is returned to the same state, only a few of the many macroscopic properties need to be specified. The macroscopic point of view is independent of any assumptions concerning the structure of matter or the mechanisms by which changes occur. Thermodynamics is the study of the relations between heat and other forms of energy, and changes in macroscopic properties, and this subject will make up the first part of our study of physical chemistry.

The microscopic point of view of matter is based upon ideas about structure and the details of the processes occurring on a molecular scale. Kinetic theory (Chapter 11) and statistical mechanics (Chapter 19) are the microscopic approaches to explaining the macroscopic properties of matter. Since they are much more difficult mathematically than thermodynamics, their discussion will come later. However, these methods will provide a deeper insight into the laws of thermodynamics.

The term thermodynamic system is used to designate a definite quantity of matter bounded by a closed surface. The surface may be imaginary, but the important point is that the amount of material in the system is constant. A system such as a mixture of liquid water and ice may exchange work and heat with its surroundings which are outside the closed surface.

Temperature. The concept of temperature is suggested by our sense perceptions, but now we want to extend the idea of temperature to

6

an objective measurement. We can readily determine whether two systems are at the same temperature by bringing them into contact and seeing whether observable changes take place in the properties of either system. If no changes occur, they are at the same temperature. It is found that, if two systems are at the same temperature as a third, they are at the same temperature as each other. This principle is assumed whenever a thermometer is used to compare the temperatures of two systems.

A number of different properties may be used to define temperature scales; these include volume and pressure of a liquid or gas, length of a solid, resistance of a wire, or electromotive force of a thermocouple. Suppose that we define the temperature t to be a linear function of one of these properties of magnitude M:

$$t = a + bM \tag{1}$$

The constants a and b may be determined by *assigning* temperatures at two values of M. In defining the centigrade scale, $t = 0$ is assigned to the equilibrium temperature of ice and air-saturated water under a pressure of 1 atm and $t = 100$ is assigned to the equilibrium temperature of pure water and water vapor under a pressure of 1 atm. Thus

$$0 = a + bM_i \tag{2}$$

$$100 = a + bM_s \tag{3}$$

where M_i and M_s are the values of the measurable property at the ice and steam points, respectively. Solving equations 2 and 3 for a and b and substituting these values into equation 1, we obtain

$$t = \frac{M - M_i}{M_s - M_i} 100 \tag{4}$$

When equation 4 is used with other properties, the temperatures obtained are, in general, different. It will be seen later, however, that the use of gases permits the unambiguous establishment of an absolute temperature scale. In Chapter 5 on thermodynamics this scale will be found identical with one based on the second law of thermodynamics, which is independent of the properties of any particular substance.

Behavior of Gases. In order to describe completely the properties of a given weight of a pure gas under a given set of conditions a number of its properties, such as pressure, volume, density, refractive index, temperature, and thermal conductivity, can be measured. However, it is found as a matter of experience that it is necessary to state only two of these properties in order to fix uniquely the values of all the others. For example, for a given weight of gas it is necessary to specify only the pressure and temperature, or pressure and volume, or volume and temperature, in order to describe completely the condition of the gas and fix all its properties. The relation between pressure, volume, and temperature for a substance is called its *equation of state*. Since the pressure P of a fixed quantity of gas is a function of the volume V and temperature t, the equation of state may be represented by

$$P = f(V,t) \qquad (5)$$

where f is the function to be determined.

Thus the pressure-volume-temperature relations of a gas may be represented by a three-dimensional diagram such as that in *Fig. 2-1*. This diagram represents the relationships for a real gas at low pressures and high temperatures and does not show the condensation and freezing which occur at lower temperatures. (These phenomena are discussed later in connection with Fig. 6-4.) As a simplification we will consider cross sections through this three-dimensional surface which are perpendicular to one of the axes.

The measurements of the volume of a gas at different pressures go back to the classical work of Robert Boyle in 1662. Boyle found that

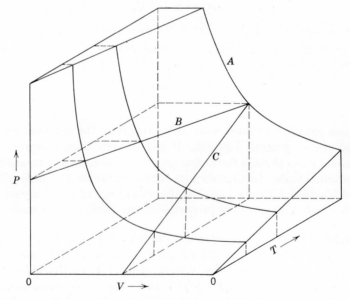

Fig. 2-1. Pressure-volume-absolute temperature relation for an ideal gas.

at constant temperature the volume of a certain weight of gas decreases when the pressure is increased; that is, the volume is inversely proportional to the applied pressure as expressed by the equation

$$V = \frac{k_1}{P} \quad \text{or} \quad PV = k_1 \qquad \text{(temperature constant)} \qquad (6)$$

where k_1 is a constant. This important relation between the pressure and volume is shown by cross sections through Fig. 2-1 at constant temperature (such as line A). This type of curve is a rectangular hyperbola.

In 1802 Gay-Lussac reported his discovery that the volume V of a given quantity of gas kept at a constant pressure increases with increasing temperature. In unpublished earlier work, Charles had found that various gases expand to the same extent when the temperature is increased at constant pressure. These investigators found that, if the pressure is kept constant, the volume V of a given quantity of gas at any temperature is equal to the volume V_0 at some reference temperature plus an increase in volume which is proportional to the difference t between the temperature and the reference temperature. Thus

$$V = V_0 + V_0 \alpha t = V_0(1 + \alpha t) \qquad (7)$$

This is the equation for a straight line obtained when V is plotted against t. The value of α varies slightly from one gas to another, but the same value is approached by all gases at very low pressures. It is convenient then to introduce the concept of the *ideal* gas for which α has the value obtained by extrapolation of α for a real gas to zero pressure. Ideal behavior is approached as the pressure is reduced and the molecules become so far apart that they exert no attractive force on each other. Experimental measurements of volume and temperature may be made at lower and lower pressures, and it is found for all gases that α is $1/273.15$ when the temperature t is taken on the centigrade scale and the data are extrapolated to zero pressure.

Thus, when temperature is expressed in degrees centigrade,

$$V = V_0 \left(1 + \frac{t}{273.15}\right) \qquad (8)$$

where V_0 is the volume at 0°C. According to this equation, V would be zero at $t = -273.15$°C. In reality the volume of a real gas will not become zero at -273.15°C because it will liquefy first, and equation 8 will not be valid.

Equation 8 may be simplified by *defining* a new temperature scale, the absolute temperature scale or Kelvin scale, in which the zero is taken as 273.15° below zero on the centigrade scale. Then

$$T°K = t°C + 273.15 \tag{9}$$

where K indicates the absolute or Kelvin scale and C the centigrade scale. The symbol T is used for Kelvin temperatures, and the symbol t for centigrade temperatures.*

The Gay-Lussac–Charles law can be expressed simply by substituting into equation 8 the value of $t°$ as given by equation 9 to obtain

$$V = \frac{V_0}{273.15} T = k_2 T \qquad \text{(pressure constant)} \tag{10}$$

Thus, an immediate advantage of the absolute scale is that the volume of a given quantity of an ideal gas is directly proportional to the absolute temperature, if the pressure is kept constant. The relationship between V and T is illustrated in Fig. 2-1, in which the line B indicates that at constant pressure the volume is directly proportional to the absolute temperature. Similarly, if the volume is held constant it can be seen from the diagram (for example, line C) that the pressure is directly proportional to the absolute temperature.

When a quantity is a function of two variables, a fundamental equation of differential calculus relates the differential of the function to the differentials of the variables and the two partial derivatives (equation 39 of the Appendix). A partial derivative is the rate of change of the function when one of the variables is changed while the others are held constant. Since for an ideal gas the volume is a function of the pressure and the absolute temperature, $V = f(P,T)$, the total differential for the volume is

$$dV = \left(\frac{\partial V}{\partial P}\right)_T dP + \left(\frac{\partial V}{\partial T}\right)_P dT \tag{11}$$

From equation 6 it is known that

$$\left(\frac{\partial V}{\partial P}\right)_T = -\frac{k_1}{P^2} \tag{12}$$

and from equation 10

$$\left(\frac{\partial V}{\partial T}\right)_P = k_2 \tag{13}$$

---

* If the temperature scale is not specified, it is assumed in this book that the centigrade scale is meant.

Substitution into equation 11 yields

$$dV = \frac{-k_1 \, dP}{P^2} + k_2 \, dT \tag{14}$$

By introducing $k_1/P = V$ and $k_2 = V/T$, equation 14 may be rearranged to give

$$\frac{dV}{V} + \frac{dP}{P} = \frac{dT}{T} \tag{15}$$

Integration yields

$$\ln P + \ln V = \ln T + \ln (\text{constant})$$

$$PV = (\text{constant})T \tag{16}$$

Avogadro's Principle. The constant in equation 16 could be determined for any given quantity of a particular gas, but a universal value of the constant for 1 mole of any ideal gas may be calculated because of Avogadro's law. Avogadro in 1811 suggested that equal volumes of different gases contain the same number of molecules if they are at the same temperature and pressure. However, it was not until 1860 that the importance of this principle for determining molecular weights, as contrasted with atomic weights, was understood. If equal volumes of gas contain the same number of molecules at the same temperature and pressure, the relative weights of the molecules may be obtained by simply weighing equal volumes of the two gases at the same pressure and temperature. Also, if equal volumes of gas contain the same number of molecules at the same temperature and pressure, it might be expected that the constant in equation 16 would be a universal constant, provided that some fixed number of gas molecules is considered. A mole of a substance is the number of grams equal to its molecular weight.

The actual number of molecules in a mole has been determined accurately in many different ways, which are entirely independent of each other, and the agreement is excellent. Avogadro's number, 6.023×10^{23} mole^{-1}, is a fundamental constant of physical chemistry. Perrin determined it from observation of the random motion of small particles; Rutherford, from a determination of the charge of alpha particles from radium; Boltwood and Curie, by direct counting of alpha particles and measurement of the volume of helium resulting from them; Millikan, from the unit charge on an oil droplet and the value of the Faraday constant of electrolysis; and others, from the density and X-ray diffraction of crystals. Although the weight of a single molecule or atom is well known $(1.008/6.023 \times 10^{23} = 1.67 \times 10^{-24}$ gram for one hydrogen atom), most of the calculations of physical chemistry are based on the mole.

In order to establish the chemical * scale of atomic and molecular weights the atomic weight of natural oxygen is arbitrarily taken as 16.0000. Thus a mole of oxygen, O_2, weighs 32.0000 grams, and it is found that the volume of this weight of oxygen at 0°C and 1 atm pressure (760 mm of mercury at 0°C) is 22.414 liters, if correction is made for nonideality. In other words the $P\overline{V}$ product approaches 22.414 liter-atm as the pressure is reduced indefinitely.

The symbol $\overline{V}$ will be used to represent the volume occupied by 1 mole of gas, whereas V is used for the volume of any specified quantity of gas.

The Ideal Gas Constant. The constant in equation 16 is designated by the symbol R when 1 mole of gas is considered:

$$P\overline{V} = RT \tag{17}$$

The value of the gas constant R may be calculated from the data just given for oxygen

$$R = \frac{P\overline{V}}{T} = \frac{(1 \text{ atm})(22.414 \text{ l mole}^{-1})}{(273.16 \text{ deg})}$$

$$= 0.08205 \text{ l-atm deg}^{-1} \text{ mole}^{-1}$$

With this known value of R the volume of 1 mole of any ideal gas at a given T and P may be calculated. It should be noted that the gas constant R has the dimensions of energy per mole divided by temperature. The term $P\overline{V}$ has the units of energy per mole. Since pressure is force per unit area, the product of pressure and volume has the units of force times distance, which is work or energy.

The gas constant can be expressed using various energy units: liter-atmospheres, ergs, joules, or calories. The *cgs* unit of energy is the *erg*, which is the work done when a force of 1 dyne acts through a distance of 1 cm. The *cgs* unit force, the *dyne*, gives a mass of 1 gram an acceler-

---

* It will be necessary later (p. 678) to distinguish between two scales of atomic weights, the chemical scale, used generally in chemistry, in which 16.0000 is assigned to natural oxygen, which is a mixture of isotopes; and the physical scale, in which 16.0000 is assigned to the most abundant isotope of oxygen. A new atomic-weight scale will probably be adopted soon by the International Union for Pure and Applied Chemistry in which the most abundant isotope of carbon is assigned the atomic weight 12.0000. The adoption of the carbon-12 scale will result in decreasing the values of atomic weights based on the present chemical scale by 43 parts in a million.

ation of 1 cm sec^{-2}. Since an erg is such a small quantity of energy, a larger unit, the *joule*, which is equal to 10^7 ergs, is more convenient.

The pressure in dynes per square centimeter corresponding to 1 atm pressure is obtained by multiplying the weight of mercury above 1 cm^2 by the acceleration * of gravity, 980.7 cm sec^{-2}. One atmosphere pressure will support 76 cm of mercury at 0°C. The density of mercury is 13.595 g cm^{-3}.

$$P = (76.00 \text{ cm})(13.595 \text{ g cm}^{-3})(980.7 \text{ cm sec}^{-2})$$
$$= 1.013 \times 10^6 \text{ dynes cm}^{-2} \tag{18}$$

The gas constant is obtained in ergs if the pressure is expressed in dynes per square centimeter and the volume in cubic centimeters.

$$R = \frac{P\overline{V}}{T} = \frac{(1.013 \times 10^6 \text{ dynes cm}^{-2})(22{,}414 \text{ cm}^3 \text{ mole}^{-1})}{(273.16 \text{ deg})}$$
$$= 8.314 \times 10^7 \text{ ergs deg}^{-1} \text{ mole}^{-1}$$
$$= 8.314 \text{ joules deg}^{-1} \text{ mole}^{-1} \tag{19}$$

The unit of energy used most frequently in physical chemistry is the *calorie*. The *kilocalorie* (kcal) is equal to 1000 calories. The 15° calorie † is the heat required to raise the temperature of a gram of water from 14.5 to 15.5°. The *calorie* as used by American physical chemists is arbitrarily defined as being equal to 4.1840 absolute joules. This value will be used throughout the book. Thus

$$R = \frac{(8.314 \text{ joules deg}^{-1} \text{ mole}^{-1})}{(4.184 \text{ joules cal}^{-1})} = 1.987 \text{ cal deg}^{-1} \text{ mole}^{-1} \tag{20}$$

In calculations on the P-V-T relations of gases it is usually convenient to express R in liter-atmospheres; in electrochemical problems involving volts and coulombs R is best expressed in joules; and in thermochemical problems R is usually expressed in calories. It is necessary to be thoroughly familiar with the different values of R and to know which units to use in a specified problem and how to convert from one set of units to another.

If n moles of ideal gas are considered rather than one, the pressure will be increased by the factor n at constant volume and temperature, or the volume will be increased by the factor n at constant pressure and temperature. Thus

$$PV = nRT \tag{21}$$

---

* The acceleration of gravity varies somewhat with position on the earth's surface, but the value 980.7 cm sec^{-2} is used for calculations in this book.

† The 15° calorie is equal to 4.1855 absolute joules.

Dalton's Law. According to Dalton's law, the total pressure of a mixture of gases is equal to the sum of the *partial pressures* of the gases in the mixture. The partial pressure of a gas is the pressure it would exert if it alone filled the volume of the container at the specified temperature. Dalton's law is exact only for ideal gases, and it may be derived from the ideal gas law as follows. The total number of moles of gas in a mixture is equal to the sum of the numbers of moles of the different gases $A, B, C, \cdots$.

$$n_{total} = n_A + n_B + n_C + \cdots \qquad (22)$$

Multiplying this equation through by RT/V, where V is the volume of the container, we obtain

$$n_{total}\frac{RT}{V} = n_A\frac{RT}{V} + n_B\frac{RT}{V} + n_C\frac{RT}{V} + \cdots \qquad (23)$$

Thus

$$P_{total} = p_A + p_B + p_C + \cdots \qquad (24)$$

where lower case p's are used to represent partial pressures, p_A, p_B, $p_C \cdots$. Equation 24 is an excellent approximation for real gases at low pressures, provided that they do not react, but marked departures are found at high pressures, just as pure gases show deviations from the ideal gas law at high pressures.

Dalton's law of partial pressures may be visualized with a vessel containing an equal number of moles of CO_2 and O_2 at a total pressure of 1 atm. If the CO_2 is absorbed by NaOH, only O_2 remains and the pressure falls to $\frac{1}{2}$ atm. If in another experiment the O_2 is removed by phosphorus, only the CO_2 remains and the total pressure falls to $\frac{1}{2}$ atm.

A corollary of Dalton's law is that the fraction of the pressure exerted by a gas is equal to the fraction of the total number of moles provided by that gas. Dividing

$$p_A = n_A\frac{RT}{V} \qquad (25)$$

by

$$P_{total} = n_{total}\frac{RT}{V} \qquad (26)$$

we obtain

$$\frac{p_A}{P_{total}} = \frac{n_A}{n_{total}} = X_A \qquad (27)$$

where X_A is the mole fraction of gas A. The mole fraction of a substance in a gas mixture or a solution is equal to the number of moles of that substance divided by the total number of moles of all the substances present. It is apparent that the sum of the mole fractions for all the components present must equal unity.

$$X_A + X_B + X_C + \cdots = 1 \tag{28}$$

or

$$\Sigma X_i = 1 \tag{29}$$

where the subscript i indicates $A, B, C, \cdots$. The mole fraction and other ways of expressing concentrations are given in the Appendix on p. 719.

Gas Density and Molecular Weight. The density of a gas is usually expressed as the weight in grams in 1 liter. Gas densities are useful in obtaining molecular weights. According to Avogadro's principle, it should be possible to determine the molecular weight of a gas by weighing a given volume at a known temperature and pressure and calculating the weight which would be contained in 22.414 liters at 0° and 760 mm pressure. For high accuracy it is necessary to make corrections for the departure of the gas from the behavior of an ideal gas.

If g grams of a pure gas are taken, the number of moles is g/M, where M is the molecular weight, and so equation 21 becomes

$$PV = (g/M)RT \tag{30}$$

In applying this equation one must be careful to use the value of R which is consistent with the units used in expressing P and V.

Example 1. Calculate the volume occupied by 20 grams of carbon dioxide at 740 mm pressure and 30°, assuming that the ideal gas law is obeyed.

$$V = \frac{gRT}{MP} = \frac{(20 \text{ g})(0.08205 \text{ l-atm deg}^{-1} \text{ mole}^{-1})(303.1 \text{ deg})}{(740/760 \text{ atm})(44.01 \text{ g mole}^{-1})}$$

$$= 11.60 \text{ liters}$$

In the *Regnault method* for determining the molecular weight of a gas, a glass bulb is weighed when evacuated and again when filled with the gas. The volume is obtained by weighing the bulb filled with water. A second bulb of the same size is used as a counterpoise to eliminate errors due to the adsorption of moisture on the surface of the bulb. Exact weighing of large bulbs is difficult.

The *Victor Meyer method* is convenient for the approximate determination of molecular weights of substances that can be weighed in the liquid state, thus avoiding the weighing of large vessels of gases. A weighed quantity of liquid in a glass bulblet is evaporated in an air-filled tube heated to a constant temperature. This drives out an equivalent volume of air, which is measured with a gas buret at known pressure and temperature.

Example 2. In a Victor Meyer apparatus the evaporation of 0.110 gram of a pure hydrocarbon, $H(CH_2)_nH$, displaced 27.0 ml of air as measured in a mercury buret at 26.1° and 743 mm. What is the molecular weight of the hydrocarbon and the value of the integer n?

$$M = \frac{gRT}{PV} = \frac{(0.110 \text{ g})(0.08205 \text{ l-atm deg}^{-1} \text{ mole}^{-1})(299.2 \text{ deg})}{(743/760 \text{ atm})(0.0270 \text{ l})}$$

$$= 102 \text{ g mole}^{-1}$$

Since $M = 14n + 2$, n must be 7.

Exact Molecular Weights. When values of molecular weights more exact than those obtainable by the simple gas-law calculation are required, determinations are made at lower and lower pressures, usually by the Regnault method. The deviations from the ideal gas law become smaller at the lower pressures and approach zero at zero pressure, but serious experimental difficulties are involved in weighing a large volume of gas at a low pressure. Precise measurements of gas densities g/V are made at constant temperature and at several low pressures, and the apparent molecular weight M' is calculated by use of equation 30. These values of M' are then plotted against pressure, as shown in *Fig. 2-2*, and extrapolated to zero pressure where the molecules are so far apart that they have no attraction for each other and the gas is ideal.

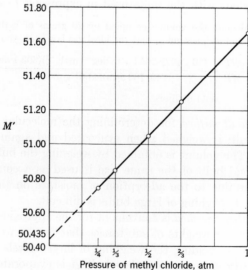

Fig. 2-2. Determination of the molecular weight of methyl chloride.

Example 3. Calculate the molecular weight of methyl chloride and the atomic weight of chlorine from the following data, being given the atomic weights of carbon and hydrogen.

Pressure, atm	1	$\frac{2}{3}$	$\frac{1}{2}$	$\frac{1}{3}$	$\frac{1}{4}$
Apparent molecular weight M'	51.6534	51.2516	51.0445	50.8473	50.7356

The value of M' extrapolated to zero pressure as shown in Fig. 2-2 is the true molecular weight M. It is 50.435 g mole^{-1}. If we subtract from 50.435 the atomic weight of carbon, 12.010, and three times the atomic weight of hydrogen, 3.024, a value of 35.401 is obtained for the atomic weight of chlorine. The accepted value is 35.457.

For permanent gases practically a straight line is produced when M' is plotted against P at pressures below 1 atm. Gases that have strong intermolecular attraction and liquefy at fairly high temperatures show greater deviations, and the linear relation does not apply until lower pressures are reached.

These methods are not used as much now because more accurate atomic and molecular weights may be determined by mass spectrometry (p. 674).

Behavior of Gases at High Pressures. Whereas the behavior of an ideal gas is described by equation 17, the behavior of real gases, especially at high pressures or low temperatures, can be described only with more complicated equations. When simple laws which apply to idealized systems have to be complicated by the addition of further terms in order to represent actual systems, the mathematical terms frequently give clues to the causes of these deviations.

Pressure-volume data for two common gases at 0° are shown in Table I, where the pressure P is given in atmospheres, and the volume $\overline{V}$ in liters mole^{-1}. If the gases were ideal, the product of pressure and molar volume would be equal to 22.414 liter-atm mole^{-1} at all pressures. The table shows that $P\overline{V}$ is far from being constant and that it varies differently with pressure for different gases. Even at 1 atm there is a slight departure from the behavior of an ideal gas.

For an ideal gas the value of the ratio $P\overline{V}/RT$ is 1.000. For real gases it is not unity, and the value of this ratio, known as the *compressibility factor*, provides one of the best ways of recording deviations from ideal behavior. The compressibility factors for H_2, O_2, and CO_2 at 0° are plotted versus pressure in *Fig. 2-3*. The behavior of an ideal gas is represented by the horizontal dashed line. In the limit of zero pressure the compressibility factor of any gas is unity.

A compressibility factor of less than unity indicates that the gas is more compressible than an ideal gas. All gases show a minimum in the plot of compressibility factor versus pressure if the temperature is

Table I. Pressure-Volume Relations of Gases at 0°

	Hydrogen			Carbon Dioxide		
P, atm	$\bar{V}$, liters mole^{-1}	$P\bar{V}$	$\dfrac{P\bar{V}}{RT}$	$\bar{V}$, liters mole^{-1}	$P\bar{V}$	$\dfrac{P\bar{V}}{RT}$
0.1	224.14	22.41	1.000	224.1	22.41	1.0000
1	22.428	22.43	1.001	22.262	22.26	0.9933
50	0.4634	23.17	1.034	0.04675	2.338	0.1043
100	0.2386	23.86	1.065	0.04497	4.497	0.2007
200	0.12712	25.42	1.134	0.04285	8.570	0.3824
300	0.09004	27.01	1.205	0.04152	12.46	0.5560
400	0.07163	28.65	1.278	0.04051	16.20	0.7229
600	0.05318	31.91	1.424	0.03894	23.36	1.042
800	0.04392	35.14	1.568	0.03779	30.23	1.349
1000	0.03837	38.37	1.712	0.03687	36.87	1.645

low enough. Hydrogen and He, which have very low boiling points, exhibit this minimum only at temperatures much below 0°.

The effect of temperature on the change of compressibility factor of N_2 with pressure is shown in *Fig. 2-4*. At 0° and low pressures N_2 is more compressible than an ideal gas, but at high pressures it is less compressible.

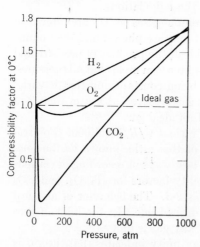

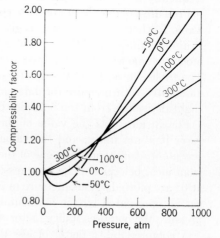

Fig. 2-3. Influence of high pressures on the compressibility factor, $P\bar{V}/RT$, for typical gases.

Fig. 2-4. Influence of temperature on the compressibility factor, $P\bar{V}/RT$, for nitrogen at different temperatures.

Abnormal Densities. Some substances dissociate in the gaseous phase (for example, N_2O_4 is partially dissociated to NO_2), and others associate (for example, acetic acid is partially associated to dimers). These phenomena cause deviations from the ideal gas law and may produce a complicated relationship between compressibility factor and pressure and temperature. For example, iodine has a molecular weight corresponding with I_2 from 200 to 600°, but at 1400° and higher it exists in monatomic form. At intermediate temperatures the apparent molecular weight ranges from that of I_2 to I. From the density of a partially associated or dissociated gas it is possible to calculate the extent of reaction and the equilibrium constant (p. 197).

The Critical Constants. At sufficiently low temperatures any gas may be made to liquefy by applying pressure, thus reducing the volume and bringing the molecules so close together that the attractive force between them becomes large enough to cause condensation. Below a certain temperature (the critical temperature) there is a meniscus between the liquid and vapor phases, but as the critical temperature is closely approached this meniscus disappears. For a pure substance the critical state may be defined by either of the following two criteria: (1) the critical state is the state of temperature and pressure at which the gas and liquid phases become so nearly alike that they can no longer exist as separate phases; or (2) the critical temperature of a pure liquid is the highest temperature at which gas and liquid phases can exist as separate phases. The critical pressure is the pressure at the critical temperature, and the critical volume is the molar volume under these conditions.

Only the first of these definitions is applicable to mixtures.* More complicated behavior is encountered with mixtures since the coexisting liquid and vapor phases are, in general, of different composition.

The appearance of the pressure-volume curves in the vicinity of the critical temperature is shown in *Fig. 2-5*. The pressure is plotted against volume for 1 mole of isopentane at the several temperatures indicated on the graph.

Lines on a graph which refer to a specified constant temperature are called *isotherms*. At 280° the pressure-volume curve is a hyperbolic curve similar to that shown in Fig. 2-1 for an ideal gas. At 200° there is a nick in the curve, showing that the molecules are close enough to exhibit some attraction for each other, thus making the volume of the gas smaller than that of an ideal gas, in which no such attraction exists.

* L. G. Roof, *J. Chem. Educ.*, *34*, 492 (1957).

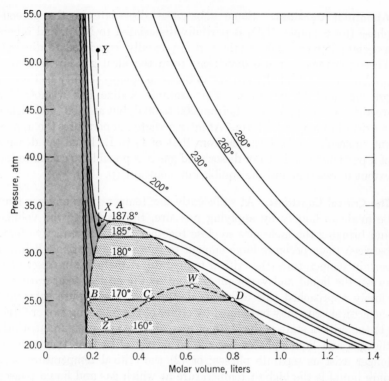

Fig. 2-5. Isotherms for isopentane showing the critical region. The two-phase region is light gray, and the liquid region is darker gray.

At all temperatures below 187.8° the isotherms in Fig. 2-5 exhibit horizontal sections. These horizontal lines indicate that an infinitesimal increase in pressure causes a very large decrease in volume, owing to the fact that the gas is liquefying. At the right of the diagram outside the two-phase region gas alone is present, and the curves follow the ideal gas law approximately. At the left of the diagram outside the two-phase region liquid alone is present; and, since the liquid is much less compressible than the gas, the isotherms are steeper than for the gas. The liquid region is marked with dots packed closely together. Along the horizontal lines gas and liquid exist together. The region in which gas and liquid are coexistent is marked with separated dots. The maximum point A gives the critical temperature, critical pressure, and critical volume. The wavy line $DWCZB$ is discussed on p. 25.

If liquid is converted to gas by a series of steps which take it through the two-phase region, a meniscus will be formed between the gas and liquid phases. However, the liquid may be converted to gas smoothly and continuously without the appearance of a meniscus. If a sample of liquid at point X is heated at constant volume to point Y, there is complete continuity between liquid and gaseous states.

The critical temperature of a pure liquid is usually obtained by observing under pressure the temperature at which the meniscus separating the gas and liquid phases disappears on warming and reappears on cooling. Although the material at the hydrostatic level at which the interface has just disappeared is at the critical temperature and pressure, it is important to realize that the pressure is not the same throughout the sample because of the acceleration of gravity, and the density ρ varies with the height in the sample. Near the critical point $d\rho/dP$ is large (actually it is infinite at the critical point) so that the material in the lower part of the sample is more dense than that in the upper part.

The critical volume, which is the volume of a mole of substance at the critical temperature and pressure, is difficult to determine accurately. It may be obtained indirectly from measurements of the density of the liquid and of the saturated vapor at temperatures just below the critical temperature. As the temperature is increased, the density of the liquid becomes smaller and the density of the saturated vapor in equilibrium with the liquid becomes greater because the vapor pressure becomes greater. The two densities approach each other and become equal at the critical temperature, as do other physical properties of the two phases. It is found that the mean of the densities of the liquid and vapor, when plotted against the corresponding temperature, lies on a straight line. This behavior is shown by the graph in *Fig. 2-6.** This relation, pointed out first by Cailletet and Mathias, is expressed mathematically by equation 31,

$$\frac{\rho_l + \rho_v}{2} = AT + B \tag{31}$$

where ρ_l and ρ_v are the densities of the liquid and saturated vapor, respectively, and A and B are constants. The measurements are carried as close to the critical temperature as is experimentally convenient, and then the curve is extrapolated as shown by the dashed lines in Fig. 2-6. The intersection of the straight line of equation 31 with this extrapolated curve gives the critical density. The molar volume $\overline{V}_c$ at the critical point is equal to the molecular weight divided by the critical density.

* From measurements of F. R. Bichowsky and W. K. Gilkey on CCl_2F_2, *Ind. Eng. Chem.*, *23*, 365 (1931).

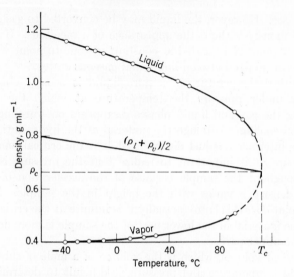

Fig. 2-6. Densities of liquid and saturated vapor of CCl_2F_2 showing the equality of the two at the critical point.

The critical constants, melting points, and boiling points for several types of molecules are given in Table II. The significance of $P_c \overline{V}_c / RT_c$, the compressibility factor at the critical temperature and volume, will be discussed later.

Van der Waals' Equation. Van der Waals in 1879 made an early attempt to introduce additional terms into the ideal gas equation and thus obtain an expression which would describe more exactly the behavior of real gases. An examination of Figs. 2-3 and 2-4 reveals that at low pressures real gases may be more compressible than an ideal gas and that at high pressures they are less compressible. The tendency to be more compressible is due to the fact that the molecules have some attraction for each other. The tendency to be less compressible at higher pressures is due to the fact that the molecules of the gas are essentially incompressible, and the volume of the molecules themselves becomes an appreciable part of the total volume when the pressure is high and the total gas volume small.

Van der Waals put these ideas into a general equation as follows:

$$\left(P + \frac{a}{\overline{V}^2} \right) (\overline{V} - b) = RT \tag{32}$$

where the constant a expresses the attraction which exists between molecules of the gas. The attraction between two small neighboring regions of gas will depend on the number of molecules in the regions.

Table II. Critical Constants, Melting Points, and Boiling Points

Gas	T_{MP}, °K	T_{BP}, °K	T_c, °K	$\dfrac{T_{BP}}{T_c}$	P_c, atm	$\bar{V}_c$, l mole^{-1}	$\dfrac{P_c \bar{V}_c}{RT_c}$
			Simple Nonpolar Molecules [1]				
He	0.9	4.2	5.3	0.79	2.26	0.0578	0.300
H_2	14.0	20.4	33.3	0.68	12.8	0.0650	0.304
Ne	24.5	27.2	44.5	0.61	25.9	0.0417	0.296
A	83.9	87.4	151	0.58	48	0.0752	0.291
Xe	133	164.1	289.81	0.57	57.89	0.1202	0.293
N_2	63.2	77.3	126.1	0.61	33.5	0.0901	0.292
O_2	54.7	90.1	154.4	0.58	49.7	0.0744	0.292
CH_4	89.1	111.7	190.7	0.59	45.8	0.0990	0.290
CO_2	...	194.6	304.2	0.64	72.8	0.0942	0.274
			Hydrocarbons				
Ethane, C_2H_6	89.98	184.6	305.5	0.60	48.2	0.139	0.267
Propane, C_3H_8	185.5	231.1	370.0	0.62	42.1	0.195	0.270
Isobutane, C_4H_{10}	113.6	261.5	407	0.64	37	0.250	0.276
n-Butane, C_4H_{10}	134.9	272.7	426	0.64	36	0.250	0.257
n-Hexane, C_6H_{14}	178.8	342.1	507.9	0.67	29.6	0.367	0.260
n-Octane, C_8H_{18}	216.6	397.7	570	0.70	24.7	0.490	0.259
Benzene, C_6H_6	278.6	352.7	561.6	0.63	47.9	0.256	0.265
Cyclohexane, C_6H_{12}	279.7	353.9	554	0.64	40.57	0.312	0.280
Ethylene, C_2H_4	103.7	169.3	282.8	0.60	50.5	0.126	0.274
Acetylene, C_2H_2	191.3	189.5	308.6	0.61	61.6	0.113	0.275
			Polar Molecules [1]				
H_2O	273.1	373.1	647.3	0.58	217.7	0.0566	0.232
NH_3	195.4	239.7	405.5	0.59	112.2	0.0720	0.243
CH_3OH	175.4	337.9	513.2	0.66	78.67	0.118	0.220
CH_3Cl	175.5	249.7	416.3	0.60	65.8	0.148	0.285
C_2H_5Cl	134.2	285.9	460.4	0.62	52	0.196	0.269

[1] Polar and nonpolar molecules are defined on p. 501. Although both types of molecules are electrically neutral, in the polar molecules there is a separation of positive and negative charge in different parts of the molecule and a resulting attraction between the molecules.

The larger the volume holding 1 mole of gas, the fewer are the molecules in a given region and the smaller the attraction. The attraction of one small region then varies inversely as the molar volume $\overline{V}$, and so does the attraction of the second region. The total intermolecular attraction between the two regions decreases as the product of the two, and the total effect per mole is $a/\overline{V}^2$. Since this attraction $a/\overline{V}^2$ augments the pressure in tending to make the volume smaller, it is added to the measured pressure P.

The term b represents the decrease in the volume in which a molecule can move due to the presence of other molecules. The volume b appears to have a value about 4 times the volume occupied by the molecules themselves if they are considered to be spheres.

When the molar volume $\overline{V}$ is large, both b and $a/\overline{V}^2$ become negligible; and van der Waals' equation reduces to the ideal gas law, $P\overline{V} = RT$. In general, all gases tend to become ideal at low pressures and approach the behavior given by the simple gas law, and all equations of state approach the ideal gas law.

Van der Waals' constants for a few gases are listed in Table III. They can be calculated from experimental measurements of P, $\overline{V}$, and T or from the three critical constants, as shown later on p. 26.

Table III. Van der Waals' Constants

Gas	a, liter²-atm mole⁻²	b, liter mole⁻¹	Gas	a, liter²-atm mole⁻²	b, liter mole⁻¹
H_2	0.2444	0.02661	CH_4	2.253	0.04278
He	0.03412	0.02370	C_2H_6	5.489	0.06380
N_2	1.390	0.03913	C_3H_8	8.664	0.08445
O_2	1.360	0.03183	$C_4H_{10}(n)$	14.47	0.1226
Cl_2	6.493	0.05622	$C_4H_{10}(iso)$	12.87	0.1142
NO	1.340	0.02789	$C_5H_{12}(n)$	19.01	0.1460
NO_2	5.284	0.04424	CO	1.485	0.03985
H_2O	5.464	0.03049	CO_2	3.592	0.04267

Example 4. Calculate the pressure exerted by 1 mole of carbon dioxide in $\frac{1}{2}$ liter at 25°, using (a) the ideal gas law and (b) van der Waals' equation.

$$(a) \quad P = \frac{RT}{\overline{V}} = \frac{(0.08205 \text{ l-atm deg}^{-1} \text{ mole}^{-1})(298 \text{ deg})}{(0.500 \text{ l mole}^{-1})} = 48.9 \text{ atm}$$

$$(b) \quad P = \frac{RT}{\overline{V} - b} - \frac{a}{\overline{V}^2} = \frac{(0.08205)(298)}{(0.5000 - 0.04267)} - \frac{3.592}{(0.5)^2}$$

$$= 53.5 - 14.3 = 39.2 \text{ atm}$$

Exercise I. Equation 32 applies to 1 mole of gas. Show that van der Waals' general equation for n moles of gas is

$$\left(P + \frac{n^2a}{V^2}\right)(V - nb) = nRT$$

where V is the volume of n moles of gas.

The attractive force between molecules which gives rise to the term $a/\overline{V}^2$ in van der Waals' equation is also responsible for the condensation of gases to liquids.

Multiplying out the terms in van der Waals' equation 32 and rearranging in descending powers of $\overline{V}$, we have

$$\overline{V}^3 - \overline{V}^2\left(b + \frac{RT}{P}\right) + \overline{V}\frac{a}{P} - \frac{ab}{P} = 0 \qquad (33)$$

At temperatures below the critical temperature this cubic equation has three real solutions, each value of P giving three values of $\overline{V}$. This equation is shown graphically by the dashed line $DWCZB$ on the 170.0° isothermal in Fig. 2-5, where the three values of $\overline{V}$ are the intersections B, C, and D on the horizontal line corresponding to a fixed value of the pressure. This dashed calculated line then appears to give a continuous transition from the gaseous phase to the liquid phase, but in reality the transition is abrupt and discontinuous, both liquid and vapor existing along the straight horizontal lines. The theoretical dashed line $DWCZB$ does not correspond to normal physical conditions; for example, the slope of the curve at C is positive, a fact which would lead to the unnatural condition that an increase in pressure produces an increase in volume. However, it is possible to have pressures of gas in an unstable condition represented by the beginning of the dashed line DW, before the supercooled vapor has a chance to liquefy and bring the pressure down to that of the horizontal line. At the critical temperature (187.8° for isopentane) and pressure there is only one real root, the critical volume $\overline{V}_c$.

The values of van der Waals' constants may be calculated from the critical constants for a gas. As may be seen in Fig. 2-5, there is an inflection point in the $P\overline{V}$ curve at the critical point so that $(\partial P/\partial\overline{V})_{T_c} = 0$ and $(\partial^2 P/\partial\overline{V}^2)_{T_c} = 0$. At the critical temperature van der Waals' equation may be written

$$P = \frac{RT_c}{\overline{V} - b} - \frac{a}{\overline{V}^2} \qquad (34)$$

Differentiating with respect to molar volume,

$$\left(\frac{\partial P}{\partial \overline{V}}\right)_{T_c} = \frac{-RT_c}{(\overline{V} - b)^2} + \frac{2a}{\overline{V}^3} \tag{35}$$

$$\left(\frac{\partial^2 P}{\partial \overline{V}^2}\right)_{T_c} = \frac{2RT_c}{(\overline{V} - b)^3} - \frac{6a}{\overline{V}^4} \tag{36}$$

At the critical point these derivatives are both equal to zero, and $\overline{V}$ is replaced by $\overline{V}_c$ and P by P_c.

Equations 34, 35, and 36 may be solved together to obtain

$$a = 3P_c\overline{V}_c^2 \qquad b = \frac{\overline{V}_c}{3} \qquad R = \frac{8P_c\overline{V}_c}{3T_c}$$

The critical constants are expressed in terms of the van der Waals' constants by

$$\overline{V}_c = 3b \qquad P_c = \frac{a}{27b^2} \qquad T_c = \frac{8a}{27bR}$$

Other Equations of State. An equation, like the ideal gas law or van der Waals' equation, which gives the relation between pressure, volume, and temperature for a substance is called an equation of state. Various equations have been designed for particular applications, and for accurate work over a wide range of conditions a large number of constants are required. For example, the Beattie-Bridgeman equation * of state for gases uses five constants in addition to R.

An especially useful equation of state is the virial equation

$$\frac{P\overline{V}}{RT} = 1 + \frac{B(T)}{\overline{V}} + \frac{C(T)}{\overline{V}^2} + \cdots \tag{37}$$

where the coefficients $B(T)$, $C(T)$, $\cdots$ which are functions of the absolute temperature T are called the second, third, $\cdots$ virial coefficients. The range of application of the virial equation is limited by the convergence of the series, so that it is useful in the study of gases at low and moderate densities. An advantage of the virial equation is that the coefficients may be expressed in terms of intermolecular attractions by means of statistical mechanics. Thus it is possible to make a quantitative interpretation of the deviations from the ideal gas law in terms of the forces between molecules.

* J. A. Beattie and O. C. Bridgeman, *J. Am. Chem. Soc.*, *49*, 1665 (1927); *50*, 3133 (1928).

The Principle of Corresponding States.* † It has been found that, if different substances are compared at equal fractions of their critical temperatures and pressures, their properties are quite similar. For example, it may be seen from the data of Table II that the standard boiling point of a substance is approximately two-thirds of its critical temperature.

The critical constants may be used to define a set of reduced variables P_r, $\overline{V}_r$, and T_r.

$$P_r = P/P_c \qquad \overline{V}_r = \overline{V}/\overline{V}_c \qquad T_r = T/T_c$$

The properties of a gas may be stated in terms of these reduced variables rather than P, $\overline{V}$, and T. When measured at their critical temperatures, all substances would tend to behave nearly alike, and according to the principle of corresponding states they would obey the same equation of state if P_r, $\overline{V}_r$, and T_r were used rather than P, $\overline{V}$, and T. This principle is not exact but is a very good approximation and forms the basis of the Hougen, Watson, and Ragatz † generalized compressibility charts. Such a chart is shown in *Fig. 2-7*, in which the compressibility factor is plotted against the reduced pressure P/P_c for several different reduced temperatures T/T_c. Such charts are especially useful at high pressures when direct experimental data are not available.

Example 5. With the Hougen, Watson, and Ragatz chart, estimate the volume occupied by a mole of oxygen at $-88°$ and 44.7 atm. The critical temperature and pressure are found in Table II.

$$\frac{T}{T_c} = \frac{273.1 - 88.0}{154.4} = 1.20 \qquad \frac{P}{P_c} = \frac{44.7}{49.7} = 0.90$$

From the chart, $P\overline{V}/RT = 0.80$,

$$\overline{V} = \frac{0.80RT}{P} = \frac{(0.80)(0.08205)(185.1)}{44.7} = 0.272 \text{ liter mole}^{-1}$$

According to the principle of corresponding states, the compressibility factor at the critical point should be the same for all gases. The compressibility factors at the critical point are given for a number of substances in Table II. It may be seen that for simple nonpolar molecules (p. 501) this ratio has a value near 0.29. The fact that the average value for hydrocarbons is somewhat lower, approximately

* J. O. Hirschfelder, C. F. Curtiss, and R. B. Bird, *The Molecular Theory of Gases and Liquids*, John Wiley & Sons, New York, 1954.

† O. A. Hougen, K. M. Watson, and R. A. Ragatz, *Chemical Process Principles*, Part II, John Wiley & Sons, New York, 1959, Chapter XII.

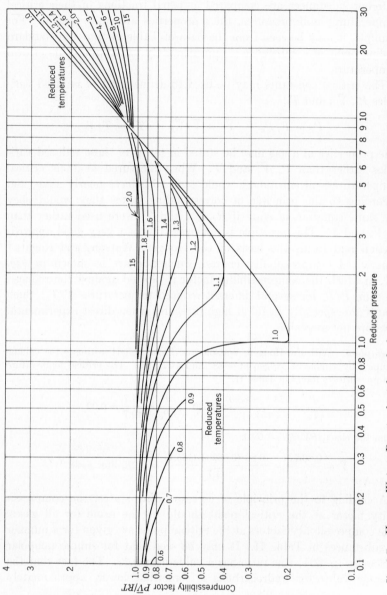

Fig. 2-7. Hougen–Watson–Ragatz chart for calculating pressure, volume, and temperature relations at high pressure.

0.27, indicates that they would follow a plot such as Fig. 2-7, which differs from that for the simpler molecules. As shown by the last group of substances, polar molecules (p. 501) give a still greater deviation. The compressibility factor at the critical point for van der Waals' gas would be $\frac{3}{8} = 0.375$.

REFERENCES

J. O. Hirschfelder, C. F. Curtiss, and R. B. Bird, *The Molecular Theory of Gases and Liquids*, John Wiley & Sons, New York, 1954.

O. A. Hougen, K. M. Watson, and R. A. Ragatz, *Chemical Process Principles*, Part I, John Wiley & Sons, New York, 1954.

M. W. Zemansky, *Heat and Thermodynamics*, McGraw-Hill Book Co., New York, 1957.

PROBLEMS

1. How much does a liter of octane gas, C_8H_{18}, weigh at 150° and 1 atm pressure?
Ans. 3.29 g.

2. Calculate the average molecular weight of air saturated with water vapor at 25° at a total pressure of 1 atm. The vapor pressure of water at this temperature is 23.7 mm. Dry air may be taken to be 80 per cent nitrogen and 20 per cent oxygen by volume. *Ans.* 28.4.

3. Estimate the number of tons of carbon dioxide over a square mile of the earth's surface if the atmospheric pressure is 760 mm, and the air contains 0.046 per cent of CO_2 by weight. *Ans.* 13.6×10^3 tons.

4. Flasks A and B are filled with oxygen and nitrogen, respectively, at 25° and connected by a stopcock.

		Volume, ml	Pressure, atm
A	O_2	500	1
B	N_2	1500	$\frac{1}{2}$

Calculate (a) the total pressure, (b) the partial pressure of each gas after the stopcock is opened and the gases are mixed at constant temperature, assuming ideality, and (c) the mole fraction of O_2 in the final mixture.
Ans. (a) 0.625 atm. (b) $p_{N_2} = 0.375$, $p_{O_2} = 0.250$ atm. (c) 0.400.

5. In a Victor Meyer experiment, 0.2350 gram of a liquid is vaporized, and the volume of displaced air measured over water in a gas buret is 40.2 ml at 23.0° and 730 mm. Since the air in the buret has become saturated with water, it is necessary to subtract the vapor pressure of the water, which is 21.0 mm, from the total pressure. What is the molecular weight of the vapor? *Ans.* 153 g mole^{-1}.

6. The weight of a certain evacuated vessel is found to increase 0.2500, 0.5535, and 0.5268 gram when oxygen, chlorine, and a compound of oxygen and chlorine, respectively, are separately admitted into the vessel under the same conditions of temperature and pressure. Given that oxygen is diatomic and has a molecular weight of 32.000, calculate from these data alone the molecular weights of chlorine and the oxide of chlorine. What can you say from these data regarding the number of atoms in the chlorine molecule and the chemical formula of the oxide of chlorine? *Ans.* 70.87, 67.45, Cl_2, ClO_2.

7. The density of ammonia in grams per liter was determined at various pressures by weighing the gas in large glass bulbs. The values of the density in grams per liter at $0°$ were as follows: 0.77169 at 1 atm, 0.51515 at $\frac{2}{3}$ atm, 0.38293 at $\frac{1}{2}$ atm, 0.25461 at $\frac{1}{3}$ atm. (a) What is the molecular weight of ammonia? (b) If the atomic weight of hydrogen is taken as 1.008, what is the atomic weight of nitrogen?

Ans. (a) 17.030. (b) 14.006.

8. The critical temperature of carbon tetrachloride is $283.1°$. The densities in grams per milliliter of the liquid ρ_l and vapor ρ_v at different temperatures are as follows:

t	$100°$	$150°$	$200°$	$250°$	$270°$	$280°$
ρ_l	1.4343	1.3215	1.1888	0.9980	0.8666	0.7634
ρ_v	0.0103	0.0304	0.0742	0.1754	0.2710	0.3597

What is the critical molar volume of CCl_4? *Ans.* 276 cm^3 $mole^{-1}$.

9. Using van der Waals' equation, calculate the pressure exerted by 1 mole of carbon dioxide at $0°$ in a volume of (a) 1.00 liter, (b) 0.05 liter. (c) Repeat the calculations at $100°$ and 0.05 liter. *Ans.* (a) 19.82, (b) 1621, (c) 2739 atm.

10. Calculate the volume of 1 mole of methane at $0°$ and 50 atm using (a) the ideal gas law and (b) van der Waals' equation. In the calculation in part (b) the solution of a cubic equation may be avoided by use of a successive approximation method. The van der Waals' equation is written as follows:

$$\bar{V} = \frac{RT}{P + (a/\bar{V}^2)} + b$$

The value of $\bar{V}$ obtained from the ideal gas law is substituted in the right-hand side of this equation, and an approximate value of $\bar{V}$ is calculated. This value is then substituted into the right-hand side of the equation to obtain a still more accurate value of $\bar{V}$. This process is continued until the calculated value of $\bar{V}$ is essentially the same as that substituted in the right-hand side of the equation.

Ans. (a) 0.448, (b) 0.391 liter.

11. Calculate the volume occupied by a kilogram of carbon dioxide at $100°$ and 50 atm using (a) the ideal gas equation, and (b) the Hougen-Watson-Ragatz chart.

Ans. (a) 13.9, (b) 12 2 liters.

12. It is stated that the density of air is about 0.0012 g ml^{-1} at room temperature. Assuming that air behaves as an ideal gas, calculate the weight of 1 ml of air at $25°$ and 1 atm if the relative humidity of the air is 70 per cent. The vapor pressure of water at $25°$ is 23.7 mm. The composition of dry air is 80 per cent nitrogen and 20 per cent oxygen by volume.

13. (a) How many grams of air are there in the atmosphere surrounding the earth, if it is assumed that the earth is a sphere with a diameter of 12 million meters and that the atmospheric pressure is 760 mm everywhere on the surface? (b) How many moles of air are there in the total atmosphere, if it is assumed that

the average molecular weight of air is 28.8? (c) How many molecules of oxygen are there in the earth's atmosphere, if one-fifth of the air by volume is oxygen?

14. A glass bulb fitted with a stopcock was evacuated and found to weigh 46.8542 grams without correcting for the buoyancy of the air. When the stopcock was opened and dry air was allowed to fill the bulb, the weight increased to 47.0465 grams. The barometric pressure was 745 mm, and the temperature was 27°. (a) Calculate the total volume of the bulb from the known average molecular weight of air, 28.8. (b) Calculate the weight if the bulb were filled with dry hydrogen at this temperature and pressure.

15. A mixture of 0.1 gram of hydrogen and 0.2 gram of nitrogen is to be stored at 760 mm pressure and 26°. (a) What must the volume of the container be? (b) What is the mole fraction of hydrogen in the mixture? (c) What is the partial pressure of H_2?

16. A certain hydrocarbon is found to have a vapor density of 2.550 g liter^{-1} at 100° and 760 mm. Chemical analysis shows that the substance contains 1 atom of carbon to 1 atom of hydrogen. What is its molecular formula?

17. A 200-ml glass bulb weighs 27.579 grams when filled with a certain gas at 25° and 743 mm pressure. After the pressure has been reduced to 150 mm by partial evacuation, the weight is 27.401 grams. What is the molecular weight of the gas?

18. The ratio of the density of ethyl chloride to the pressure in atmospheres at three different pressures at 0° is as follows: 2.9002 g l^{-1} atm^{-1} at 760 mm, 2.8919 at 475 mm, 2.8863 at 285 mm. Calculate the molecular weight of ethyl chloride and the atomic weight of chlorine by the method of Fig. 2-2, taking the atomic weights of carbon and hydrogen as known.

19. The densities of liquid and vapor methyl ether in grams per cubic centimeter at various temperatures are as follows:

°C	30	50	70	100	120
ρ_l	0.6455	0.6116	0.5735	0.4950	0.4040
ρ_v	0.0142	0.0241	0.0385	0.0810	0.1465

Calculate the critical density and temperature.

20. From the critical constants of helium given in Table II calculate van der Waals' constants.

21. Correction for gas imperfection by use of Berthelot's equation

$$M = \frac{gRT}{PV}\left[1 + \frac{9}{128}\frac{P}{P_c}\frac{T_c}{T}\left(1 - 6\frac{T_c^2}{T^2}\right)\right]$$

makes possible the calculation of more accurate molecular weights than if the ideal gas law is used. Calculate the atomic weight of nitrogen from the fact that the density of nitric oxide, NO, at 0° and 760 mm is 1.3402 g liter^{-1}. The critical constants of NO are 177.1°K and 64 atm. The accepted atomic weight of nitrogen is 14.008.

22. Calculate the number of grams of hydrogen in a vessel of 500-ml capacity when hydrogen is forced in at 100 atm at 200°, using (a) simple gas laws, (b) van der Waals' equation, (c) the Hougen-Watson-Ragatz chart.

23. If the atmospheric pressure is 740 mm, how many kilograms of oxygen are there over a square meter of land? The per cent by weight of oxygen in air is 22.8.

24. The melting point of ice is 0.000°C or 32.000°F; the boiling point of water at 760 mm pressure is 100.000°C or 212.000°F. (a) Devise an equation for converting °F to °C. (b) At what temperature do the centigrade and Fahrenheit scales give the same reading?

25. Calculate the values of the factors for converting from (a) calories to liter-atmospheres, (b) joules to liter-atmospheres, and (c) ergs to calories.

26. Exactly 1.100 grams of carbon dioxide was introduced into a 1-liter flask which contained some pure oxygen before being subjected to partial evacuation. The flask was warmed to 100° and the pressure found to be 608 mm Hg. Considering oxygen and carbon dioxide to be the only gases present, calculate the weight of oxygen in the flask.

27. Four hundred milliliters of an organic vapor weighed 0.5220 gram at 27° and 750 mm. Chemical analysis gave carbon 37.52 per cent, hydrogen 12.56 per cent, and oxygen 49.90 per cent by weight. What is the formula of the organic substance?

28. Ordinary carbon contains 98.9 per cent of an isotope with a mass of 12.00 and 1.1 per cent of an isotope with a mass of 13.00. By a certain physical-chemical operation (p. 678) the concentration of this isotope is increased from 1.1 to approximately 2.0 per cent. It is planned to determine the exact percentage of this heavier isotope by measuring the density of carbon dioxide with a gas-density balance. If this concentration of 2 per cent must be known to 1 part in 500 for the experiment planned, how accurately in parts per million must the gas density of the CO_2 be measured? To what fraction of a degree must the temperature be known at about 25° and to what fraction of a millimeter must the pressure be known at about 740 mm in order to achieve this accuracy?

29. Baxter and Starkweather found the density of nitrogen to be 0.41667 g liter^{-1} at 253.3 mm of mercury and 0°. The ratio of density to pressure was not detectably different at pressures up to 1 atm. Calculate an accurate atomic weight for nitrogen from these data.

30. Calculate the critical temperature and volume of hydrogen from the following densities (in grams per cubic centimeter) of liquid ρ_l and vapor ρ_v:

°C	−246	−244	−242	−241
ρ_l	0.061	0.057	0.051	0.047
ρ_v	0.0065	0.0095	0.014	0.017

31. (a) Using the Hougen-Watson-Ragatz chart, estimate the volume of a vessel necessary to hold 1000 grams of n-octane, C_8H_{18}, at 354° under a pressure of 50 atm. (b) How is this chart to be interpreted if 1000 grams of octane is placed in this vessel under 50 atm pressure at 183°?

32. Show that van der Waals' equation can be written in terms of the reduced temperature T_r, reduced pressure P_r, and reduced volume $\overline{V}_r$ as

$$\left(P_r + \frac{3}{\overline{V}_r^2} \right) (3\overline{V}_r - 1) = 8T_r$$

if a, b, and R are also expressed in terms of the critical constants. It may be noted that all constants connected with the individual nature of the gas have vanished.

FIRST LAW OF THERMODYNAMICS

3

This chapter provides an introduction to the applications of the concepts of heat, work, energy, and heat capacity in physical chemistry. It is followed by a chapter on the measurement of the heats of chemical reactions. Much of physical chemistry is based upon thermodynamics, which deals with the heat and work accompanying chemical and physical processes.

Forms of Energy. Energy is a measure of the capacity to do work. Only when a force acts over a distance is work done, and the work is defined as the product of the magnitude of the displacement and the component of the force in the direction of the displacement. When a body does work (for example, water flowing through a turbine), there is a decrease in its capacity to do work and therefore in its energy. Energy is measured in the same units as work, *ergs* in the cgs system.* In chemistry calories are used more often to express work and energy.

A body may have energy by virtue of its motion (kinetic energy) or by virtue of its position or interaction of its parts (potential energy). The translational kinetic energy of an object is given by $\frac{1}{2}mv^2$, where v is its velocity and m its mass. The rotational kinetic energy of an object is given by $\frac{1}{2}I\omega^2$, where ω is the angular velocity in radians per second and I is the moment of inertia.

$$I = \Sigma m_i r_i^2 \tag{1}$$

* The MKSA system with meters, kilograms, seconds, and amperes is being considered by the International Union of Pure and Applied Chemistry. It is particularly advantageous for electrochemistry. Its unit of energy is the joule, which is a unit of convenient size. The chemical mole is not changed; 1 mole of oxygen gas is 0.032 kg instead of 32 grams. The constants of physical chemistry remain unchanged.

Here m_i is the mass of a particle of the body, r_i is its perpendicular distance from the axis of rotation, and the summation is extended over all particles of the body.

A body may have potential energy because of its position in the earth's gravitational field, because of elastic deformation, because of electric charge and the existence of an electrical field, or because of other attractive or repulsive forces. The potential energy of a body in a certain position or configuration with respect to its potential energy in another position or configuration is equal to the negative of the work done by the gravitational, elastic, electrostatic, etc., forces during the change in position or configuration. For example, when a weight falls, work is done by the force of gravity and the potential energy of the weight *decreases*. When a kilogram weight falls 10 cm under the force of gravity the change in potential energy is

$$-(1000 \text{ g})(980.7 \text{ cm sec}^{-2})(10 \text{ cm}) = -9.807 \times 10^6 \text{ ergs}$$

The amount of work required to lift the weight 10 cm is 9.807×10^6 ergs. Only *differences* in potential energy at two levels have physical significance.

Kinetic energy may be converted into potential energy and vice versa. When a weight or molecule is projected upward in the earth's gravitational field it loses kinetic energy as it gains potential energy. In this motion kinetic energy is converted into potential energy as work is done against gravity. The oscillation of a particle is said to be simple harmonic if the restoring force is proportional to the displacement from the mean position. The energy of the system is alternately all in the form of potential energy (when the displacement is a maximum) or all in the form of kinetic energy (when the displacement is a zero).

Electrical energy, mechanical energy, and other forms of energy can be converted completely into heat, but heat cannot be completely converted into work in a cyclic process (cf. p. 85). In 1849 Joule showed that a given amount of mechanical work always produces the same amount of heat irrespective of the way in which it is transformed into a temperature rise in a body of water. For example, a given amount of mechanical work produced the same temperature rise whether the water was stirred, or heat was produced by rubbing two iron blocks together under the water. Since the ratios of heat evolved to various types of work done are independent of the experimental arrangement, suitable units may be chosen so that heat and the various types of work can be combined into a single function, called energy. If work is converted completely into heat, 4.1840 joules or 4.1840×10^7 ergs produces 1 calorie of heat.

The total energy of a body is unknown, but the change in energy which occurs in various processes can be determined. For example, when coal is burned the energy released upon changing carbon and oxygen to carbon dioxide can be measured, but the total energy which still resides in the carbon dioxide is unknown.

Work may be expressed as the product of two factors—an intensity factor and a capacity factor. Examples are given in Table I. The differential quantity of work done by a force f operating over a distance dl

Table I.　Intensity and Capacity Factors for Various Types of Work

Type of Work	Intensity Factor	Capacity Factor
Mechanical (ergs)	Force (dynes)	Change in distance (cm)
Volume expansion (ergs)	Pressure (dynes cm^{-2})	Change in volume (cm^3)
Surface increase (ergs)	Surface tension (dynes cm^{-1})	Change in area (cm^2)
Electrical (joules)	Potential difference (volts)	Quantity of electricity (coulombs = amp $\times$ sec)
Gravitational (ergs)	Gravitational potential (height $\times$ acceleration) ($cm^2 sec^{-2}$)	Mass (grams)

is $f\,dl$. Since pressure P is force per unit area, the force on a piston is PA, where A is the surface area perpendicular to the direction of motion of the piston. Thus the differential quantity of work done by an expanding gas which causes the piston to move distance dl is $PA\,dl$. But $A\,dl = dV$, and so the differential quantity of work is $P\,dV$. In general, the pressure in this expression is not the pressure of the gas, but the opposing pressure.

It is evident that different kinds of work may be compared but that no relation exists between the intensity factors alone or between the capacity factors alone. It is clear also that the same quantity of work can be accomplished by a small quantity of water passing through a turbine from a great height as by a large quantity of water falling from a lower level.

The First Law of Thermodynamics.　Only work and heat can be measured directly, but it is helpful to define *energy*, which includes the internal energy of a substance as well as heat and work. The internal energy of a substance depends only upon its state, that is, its temperature, pressure, volume, crystal form, etc. If work is done on an insulated body, there is a change in the internal energy of the body which is equal to the amount of work done. The *same* change in the temperature of the body may be produced by the addition of heat transferred by direct contact with a hotter body. The discovery of Joule that the ratios of various types of work to each other are constant and independent of the method of conversion is in agreement with the fact that it has not been possible to develop a perpetual-motion machine.

The first law of thermodynamics is commonly known as the law of conservation of energy. Energy may be transformed from one form to another, but it cannot be created or destroyed, and the total energy of an isolated system is constant.

According to the first law of thermodynamics, the amount of work alone or heat alone required to take the insulated body from one state to another is equal to the change in energy of the body and is independent of the path between these states. Thus, by introducing the concept of internal energy in this way, the total of heat, work, and energy change for a process is zero.

Exercise I. Explain the application of the first law of thermodynamics if work is done in winding up a steel spring and the coiled spring is then dissolved in acid.

Nuclear reactions do not contradict the first law, for, according to the theory of relativity, a certain rest mass is equivalent to a certain amount of energy, and the large amount of energy produced by nuclear reactions (p. 683) is due to a decrease in rest mass. The rest mass is measured when the body is stationary; the relativistic mass depends upon velocity (p. 449). Einstein showed that, if there is a change in rest mass, Δm_0, the energy change

$$\Delta E = c^2 \, \Delta m_0 \tag{2}$$

where c is the velocity of light $(3 \times 10^{10} \text{ cm sec}^{-1})$. Thus 1 gram of matter is equivalent to 9×10^{20} ergs of energy. It is evident that the law of conservation of energy and the law of the conservation of mass are essentially one and the same. However, nuclear transformations and detectable changes in total mass are not involved in ordinary chemical and physical phenomena, and their discussion is reserved for Chapter 24. Equation 2 is of no importance in most chemical phenomena.

Internal Energy. The *internal energy* E of a substance is the total energy it possesses due to the kinetic and potential energies of its component molecules, atoms, and subatomic particles. This includes the energies of translational, rotational, and vibrational motions and the potential energies due to the attractive and repulsive forces acting between molecules, atoms, and subatomic particles. The internal energy does not include the potential energy due to position or the kinetic energy of motion through space, but it may include additional energies like surface energy.

The internal energy of a substance depends upon its physical state and is independent of the path by which the substance was brought to that state. The internal energy is an extensive property; that is, it depends upon the quantity of matter being considered. Although it is not possible to determine the total internal energy of a substance, the *changes* in internal energy for various processes may be determined. For example, if E_1 represents the internal energy of a substance in state 1, and E_2 the internal energy in state 2, the change in internal energy ΔE for the process

$$\text{State } 1 \to \text{State } 2 \tag{3}$$

is given by

$$\Delta E = E_2 - E_1 \tag{4}$$

The symbol Δ is used to represent a difference and always refers to the value for the *final* state (the products) given at the right of the arrow minus the value for the *initial* state (the reactants) given at the left.

Since the internal energy of a substance depends only upon its physical state, the value of ΔE for a process is the same whether that process is carried out by one or several steps, reversibly or irreversibly (as defined in a following section). The amount of heat absorbed q and work done w in a process, on the other hand, depend very much on how the process is carried out.

The change in internal energy of a system produced by a given process may be obtained by determining the work w and heat exchange q involved in the process. A *system* is simply a specified part of the universe which is isolated for special consideration. In order to keep the bookkeeping straight it is necessary to adopt conventions about the signs of q and w. A positive value of w indicates that the work is done by the system on its surroundings. A negative value of w indicates that the surroundings do work on the system, as, for example, when a gas is compressed by the application of external pressure. The heat exchange is designated by q; a positive value of q means that heat is absorbed by the system from its surroundings, as in the melting of ice; and a negative value means that the system gives up heat to its surroundings, as in the combustion of carbon. It follows from the first law of thermodynamics that for a process such as that represented by equation 3 the internal energy of the final state E_2 must be equal to the internal energy of the initial state plus the heat absorbed by the system minus the work done by the system.

$$E_2 = E_1 + q - w \tag{5}$$

$$\Delta E = E_2 - E_1 = q - w \tag{6}$$

This equation is the mathematical formulation of the *first law of thermodynamics* which we will use.

If there is no change of internal energy (as in the isothermal expansion of an ideal gas, p. 41), the work done must be exactly equal to the heat absorbed or both must be equal to zero. Again, if there is a chemical reaction and the internal energy of the system decreases, that is, E_2 is less than E_1, the released energy will appear as heat evolved and work done. Nothing is stated regarding the relative amounts of heat and work, but the two taken together $(q - w)$ must be equal to the change in internal energy. Under special conditions it is possible to have either q or w equal to zero.

If pressure-volume work is the only kind of work which can be done in a specified system and the process is carried out at constant volume, then $w = 0$, and

$$\Delta E = q_V* \tag{7}$$

In words, the *heat absorbed in a process involving only mechanical work, measured under conditions of constant volume, is equal to the increase in internal energy.* Or, put in another way, if no work is done, the heat evolved is equal to the decrease in the internal energy.

The First Law of Thermodynamics for an Infinitesimal Process and a Cyclic Process. If an infinitesimal quantity of heat is absorbed by a system and an infinitesimal amount of work is done by the system, the infinitesimal increment in the internal energy is given by the differential form of equation 6.

$$dE = \delta q - \delta w \tag{8}$$

where δ is used rather than d to indicate inexact differentials. Since E is a function of the state of the system, dE may be integrated and $E_2 - E_1$ depends only upon the initial and final states 1 and 2. However, δq and δw are not the differentials of a function of the state of the system, and so their integrals, which are simply written q and w, respectively, rather than $q_2 - q_1$ and $w_2 - w_1$, depend upon the particular path which is followed between state 1 and state 2. For example,

---

* A subscript below a quantity indicates that the property represented by the subscript is kept constant; thus, q_V shows that the process is carried out at constant volume.

when a gas is allowed to expand, the amount of work obtained may vary from zero (if the gas is allowed to expand into a vacuum) to a maximum value which is obtained if the expansion is carried out reversibly as described in the next section. Differentials like dE and dV whose integrals depend only upon the initial and final states are called *exact* differentials. Differentials like δq and δw whose integrals depend upon the path chosen are called *inexact* differentials.

A cyclic process is a process in which a system is carried through a series of steps which eventually bring the system back to its *initial* conditions. The change in internal energy for a cyclic process is zero since the internal energy is a function only of the state of the system. This may be represented by

$$\oint dE = 0 \qquad (9)$$

which indicates integration around a cycle. The cyclic integrals of q and w are not in general equal to zero, and their values will depend upon the path followed.

Reversible Processes. A reversible process is a process which may be reversed at any moment by changing an independent variable by an infinitesimal amount. Thus in the reversible expansion of a gas the expansion can be stopped at any point by increasing the pressure exerted by the piston by an infinitesimal amount. A reversible process is often spoken of as one which consists of a series of successive equilibria. Such processes are idealizations which may be closely approached, but not actually reached, in the laboratory. To carry out a finite process reversibly would require an infinite time. Reversible processes are of great importance because they yield the maximum amount of work which may be obtained from a given net change. This amount of work is just sufficient to return the system to its original conditions. When a process is carried out irreversibly, less work is obtained than would be required to return the system to its initial state.

Imagine a gas enclosed in a cylinder fitted with a frictionless and weightless piston. The external pressure on the piston is decreased by an infinitesimal amount, dP, and the gas expands by an amount dV. In this expansion the pressure of the gas in the cylinder decreases until it becomes equal to the external pressure, and then the piston ceases to move. A second infinitesimal decrease in pressure produces a second expansion dV; as the pressure is decreased in successive amounts, the volume undergoes a series of increases. During each little expansion the pressure throughout the gas is constant (within an infinitesimal amount). In each little expansion the work done is the external pressure multiplied by dV, and the total work obtainable in expanding the gas reversibly from the *initial* volume V_1 to the *final* volume V_2 is equal to the integral of the pressure times the differential of the volume.

$$w_{\text{rev}} = \int_{V_1}^{V_2} P \, dV \tag{10}$$

Since the gas is at its equilibrium pressure (within an infinitesimal amount) at each stage in the expansion, we may substitute an expression for the dependence of pressure on volume obtained from equilibrium measurements. If the gas was allowed to expand rapidly, the pressure would not be uniform throughout the volume of the gas, and so such a substitution could not be made. *Only if the expansion is carried out reversibly can sufficient energy be obtained to reverse the process, compressing the gas to its original conditions.*

A number of processes may be carried out essentially reversibly in the laboratory. A liquid may be vaporized reversibly as described in the next section. In the reversible discharge of an electrochemical cell the applied voltage from the potentiometer is kept within an infinitesimal voltage of the electromotive force of the electrochemical cell.

Reversible Vaporization of a Liquid. Imagine that a liquid is placed in a cylinder provided with a weightless, frictionless piston and that the cylinder is set into a large heat reservoir at the boiling temperature of the liquid. (The fact that no machine can be built with a weightless, frictionless piston in no way affects the conclusions drawn from this idealized process.) The vapor pressure of the liquid at this temperature is exactly equal to the atmospheric pressure, and the whole system is in a state of equilibrium. Now, if the temperature of the reservoir is raised by an infinitesimal amount, the vapor pressure of the liquid will be slightly greater, and the piston will be pushed back against the atmospheric pressure. As the volume increases, more liquid evaporates and the pressure in the cylinder is thus maintained constant; heat flows in from the heat reservoir to supply energy for the vaporization process and maintain the temperature constant.

This process of absorbing heat and doing external work is reversible, because at any time the vaporization can be stopped by decreasing the temperature by an infinitesimal amount or by increasing the pressure by an infinitesimal amount, thus making internal and external pressures exactly equal. Increasing the pressure still further by an infinitesimal amount causes the vapor to condense and give back the heat of vaporization to the reservoir.

If the liquid in the cylinder is water and the pressure is 1 atm, the temperature of vaporization will be 100°; and when 1 mole has been evaporated, the increase in volume can be calculated on the assumption that water vapor behaves as an ideal gas and that the volume of the liquid (0.018 liter) is negligible:

$$w = P\,\Delta\overline{V} = (1\text{ atm})(22.41\text{ l mole}^{-1})\frac{373.1\text{ deg}}{273.1\text{ deg}} = 30.6\text{ l-atm mole}^{-1}$$

Since it is assumed that the ideal gas law is obeyed, and we are considering the vaporization of 1 mole of water, RT may be substituted for $P\,\Delta\overline{V}$. Then,

$$w = RT = (0.08205\text{ l-atm deg}^{-1}\text{ mole}^{-1})(373.1\text{ deg})$$

$$= 30.6\text{ l-atm mole}^{-1}$$

or

$$w = RT = (1.987\text{ cal deg}^{-1}\text{ mole}^{-1})(373.1\text{ deg}) = 741.3\text{ cal mole}^{-1}$$

The work done in vaporizing 1 mole to give an ideal gas depends only on the temperature and is independent of the pressure or volume. If the pressure is doubled, the volume change is halved and the product $P\,\Delta\overline{V}$ is the same. In very exact work it is not accurate to consider a vapor at its boiling point as an ideal gas; the volume change must be measured experimentally or calculated with a more exact equation of state.

The energy required to do this pressure-volume work comes from heat absorbed from the reservoir by the evaporating liquid. A great deal more energy than that required to do the pressure-volume work must be absorbed from the reservoir, however, in order to separate the molecules from their neighboring molecules in the liquid. To vaporize a gram of water at 373.1°K and atmospheric pressure, 539.7 cal is required. Thus

$$q = (18.02)(539.7) = 9725\text{ cal mole}^{-1}$$

By use of equation 6 the change in internal energy of a mole of water upon vaporization is given by

$$\Delta\overline{E} = q - w = 9725 - 741 = 8984\text{ cal mole}^{-1}$$

The bar in $\Delta\overline{E}$ indicates that 1 mole is considered.

Reversible Isothermal Expansion of a Gas. The maximum work that can be obtained from the *isothermal* expansion of an ideal gas may readily be calculated. If the expansion is carried out reversibly, the pressure is always given by $P = RT/\overline{V}$ for 1 mole of ideal gas. Substituting this relation into equation 10, we obtain

$$w_{rev} = \int_{\overline{V}_1}^{\overline{V}_2} \frac{RT}{\overline{V}}\, d\overline{V} \tag{11}$$

Since R is a constant and the process is isothermal,

$$w_{rev} = RT \int_{\overline{V}_1}^{\overline{V}_2} \frac{d\overline{V}}{\overline{V}} = RT \ln \frac{\overline{V}_2}{\overline{V}_1} = 2.303RT \log \frac{\overline{V}_2}{\overline{V}_1} \tag{12}$$

For n moles of an ideal gas $w_{rev} = 2.303nRT \log (V_2/V_1)$.

In integration the lower limit always refers to the initial state and the upper limit to the final state. If the gas is compressed, the final volume is smaller and w_{rev} is negative. The negative value means that work is done on the gas.

Example 1. What is the maximum work which can be obtained by the reversible isothermal expansion of 1 mole of an ideal gas at 0° from 2.24 to 22.4 liters?

$$w_{rev} = 2.303RT \log (\overline{V}_2/\overline{V}_1) = (2.303)(1.987)(273.1) \log 10 = 1250 \text{ cal}$$

Then 1250 cal is also the minimum amount of work required to compress the gas from 22.4 to 2.24 liters at 0°, and $w_{rev} = -1250$ cal.

The reversible work obtainable from the reversible isothermal expansion of 1 mole of gas may be expressed in terms of pressures instead of volumes, since at constant temperature $\overline{V}_2/\overline{V}_1 = P_1/P_2$. Then,

$$w_{rev} = RT \ln \frac{P_1}{P_2} = -2.303RT \log \frac{P_2}{P_1} \tag{13}$$

Enthalpy.* Constant-pressure processes are more common in chemistry than constant-volume processes because most operations are carried out in open vessels. If only pressure-volume work is done and the pressure is constant, equation 6 may be written

$$q_P = \Delta E + P\, \Delta V \tag{14}$$

It is convenient to introduce a new quantity, the *enthalpy*, H, which is defined by

$$H = E + PV \tag{15}$$

or, for 1 mole, $\overline{H} = \overline{E} + P\overline{V}$.

Like the internal energy E, the enthalpy depends only on the state of the system and does not depend upon the path involved in going

---

* Pronounced *enthal'py* to distinguish it from *en'tropy* (p. 88).

from the initial state to the final state. Then from equation 15

$$\Delta H = \Delta E + \Delta(PV) \tag{16}$$

At constant pressure

$$\Delta H = \Delta E + P \Delta V \tag{17}$$

For the special case that the only work which can be done is pressure-volume work and the pressure is constant, equation 14 can be written

$$\Delta E = q_P - P \Delta V \tag{18}$$

Substituting equation 18 into equation 17,

$$\Delta H = q_P \tag{19}$$

In words, *the heat absorbed in a process at constant pressure is equal to the change in enthalpy if the only work done is pressure-volume work.*

When pressure-volume work is the only kind of work (electrical and other kinds being excluded), it is easy to visualize ΔE and ΔH; in a *constant-volume* calorimeter the evolution of heat is a measure of the decrease in internal energy E, and in a *constant-pressure* calorimeter the evolution of heat is a measure of the decrease in enthalpy, H.

Internal Energy of Gases. Imagine two gas bottles connected with a valve and immersed in a stirred liquid in a thermally isolated container. The first is filled with a gas under pressure, and the second is evacuated. When the valve is opened, gas rushes from the first bottle into the second. The first becomes cooler because work is done against the (increasing) opposing pressure, and the second becomes warmer on account of the compression of the gas. When equilibrium is reached, however, and the same pressure is established throughout the two vessels, the heating and cooling effects will exactly balance if the gas is ideal. In other words, the temperature of the stirred liquid remains constant. Thus, when an ideal gas expands into an evacuated space, there is no absorption or evolution of heat by the gas as a whole. Moreover, since the total volume of the system, consisting of the two vessels, remains unchanged, no external work is done.

Since $q = 0$ and $w = 0$, it follows from equation 6 that ΔE must be zero for the expansion of an ideal gas. In other words, the internal energy of an ideal gas is independent of the volume or the pressure at constant temperature:

$$\left(\frac{\partial E}{\partial V}\right)_T = 0 \tag{20}$$

$$\left(\frac{\partial E}{\partial P}\right)_T = 0 \tag{21}$$

These criteria of an ideal gas are not really separate from the ideal gas law, since they may be derived (p. 122) from the second law of thermodynamics using the ideal gas law.

The change in internal energy or enthalpy of nonideal gases with pressure is so small that temperature changes in the type of expansion just discussed are difficult to detect. A flow method involving larger quantities of material is used as described in the following section.

Joule-Thomson Effect. Joule and Thomson investigated the temperature change which occurs when a gas is allowed to expand through a porous plug in an apparatus such as that represented schematically in *Fig. 3-1.* The pressure on the left side is maintained constant at

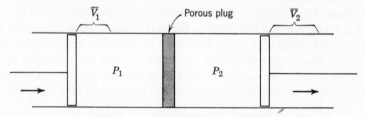

Fig. 3-1. Joule-Thomson experiment.

P_1, and that on the right side is maintained constant at a lower value, P_2. The volume at the left decreases by $\overline{V}_1$ per mole of gas passing through the plug, and the volume at the right increases by $\overline{V}_2$ per mole. The apparatus is insulated so that the process is adiabatic (p. 47).

The work done on the gas by the piston at the left is $P_1\overline{V}_1$, and the work done by the gas on the piston on the right is $P_2\overline{V}_2$. Since the process is adiabatic, $q = 0$ and the first law may be written

$$\overline{E}_2 - \overline{E}_1 = -w = -(P_2\overline{V}_2 - P_1\overline{V}_1) \tag{22}$$

$$\overline{E}_2 + P_2\overline{V}_2 = \overline{E}_1 + P_1\overline{V}_1 \tag{23}$$

$$\overline{H}_2 = \overline{H}_1$$

Thus the enthalpy of the gas does not change in the expansion.

The Joule-Thomson coefficient μ is defined by

$$\mu = \left(\frac{\partial T}{\partial P}\right)_{\overline{H}} \tag{24}$$

It is equal to the temperature change per atmosphere difference in pressure measured at constant enthalpy in the system described in Fig. 3-1.

With most gases other than hydrogen and helium a cooling effect is obtained at room temperature, and so the Joule-Thomson coefficient is positive. For an ideal gas the Joule-Thomson coefficient is zero. For hydrogen at room temperature the Joule-Thomson coefficient is negative, but there is a temperature, the inversion temperature, at $-78°$, below which the Joule-Thomson coefficient is positive and hydrogen is cooled by the expansion. The inversion temperature of a gas depends upon the pressure.

The Joule-Thomson effect is of practical importance for the liquefaction of gases. In order to obtain a cooling effect the gas must be precooled to a temperature below its inversion temperature.

The following principles are involved in the liquefaction of gases: (1) the gas must be below its critical temperature; (2) the pressure must be great enough to cause liquefaction, and the lower the temperature, the lower is the required pressure; (3) the incoming gas is cooled in a heat exchanger by the outgoing gas, which has been cooled by expansion; (4) the gas is cooled by doing external mechanical work in an engine, or by expanding against the force of attraction between the molecules in a Joule-Thomson expansion. The latter expansion is often used rather than the expansion in an engine because of the difficulty of operating an engine at such a low temperature.

Many gas mixtures can be separated by liquefaction and fractional distillation; for example, oxygen and neon are obtained from air, helium from natural gas, and propane and butane from petroleum products.

The important specific heat measurements at low temperatures are dependent on liquid nitrogen (b.p. $77.3°K$), liquid hydrogen (b.p. $20.4°K$), and liquid helium (b.p. $4.2°K$). At low temperatures obtainable with liquid helium, interesting new phenomena can be studied, such as superconductivity (the disappearance of electrical resistance of metals) and the extraordinary ability of helium to flow, apparently without friction, at temperatures below $2.2°K$.

Heat Capacity. The *specific heat* of a substance is defined as the quantity of heat required to raise the temperature of 1 gram of the substance 1 degree centigrade. A general term which may be applied to any quantity of material, or even to a heterogeneous system, is the *heat capacity* C. The average heat capacity over a range of temperature T_1 to T_2 is given by

$$C_{\text{avg}} = \frac{q}{T_2 - T_1} \tag{25}$$

where q is the heat absorbed by the system. Since the heat capacity depends upon the temperature, it is defined more accurately as the limit of equation 25 as $T_2 - T_1$ becomes smaller and smaller.

$$C = \frac{\delta q}{dT} \tag{26}$$

where the δ in the inexact differential δq emphasizes that the amount of heat absorbed depends upon how the process is carried out and does not depend on the initial and final states alone.

If a system is heated at constant volume, no pressure-volume work can be done, and if no other kind of work is done, $\delta q = dE$; equation 26 becomes

$$C_V = \left(\frac{\partial E}{\partial T}\right)_V \tag{27}$$

The partial derivative, indicated by ∂, is used because E is a function of more than one variable, and the subscript V reminds us that the volume is kept constant.

If one mole of pure substance is considered, the heat capacity at constant volume is the *molar heat capacity* $\overline{C}_V$.

$$\overline{C}_V = \left(\frac{\partial \overline{E}}{\partial T}\right)_V$$

If a system is heated at constant pressure, $\delta q = dH$, provided that pressure-volume work is the only kind of work done. Thus equation 26 becomes

$$C_P = \left(\frac{\partial H}{\partial T}\right)_P \tag{28}$$

For 1 mole of pure substance

$$\overline{C}_P = \left(\frac{\partial \overline{H}}{\partial T}\right)_P$$

Relation between C_P **and** C_V. The heat capacity at constant pressure C_P is always larger than the heat capacity at constant volume C_V because pressure-volume work is done when a substance is heated at constant pressure. The equation for the difference $C_P - C_V$ may be derived as follows:

$$C_P - C_V = \left(\frac{\partial H}{\partial T}\right)_P - \left(\frac{\partial E}{\partial T}\right)_V \tag{29}$$

$$= \left[\frac{\partial(E + PV)}{\partial T}\right]_P - \left(\frac{\partial E}{\partial T}\right)_V \tag{30}$$

$$= \left(\frac{\partial E}{\partial T}\right)_P + P\left(\frac{\partial V}{\partial T}\right)_P - \left(\frac{\partial E}{\partial T}\right)_V \tag{31}$$

Since dE is an exact differential, it follows that

$$dE = \left(\frac{\partial E}{\partial T}\right)_V dT + \left(\frac{\partial E}{\partial V}\right)_T dV \tag{32}$$

and differentiating with respect to T at constant pressure gives

$$\left(\frac{\partial E}{\partial T}\right)_P = \left(\frac{\partial E}{\partial T}\right)_V + \left(\frac{\partial E}{\partial V}\right)_T \left(\frac{\partial V}{\partial T}\right)_P \tag{33}$$

Substituting in equation 31,

$$C_P - C_V = \left(\frac{\partial E}{\partial V}\right)_T \left(\frac{\partial V}{\partial T}\right)_P + P \left(\frac{\partial V}{\partial T}\right)_P$$

$$= \left[P + \left(\frac{\partial E}{\partial V}\right)_T\right] \left(\frac{\partial V}{\partial T}\right)_P \tag{34}$$

and for one mole

$$\bar{C}_P - \bar{C}_V = \left[P + \left(\frac{\partial \bar{E}}{\partial \bar{V}}\right)_T\right] \left(\frac{\partial \bar{V}}{\partial T}\right)_P$$

For an ideal gas $(\partial \bar{E}/\partial \bar{V})_T = 0$ and $(\partial \bar{V}/\partial T)_P = R/P$, so that

$$\bar{C}_P - \bar{C}_V = R \tag{35}$$

This relationship may be visualized quite easily for an ideal gas. When a mole of ideal gas is heated at constant pressure, the work done in pushing back a piston is $P \, \Delta \bar{V} = R \, \Delta T$. For a 1°C change in temperature the amount of work done is R, and this is just the extra energy required to heat a mole of ideal gas at constant pressure over that required to heat it 1°C at constant volume.

A relation for calculating the change in internal energy of an ideal gas with temperature may be derived by considering equation 32. Since for an ideal gas $(\partial E/\partial V)_T = 0$,

$$dE = \left(\frac{\partial E}{\partial T}\right)_V dT = C_V \, dT \tag{36}$$

The change in internal energy for a mole of gas heated from T_1 to T_2 is

$$\Delta \bar{E} = \int_{T_1}^{T_2} \bar{C}_V \, dT \tag{37}$$

Reversible Adiabatic Expansion of a Gas. An *adiabatic* process is one in which there is no loss or gain of heat, that is, one in which the system under investigation is thermally isolated from its environment so that $q = 0$. In an adiabatic expansion external work is done at the expense of the internal energy of the gas and the temperature drops. Thus, when a gas expands adiabatically to a larger volume and a lower pressure, the volume is smaller than it would be after an isothermal expansion to the same pressure. Plots of pressure versus volume for adiabatic and isothermal expansions are shown in *Fig. 3-2*.

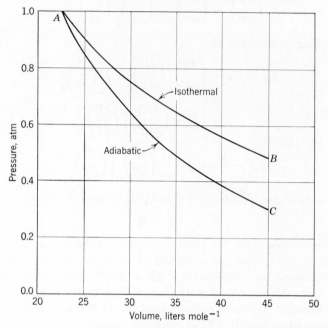

Fig. 3-2. Isothermal and adiabatic expansion of a gas.

One mole of helium at A occupying 22.4 liters under 1 atm and at $0°$ expands isothermally to B, where the volume is 44.8 liters at 0.5 atm still at $0°$. When the mole of helium at A expands adiabatically toward C, at 0.5 atm it occupies 33.6 liters and the temperature is $-66°$. If it is allowed to expand still further to 44.8 liters at C, the temperature is $-101°$ and the pressure is 0.32 atm.

The work done by the isothermal reversible expansion of the gas, represented by the area under AB, is larger than the work done by the adiabatic expansion, represented by the area under AC. The energy for doing the additional work in the isothermal expansion is provided by heat absorbed from the constant-temperature reservoir. The energy for doing work in the adiabatic expansion comes only from the cooling of the gas itself.

Now let us consider the reversible adiabatic expansion of 1 mole of ideal gas. Since for an adiabatic process $\delta q = 0$, then, by the first law,

$$d\bar{E} = -\delta w = -P\, d\bar{V} \tag{38}$$

Since, according to equation 36, $d\bar{E} = \bar{C}_V\, dT$, equation 38 shows that the amount of work obtainable from a reversible adiabatic expansion is

$$w_{\text{rev}} = -\int_{T_1}^{T_2} \bar{C}_V\, dT \tag{39}$$

Combining equations 36 and 38,

$$\bar{C}_V\, dT = -P\, d\bar{V} \tag{40}$$

Since, for 1 mole of an ideal gas, $P = RT/\bar{V}$, it follows that

$$\bar{C}_V\, dT = -RT\, \frac{d\bar{V}}{\bar{V}} \tag{41}$$

and

$$\bar{C}_V\, \frac{dT}{T} = -R\, \frac{d\bar{V}}{\bar{V}} \tag{42}$$

If $\bar{V}_1$ is the volume of 1 mole of the gas at the initial temperature T_1, and $\bar{V}_2$ is the volume at the final temperature T_2, and if $\bar{C}_V$ is independent of temperature, integration between these limits gives

$$\bar{C}_V \ln \frac{T_2}{T_1} = -R \ln \frac{\bar{V}_2}{\bar{V}_1} \tag{43}$$

for an ideal gas.

For an expansion $\bar{V}_2 > \bar{V}_1$, so it is apparent that for an adiabatic expansion $T_2 < T_1$. In other words, the gas cools. Conversely the adiabatic compression of the gas produces an increase in temperature.

Example 2. If a gas is compressed so rapidly that there is no opportunity to transfer heat to the container, the compression will be adiabatic. Calculate the temperature increase and final pressure of helium if a mole is compressed adiabatically and reversibly from 44.8 liters at 0° to 22.4 liters. The molar heat capacity $\bar{C}_V$ of helium is constant and equal to 3.00 cal deg^{-1} mole^{-1}. It is necessary of course to express R in the same units.

$$\bar{C}_V \ln (T_2/T_1) = -R \ln (\bar{V}_2/\bar{V}_1)$$
$$(3.00)(2.303) \log (T_2/273.1) = (-1.987)(2.303) \log (22.4/44.8)$$
$$\log T_2 = -(1.987/3.00)(\log \tfrac{1}{2}) + \log 273.1$$
$$T_2 = 432.4°\text{K}$$
$$\text{Increase in temperature} = 432.4 - 273.1 = 159.3°$$

Substitution into the ideal gas law shows that the final pressure is 1.59 atm.

Exercise II. Starting with equations 35 and 43, show that for reversible adiabatic expansion of an ideal gas

$$\bar{C}_P \log (T_2/T_1) = R \log (P_2/P_1)$$

Equation 43 may be written

$$\frac{T_2}{T_1} = \left(\frac{\bar{V}_1}{\bar{V}_2}\right)^{R/\bar{C}_V} = \left(\frac{\bar{V}_1}{\bar{V}_2}\right)^{(\bar{C}_P - \bar{C}_V)/\bar{C}_V} \tag{44}$$

where the last form is obtained by introducing equation 35. If the ratio $\bar{C}_P/\bar{C}_V$ is represented by γ,

$$\frac{T_2}{T_1} = \left(\frac{\bar{V}_1}{\bar{V}_2}\right)^{\gamma - 1} \tag{45}$$

For an ideal gas

$$\frac{T_2}{T_1} = \frac{P_2 \bar{V}_2}{P_1 \bar{V}_1} \tag{46}$$

Therefore, combining equations 45 and 46,

$$\frac{P_2}{P_1} = \left(\frac{\bar{V}_1}{\bar{V}_2}\right)^{\gamma} \tag{47}$$

or

$$P_1 \bar{V}_1{}^{\gamma} = P_2 \bar{V}_2{}^{\gamma} \tag{48}$$

Sometimes it is more convenient to use this equation rather than equation 43 in doing calculations on adiabatic processes with ideal gases. In engineering calculations it is sometimes useful to use $P\bar{V}^k = constant$ for calculations or processes which are intermediate between isothermal and adiabatic. The constant k is determined empirically, and of course $1 < k < \gamma$.

Example 3. Calculate the final pressure of the helium after the adiabatic compression described in example 2. As shown in Table II, the value of γ for helium is 1.67.

$$P_2 = P_1(\bar{V}_1/\bar{V}_2)^{\gamma}$$

$$= (0.500)(44.8/22.4)^{1.67}$$

$$= 1.59 \text{ atm}$$

This calculation may be made by taking logarithms of both sides of the equation.

Heat Capacity of Gases. When a gas is heated, energy is absorbed by increased translational kinetic energy and, in the case of polyatomic molecules, by increased rotational and vibrational motions. Experimental values of $\bar{C}_V$ and $\bar{C}_P$ for various gases at 25° are given in Table II. Since work is done by a gas which is heated at constant pressure, $\bar{C}_P > \bar{C}_V$. It may be seen from the table that for most of these

Table II. Molar Heat Capacities of Gases

(In cal deg^{-1} $mole^{-1}$ at 25°)

Gas	$\bar{C}_P$	$\bar{C}_V$	$\bar{C}_P/\bar{C}_V = \gamma$
Argon, A	4.97	2.98	1.67
Helium, He	4.97	2.98	1.67
Mercury, Hg	4.97	2.98	1.67
Hydrogen, H_2	6.90	4.91	1.41
Oxygen, O_2	7.05	5.05	1.40
Nitrogen, N_2	6.94	4.95	1.40
Chlorine, Cl_2	8.25	6.14	1.34
Nitric oxide, NO	7.11	5.11	1.39
Carbon monoxide, CO	6.97	4.97	1.40
Hydrogen chloride, HCl	7.05	5.01	1.41
Carbon dioxide, CO_2	8.96	6.92	1.29
Nitrous oxide, N_2O	9.33	7.29	1.28
Sulfur dioxide, SO_2	9.4	7.3	1.29
Ammonia, NH_3	8.63	6.57	1.31
Methane, CH_4	8.60	6.59	1.31
Ethane, C_2H_6	12.71	10.65	1.19
Dimethyl ether, C_2H_6O	15.89	13.75	1.16

gases $\bar{C}_P - \bar{C}_V = R$ as required for an ideal gas. For dimethyl ether, however, $\bar{C}_P - \bar{C}_V = 2.14$ cal deg^{-1} $mole^{-1}$ because the gas is not an ideal gas. This difference for a nonideal gas will depend on pressure and temperature.

The theoretical calculation of the heat capacities of gases is discussed in Chapter 11 on kinetic theory and again in Chapter 19 on statistical mechanics. It is shown that for a monatomic ideal gas $\bar{C}_V$ is expected to have a value of $\frac{3}{2}R = 2.98$ cal deg^{-1} $mole^{-1}$, in agreement with the values for A, He, and Hg in Table II. For diatomic molecules for which the vibrational energy is negligible, $\bar{C}_V$ is expected to have a value of $\frac{3}{2}R + R = 4.97$ cal deg^{-1} $mole^{-1}$ in agreement with the values for H_2, O_2, N_2, CO, and HCl in Table II.

The dependence of C_P on temperature is shown for a number of gases in *Fig. 3-3*. It was not possible to explain this temperature dependence until the development of quantum mechanics (Chapter 16), according to which a certain minimum amount of energy is required to bring about a specified vibration or a rotation of a molecule. At low temperatures the energy units are not large enough to produce these motions, but as the temperature rises the energy for the different

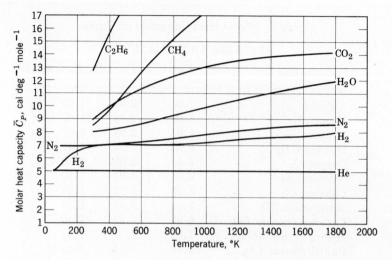

Fig. 3-3. Influence of temperature on the molar heat capacities of gases.

motions is utilizable and the heat capacity increases. Theoretical calculations are given on p. 565.

In general, the more complex the molecule, the greater is its molar heat capacity, the greater is the temperature effect, and the smaller is γ, although this ratio cannot become as small as 1. The values of empirical constants for calculating the heat capacities of common gases at temperatures in the range 300–1500°K are given in Table VI of Chapter 4.

Heat Capacity of Solids. Dulong and Petit in 1819 found that *at room temperature the product of the specific heat at constant pressure and the atomic weight of the solid elements is a constant, $\bar{C}_P$, equal to approximately 6.4 cal deg^{-1} g-atom^{-1}.* This law of Dulong and Petit played an important part in the determination of atomic weights because it could be used to select the multiple of the known equivalent weight (obtained from quantitative analysis) required to give the atomic weight.

Example 4. Estimate the specific heat C_P of zinc at constant pressure at room temperature from the fact that its atomic weight is 65.38 grams g-atom^{-1}.

$$65.38 \text{ grams g-atom}^{-1} \, C_P = 6.4 \text{ cal deg}^{-1} \text{ g-atom}^{-1}$$

$$C_P = 0.096 \text{ cal deg}^{-1} \text{ g}^{-1}$$

The atomic heat capacity of solid elements at constant volume is more nearly the same for different elements than the atomic heat capacity at constant pressure. When a substance is heated at constant pressure, it expands; and, since work is done, more heat is absorbed. Lewis and Gibson * found that the atomic heat capacity at constant volume and room temperature is 5.90 cal deg^{-1} $g\text{-atom}^{-1}$ within 0.09 for all the elements heavier than potassium for which data were available. This value of the heat capacity of a solid may be accounted for by classical physics, and this theoretical interpretation of heat capacity is discussed later (p. 566). However, the heat capacities of all solids decrease with decreasing absolute temperature; this effect cannot be explained by classical physics but is explained on the basis of quantum theory.

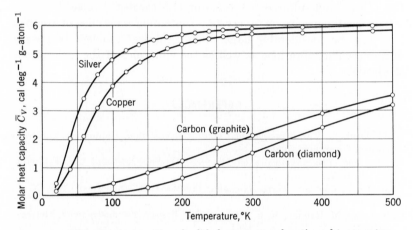

Fig. 3-4. Molar heat capacities of solid elements as a function of temperature.

The dependence of heat capacity on temperature is shown for several solids in *Fig. 3-4*. As the absolute temperature approaches zero, the heat capacity approaches zero. Debye showed that at sufficiently low temperatures the heat capacity is proportional to the cube of the absolute temperature,† as given by equation 49.

$$\bar{C}_V = \tfrac{12}{5}\pi^4 R \left(\frac{T}{\theta}\right)^3 \tag{49}$$

The quantity θ, called the characteristic temperature of a substance, is usually of the order of $100\text{-}400°K$. For substances which approach a heat capacity of 6 cal deg^{-1} $mole^{-1}$ only at quite high temperatures, the value of θ is larger; for diamond it is $1860°K$. This behavior is

* G. N. Lewis and G. E. Gibson, *J. Am. Chem. Soc.*, *39*, 2554 (1917).

† For graphite and certain other anisotropic solids the heat capacity is proportional to T^2.

characteristic of solids with strong interatomic forces. For metals like copper and silver, which are soft and malleable and have low melting points, θ is smaller (315 and 215°K, respectively), and $\bar{C}_V$ rises rapidly at lower temperatures. For such solids the forces between atoms in the lattice are weak. Equation 49 is useful for calculating heat capacities below 15°K, where it is more difficult to obtain experimental values.

The molar heat capacities of simple salts can be estimated approximately by totaling the atomic heat capacities of the elements. For example, the molar heat capacity of lead sulfide, PbS, is 12.3 cal deg^{-1} mole^{-1} at room temperature, and the sum of the atomic heat capacities of lead and sulfur is 6.3 + 5.5 or 11.8 cal deg^{-1} mole^{-1}.

The heat capacity of a crystal, containing molecules or complex ions, may be considerably larger than 6 cal deg^{-1} mole^{-1} because of intramolecular vibrations as well as the vibrations of the molecules in the lattice.

REFERENCES

K. G. Denbigh, *The Principles of Chemical Equilibrium*, Cambridge University Press, Cambridge, 1955.

S. Glasstone, *Thermodynamics for Chemists*, D. Van Nostrand Co., Princeton, N. J., 1947.

I. M. Klotz, *Chemical Thermodynamics*, Prentice-Hall, Englewood Cliffs, N. J., 1950.

G. N. Lewis, M. Randall, K. S. Pitzer, and L. Brewer, *Thermodynamics*, McGraw-Hill Book Co., New York, 1961.

F. D. Rossini, *Chemical Thermodynamics*, John Wiley & Sons, New York, 1950.

F. T. Wall, *Chemical Thermodynamics*, W. H. Freeman & Co., San Francisco, 1958.

PROBLEMS

1. Thirty-five liters of hydrogen is produced at a total pressure of 1 atm by the action of acid on a metal. Calculate the work done by the gas in pushing back the atmosphere in (a) liter-atmospheres, (b) calories, (c) joules, and (d) ergs.

   Ans. (a) 35 l-atm. (b) 847 cal. (c) 3540 joules. (d) 3540 × 10^7 ergs.

2. A 900-gram weight falls 120 meters. (a) How many ergs of heat are liberated when it strikes the ground? (b) How many joules? (c) How many calories? (d) How many liter-atmospheres?

   Ans. (a) 1.059 × 10^{10} ergs. (b) 1059 joules. (c) 253.1 cal. (d) 10.45 l-atm.

3. How many degrees will a 500-watt electric heater raise the temperature of 10 liters of water in 1 hour if no heat is lost? The specific heat of water may be taken as 1 cal deg^{-1} g^{-1}, and the density of water as 1 g cm^{-3} independent of temperature. *Ans.* 43.1°.

4. One hundred grams of benzene is vaporized at its boiling point of 80.2° at 760 mm. The heat of vaporization is 94.4 cal g^{-1}. Calculate (a) w_{rev}, (b) q, (c) ΔH, (d) ΔE.   Ans. (a) 898, (b) 9440, (c) 9440, (d) 8542 cal.

5. One hundred grams of nitrogen at 25° and 760 mm is expanded reversibly and isothermally to a pressure of 100 mm. (a) What is the maximum work in calories that can be obtained by this expansion? (b) What is the maximum work that can be obtained if the temperature is 100°?   Ans. (a) 4290, (b) 5370 cal.

6. (a) Calculate the work in calories done when a mole of sulfur dioxide gas expands isothermally and reversibly at 27° from 2.46 to 24.6 liters, assuming that the gas is ideal. (b) Would an attractive force between molecules of the gas tend to make the work done larger or smaller?   Ans. (a) 1370 cal mole^{-1}. (b) Smaller.

7. (a) Show that for the isothermal reversible expansion from $\overline{V}_1$ to $\overline{V}_2$ of 1 mole of a gas obeying van der Waals' equation the work done by the gas is given by

$$w = RT \ln \left(\frac{\overline{V}_2 - b}{\overline{V}_1 - b} \right) + a \left(\frac{1}{\overline{V}_2} - \frac{1}{\overline{V}_1} \right)$$

Calculate the work which could be obtained from an isothermal reversible expansion of a mole of chlorine from 1 to 50 liters at 0°, (b) assuming ideal gas behavior and (c) assuming van der Waals' behavior.
          Ans. (b) 87.4 l-atm mole^{-1}. (c) 82.4 l-atm mole^{-1}.

8. Calculate the molar heat capacity of glycol, $(CH_2OH)_2$, at 2° from the following data. One hundred grams of glycol was weighed into a copper container equipped with an electric heater and a sensitive resistance thermometer. The copper container or calorimeter was suspended by fine cords inside a metal shield, suspended in turn inside an outer container which could be evacuated. The shield carried heaters and thermocouples by means of which its temperature was kept so close to that of the calorimeter that the heat leak to the calorimeter was negligible. The apparatus was immersed in an ice bath; and, after it had cooled to nearly 0°, the air space was evacuated. With the shield maintained at the temperature of the calorimeter, 955 joules was required to heat the calorimeter from 0.500 to 3.500°. The heat capacity of the calorimeter was found to be 20.00 cal deg^{-1} at 2°.
          Ans. 34.7 cal deg^{-1} mole^{-1}.

9. How much heat is required to raise the temperature of 10 grams of argon (a monatomic gas) through 10° (a) at constant volume, (b) at constant pressure?
          Ans. (a) 7.47, (b) 12.5 cal.

10. One mole of argon at 25° and 1 atm pressure is allowed to expand reversibly to a volume of 50 liters (a) isothermally and (b) adiabatically. Calculate the final pressure in each case, assuming ideal gas behavior. Ans. (a) 0.489, (b) 0.303 atm.

11. Ten liters of nitrogen at 1 atm and 25° is allowed to expand reversibly and adiabatically to 20 liters. What are the final pressure and temperature?
          Ans. 0.379 atm, 226°K.

12. (a) Calculate the maximum work of isothermal expansion of 10 grams of helium from a volume of 10 liters to a volume of 50 liters at 25°. (b) Calculate the maximum work of adiabatic expansion, starting with the same conditions and allowing the gas to expand to 50 liters.   Ans. (a) 2390, (b) 1460 cal.

13. Lead chloride is found by analysis to contain 74.5 per cent lead and 25.5 per cent chlorine by weight. The atomic weight of chlorine is 35.45. The specific heat of lead is approximately 0.0309 cal g^{-1}. Using this information, which of the following formulas are possible: Pb_2Cl, $PbCl$, $PbCl_2$, $PbCl_3$, Pb_2Cl_2, Pb_2Cl_4? Calculate the possible atomic weights of lead. *Ans.* $PbCl_2$, 207.2; or Pb_2Cl_2, 414.4.

14. Estimate from Dulong and Petit's relation the specific heat of iron at room temperature. *Ans.* 0.115 cal g^{-1}.

15. A 50-gram bullet is moving with a velocity of 2000 ft sec^{-1}. Calculate its kinetic energy in (*a*) joules and (*b*) calories.

16. The surface tension of water is 72 dynes cm^{-1} (72 ergs cm^{-2}) at 25°; calculate the surface energy in calories of 1 mole of water dispersed as a mist containing droplets 1 micron (10^{-4} cm) in radius. The density of water may be taken as 1.00 g cm^{-3}.

17. What current must be passed through a 100-ohm heater to heat a 10-liter water thermostat 0.1 deg min^{-1}? The specific heat of water may be taken as 1 cal deg^{-1} g^{-1}, and the density as 1 g cm^{-3}.

18. A mole of ammonia gas is condensed at its standard boiling point of $-33.4°C$ by the application of a pressure infinitesimally greater than 1 atm. To evaporate a gram of ammonia at its boiling point requires the absorption of 327 cal. Calculate (*a*) w_{rev}, (*b*) q, (*c*) $\Delta \bar{H}$, (*d*) $\Delta \bar{E}$.

19. One mole of ideal gas at 25° and 100 atm is allowed to expand reversibly and isothermally to 5 atm. Calculate (*a*) the work done by the gas in liter-atmospheres, (*b*) the heat absorbed in calories, (*c*) $\Delta \bar{E}$, and (*d*) $\Delta \bar{H}$.

20. Calculate the maximum work obtained in the isothermal expansion of 10 grams of helium from 10 to 50 liters at 25°, assuming ideal gas behavior. Express the answer in (*a*) calories, (*b*) ergs, and (*c*) liter-atmospheres.

21. Ten moles of carbon dioxide contained in a volume of 20 liters is allowed to expand to a volume of 200 liters at 25°. Calculate the maximum work which may be done if (*a*) the gas is assumed to be ideal and (*b*) van der Waals' equation is used (see equation in problem 7).

22. One hundred liters of helium at 0° and 1 atm is heated in a closed vessel to 800°. (*a*) Calculate the change in internal energy in kilocalories. (*b*) How much more heat would be required if the gas were heated at a constant pressure of 1 atm?

23. Ten cubic feet of oxygen under pressure at 25° is allowed to expand reversibly and adiabatically to a volume of 30 ft^3. Considering oxygen to be an ideal gas with the heat capacity given in Table II, calculate the final temperature.

24. One mole of hydrogen at 25° and 1 atm is compressed adiabatically and reversibly into a volume of 5 liters. Calculate (*a*) the final temperature, (*b*) the final pressure, and (*c*) the work done on the gas.

25. Derive the equation for the adiabatic expansion of a gas obeying the equation of state $P(\bar{V} - b) = RT$.

26. Derive the relation for $\bar{C}_P - \bar{C}_V$ for a gas which follows van der Waals' equation.

27. The specific heat of zinc is 0.0978 cal deg^{-1} g^{-1}, and it has been established that 10.00 grams of zinc combines with 10.85 grams of chlorine to form a stable zinc chloride. What is the atomic weight of zinc, and what is the formula for the zinc chloride if the valence of chlorine is 1 and its atomic weight 35.45?

28. How much work is done when a man weighing 75 kg (165 lb) climbs the Washington monument, 555 ft high? How many kilocalories must be supplied to do this muscular work, assuming that 25 per cent of the energy produced by the oxidation of food in the body can be converted into muscular mechanical work?

29. How far will a 100-gram ball with a velocity of 100 ft sec^{-1} rise vertically, ignoring air friction?

30. The heat loss from a furnace is 100 cal min^{-1}. What current must be passed through a 50-ohm heater to compensate for this heat loss?

31. One hundred liters of water vapor at 100° and $\frac{1}{2}$ atm is compressed isothermally and reversibly to 1 atm and further until the volume is 10 liters. Neglecting the volume of the water condensed in comparison with the volume of the vapor and assuming that the vapor behaves as an ideal gas, calculate the work required for the compression and the heat evolved.

32. Show that for an isothermal expansion of an ideal gas $\Delta \bar{H} = 0$.

33. What is the minimum number of calories of work required to compress isothermally 1 mole of ammonia at 1 atm and 150° to a volume of 10 liters: (a) assuming that it follows the ideal gas law, (b) assuming that it follows van der Waals' equation with $a = 4.170$ liter^2-atm mole^{-2} and $b = 0.03707$ liter mole^{-1}?

34. A mole of ideal gas expands isothermally and reversibly from a state of P_1 and $\bar{V}_1$ to a state of P_2 and $\bar{V}_2$. Calculate the work done by the gas. A real gas which obeys the relation $P(\bar{V} - b) = RT$, where b is a constant, expands isothermally and reversibly from a state of P_1 and $\bar{V}_1$ to a state of P_2 and $\bar{V}_2$. Calculate the work done by the gas. What general conclusion can be drawn from these results?

35. (a) Calculate the change in internal energy of oxygen when it is heated from 0° to 100° at constant volume. (b) Calculate the change in enthalpy for this process.

36. A mole of oxygen at 5 atm and in a volume of 4 liters is allowed to expand reversibly and adiabatically to a final pressure of 1 atm. What are the final (a) volume and (b) temperature?

37. A tank contains 20 liters of compressed nitrogen at 10 atm and 25°. Calculate the maximum work (in calories) which can be obtained when the gas is allowed to expand to 1 atm pressure (a) isothermally and (b) adiabatically.

38. One mole of an ideal gas is confined in a cylinder by a piston. The pressure is P, the volume is $\bar{V}$, and the cylinder is immersed in a thermostat at temperature T. The following cycle is carried out: (1) the temperature of the thermostat is raised 1°, the pressure being kept constant; (2) the pressure is gradually increased until the volume is decreased to the original value $\bar{V}$, with no change in temperature; and (3) the temperature of the thermostat is lowered 1°, the volume being kept constant. Make a table showing the initial and final pressures, volumes, and temperatures, and q, w, and $\Delta \bar{E}$, for each step. Since $\Delta \bar{E}$ for the cycle is 0, show that $\bar{C}_P - \bar{C}_V = R$.

39. Estimate the maximum rise in temperature of a 500-kg iron weight when it hits a surface after falling through 500 meters (neglecting air resistance and assuming that half the heat goes into the iron weight). The atomic weight of iron is 55.85.

40. Estimate how many more calories of heat will be required to heat 100 grams of aluminum from 25° to 300° than will be required to heat the same weight of silver through the same temperature interval.

41. Ten moles of helium is heated from 25° to 125° at constant pressure by introducing some silver metal at 200° and allowing the system to come to thermal equilibrium. How many grams of silver were used?

THERMOCHEMISTRY

4

Thermochemistry is concerned with the heat that accompanies chemical reaction. Since the internal energy and enthalpy of a substance depend upon the temperature, pressure, and state of aggregation and not upon the past history, the change in internal energy or enthalpy for a physical process or chemical reaction is independent of the way the process or reaction is carried out. Thermochemical data are usually expressed by writing the equation for the chemical reaction and giving the value of ΔH or ΔE for the reaction as written. *Exothermic* reactions evolve heat and have negative values of ΔH or ΔE, and *endothermic* reactions absorb heat and have positive values of ΔH or ΔE. The combustion of graphite with pure oxygen at 1 atm pressure to form pure carbon dioxide at 1 atm pressure yields 94,051.8 cal mole $^{-1}$ at 25°. This is represented by

$$C(\text{graphite}) + O_2(g) = CO_2(g) \qquad \Delta H_{298} = -94{,}051.8 \text{ cal mole}^{-1}$$

Standard States. It is very important to specify the states of the reactants and products. To facilitate the tabulation of thermodynamic data certain standard states are adopted. The standard state of a gas is the pure gas at 1 atm pressure; for a liquid it is the pure liquid at 1 atm; for a solid substance it is a specified crystalline state at 1 atm, for example, graphite for carbon and rhombic sulfur for sulfur. In writing equations, solids, liquids, and gases are designated by (s), (l), and (g), respectively, since the enthalpy change depends upon the physical states of the reactants and products. The standard state refers to a temperature of 25° unless otherwise specified.

When the reactants and products are in their standard states, there should, strictly speaking, be a superscript degree sign on ΔH. How-

58

ever, these superscripts will be neglected in the present chapter (except in tables of data) in order to simplify the notation.

The heat absorbed at constant pressure in reactions where pressure-volume work is the only work done is equal to ΔH, the enthalpy of the products minus the enthalpy of the reactants. In chemical reactions $\Delta H = H_2 - H_1$, where H_2 is the enthalpy of the indicated number of moles of products written at the right-hand side of the equality sign and H_1 is the enthalpy of all the moles of reactants written at the left. The absolute values of the enthalpy are unknown, but changes in enthalpy can be determined. In the oxidation of carbon, heat is evolved, and the enthalpy of the system is thereby decreased, so that ΔH has a negative value.

Calorimetric Measurements. Calorimeters are used for measuring the heat changes that accompany chemical reactions. In the most common type, the reaction is allowed to take place in a reaction chamber surrounded by a weighed quantity of water in an insulated vessel, and the rise in temperature is measured with a sensitive thermometer. The product of the rise in temperature and the total heat capacity of the water and calorimeter is equal to the heat evolved. The heat capacity of the surrounding water is obtained by weighing the water and multiplying by its known specific heat; the heat capacity of the calorimeter is determined by carrying out a reaction of known heat evolution in the calorimeter or by introducing a known quantity of heat with an electric heater. The temperature change of the calorimeter is obtained by plotting temperature versus time before and after the reaction and extrapolating both lines back to the time of reaction. The difference between the extrapolated final and initial temperatures is the temperature rise which would have been obtained if there had been no loss of heat from the calorimeter during the period of observation. In adiabatic calorimetry the cooling correction is rendered unnecessary by heating the outer jacket electrically at a controlled rate so that the jacket is always kept at the same temperature as the calorimeter.

Since only rapid, complete reactions are suitable for thermochemical measurement, heats of combustion comprise the most important data of thermochemistry. In order to be sure that combustions will be complete, the material is ignited electrically in a heavy steel bomb containing oxygen under a pressure of 25 atm. Under these conditions all hydrocarbons are burned to water and carbon dioxide. Some reactions present difficulties since they do not go rapidly and completely to definite products. For example, the heat of combustion of a substance like ethyl chloride is not known with high accuracy because an uncertain mixture of products may be obtained.

Standard Enthalpy of Reaction. In order to facilitate the comparison of various reactions, experimental thermochemical data are usually corrected to give the *standard enthalpy of reaction* at 25°. The standard enthalpy of combustion of an organic substance is the standard enthalpy of reaction for complete oxidation of 1 mole of the substance to $CO_2(g)$ and $H_2O(l)$.

Several compilations of accurate thermochemical data have been published by the National Bureau of Standards, and the values in Table I have been obtained from this source.

Table I.[1] Heats of Combustion [to $H_2O(l)$ and $CO_2(g)$] at Constant Pressure and 25°

Substance	$\Delta H°$	
	In kcal mole^{-1}	In kcal g^{-1}
Hydrogen, $H_2(g)$	-68.3174	-33.8876
Graphite, $C(s)$	-94.0518	-7.8311
Carbon monoxide, $CO(g)$	-67.6361	-2.4147
Methane, $CH_4(g)$	-212.798	-13.2651
Ethane, $C_2H_6(g)$	-372.820	-12.3992
Propane, $C_3H_8(g)$	-530.605	-12.0335
n-Butane, $C_4H_{10}(g)$	-687.982	-11.8373
Isobutane, $C_4H_{10}(g)$	-686.342	-11.8091
n-Pentane, $C_5H_{12}(g)$	-845.16	-11.7146
n-Hexane, $C_6H_{14}(l)$	-995.01	-11.5468
n-Heptane, $C_7H_{16}(l)$	-1151.27	-11.4899
n-Octane, $C_8H_{18}(l)$	-1307.53	-11.4471
Ethylene, $C_2H_4(g)$	-337.234	-12.0217
Propylene, $C_3H_6(g)$	-491.987	-11.6923
1-Butene, $C_4H_8(g)$	-649.757	-11.5813
Acetylene, $C_2H_2(g)$	-310.615	-11.9302
Cyclopentane, $C_5H_{10}(l)$	-786.54	-11.2155
Cyclohexane, $C_6H_{12}(l)$	-936.88	-11.1327
Benzene, $C_6H_6(l)$	-780.98	-9.9987
Toluene, $C_7H_8(l)$	-934.50	-10.1428

[1] From F. D. Rossini, K. S. Pitzer, W. J. Taylor, J. P. Ebert, J. E. Kilpatrick, C. W. Beckett, M. G. Williams, and H. G. Werner, "Selected Values of Properties of Hydrocarbons," *Natl. Bur. Standards Circ.* C 461, U. S. Government Printing Office, Washington, D. C., 1947.

Heats of combustion are useful in calculating other thermochemical data. Also they have practical as well as theoretical importance. The purchaser of coal is more interested in its heat of combustion than in its weight. The dietician must know, among other factors, the number of calories obtainable from various foods. In nutrition work the term "calorie" refers to kilocalorie.

Calculation of Heat of Reaction at Constant Pressure from Heat of Reaction at Constant Volume. For a constant-pressure process

$$(\Delta H)_P = (\Delta E)_P + P\,\Delta V \tag{1}$$

For reactions involving only liquids and solids $P\,\Delta V$ is usually negligible in comparison with $(\Delta E)_P$, and the heat absorbed at constant volume and the heat absorbed at constant pressure are the same for all practical purposes. However, for reactions involving gases $P\Delta V$ may be significant. In calculating $P\Delta V$ it is generally sufficiently accurate to assume that the gases are ideal. If Δn represents the number of moles of gaseous products minus the number of moles of gaseous reactants, $P\,\Delta V = RT\,\Delta n$. Thus

$$(\Delta H)_P = (\Delta E)_P + RT\,\Delta n \tag{2}$$

As has been shown on p. 43, the heat absorbed at constant pressure q_P is equal to $(\Delta H)_P$, and the heat absorbed at constant volume q_V is equal to $(\Delta E)_V$. For most purposes the difference between $(\Delta E)_V$ and $(\Delta E)_P$ is sufficiently small that equation 2 may be written:

$$q_P = q_V + RT\Delta n \tag{3}$$

This equation is useful for calculating q_P for a reaction from the heat q_V measured in a bomb calorimeter. In calculating Δn it is important to note the temperature and determine whether a given product or reactant is in the gaseous or liquid state.

Example 1. The heat of combustion of n-heptane at constant volume and $25°$ is 1148.93 kcal mole^{-1}.

$$C_7H_{16}(l) + 11O_2(g) = 7CO_2(g) + 8H_2O(l) \qquad \Delta E = -1148.93 \text{ kcal mole}^{-1}$$

What is the heat absorbed at constant pressure?

$$q_P = q_V + RT\,\Delta n = -1,148,930 - (1.987)(298.1)(4)$$

$$= -1,148,930 - 2370$$

$$= -1,151,300 \text{ cal mole}^{-1} \quad \text{or} \quad -1151.30 \text{ kcal mole}^{-1}$$

Application of First Law to Thermochemistry. Lavoisier and Laplace recognized in 1780 that the heat absorbed in decomposing a compound must be equal to the heat evolved in its formation under the same conditions. Thus, if the reverse of a chemical reaction is written, the sign of ΔH is changed. Hess pointed out in 1840 that the over-all heat of a chemical reaction at constant pressure is the same, regardless of the intermediate steps involved. These principles are both corollaries of the first law of thermodynamics. They follow from the experience of Chapter 3, since the enthalpy change ΔH for a reaction depends only on the initial and final states and is not affected by the path of the reaction. This makes it possible to calculate the enthalpy changes for reactions that cannot be studied directly. For example, it is not practical to measure the heat evolved when carbon burns to carbon monoxide in a limited amount of oxygen because the product will be an uncertain mixture of carbon monoxide and carbon dioxide. However, carbon may be burned completely to carbon dioxide in an excess of oxygen and the heat of reaction measured. Thus, for graphite

$$C(s) + O_2(g) = CO_2(g) \qquad \Delta H = -94.0518 \text{ kcal}$$

The heat evolved when carbon monoxide burns to carbon dioxide can be readily measured also:

$$CO(g) + \tfrac{1}{2}O_2(g) = CO_2(g) \qquad \Delta H = -67.6361 \text{ kcal}$$

Writing these equations in such a way as to obtain the desired reaction, adding, and canceling:

$$
\begin{aligned}
C(s) + O_2(g) &= CO_2(g) & \Delta H &= -94.0518 \text{ kcal} \\
CO_2(g) &= CO(g) + \tfrac{1}{2}O_2(g) & \Delta H &= 67.6361 \text{ kcal} \\
\hline
C(s) + \tfrac{1}{2}O_2(g) &= CO(g) & \Delta H &= -26.4157 \text{ kcal}
\end{aligned}
$$

It will be noticed that, since the second reaction has been reversed, the sign of ΔH is changed from minus to plus. This indicates that 67.6361 kcal would be absorbed if the reaction $CO_2(g) = CO(g) + \tfrac{1}{2}O_2(g)$ occurred.

The indirect calculation of heats of reaction is illustrated with another example.

Example 2. Calculate ΔH for the transition of 1 mole of monoclinic sulfur to rhombic sulfur at room temperature. Although this is a spontaneous transition at room temperature, the change is too slow for accurate calorimetric measurements. Accordingly, a rapid reaction is carried out with the two different forms, and the difference in heats of reaction is equal to the heat of transition.

$$
\begin{aligned}
S(\text{monoclinic}) + O_2(g) &= SO_2(g) & \Delta H &= -71.03 \text{ kcal} \\
SO_2(g) &= S(\text{rhombic}) + O_2(g) & \Delta H &= 70.96 \text{ kcal} \\
\hline
S(\text{monoclinic}) &= S(\text{rhombic}) & \Delta H &= -0.07 \text{ kcal}
\end{aligned}
$$

Enthalpy of Formation. As has been shown in the preceding section, the enthalpy changes of many new reactions may be calculated from the enthalpy changes of reactions which have already been measured. Such calculations are greatly facilitated by the introduction of an *enthalpy of formation* $\Delta \bar{H}°_f$, which is the enthalpy change for the reaction in which 1 mole of the substance is formed in its standard state from its constituent elements, each in its standard state. The bar indicates that we are considering 1 mole of substance. It follows from the reaction on p. 58 that the enthalpy of formation of CO_2 at 25° is -94.0518 kcal. Since the enthalpy of combustion of hydrogen is $-68,317.4$ cal mole^{-1} (Table I), the enthalpy of formation of $H_2O(l)$ is $-68,317.4$ cal mole^{-1}. The enthalpy of formation of liquid water is less negative by the molar heat of vaporization of H_2O at 25°, which is 10,519.5 cal mole^{-1}. Therefore the enthalpy of formation of H_2O (g) at 25° is $-57,979.9$ cal mole^{-1}.

When a substance cannot be formed directly in a rapid reaction from its elements, the enthalpy changes for a series of suitable reactions may be utilized in calculating the enthalpy of formation.

Example 3. Calculate the enthalpy of formation of $H_2SO_4(l)$ from the enthalpy change for the combustion of sulfur to SO_2, the oxidation of SO_2 to SO_3 using a platinum catalyst, and the heat of solution of SO_3 in H_2O to give $H_2SO_4(l)$. The desired reaction is the sum of the following reactions, and the sum of the enthalpy changes is the enthalpy of formation of $H_2SO_4(l)$.

$$S(s) + O_2(g) = SO_2(g) \qquad \Delta H = -70.96 \text{ kcal}$$
$$SO_2(g) + \tfrac{1}{2}O_2(g) = SO_3(g) \qquad \Delta H = -23.49 \text{ kcal}$$
$$SO_3(g) + H_2O(l) = H_2SO_4(l) \qquad \Delta H = -31.14 \text{ kcal}$$
$$H_2(g) + \tfrac{1}{2}O_2(g) = H_2O(l) \qquad \Delta H = -68.32 \text{ kcal}$$

$$S(s) + 2O_2(g) + H_2(g) = H_2SO_4(l) \qquad \Delta \bar{H}_f = -193.91 \text{ kcal}$$

Enthalpies of formation may be used to calculate enthalpies of reaction. The enthalpy change of a reaction is equal to the sum of the enthalpies of formation of the products, each multiplied by its stoichiometric coefficient ν_i in the balanced chemical equation, minus the sum of the enthalpies of formation of the reactants, each multiplied by its stoichiometric coefficient ν_j.

$$\Delta H = \Sigma \nu_i \, \Delta \bar{H}_{f,\text{prod}} - \Sigma \nu_j \, \Delta \bar{H}_{f,\text{react}} \qquad (4)$$

Since the enthalpies of formation of CO_2 and H_2O are known, the enthalpies of formation of organic compounds may readily be calculated from heats of combustion.

Example 4. Calculate the enthalpy of formation of acetylene from the fact that the enthalpy change for combustion is -310.615 kcal.

$$C_2H_2(g) + 2\tfrac{1}{2}O_2(g) = 2CO_2(g) + H_2O(l) \qquad \Delta H = -310.615 \text{ kcal}$$

$$\Delta H = -310.615 = 2\Delta \bar{H}_{f,CO_2} + \Delta \bar{H}_{f,H_2O} - \Delta \bar{H}_{f,C_2H_2}$$

$$= -188.104 + (-68.3174) - \Delta \bar{H}_{f,C_2H_2}$$

$$\Delta \bar{H}_{f,C_2H_2} = 54.194 \text{ kcal mole}^{-1}$$

Since the enthalpies of formation are obtained by taking differences between heats of combustion, a fairly small percentage error in the large heats of combustion may introduce a large percentage error in their difference.

Example 5. What percentage error in the calculation of the heat of formation of n-butane will be introduced by an error of 0.2 per cent in the heat of combustion of n-butane?

$$C_4H_{10}(g) + 6\tfrac{1}{2}O_2(g) = 4CO_2(g) + 5H_2O(l) \qquad \Delta H = -687.982 \text{ kcal}$$

$$\Delta \bar{H}_{f,n\text{-butane}} = 687.982 - 4(94.0518) - 5(68.3174)$$

$$= -29.812 \text{ kcal mole}^{-1}$$

An error of 0.2 per cent in the heat of combustion would be 1.4 kcal. An error of 1.4 kcal in the heat of formation of n-butane is an error of $(100)(1.4)/(29.8)$ or 4.7 per cent.

The enthalpies of formation of many compounds, ions, and atoms are accurately known, and a few selected values from *Circular* 500 and *Circular* 461 of the National Bureau of Standards are given in Table II. In obtaining these accurate data great precision in calorimetry and great care in purification of the substances were required. From these enthalpies of formation the enthalpy changes for many reactions may be calculated by use of equation 4.

Example 6. Calculate the enthalpy change at 25° for the reaction

$$Fe_2O_3(s) + 2Al(s) = Al_2O_3(s) + 2Fe(s)$$

The enthalpies of formation of the elements are equal to zero. Using values from Table II, we calculate the enthalpy change for the reaction as follows:

$$\Delta H = \Delta \bar{H}_{f,Al_2O_3} - \Delta \bar{H}_{f,Fe_2O_3}$$

$$= -399.1 - (-196.5) = -202.6 \text{ kcal}$$

The standard state of a solute in aqueous solution is taken as the hypothetical ideal state of unit molality, in which the enthalpy of the solute is the same as in the infinitely dilute solution.

Heat of Solution. When a solute is dissolved in a solvent, heat may be absorbed or evolved; in general, the heat of solution depends upon the concentration of the final solution. The *integral heat of solution*

Table II.[1] Enthalpy of Formation at 25°

$(\Delta \bar{H}^\circ_f$ in kcal mole$^{-1})$

Elements and Inorganic Compounds

$O_3(g)$	34.0	$CO(g)$	-26.4157
$H_2O(g)$	-57.7979	$CO_2(g)$	-94.0518
$H_2O(l)$	-68.3174	$PbO(s)$	-52.5
$HCl(g)$	-22.063	$PbO_2(s)$	-66.12
$Br_2(g)$	7.34	$PbSO_4(s)$	-219.50
$HBr(g)$	-8.66	$Hg(g)$	14.54
$HI(g)$	6.20	$Ag_2O(s)$	-7.306
S(monoclinic)	0.071	$AgCl(s)$	-30.362
$SO_2(g)$	-70.96	$Fe_2O_3(s)$	-196.5
$SO_3(g)$	-94.45	$Fe_3O_4(s)$	-267.0
$H_2S(g)$	-4.815	$Al_2O_3(s)$	-399.09
$H_2SO_4(l)$	-193.91	$UF_6(g)$	-505
$NO(g)$	21.600	$UF_6(s)$	-517
$NO_2(g)$	8.091	$CaO(s)$	-151.9
$NH_3(g)$	-11.04	$CaCO_3(s)$	-288.45
$HNO_3(l)$	-41.404	$NaF(s)$	-136.0
$P(g)$	75.18	$NaCl(s)$	-98.232
$PCl_3(g)$	-73.22	$KF(s)$	-134.46
$PCl_5(g)$	-95.35	$KCl(s)$	-104.175
C(s, diamond)	0.4532		

Organic Compounds

Methane, $CH_4(g)$	-17.889	Propylene, $C_3H_6(g)$	4.879
Ethane, $C_2H_6(g)$	-20.236	1-Butene, $C_4H_8(g)$	0.280
Propane, $C_3H_8(g)$	-24.820	Acetylene, $C_2H_2(g)$	54.194
n-Butane, $C_4H_{10}(g)$	-29.812	Formaldehyde, $CH_2O(g)$	-27.7
Isobutane, $C_4H_{10}(g)$	-31.452	Acetaldehyde, $CH_3CHO(g)$	-39.76
n-Pentane, $C_5H_{12}(g)$	-35.00	Methanol, $CH_3OH(l)$	-57.02
n-Hexane, $C_6H_{14}(g)$	-39.96	Ethanol, $C_2H_5OH(l)$	-66.356
n-Heptane, $C_7H_{16}(g)$	-44.89	Formic acid, $HCOOH(l)$	-97.8
n-Octane, $C_8H_{18}(g)$	-49.82	Acetic acid, $CH_3COOH(l)$	-116.4
Benzene, $C_6H_6(g)$	19.820	Oxalic acid, $(CO_2H)_2(s)$	-197.6
Benzene, $C_6H_6(l)$	11.718	Carbon tetrachloride, $CCl_4(l)$	-33.3
Ethylene, $C_2H_4(g)$	12.496	Glycine, $H_2NCH_2CO_2H(s)$	-126.33

Ions in Water

H^+	0.000	$SO_4{}^{2-}$	-216.90	Cu^{2+}	15.39
OH^-	-54.957	HS^-	-4.22	Ag^+	25.31
F^-	-78.66	$NO_3{}^-$	-49.372	Mg^{2+}	-110.41
Cl^-	-40.023	$NH_4{}^+$	-31.74	Ca^{2+}	-129.77
$ClO_4{}^-$	-31.41	$PO_4{}^{3-}$	-306.9	Li^+	-66.554
Br^-	-28.90	$CO_3{}^{2-}$	-161.63	Na^+	-57.279
I^-	-13.37	Zn^{2+}	-36.43	K^+	-60.04
S^{2-}	10.0	Cd^{2+}	-17.30		

Gaseous Atoms

H	52.089	Br	26.71	N	85.565
F	18.3	I	25.482	C	171.698
Cl	29.012				

[1] These data have been obtained from F. D. Rossini, D. D. Wagman, W. H. Evans, S. Levine, and I. Jaffe, "Selected Values of Chemical Thermodynamic Properties," *Natl. Bur. Standards Circ.* 500, U. S. Government Printing Office, Washington, D. C., 1952, and F. D. Rossini, K. S. Pitzer, W. J. Taylor, J. P. Ebert, J. E. Kilpatrick, C. W. Beckett, M. G. Williams, and H. G. Werner, "Selected Values of Properties of Hydrocarbons," *Natl. Bur. Standards Circ.* C 461, U. S. Government Printing Office, Washington, D. C., 1947.

is the enthalpy change for the solution of 1 mole of solute in n_1 moles of solvent. The solution process may be represented by a chemical equation such as

$$\text{HCl}(g) + 5\text{H}_2\text{O}(l) = \text{HCl in } 5\text{H}_2\text{O} \qquad \Delta H = -15.31 \text{ kcal}$$

where "HCl in $5\text{H}_2\text{O}$" represents a solution of 1 mole of HCl in 5 moles of H_2O. The integral heats of solution of HCl, NaOH, and NaCl are plotted versus the number of moles of water per mole of solute in *Fig. 4-1*. The integral heat of solution depends upon the number of moles of solvent used. The symbol aq is used to represent an aqueous solution which is so dilute that additional dilution produces no thermal effect. As an illustration

$$\text{HCl}(g) + aq = \text{HCl}(aq) \qquad \Delta H = -17.96 \text{ kcal}$$

Integral heats of solution of a number of solutes are given in Table III.

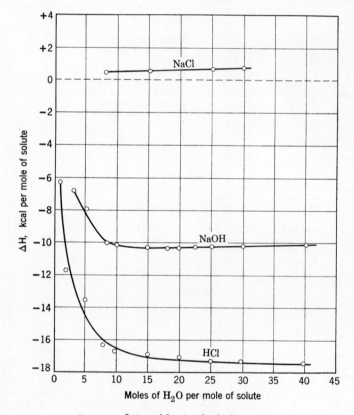

Fig. 4-1. Integral heats of solution at 25°.

Table III.[1]   Integral Heats of Solution in Water at 25°

Solute	Moles H_2O	$\Delta H°$, kcal mole^{-1}	Solute	Moles H_2O	$\Delta H°$, kcal mole^{-1}
$HCl(g)$	5	-15.31	$NH_4NO_3(s)$	5	4.24
	200	-17.74		200	6.08
	10,000	-17.92	$CH_3CO_2H(l)$	200	-0.32
	∞	-17.96	$CuSO_4(s)$	200	-16.20
$HBr(g)$	200	-20.05	$KOH(s)$	5	-11.53
$HI(g)$	200	-7.02		200	-13.04
$H_2SO_4(l)$	200	-17.91	$KCl(s)$	200	4.20
$HNO_3(l)$	200	-7.84	$NaOH(s)$	5	-9.03
$NH_3(g)$	200	-8.28		200	-10.11
$CH_3OH(l)$	10	-1.43	$NaCl(s)$	200	1.02

[1] *Natl. Bur. Standards Circ.* 500, U. S. Government Printing Office, Washington, D. C., 1952.

When a solute is dissolved in a solvent which is chemically quite similar and there are no complications of ionization or solvation, the heat of solution may be nearly equal to the heat of fusion of the solute.* In general it might be expected that heat would always be absorbed in overcoming the attraction between the molecules or ions of the solid solute. However, another process which commonly occurs is combination with the solvent, referred to as solvation, which evolves heat.

The importance of this attraction of the solvent for the solute in the process of solution may be illustrated by the dissolving of sodium chloride in water. In the crystal lattice of sodium chloride, positive sodium ions and negative chloride ions attract each other strongly. The energy required to separate them is so great that nonpolar solvents like benzene and carbon tetrachloride do not dissolve sodium chloride; but a solvent like water, which has a high dielectric constant and a large dipole moment, has a strong attraction for the sodium and chloride ions and solvates them with the evolution of a large amount of heat. When, as in sodium chloride, the heat absorbed in breaking up the crystal is about equal to that evolved by solvation, the result is nearly zero and there is little heating or cooling. With many crystals the heat evolved by solvation is less than the heat

* J. H. Hildebrand and R. L. Scott, *Solubility of Non-Electrolytes*, Reinhold Publishing Corp., New York, 1950.

absorbed in the solution process, and so heat is absorbed in the solution process. With a few salts, such as anhydrous sodium sulfate, the energy of solvation is more than the energy of crystal disintegration, and so heat is evolved.

Since a larger heat effect per mole is obtained in forming dilute solutions than in forming concentrated ones, dilution of concentrated solutions causes the evolution or absorption of heat. The integral heat of dilution between two molalities m_1 and m_2 is the heat accompanying the dilution of an amount of solution of concentration m_2 containing 1 mole of solute with pure solvent to make a solution of concentration m_1. The integral heat of dilution from one concentration to another is equal to the difference between the integral heats of solution for these concentrations.

Example 7. Calculate the integral heat of dilution for the addition of 195 moles of H_2O to 1 mole of HCl in 5 moles of H_2O, using data from Table III.

$$HCl(g) + 200H_2O(l) = HCl \text{ in } 200H_2O \qquad \Delta H = -17.74 \text{ kcal}$$
$$HCl \text{ in } 5H_2O = HCl(g) + 5H_2O(l) \qquad \Delta H = 15.31 \text{ kcal}$$

$$HCl \text{ in } 5H_2O + 195H_2O(l) = HCl \text{ in } 200H_2O \qquad \Delta H = -2.43 \text{ kcal}$$

Heat-of-solution experiments may be used to determine the heat of hydration of a solid. Such enthalpy changes cannot be measured directly because of the slowness of the phase transformation. However, the heat of hydration is equal to the difference between the integral heats of solution of the two forms.

Example 8. Calculate the heat of hydration of $Na_2SO_4(s)$ from the integral heats of solution of $Na_2SO_4(s)$ and $Na_2SO_4 \cdot 10H_2O(s)$ in infinite amounts of H_2O, which are -0.56 kcal and $+18.85$ kcal, respectively.

$$Na_2SO_4(s) + aq = Na_2SO_4(aq) \qquad \Delta H = -0.56$$
$$Na_2SO_4(aq) = Na_2SO_4 \cdot 10H_2O(s) + aq \qquad \Delta H = -18.85$$

$$Na_2SO_4(s) + 10H_2O(l) = Na_2SO_4 \cdot 10H_2O(s) \qquad \Delta H = -19.41$$

The symbol aq represents an excess of water so that $10H_2O$ may be taken from it.

The *differential heat of solution* is the heat of solution of 1 mole of solute in such a large volume of solution that the addition of 1 more mole of solute does not change the concentration appreciably. The differential heat of solution depends upon the concentration of the solution. It is impractical to measure the differential heat of solution directly, but it can be calculated from data on the integral heat of solution. The heat effect for the formation of a solution containing m moles of solute and 1000 grams of solvent is $m \Delta H$, where ΔH is the integral heat of solution per mole of solute. If this quantity is plotted against the number of moles of solute m, the slope of the graph at a given concentration is the heat effect per mole of solute or the differential heat of solution, $d(m \, \Delta H)/dm$, at that concentration.

Enthalpies of Formation of Solutes. Enthalpies of formation of solutes may be defined similarly to the enthalpies of formation of gases, liquids, and solids. The enthalpy of formation of water is neglected in calculations if there is the same number of moles of water on both sides of the balanced chemical equation. Also, the enthalpy of formation of pure water is used for water in aqueous solution. This is done arbitrarily, much as the enthalpies of formation of the elements are taken equal to zero. The calculation of the enthalpy of formation of a solute is illustrated in the following example.

Example 9. Calculate the enthalpy of formation of HCl in 200 moles of H_2O from the enthalpy of solution:

$$HCl(g) + 200H_2O(l) = HCl \text{ in } 200H_2O \qquad \Delta H_{298} = -17.74 \text{ kcal}$$

$$\Delta H_{298} = \Delta \bar{H}_{f,HCl \text{ in } 200H_2O} - \Delta \bar{H}_{f,HCl(g)}$$

$$-17.74 = \Delta \bar{H}_{f,HCl \text{ in } 200H_2O} - (-22.063)$$

$$\Delta \bar{H}_{f,HCl \text{ in } 200H_2O} = -39.80 \text{ kcal mole}^{-1}$$

The enthalpies of formation of a number of solutes are given for three concentrations in Table IV. The enthalpies of formation of

Table IV.[1] Enthalpies of Formation of Solutes in Aqueous Solution at 25°

$$(\Delta \bar{H}°_f \text{ in kcal mole}^{-1})$$

Solute	In $100H_2O$	In $200H_2O$	In ∞H_2O
NaOH	-112.108	-112.1	-112.236
NaCl	-97.250	-97.216	-97.302
$NaNO_3$	-106.83	-106.70	-106.651
$NaC_2H_3O_2$	-173.827	-173.890	-174.122
$HC_2H_3O_2$	-116.705	-116.724	-116.743
HCl	-39.713	-39.798	-40.023
HNO_3	-49.231	-49.244	-49.372

[1] *Natl. Bur. Standards Circ.* 500, U. S. Government Printing Office, Washington, D. C., 1952.

solutes are useful for calculating the enthalpy changes for solution reactions, as illustrated in example 10.

Example 10. Calculate ΔH_{298} for the reaction

$$\text{HCl in } 100\text{H}_2\text{O} + \text{NaOH in } 100\text{H}_2\text{O} = \text{NaCl in } 200\text{H}_2\text{O} + \text{H}_2\text{O}(l)$$

$$\Delta H_{298} = -97.216 - 68.3174 + 39.713 + 112.108$$

$$= -13.712 \text{ kcal}$$

For dilute solutions it is found that the heat of reaction of strong bases, like NaOH and KOH, with strong acids, like HCl and HNO_3, is independent of the nature of the acid or base. This constancy of the heat of neutralization is a result of the complete ionization of strong acids and bases and the salts formed by neutralization. Thus, when a dilute solution of a strong acid is added to a dilute solution of a strong base, the only chemical reaction is

$$\text{OH}^- + \text{H}^+ = \text{H}_2\text{O} \qquad \Delta H = -13.70 \text{ kcal mole}^{-1}$$

When a dilute solution of a weak acid or base is neutralized, the heat of neutralization may be somewhat less because of the absorption of heat in the dissociation of the weak acid or base. For example, the neutralization of HCN by NaOH evolves only 2.9 kcal mole^{-1}.

When dilute solutions of salts of strong acids and strong bases are mixed with each other or with solutions of strong acids or strong bases, there is no appreciable heat effect, provided that a chemical reaction does not occur. For example, when dilute solutions of NaCl and KBr are mixed, no heat is evolved or absorbed. The reason is that strong electrolytes are completely dissociated and their heats of dilution are very small for dilute solutions. Thus the reaction could be represented by

$$\text{Na}^+(aq) + \text{Cl}^-(aq) + \text{K}^+(aq) + \text{Br}^-(aq) = \text{Na}^+(aq)$$
$$+ \text{Cl}^-(aq) + \text{K}^+(aq) + \text{Br}^-(aq)$$

and it is apparent that no heat effect would be expected.

Enthalpies of Formation of Ions. Since for strong electrolytes in dilute solution the thermal properties of the ions are essentially independent of the accompanying ions, it is convenient to use relative enthalpies of formation of individual ions. The sum of the enthalpies of formation of H^+ and OH^- ions may be calculated from

$$\text{H}_2\text{O}(l) = \text{H}^+(aq) + \text{OH}^-(aq) \qquad \Delta H = 13.70 \text{ kcal}$$
$$\text{H}_2(g) + \tfrac{1}{2}\text{O}_2(g) = \text{H}_2\text{O}(l) \qquad\qquad\qquad \Delta H = -68.31 \text{ kcal}$$

$$\text{H}_2(g) + \tfrac{1}{2}\text{O}_2(g) = \text{H}^+(aq) + \text{OH}^-(aq) \qquad \Delta H = -54.61 \text{ kcal}$$

The separate enthalpies of formation of H^+ and OH^- cannot be calculated, but if it is assumed that the enthalpy of formation of $H^+(aq)$ is zero, it is possible to calculate *relative* enthalpies of formation for other ions. Denoting the electron by e, the convention is that

$$\tfrac{1}{2}H_2(g) + aq = H^+(aq) + e \qquad \Delta H = 0$$

Therefore the enthalpy of formation of OH^- is given by

$$\tfrac{1}{2}H_2(g) + \tfrac{1}{2}O_2(g) + aq + e = OH^-(aq) \qquad \Delta H = -54.61 \text{ kcal}$$

On the basis of these values for the enthalpies of formation of H^+ and OH^-, the enthalpies of formation of other ions of strong electrolytes may be calculated.

From the enthalpy of formation of $HCl(aq)$ it is possible to calculate the enthalpy of formation of $Cl^-(aq)$.

$$\tfrac{1}{2}H_2(g) + \tfrac{1}{2}Cl_2(g) + aq = H^+(aq) + Cl^-(aq) \qquad \Delta H = -40.023 \text{ kcal}$$

$$\tfrac{1}{2}Cl_2(g) + aq + e = Cl^-(aq) \qquad \Delta H = -40.023 \text{ kcal}$$

These and other enthalpies of formation of ions are given in Table II.

Thermochemical Constants. Thermochemical data are necessary for many calculations of chemical equilibria and the interpretation of reaction rates. It will be shown on pp. 96 and 210, for example, that, when the heat capacities of reactants and products are known down to the neighborhood of absolute zero, a knowledge of the heat of reaction permits a simple and accurate calculation of the equilibrium constant of a chemical reaction. In many of these calculations the heats of reaction constitute the least satisfactory part of the available data.

If needed thermochemical data are not available, various methods may be used to obtain an estimate of the enthalpy of formation from data on related compounds. In the method developed by Andersen, Beyer, and Watson,* each compound is regarded as a fundamental group which is modified by replacing its atoms with new groups. For example, a paraffin hydrocarbon is derived from methane by successive substitutions of CH_3 groups for hydrogen atoms. Definite values of $\Delta(\Delta \bar{H}_f)$ are assigned to various group replacements such as OH, C_6H_5, NH_2, and Cl and to the replacement of single bonds by multiple bonds.

---

* O. A. Hougen, K. M. Watson, and R. A. Ragatz, *Chemical Process Principles,* Part II, John Wiley & Sons, New York, 1959.

72   PHYSICAL CHEMISTRY

Bond Energies.* In order to estimate the ΔH of reactions involving compounds for which $\Delta \bar{H}_f$ is not known, bond energies are often used. The bond energy of a diatomic molecule may be determined with accuracy by measuring the degree of dissociation at a series of temperatures (p. 214). Also, dissociation energies can be calculated from spectroscopic measurements as shown by the values in Table III of Chapter 18. The energy required to break certain bonds in more complicated molecules may be estimated by chemical kinetic methods and by determining the lowest energy of accelerated electrons required to produce a given ion by dissociation and ionization, using a mass spectrometer (p. 676).

The bond energy for a particular type of bond in a polyatomic molecule is an average for the various bonds of this type. For example, the C—H bond energy in CH_4 is one-fourth of the energy required to separate CH_4 into atoms. This ΔH may be obtained by summing the following reactions:

$$C(\text{graphite}) + 2H_2(g) = CH_4(g) \qquad \Delta \bar{H}_f = -18 \text{ kcal}$$
$$4H(g) = 2H_2(g) \qquad \Delta H = -206$$
$$C(g) = C(\text{graphite}) \qquad \Delta H = -170$$

$$C(g) + 4H(g) = CH_4(g) \qquad \Delta H = 394 \text{ kcal}$$

Thus the C—H bond energy in CH_4 is $394/4 = 98$ kcal. This may be compared with the energy of dissociation of the successive hydrogen atoms of methane.

$$CH_4(g) = CH_3(g) + H(g) \qquad \Delta H = 102 \text{ kcal}$$
$$CH_3(g) = CH_2(g) + H(g) \qquad \Delta H > 100$$
$$CH_2(g) = CH(g) + H(g) \qquad \Delta H < 110$$
$$CH(g) = C(g) + H(g) \qquad \Delta H = 82$$

The heat of sublimation of carbon has long resisted accurate determination,† but now various types of experimental evidence support the value of 170 kcal used above. This value may be obtained from measurements of the vapor pressure of carbon over graphite at high temperatures and from measurements of the spectroscopic dissociation energies of simple gas molecules containing carbon, such as CO, C_2H_2, and C_2N_2.

* T. L. Cottrell, *The Strengths of Chemical Bonds*, Butterworths Scientific Publications, London, 1954.
† D. M. Kern, *J. Chem. Educ.*, *33*, 272 (1956).

Bond-dissociation energies are generally given for $0°K$ rather than $298°K$. There are effects on bond energies of other parts of the molecule, and so a given type of bond does not have an exact energy. The bond energies in Table V represent averages of the best available data

Table V.[1] ΔH of Bond Dissociation (Bond Energies)

(In kcal mole^{-1})

Bond	ΔH	Bond	ΔH
C—C	80.5	O—O	34
C=C	145	O—H	109.4
C≡C	198	H—H	103.2
C—H	98.2	N—N	37
C—Cl	78	N—H	92.2
C—O	79	H—Cl	102.1
C=O	173	Cl—Cl	57.1
C—Br	54	Br—Br	46

[1] K. S. Pitzer, *Quantum Chemistry*, Prentice-Hall, Englewood Cliffs, N. J., 1953, p. 170.

for different compounds. Estimates of ΔH based on bond energies have been found to be quite satisfactory, provided that the molecules involved can each be represented by a single structural formula. When a molecule can exist with two or more different electronic configurations, its stability is increased and a greater amount of energy is required to break the bond (p. 492).

The heat of a reaction may be estimated by adding the bond energies for the bonds that are broken and subtracting from this total the bond energies for the new bonds formed in the reaction. This may be illustrated with the reaction

$$
\begin{array}{ccc}
\text{H} & \text{H} & \qquad\qquad \text{H} \quad \text{H} \\
| & | & \qquad\qquad | \quad\quad | \\
\text{C} & =\text{C} + \text{H—H} = & \text{H—C—C—H} \\
| & | & \qquad\qquad | \quad\quad | \\
\text{H} & \text{H} & \qquad\qquad \text{H} \quad \text{H}
\end{array}
$$

H—H bond is broken	$\Delta H =$	103.2 kcal
C=C bond is broken	$\Delta H =$	145 kcal
C—C bond is formed	$\Delta H =$	-80.5 kcal
2(C—H) bonds are formed	$\Delta H =$	-196.4 kcal
	$\Delta H =$	-29 kcal

According to these estimates, the hydrogenation of ethylene should evolve 29 kcal mole^{-1}. The experimental value is 32.73 kcal mole^{-1}.

Dependence of Heat Capacity on Temperature. In Chapter 3 it was found that the heat capacity of a monatomic gas at constant pressure is 5.0 cal mole^{-1} deg^{-1} independent of temperature, and that the heat capacities of polyatomic gases are greater than this value and increase with increasing temperature, as illustrated in Fig. 3-3. The parameters for an empirical equation giving the molar heat capacities of a number of gases as a function of temperature are recorded in Table VI. The

Table VI.^{1} Molar Heat Capacity of Gases at Constant Pressure

(In cal deg^{-1} mole^{-1})

$$\bar{C}_P = a + bT + cT^2$$

Gas	a	$b \times 10^3$	$c \times 10^7$
H$_2$	6.9469	−0.1999	4.808
N$_2$	6.4492	1.4125	−0.807
O$_2$	6.0954	3.2533	−10.171
Cl$_2$	7.5755	2.4244	−9.650
CO	6.3424	1.8363	−2.801
CO$_2$	6.3957	10.1933	−35.333
HCl	6.7319	0.4325	3.697
HBr	6.5776	0.9549	1.581
H$_2$O	7.1873	2.3733	2.084
CO$_2$	6.3957	10.1933	−35.333
NH$_3$	6.189	7.887	−7.28
CH$_4$	3.422	17.845	−41.65
C$_2$H$_6$	1.375	41.852	−138.27
C$_3$H$_8$	0.410	64.710	−225.82

^{1} The constants are applicable in the range 300–1500°K. H. M. Spencer and J. L. Justice, *J. Am. Chem. Soc.*, *56*, 2311 (1934); H. M. Spencer and G. N. Flannagan, *J. Am. Chem. Soc.*, *64*, 2511 (1942).

molar heat capacities of simple gases can be calculated more accurately than they can be determined experimentally, especially at high temperatures (see Chapter 19).

To calculate the heat absorbed per mole at constant pressure when the temperature of a substance is raised, the equation $d\bar{H} = \bar{C}_P\, dT$ is integrated between the desired temperature limits.

$$\Delta \bar{H} = \bar{H}_{T_2} - \bar{H}_{T_1} = \int_{T_1}^{T_2} \bar{C}_P \, dT = \int_{T_1}^{T_2} (a + bT + cT^2) \, dT$$

$$= a(T_2 - T_1) + \frac{b}{2}(T_2^2 - T_1^2) + \frac{c}{3}(T_2^3 - T_1^3) \tag{5}$$

Example 11. Calculate the heat required to raise the temperature of 1 mole of oxygen from 300 to 1000°K at constant pressure.

$$\Delta \bar{H} = \int_{300}^{1000} \bar{C}_P \, dT = \int_{300}^{1000} (6.0954 + 3.2533 + 10^{-3}T - 1.0171 \times 10^{-6}T^2) \, dT$$

$$= (6.0954)(700) + \frac{3.2533 \times 10^{-3}}{2}(1000^2 - 300^2)$$

$$- \frac{1.0171 \times 10^{-6}}{3}(1000^3 - 300^3)$$

$$= 4267 + 1480 - 330 = 5417 \text{ cal mole}^{-1}$$

When the temperature change or the variation of heat capacity with temperature is small, it is satisfactory to use the average heat capacity in this temperature range. Then the heat absorbed in heating a mole of substance is given by the expression

$$\Delta \bar{H} = \bar{C}_{P_{\text{avg}}}(T_2 - T_1) \tag{6}$$

For ideal gases the equations for the heat capacities at constant pressure as given in Table VI can be transformed into the corresponding equations for the heat capacities at constant volume by subtracting 1.987 cal deg^{-1} mole^{-1} from the first term, in agreement with the relation developed in equation 35 of Chapter 3, $\bar{C}_P - \bar{C}_V = R$. The molar heat capacities of liquids and solids are only slightly different at constant pressure and constant volume.

Dependence of the Heat of Reaction on Temperature. Let us consider the simple process $A \rightarrow B$, which may be carried out either at temperature T_1 or at temperature T_2. If we know the enthalpy of reaction at temperature T_1, we can calculate the enthalpy of reaction at temperature T_2 by means of the following two paths from A at temperature T_2 to B at temperature T_2, provided that the heat capacities of A and B are known:

$$
\begin{array}{ccc}
 & A \xrightarrow[T_2]{\Delta H_2} B & \\
\int_{T_2}^{T_1} \bar{C}_{P,A} \, dT \downarrow & & \uparrow \int_{T_1}^{T_2} \bar{C}_{P,B} \, dT \\
 & A \xrightarrow[T_1]{\Delta H_1} B &
\end{array}
\tag{7}
$$

The enthalpy change of reaction at T_2 is equal to the sum of three terms:

$$\Delta H_2 = \int_{T_2}^{T_1} \bar{C}_{P,A}\, dT + \Delta H_1 + \int_{T_1}^{T_2} \bar{C}_{P,B}\, dT \tag{8}$$

since the enthalpy change is independent of the path chosen between two states. It is convenient to write this equation

$$\Delta H_2 = \Delta H_1 + \int_{T_1}^{T_2} \Delta \bar{C}_P\, dT \tag{9}$$

where $\Delta \bar{C}_P = \bar{C}_{P,B} - \bar{C}_{P,A}$. If the heat capacities of reactant and product are independent of temperature between T_1 and T_2, $\Delta \bar{C}_P$ may be placed in front of the integration sign and

$$\Delta H_2 = \Delta H_1 + \Delta \bar{C}_P(T_2 - T_1) \tag{10}$$

Example 12. Calculate the heat evolved in the freezing of water at constant pressure and a temperature of $-10°$.

$$H_2O(l) = H_2O(s)$$

Given: $\Delta H_{273} = -79.7$ cal g^{-1}; $C_{P,\mathrm{H_2O}(l)} = 1.00$ cal deg^{-1} g^{-1}; $C_{P,\mathrm{H_2O}(s)} = 0.49$ cal deg^{-1} g^{-1}. The following calculation is carried out for 1 gram of H_2O rather than 1 mole.

$$\Delta H_{263} = \Delta H_{273} + [C_{P,\mathrm{H_2O}(s)} - C_{P,\mathrm{H_2O}(l)}](263 - 273)$$

$$\Delta H_{263} = \Delta H_{273} + (-0.51)(-10)$$

$$= -79.7 + 5.1 = -74.6 \text{ cal g}^{-1}$$

General Treatment of the Effect of Temperature on the Enthalpy of Reaction. For a general chemical reaction

$$aA + bB = gG + hH \tag{11}$$

the enthalpy change is

$$\Delta H = g\bar{H}_G + h\bar{H}_H - a\bar{H}_A - b\bar{H}_B \tag{12}$$

The rate of change of ΔH with temperature is obtained by differentiating equation 12 with respect to temperature at constant pressure.

$$\left[\frac{d(\Delta H)}{dT}\right]_P = g\left(\frac{d\bar{H}_G}{dT}\right)_P + h\left(\frac{d\bar{H}_H}{dT}\right)_P - a\left(\frac{d\bar{H}_A}{dT}\right)_P - b\left(\frac{d\bar{H}_B}{dT}\right)_P \tag{13}$$

Remembering that $(d\bar{H}/dT)_P = \bar{C}_P$,

$$\left[\frac{d(\Delta H)}{dT}\right]_P = g\bar{C}_{P,G} + h\bar{C}_{P,H} - a\bar{C}_{P,A} - b\bar{C}_{P,B} = \Delta \bar{C}_P \tag{14}$$

This equation may be stated in words as follows: the change in enthalpy of reaction at constant pressure per degree rise in temperature is equal to the sum of the heat capacities of the products each multiplied by its coefficient in the chemical equation minus the sum of the heat capacities of the reactants each multiplied by its coefficient in the chemical equation.

Equation 14 may be integrated between two temperatures T_1 and T_2 to obtain the relation between the enthalpy changes at these two temperatures.

$$\int_{\Delta H_1}^{\Delta H_2} d(\Delta H) = \Delta H_2 - \Delta H_1 = \int_{T_1}^{T_2} \Delta \bar{C}_P \, dT \tag{15}$$

By use of this equation it is possible to calculate ΔH for a reaction at another temperature if it is known at one temperature and if the values of $\bar{C}_P$ for the reactants and products are known in the intervening temperature range. The empirical equations for expressing $\bar{C}_P$ as a function of absolute temperature are very useful for this purpose.

Example 13. Calculate the heat of combustion of hydrogen at 1500°K.

$$2H_2(g) + O_2(g) = 2H_2O(g) \qquad \Delta H_{298} = -115{,}595.8 \text{ cal}$$

The molar heat capacities of Table VI are substituted into the following equation:

$$\Delta H_{1500} = \Delta H_{298} + \int_{298}^{1500} (2\bar{C}_{P,H_2O} - \bar{C}_{P,O_2} - 2\bar{C}_{P,H_2}) \, dT$$

to obtain

$$\Delta H_{1500} = -115{,}595.8 + \int_{298}^{1500} (-5.6146 + 1.8931 \times 10^{-3}T + 4.723 \times 10^{-7}T^2) \, dT$$

$$= -119{,}767 \text{ cal}$$

Equation 15 is applicable only if there are no changes in phase in going from T_1 to T_2; additional terms must be introduced for the enthalpy changes accompanying phase transformations such as melting or vaporization.

REFERENCES

F. R. Bichowsky and F. D. Rossini, *The Thermochemistry of the Chemical Substances*, Reinhold Publishing Corp., New York, 1936.

F. Daniels, J. H. Mathews, J. W. Williams, P. Bender, and R. A. Alberty, *Experimental Physical Chemistry*, McGraw-Hill Book Co., New York, 1955.

O. A. Hougen, K. M. Watson, and R. A. Ragatz, *Chemical Process Principles*, Part I, John Wiley & Sons, New York, 1954.

I. M. Klotz, *Chemical Thermodynamics*, Prentice-Hall, Englewood Cliffs, N. J., 1950.

G. N. Lewis, M. Randall, K. S. Pitzer, and L. Brewer, *Thermodynamics*, McGraw-Hill Book Co., New York, 1961.

F. D. Rossini, K. S. Pitzer, W. J. Taylor, J. P. Ebert, J. E. Kilpatrick, C. W. Beckett, M. G. Williams, and H. G. Werner, "Selected Values of Properties of Hydrocarbons," *Natl. Bur. Standards Circ.* C 461, U. S. Government Printing Office, Washington, D. C., 1947.

F. D. Rossini, D. D. Wagman, W. H. Evans, S. Levine, and I. Jaffe, "Selected Values of Chemical Thermodynamic Properties," *Natl. Bur. Standards Circ.* 500, U. S. Government Printing Office, Washington, D. C., 1952.

R. R. Wenner, *Thermochemical Calculations*, McGraw-Hill Book Co., New York, 1941.

PROBLEMS

1. In an adiabatic calorimeter, oxidation of 0.4362 gram of naphthalene caused a temperature rise of $1.707°$. The heat capacity of the calorimeter and water was 2460 cal $\deg^{-1}$. If corrections for oxidation of the wire and residual nitrogen are neglected, what is the enthalpy of combustion of naphthalene per mole?

Ans. -1232 kcal mole^{-1}.

2. The following reactions might be used to power rockets:

$$(1) \quad H_2(g) + \tfrac{1}{2}O_2(g) = H_2O(g)$$

$$(2) \quad CH_3OH(l) + 1\tfrac{1}{2}O_2(g) = CO_2(g) + 2H_2O(g)$$

$$(3) \quad H_2(g) + F_2(g) = 2HF(g)$$

(a) Calculate the enthalpy changes at $25°$ for each of these reactions per kilogram of fuel plus the required amount of oxidizer. (For HF(g), $\Delta \bar{H}°_f = -64.2$ kcal.) (b) Since the thrust is greater when the molecular weight of the exhaust gas is lower, divide the heat per kilogram by the molecular weight of the product (or the average molecular weight in the case of reaction 2) and arrange the above reactions in order of effectiveness on the basis of thrust.

Ans. (a) $-3210, -1908, -3210$ kcal kg^{-1}. (b) (1) > (3) > (2).

3. Calculate the heat evolved when 1 gram of ethylene is exploded (a) at constant pressure at $25°$ with an excess of air, (b) with an excess of pure oxygen at 20 atm pressure in a closed bomb at $25°$. *Ans.* (a) -12.02, (b) -11.98 kcal.

4. Calculate the enthalpy of formation of PCl$_5$(s), given the heats of the following reactions at $25°$:

$$2P(s) + 3Cl_2(g) = 2PCl_3(l) \qquad \Delta H = -151,800 \text{ cal}$$

$$PCl_3(l) + Cl_2(g) = PCl_5(s) \qquad \Delta H = -32,810 \text{ cal}$$

Ans. -108.71 kcal mole^{-1}.

5. Using the data in Table II on enthalpies of formation, calculate the enthalpies of combustion at $25°$ of the following substances to $H_2O(l)$ and $CO_2(g)$: (a) *n*-butane, (b) methanol, (c) acetic acid.

Ans. (a) -687.982, (b) -173.66, (c) -208.3 kcal mole^{-1}.

6. For acetone, $(CH_3)_2CO$, $\Delta \bar{H}°_f$ is -61.4 kcal mole^{-1} at $25°$. (a) Calculate the heat of combustion of $(CH_3)_2CO$ at constant pressure. (b) Calculate the heat evolved when 2 grams of $(CH_3)_2CO$ is burned under pressure in a closed bomb at $25°$.

Ans. (a) -425.7 kcal mole^{-1}. (b) 14.64 kcal.

7. Calculate ΔH_{298} for the reaction

(1) $$CdSO_4(s) + H_2O(g) = CdSO_4 \cdot H_2O(s)$$

using the information that

(2) $CdSO_4(s) + 400H_2O(l) = CdSO_4$ in $400H_2O$ $\qquad \Delta H = -10,977$ cal

(3) $CdSO_4 \cdot H_2O(s) + 399H_2O(l) = CdSO_4$ in $400H_2O$ $\qquad \Delta H = -6,095$ cal

(4) $H_2O(g) = H_2O(l)$ $\qquad \Delta H = -9,717$ cal

By means of heat-capacity measurements down to the neighborhood of absolute zero and measurements of equilibrium water-vapor pressures, M. N. Papadopoulos and W. F. Giauque [*J. Am. Chem. Soc.*, 77, 2740 (1955)] have obtained $-15,451$ cal mole^{-1} for ΔH_{298} of reaction 1. $\qquad$ *Ans.* -14.599 kcal mole^{-1}.

8. Using the data of Table III, calculate the enthalpy change when a solution of 1 mole of hydrochloric acid in 5 moles of water is diluted by the addition of a large excess of water. $\qquad$ *Ans.* -2.65 kcal.

9. Calculate the enthalpies of reaction at $25°$ for the following reactions in dilute aqueous solutions:

(1) $HCl(aq) + NaBr(aq) = HBr(aq) + NaCl(aq)$

(2) $CaCl_2(aq) + Na_2CO_3(aq) = CaCO_3(s) + 2NaCl(aq)$

(3) $Li(s) + \frac{1}{2}Cl_2(g) + aq = Li^+(aq) + Cl^-(aq)$

$\qquad$ *Ans.* (1) 0, (2) -2.95, (3) -106.577 kcal.

10. The heat of the reaction

$$6C(g) + 6H(g) = C_6H_6(g)$$

is to be calculated (a) from the bond energies of Table VI, assuming that benzene, C_6H_6, has three $C\!=\!C$ and three $C\!-\!C$ bonds and six $C\!-\!H$ bonds, and (b) from the heat of formation of $C_6H_6(g)$, $C(g)$, and $H(g)$ in Table II. (c) Calculate the resonance energy (p. 492) of C_6H_6, which is equal to the difference between these two values. $\qquad$ *Ans.* (a) -1265.7, (b) -1322, (c) 56 kcal mole^{-1}.

11. The equation for the molar heat capacity of n-butane is

$$\bar{C}_P = 4.64 + 0.0558T$$

Calculate the heat necessary to raise the temperature of 1 mole from 25 to $300°$ at constant pressure. $\qquad$ *Ans.* 7940 cal.

12. Calculate ΔH at $1000°K$ for the reaction

$$CH_4(g) + 2O_2(g) = CO_2(g) + 2H_2O(g)$$

$\qquad$ *Ans.* -212.466 kcal.

13. As a rough approximation, the molar heat capacity of a solid is the same as the sum of the atomic heat capacities of the solid elements of which the solid compound is formed. What general statement can be made regarding the influence of temperature on the heat of reactions of solids to give solids, as, for example, the reaction $Fe(s) + S(s) = FeS(s)$? $\qquad$ *Ans.* $[\partial(\Delta H)/\partial T]_P \cong 0$.

14. In a bomb calorimeter the combustion of 1.753 grams of sucrose produces a temperature rise of 2.907°. The enthalpy change for the combustion of sucrose is 1349.7 kcal mole^{-1}. (a) What is the total heat capacity of the water and the calorimeter? (b) If the calorimeter contains 1850 grams of water (specific heat = 1.0 cal deg^{-1} g^{-1}), what is the heat capacity of the calorimeter? In this problem, corrections for the oxidation of the wire and residual nitrogen may be neglected.

15. How many grams of cane sugar, $C_{12}H_{22}O_{11}$, must be oxidized to give the same number of calories of *heat* as the number of calories of work done by a 160-lb (72.7-kg) man in climbing a mountain 1 mile (1.609 km) high? The heat of combustion of $C_{12}H_{22}O_{11}$ is 1349.7 kcal mole^{-1}. It is found empirically that only about 25 per cent of the heat value of food can be converted into useful work by men or animals, and accordingly the calculated grams of $C_{12}H_{22}O_{11}$ could be multiplied by approximately 4 to give the amount which would actually be oxidized.

16. The combustion of oxalic acid in a bomb calorimeter yields 673 cal g^{-1} at 25°. Calculate (a) ΔE and (b) ΔH for the combustion of 1 mole of oxalic acid ($M = 90.0$).

17. The enthalpy change for the combustion of toluene to $H_2O(l)$ and $CO_2(g)$ is -934.50 kcal mole^{-1} at 25°. Calculate the enthalpy of formation of toluene.

18. At 25° the enthalpy change for the combustion of liquid carbon disulfide, CS_2, to CO_2 and SO_2 is -256.97 kcal mole^{-1}. Calculate the enthalpy of formation $\Delta \bar{H}°_f$ of liquid CS_2.

19. Calculate the heat evolved at 25° in the reaction

$$3Mg(s) + Fe_2O_3(s) = 3MgO(s) + 2Fe(s)$$

The enthalpy of formation of $MgO(s)$ is $\Delta \bar{H}°_{f,298} = -145,700$ cal mole^{-1}.

20. The following heats of solution are obtained at 18° when a large excess of water is used:

$$CaCl_2(s) + aq = CaCl_2(aq) \qquad \Delta H = -18.0 \text{ kcal}$$

$$CaCl_2 \cdot 6H_2O(s) + aq = CaCl_2(aq) \qquad \Delta H = +4.5 \text{ kcal}$$

Calculate the heat of hydration of $CaCl_2$ to give $CaCl_2 \cdot 6H_2O$ by (a) $H_2O(l)$ and (b) $H_2O(g)$. The heat of vaporization of water at this temperature is 586 cal g^{-1}.

21. Using these data for the integral heat of solution of cadmium nitrate in water, plot ΔH against the molality m, and determine the differential heat of solution of cadmium nitrate in a 4-molal solution:

m (molality)	1.063	1.799	2.821	4.251	6.372	9.949
ΔH, joule mole^{-1}	-34.2	-56.7	-88.3	-126.0	-174.4	-228.5

22. Using the enthalpies of formation of $NaOH(aq)$ and $NaNO_3(aq)$ in infinitely dilute solution (Table IV) and the value for $\Delta \bar{H}°_{f,OH^-}$, show how the value for $\Delta \bar{H}°_f$ for NO_3^- in Table II is obtained.

23. (a) Estimate from enthalpies of formation and bond energies the heat of dissociation of $HCl(g)$ into atoms. (b) Estimate the heats of the following reactions at constant pressure:

$$C_2H_4(g) + Cl_2(g) = C_2H_4Cl_2(g)$$

$$C_2H_6(g) + 2Cl_2(g) = C_2H_4Cl_2(g) + 2HCl(g)$$

24. One mole of methane (considered to be an ideal gas) initially at $25°$ and 1 atm pressure is heated at constant pressure until the volume has doubled. The variation of the molar heat capacity with absolute temperature is given by

$$\bar{C}_P = 5.34 + 11.5 \times 10^{-3}T$$

Calculate (a) $\Delta \bar{H}$, and (b) $\Delta \bar{E}$.

25. Calculate the molar heat of combustion of carbon monoxide at constant pressure and $1327°$.

26. Calculate the heat of vaporization of water at $25°$. The specific heat of water may be taken as 1 cal $\deg^{-1}$ g^{-1}. The heat capacity of water vapor at constant pressure in this temperature range is 8.0 cal $\deg^{-1}$ $mole^{-1}$, and the heat of vaporization of water at $100°$ is 539.7 cal g^{-1}.

---

27. The heat of formation of nitric oxide, NO, from nitrogen and oxygen has been calculated from spectroscopic data. A direct calorimetric determination is desirable, however. It has been found that phosphorus will burn completely to P_2O_5 in NO, leaving nitrogen, if the phosphorus is thoroughly ignited with a hot arc. Calculate the enthalpy of formation of NO from the following data.

Phosphorus was burned in a calorimeter in a stream of NO for 12.00 min and produced 1.508 grams of H_3PO_4. The calorimeter was surrounded by 1386 grams of water. The observed temperature rise was $2.222°$, and the cooling correction amounted to $0.037°$. The correction for the heat of stirring was 11.1 cal evolved per min. The heat capacity of the calorimeter, as determined with an electric heater, was 244 cal $\deg^{-1}$.

In a second experiment the NO was replaced by a mixture of half nitrogen and half oxygen. The amount of H_3PO_4 produced in 10.00 min was 2.123 grams. The observed temperature rise was $2.398°$, and the cooling correction was $0.032°$. The correction for heat of stirring was 12.2 cal evolved per min. The weight of water was the same as in the first experiment. What is the enthalpy of formation of NO?

28. Estimate the enthalpy of combustion of n-nonane, C_9H_{20}, from the data in Table I on n-heptane, n-hexane, and n-octane.

29. One hundred grams of iron is dissolved in dilute acid at $25°$, giving a ferrous salt. Will more heat be evolved when the reaction is carried out in an open beaker or in a closed bomb? How much more?

30. Calculate the enthalpy of formation for 1 mole of HI(g) from the following data:

(a) $H_2(g) + Cl_2(g) = 2HCl(g)$ $\qquad \Delta H = -44.12 \, kcal$

(b) $HCl(g) + aq = HCl(aq)$ $\qquad \Delta H = -17.96 \, kcal$

(c) $HI(g) + aq = HI(aq)$ $\qquad \Delta H = -19.21 \, kcal$

(d) $KOH(aq) + HCl(aq) = KCl(aq)$ $\qquad \Delta H = -13.74 \, kcal$

(e) $KOH(aq) + HI(aq) = KI(aq)$ $\qquad \Delta H = -13.67 \, kcal$

(f) $Cl_2(g) + 2KI(aq) = 2KCl(aq) + I_2(s)$ $\qquad \Delta H = -52.42 \, kcal$

31. From Table II of the enthalpies of formation calculate the heats of combustion at constant pressure at $25°$ of (a) CO, (b) H_2, (c) C_2H_6, and (d) C_2H_5OH.

32. The integral heat of solution of 1 mole of H_2SO_4 in n moles of water is given in calories by the equation

$$\Delta H = \frac{-18,070n}{n + 1.798}$$

Calculate ΔH for the following reactions: (a) solution of 1 mole of H_2SO_4 in 5 moles of water; (b) solution of 1 mole of H_2SO_4 in 10 moles of water; (c) solution of 1 mole of H_2SO_4 in a large excess of water, 100,000 moles for example; (d) addition of a large excess of water to a solution containing 1 mole of H_2SO_4 in 10 moles of water; (e) addition of 5 moles of water to a solution containing 1 mole of H_2SO_4 in 5 moles of water.

33. Using the data of Table III, calculate the enthalpy change when a solution of 1 mole of NaOH in 5 moles of water is diluted by the addition of 195 moles of water.

34. Calculate the enthalpies of reaction at 25° for the following reactions in dilute aqueous solutions:

$$(1) \quad AgNO_3(aq) + KCl(aq) = AgCl(s) + KNO_3(aq)$$

$$(2) \quad Zn(s) + 2HCl(aq) = ZnCl_2(aq) + H_2(g)$$

35. Calculate the quantity of heat required to raise 1 mole of CO_2 from 0 to 300° (a) at constant pressure and (b) at constant volume. $\bar{C}_P$ in calories per degree per mole is given by

$$\bar{C}_P = 6.40 + 10.2 \times 10^{-3}T - 35 \times 10^{-7}T^2$$

36. Calculate the heat evolved in the reaction $H_2(g) + Cl_2(g) = 2HCl(g)$ at 1023° and constant pressure.

37. Using data in this chapter and $\bar{C}_P$ for graphite

$$\bar{C}_P = 2.673 + 0.002617T - \frac{1.169 \times 10^5}{T^2}$$

calculate ΔH for the following reaction at 600°K:

$$H_2O(g) + C(s) = CO(g) + H_2(g)$$

38. Calculate the theoretical flame temperature for the burning of ethane with a stoichiometric amount of oxygen. The heat evolved in the reaction is used to heat the products to the flame temperature, it being assumed that the reaction goes to completion and no heat is lost by radiation. The flame temperature obtained experimentally would be less than this theoretical value because at high temperatures the reaction is incomplete, there being some dissociation of the products into atoms and free radicals with a consequent absorption of heat.

39. Calculate the enthalpy change for the dissociation of $N_2(g)$ at 25°, using data from Table II. Explain why this result differs from that given in Table V.

40. Calculate the enthalpy change at 25° for the reaction of a dilute aqueous solution of $AgNO_3$ with a dilute aqueous solution of NaCl.

SECOND AND THIRD LAWS OF THERMODYNAMICS

5

The first law of thermodynamics states that when one form of energy is converted into another the total energy is conserved, but it does not indicate any other restriction on this process. Although various forms of work can be converted completely into heat and ideally may be transformed completely into one another, it is found that only a fraction of a quantity of heat may be converted into work in a cyclic process. The second law of thermodynamics provides a means for calculating the maximum value that this fraction may have and is directly concerned with the question of whether or not a given change is spontaneous. Since the second law provides a criterion for predicting whether a process will occur spontaneously, it is of great importance for chemistry. Equilibrium conditions are independent of mechanism, and it is the great strength, and weakness, of thermodynamics that it is not concerned with mechanisms or models (as, for example, molecules) or with time.

Spontaneous and Nonspontaneous Changes. We are familiar with the fact that many changes occur spontaneously; that is, when systems are simply left to themselves. Water runs downhill; gases expand from regions of high pressure to regions of low pressure; chemical reactions proceed to equilibrium; and heat flows from hotter bodies to cooler bodies. For any spontaneous change it is possible to devise, in principle at least, a means for getting useful work. Thus, falling water can turn a turbine; an expanding gas can push a piston; a chemical reaction may be harnessed in a battery; and hot and cold reservoirs may be used to run a heat engine. Since work can be obtained from a spontaneous change, it is evident that in the occurrence of a spontaneous change the system loses capacity to do useful work.

It is a matter of experience that spontaneous changes do not reverse themselves; that is, water does not run uphill. The term *nonspontaneous* is applied to the reverse of a spontaneous change, for example, water flowing uphill. Nonspontaneous changes can be made to occur only by supplying energy from outside the system. For example, energy is required to pump water uphill, to compress a gas, and to transfer heat from a cold reservoir to a hot one, as in a refrigerator. Since the energy required can be supplied only by a spontaneous change, it is apparent that a spontaneous change may be reversed only by harnessing, in some way, energy from another spontaneous change.

Spontaneous changes may be carried out either *reversibly* or *irreversibly*. Although the meaning of these terms has been discussed earlier (p. 39), it is worth re-emphasizing them here. In order to carry out a spontaneous change reversibly, it is necessary to oppose it in such a way that the change is carried out very slowly and, in fact, can be reversed at any time by making an infinitesimal change in the opposing force. The expansion of a gas with an idealized piston with a slowly changing opposing pressure, and the discharge of a battery with a potentiometer to supply an opposing potential, are examples of idealized reversible *processes* for carrying out spontaneous *changes*. When a change is carried out reversibly, the maximum amount of work is obtained. Actually, it is not possible to obtain the maximum work from any system with a real machine because of losses due to friction and the fact that a truly reversible process must be carried out infinitely slowly. Thus actual processes are always irreversible to a certain extent, and the work obtained is less than the theoretical maximum amount. The actual amount of work secured from a spontaneous change can be anything from zero, as, for example, when a gas is allowed to expand into a vacuum or a chemical reaction is allowed to occur in a beaker, up to the maximum amount obtained when the change is carried out reversibly.

Perpetual Motion and the Second Law. The first law of thermodynamics denies the possibility of constructing a machine which will create energy. The second law denies the possibility of constructing a machine which will, by *only* cooling its surroundings, transform heat taken from the surroundings into work.

Work may be obtained from the expansion of an ideal gas which is in thermal contact with a reservoir of constant temperature. Since the internal energy of an ideal gas is independent of pressure at constant temperature (p. 43), there is no change in internal energy in the expansion and $\Delta E = q - w = 0$. Thus the work done is equal to the heat transferred from the reservoir to the gas. However, this process of obtaining work does not violate the second law, since the conversion of heat into work is not the *only* final result of the process; the final pressure of the gas is lower than its initial pressure.

Carnot Cycle. Heat can be partially transformed into work if there are available two heat reservoirs at different temperatures T_1 and T_2. By employing a cyclic process, a gas, or other working fluid, may be used to obtain work in such a way that the only final result is the transfer of heat from one reservoir to the other and the performance of a certain amount of work. A cyclic process is a series of steps which brings a system back to its initial state. Since the quantities E and H are functions only of the state of the system and the system is returned to its initial state, $\Delta E = 0$ and $\Delta H = 0$ for the working fluid for the cycle. The surroundings are in general not returned to their initial state.

A *Carnot cycle* is a *reversible* cycle in which a working fluid is subjected to four successive processes in a cylinder, as illustrated in *Fig. 5-1: AB*,

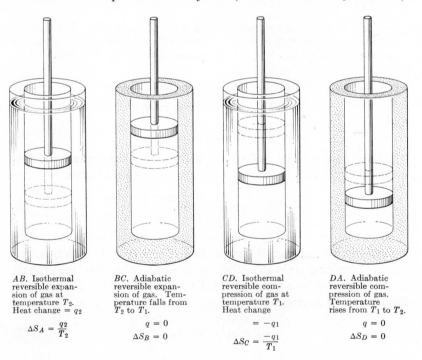

AB. Isothermal reversible expansion of gas at temperature T_2. Heat change $= q_2$

$$\Delta S_A = \frac{q_2}{T_2}$$

BC. Adiabatic reversible expansion of gas. Temperature falls from T_2 to T_1.

$$q = 0$$
$$\Delta S_B = 0$$

CD. Isothermal reversible compression of gas at temperature T_1. Heat change

$$= -q_1$$
$$\Delta S_C = \frac{-q_1}{T_1}$$

DA. Adiabatic reversible compression of gas. Temperature rises from T_1 to T_2.

$$q = 0$$
$$\Delta S_D = 0$$

Fig. 5-1. Conversion of heat into work.

reversible isothermal expansion at a constant temperature T_2; BC, reversible adiabatic expansion to a lower temperature T_1; CD, reversible isothermal compression at a constant temperature T_1; and DA, reversible adiabatic compression to temperature T_2 and the original volume and pressure. Heat q_2 is absorbed from the reservoir in the isothermal expansion at the higher temperature, and heat $-q_1$ passes from the working fluid to the reservoir at the lower temperature. The cycle is represented in a plot of P versus V in *Fig. 5-2.*

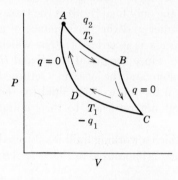

Fig. 5-2. Diagrammatic representations of a Carnot cycle in terms of pressure and volume.

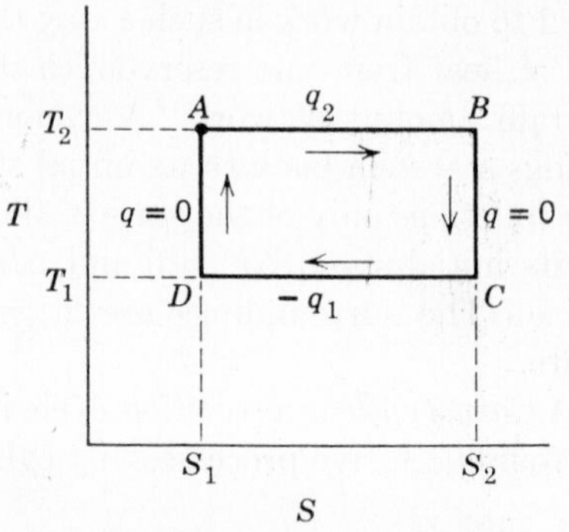

Fig. 5-3. Diagrammatic representation of a Carnot cycle in terms of temperature and entropy (cf. p. 89).

Since the working fluid is returned to its initial state,

$$\Delta E = 0 = q_2 - q_1 - w \tag{1}$$

and

$$w = q_2 - q_1$$

The fraction of the heat q_2 absorbed at the higher temperature which is converted into work is called the *efficiency* of the heat engine.

$$\text{Efficiency} = \frac{w}{q_2} = \frac{q_2 - q_1}{q_2} \tag{2}$$

The efficiency is readily calculated for a *reversible* Carnot cycle with 1 mole of an ideal gas. As mentioned in the preceding section, the amount of work done in an isothermal expansion of an ideal gas is equal to the amount of heat absorbed. If the volume of an ideal gas increases from $\overline{V}_A$ to $\overline{V}_B$ at temperature T_2, the amount of work done is given by

$$w_2 = q_2 = RT_2 \ln \frac{\overline{V}_B}{\overline{V}_A} \tag{3}$$

In the isothermal compression at temperature T_1 work must be performed on the gas, and the amount of work w_1 and the quantity of heat

$- q_1$ are given by

$$- q_1 = w_1 = RT_1 \ln \frac{\overline{V}_D}{\overline{V}_C} \tag{4}$$

For the adiabatic steps, we have from equation 45 in Chapter 3 for an ideal gas

$$T_1 \overline{V}_C{}^{\gamma-1} = T_2 \overline{V}_B{}^{\gamma-1}$$

$$T_1 \overline{V}_D{}^{\gamma-1} = T_2 \overline{V}_A{}^{\gamma-1}$$

Dividing one equation by the other and taking the $\gamma - 1$ root,

$$\frac{\overline{V}_C}{\overline{V}_D} = \frac{\overline{V}_B}{\overline{V}_A} \tag{5}$$

Dividing equation 4 by equation 3 and utilizing equation 5 yields

$$\frac{q_1}{q_2} = \frac{T_1}{T_2} \tag{6}$$

Thus the maximum efficiency (cf. eq. 2) for a Carnot cycle with an ideal gas is

$$\text{Efficiency} = \frac{w_{max}}{q_2} = \frac{T_2 - T_1}{T_2} \tag{7}$$

The Carnot cycle may be carried out in the reverse manner $ADCBA$, and then net work must be done on the ideal gas by an outside source, heat is absorbed at the lower temperature, and heat is evolved at the higher temperature. A device used in this way is called a heat pump, and this principle is involved in refrigeration.

Now we must consider the question of whether equation 7 is general or applies only when the working fluid is an ideal gas. If this expression were not generally true for reversible Carnot cycles, we could devise a perpetual-motion machine of the first kind using two Carnot cycles. The device with the higher efficiency would be used to produce work while absorbing a certain amount of heat at temperature T_2. The less efficient device would then serve as a heat pump to restore heat to the reservoir at the higher temperature. Less work would be required than was produced with the first device, and so net work would have been obtained without a change in any system. Thus we conclude that for reversible cycles the efficiency is independent of the working fluid.

Equation 7 is important in engineering and explains why internal-combustion engines with their high temperatures are efficient and why large steam-power plants are now operated at very high pressures and temperatures. A great deal of research is being directed toward finding materials for turbines and rockets which will permit the use of still higher temperatures.

Example 1. What is the maximum work that can be obtained from 1000 cal of heat supplied to a water boiler at 100° if the condenser is at 20°?

$$w_{max} = q_2 \frac{T_2 - T_1}{T_2} = (1000) \frac{373.1 - 293.1}{373.1} = 214 \text{ cal}$$

If the boiler temperature is raised to 150° by the use of superheated steam under pressure, how much more work can be obtained?

$$w_{max} = (1000) \frac{423.1 - 293.1}{423.1} = 307 \text{ cal}$$

$$307 - 214 = 93 \text{ cal}$$

Exercise 1. How can a kilowatt-hour of electricity be used in a heat pump to give more heat than corresponds to the kilowatt-hour of heat obtained from the electricity in a resistance heater?

Entropy. The second law of thermodynamics may be stated in many ways which appear to be quite different but really amount to the same thing. The most useful form of the second law for physical-chemical applications is expressed in terms of an additional thermodynamic function, the *entropy*.

Entropy is an extensive thermodynamic quantity designated by S. It is a function of the state of a system and has the following properties:

For an infinitesimal reversible process: $dS = \delta q/T$ (8)

For an infinitesimal spontaneous process: $dS > \delta q/T$ (9)

It is seen that the entropy has the dimensions of energy divided by temperature; it is usually given in units of calories per degree per mole. The use of δq rather than dq reminds us that q is not a perfect differential but depends upon the path used in making the change. Relations 8 and 9 also define an absolute temperature scale T for which these relations are true.

The entropy is a function of the state of the system, so that its value is independent of the past history of the system, and the entropy change for a given change in state is *independent of path*. However, since equation 8 applies only to a reversible process, the entropy change can be calculated only from measurements of heat and temperature along a *reversible path*. The entropy change for a finite change from state 1 to state 2 is given by the integral of equation 8 along a reversible path.

$$\Delta S = S_2 - S_1 = \int_1^2 \frac{\delta q}{T}$$ (10)

There are a number of reversible processes for which the entropy change may readily be calculated. By considering the entropy changes in a reversible Carnot cycle we can easily derive the expression for the maximum efficiency of a heat engine. The steps are indicated in the temperature-entropy diagram in *Fig. 5-3* on p. 86. The T-S diagram is simple, the isothermal steps being represented by horizontal lines and the reversible adiabatic steps by vertical lines, since $q = 0$ and the entropy is constant.

Since the gas is returned to its initial state, the total entropy change for the working fluid is zero for the four steps. Then, using equation 10, the entropy change for the working substance is given by

$$\Delta S = \Delta S_{AB} + \Delta S_{BC} + \Delta S_{CD} + \Delta S_{DA} = 0$$

$$= \frac{q_2}{T_2} + 0 + \frac{-q_1}{T_1} + 0 = 0$$

Since $\Delta E = 0$ for the cycle, $w = q_2 - q_1$ and substituting $q_1 = q_2(T_1/T_2)$,

$$\frac{w_{\max}}{q_2} = \frac{T_2 - T_1}{T_2} \tag{11}$$

which is the same as equation 7.

The temperature used in deriving equation 11 was introduced in equations 8 and 9 as the thermodynamic absolute temperature, whereas the temperature used in the derivation of equation 7 was the absolute temperature defined in terms of the properties of an ideal gas. Since both derivations lead to the same equation, the two scales of absolute temperature are proportional to each other. By picking the same fixed point, the thermodynamic temperature scale becomes identical with the absolute temperature scale based on the ideal gas law. Moreover it is seen that the statement of the second law as $dS \geqslant \delta q/T$ is equivalent to the statement of the maximum efficiency of a heat engine given by equation 7.

Entropy Changes for Reversible Processes. The transfer of heat from one body to another at an infinitesimally lower temperature is a reversible process, since the direction of heat flow can be reversed by an infinitesimal change in the temperature of one of the bodies. The fusion of a solid at its melting point and the evaporation of a liquid at a constant partial pressure of the substance equal to its vapor pressure are examples of isothermal processes which can be reversed by an infinitesimal change in temperature. For these processes the entropy change is easily calculated. Since T is constant, performing the integration in equation 10 yields

$$S_2 - S_1 = \Delta S = \frac{q_{\text{rev}}}{T} \tag{12}$$

where q_{rev} represents the heat absorbed in the reversible process.

For a mole of substance at constant temperature and pressure

$$\bar{S}_2 - \bar{S}_1 = \Delta \bar{S} = \frac{\Delta \bar{H}}{T}$$

Example 2. n-Hexane boils at 68.7°, and the heat of vaporization at constant pressure is 6896 cal mole^{-1} at this temperature. If liquid is vaporized into the saturated vapor at this temperature, the process is reversible and the entropy change per mole is given by

$$\Delta \bar{S} = \Delta \bar{H}/T = 6896/341.8 = 20.18 \text{ cal deg}^{-1}\text{mole}^{-1}$$

The molar entropy of a vapor is always greater than that of the liquid with which it is in equilibrium, and the molar entropy of the liquid is always greater than that of the solid at the melting point.

According to the disorder concept of entropy to be discussed later on p. 94, in which the entropy is a measure of the disorder of the system, the molecules of the gas are more disordered than those of the liquid, and the molecules of the liquid more disordered than those of the solid.

The same method is used for the calculation of the entropy of sublimation, the entropy of fusion, or the entropy change for a transition between two forms of a solid. Since the heat gained by the system is equal to that lost by the surroundings, the entropy change for the surroundings is the negative of the entropy change for the system; for both the system and surroundings taken together, ΔS is zero if the transfer of heat is carried out reversibly.

The increase in the entropy of a substance due to raising its temperature can be calculated, since the temperature change can be carried out in a reversible manner. The heat absorbed in each infinitesimal step is equal to the heat capacity C multiplied by the differential increase in temperature dT, and

$$dS = \frac{C \, dT}{T} \tag{13}$$

Integrating equation 13 between the limits T_1 and T_2 gives

$$\int_{S_1}^{S_2} dS = \int_{T_1}^{T_2} \frac{C \, dT}{T} \tag{14}$$

If C is independent of temperature,

$$S_2 - S_1 = C(\ln T_2 - \ln T_1) = C \ln \frac{T_2}{T_1} = 2.303C \log \frac{T_2}{T_1} \tag{15}$$

The fact that the entropy is always larger at the higher temperature agrees with the fact that the motion of the molecules is more disordered at the higher temperature. This equation is applicable for constant pressure or constant volume. If the heating is carried out at constant pressure, C_P is used; if the volume is constant, C_V is used.

Example 3. Calculate the increase in entropy of a gram-atomic weight of silver which is heated at constant pressure from 0 to 30°, if the value of $\bar{C}_P$ in this temperature range is considered to be constant at 6.09 cal deg^{-1} mole^{-1}.

$$\Delta\bar{S} = \bar{S}_2 - \bar{S}_1 = (2.303)(6.09)\log\tfrac{303}{273} = 0.640 \text{ cal deg}^{-1}\text{ mole}^{-1}$$

If the heat capacities change during the heating process, an empirical equation of the sort introduced on p. 74 may be inserted into equation 14 before integration.

Example 4. Calculate the increase in entropy of gaseous oxygen when a mole is heated at constant pressure from 25 to 600°, using data from Table VI of Chapter 4.

$$\Delta\bar{S} = \int_{298}^{873}\frac{(6.0954 + 3.2533 \times 10^{-3}T - 10.71 \times 10^{-7}T^2)\,dT}{T}$$

$$= (6.0954)(2.303)\log\tfrac{873}{298} + 3.2533 \times 10^{-3}(873 - 298)$$

$$\quad - \frac{10.71 \times 10^{-7}}{2}(873^2 - 298^2)$$

$$= 6.56 + 1.87 - 0.36$$

$$= 8.07 \text{ cal deg}^{-1}\text{ mole}^{-1}$$

The equation for the calculation of the change in entropy of 1 mole of an ideal gas with volume and temperature at constant pressure may be obtained by writing the second law of thermodynamics in differential form (p. 38).

$$\delta q = d\bar{E} + P\,d\bar{V}$$

$$= \bar{C}_V\,dT + \frac{RT\,d\bar{V}}{\bar{V}} \tag{16}$$

The infinitesimal entropy change accompanying an infinitesimal change in temperature dT and in volume $d\bar{V}$ is given by

$$d\bar{S} = \frac{\delta q}{T} = \bar{C}_V\frac{dT}{T} + R\frac{d\bar{V}}{\bar{V}} \tag{17}$$

Assuming that $\bar{C}_V$ is independent of temperature and volume, integration yields

$$\Delta\bar{S} = \bar{S}_2 - \bar{S}_1 = \bar{C}_V\ln\frac{T_2}{T_1} + R\ln\frac{\bar{V}_2}{\bar{V}_1} \tag{18}$$

If the volume is held constant, this equation reduces to equation 15.

If the temperature is held constant,

$$\Delta \bar{S} = R \ln \frac{\bar{V}_2}{\bar{V}_1} \tag{19}$$

It can be seen from this equation that for a tenfold increase in volume of an ideal gas $\Delta \bar{S} = (1.987)(2.303) = 4.59$ cal $\deg^{-1}$ mole^{-1}. The entropy of the gas will change by this amount whether the isothermal expansion is carried out reversibly or irreversibly because $\Delta \bar{S}$ depends only on the entropies of the initial and final states.

Entropy Changes for Irreversible Processes. The entropy change for an irreversible process may be calculated by considering a path by which the process can be carried out in a series of *reversible* steps. Calculations of this type will be illustrated for the freezing of water below its freezing point.

The freezing of a mole of supercooled water at $-10°$ is an irreversible process, but it can be carried out in a reversible way by means of the following three steps for which the entropy changes are indicated:

$$\text{H}_2\text{O}(l) \text{ at } -10° \rightarrow \text{H}_2\text{O}(l) \text{ at } 0° \qquad \Delta \bar{S} = \int_{263}^{273} \bar{C}_{\text{liq}} \frac{dT}{T}$$

$$\text{H}_2\text{O}(l) \text{ at } 0° \rightarrow \text{H}_2\text{O}(s) \text{ at } 0° \qquad \Delta \bar{S} = \frac{q_{\text{rev}}}{T}$$

$$\text{H}_2\text{O}(s) \text{ at } 0° \rightarrow \text{H}_2\text{O}(s) \text{ at } -10° \qquad \Delta \bar{S} = \int_{273}^{263} \bar{C}_{\text{ice}} \frac{dT}{T}$$

For the crystallization of liquid water at $0°$, $q_{\text{rev}} = -79.7$ cal g^{-1}. The specific heat of water may be taken to be 1.0 cal $\deg^{-1}$ g^{-1}, and that of ice may be taken to be 0.5 cal $\deg^{-1}$ g^{-1} over this range. Then the total entropy change of the water when 1 mole of liquid water at $-10°$ changes to ice at $-10°$ is simply the sum of the above entropy changes:

$$\Delta \bar{S} = (18 \text{ g mole}^{-1})(1.0 \text{ cal deg}^{-1} \text{ g}^{-1})(2.303) \log \tfrac{273}{263}$$

$$+ \frac{(18 \text{ g mole}^{-1})(-79.7 \text{ cal g}^{-1})}{273 \text{ deg}}$$

$$+ (18 \text{ g mole}^{-1})(0.5 \text{ cal deg}^{-1} \text{ g}^{-1})(2.303) \log \tfrac{263}{273}$$

$$= 0.67 - 5.26 - 0.34 = -4.93 \text{ cal deg}^{-1} \text{ mole}^{-1}$$

Entropy Change for a Process in an Isolated System. When the system is isolated, the process is adiabatic and $q = 0$. Therefore, according to the second law, if the process is a *reversible* one

$$dS = 0 \quad \text{and} \quad \Delta S = 0 \qquad (20)$$

Any spontaneous process is *irreversible* to a certain extent, and so for a spontaneous process in an isolated system

$$dS > 0 \quad \text{and} \quad \Delta S > 0 \qquad (21)$$

according to equation 9. Thus the entropy of an isolated system increases when a spontaneous process occurs in it. For an isolated system this is the thermodynamic criterion for a spontaneous process. An isolated system goes spontaneously to a state of greater disorder in which the entropy is greater. *As a spontaneous process occurs in an isolated system, the entropy of the system increases to a maximum as the system reaches the equilibrium state.* This statement may be illustrated by reconsideration of the example of the preceding section.

If a mole of supercooled water at $-10°$ is in contact with a large heat reservoir at this temperature in an isolated system, the entropy change for the isolated system upon freezing includes the entropy change of the reservoir as well as the entropy change of the water. If the heat reservoir is large, the heat evolved by the water upon freezing is absorbed by the reservoir with only an infinitesimal change in temperature. Since the heat of fusion of water at $-10°$ is 74.6 cal g^{-1} (p. 76), the entropy change of the reservoir is

$$\Delta S = (18 \text{ g mole}^{-1})(74.6 \text{ cal g}^{-1})/(263 \text{ deg})$$

$$= 5.10 \text{ cal deg}^{-1} \text{ mole}^{-1}$$

The entropy change of the water is -4.93 as just shown, and the total entropy change of the isolated system is

$$\Delta S = 5.10 - 4.93 = 0.17 \text{ cal deg}^{-1} \text{ mole}^{-1}$$

Thus the total entropy of the isolated system, including water and reservoir, increases, as it always must when an irreversible process occurs.

Entropy of Mixing Gases. If two gases at the same pressure and temperature are brought together, they will spontaneously diffuse into each other until the gas phase is macroscopically homogeneous. Since there is no interaction between molecules of ideal gases, the entropy change for the mixing process of two ideal gases is the same as the entropy change which results when the gases are each allowed to expand from their initial pressure P to their partial pressures X_1P and X_2P in the equilibrium mixture, where X_1 and X_2 are the mole fractions. Since the process is isothermal, equation 19 may be used in the form

$$\Delta \bar{S} = R \ln \frac{P_1}{P_2} \tag{22}$$

where P_1 represents the initial pressure and P_2 the final pressure. The sum of the entropy changes for a total of a mole of the two gases is given by

$$\Delta \bar{S} = X_1 R \ln \frac{P}{X_1P} + X_2 R \ln \frac{P}{X_2P} \tag{23}$$

$$= -R(X_1 \ln X_1 + X_2 \ln X_2) \tag{24}$$

The entropy of mixing is positive since $X_1 < 1$ and $X_2 < 1$. This constitutes the thermodynamic proof that the diffusion of one gas into another is spontaneous and irreversible.

Example 5. Calculate the entropy change when 1 mole of hydrogen at 1 atm pressure is mixed with 1 mole of nitrogen at 1 atm.

Assuming that the gases are ideal,

$$\Delta S = -2.303nR \ (X_1 \log X_1 + X_2 \log X_2)$$

$$= -(2.303)(2)(1.987)(0.5 \log 0.5 + 0.5 \log 0.5)$$

$$= 2.76 \ \text{cal deg}^{-1} \text{mole}^{-1}$$

The Statistical Interpretation of Entropy. As stated earlier, thermodynamics is not concerned with molecules or particular models of systems. However, in order to develop an intuitive feeling for thermodynamic functions it is very helpful to think in terms of molecules, and this is particularly true of entropy. The statistical-mechanical explanation of entropy will be discussed in detail later (p. 558), but a rather heuristic introduction to this subject will be given here.

According to equation 9, there is always an increase in entropy for a spontaneous change in an isolated system. It may be noted that in the spontaneous changes we have discussed, such as the expansion of a gas, the vaporization of a liquid, and the mixing of two gases, there is an increase in disorder. Boltzmann introduced the hypothesis that such processes are spontaneous because the final state is more *probable* than the initial state. By more probable he meant that there are a greater number of microscopic states, or possible ways in which a molecule can exist, in the vapor than in the liquid.

Since the entropy is an extensive property, the entropy of a system consisting of two parts is simply the sum of the entropies of the two parts of the system: $S = S_1 + S_2$. If the number of equally probable microscopic states for one part of the system is Ω_1 and for the other is Ω_2, the number of equally probable microscopic states for the whole system is $\Omega_1\Omega_2$, since any state of the first system can be combined with any state of the second to specify a state for the whole system. If we assume that the entropy is given by a function $f(\Omega)$ of the number of equally probable microscopic states,

$$S = S_1 + S_2$$

$$f(\Omega_1\Omega_2) = f(\Omega_1) + f(\Omega_2) \tag{25}$$

In order for this to be true there must be a logarithmic relation between S and Ω. Boltzmann postulated

$$S = k \ln \Omega \tag{26}$$

where k is the Boltzmann constant, that is, the molecular gas constant R/N_0, where N_0 is Avogadro's number. The general quantitative expression for Ω will be given in Chapter 19 after a discussion of the possible quantum states of a system, but we can illustrate the use of equation 26 now by application to a model of an ideal gas.

We will consider the change in entropy of an ideal gas which is allowed to expand from volume V_1 to volume V_2. These volumes will be considered to be divided into a very large number of cells of volume v. The number of cells in a given volume will be represented by m, and this number is large compared with the number n of molecules. If the n molecules were distinguishable, there would be m^n different ways in which they could be placed in the m cells without any restriction on the number of molecules per box. If the volume of the cell v is properly chosen, m^n would be the number of equally probable microscopic states, Ω. The first molecule could be placed in any one of m boxes, and the second, third, etc., molecules could also be placed in any one of the m boxes.

However, since according to quantum mechanics the gas molecules cannot be distinguished from each other, there are not as many *different* ways of placing them in the m cells as we have counted above. To obtain the correct result we must divide by the number of possible arrangements of n molecules among n positions, since these arrangements make up one microscopic state. This number is $n!$ (factorial n), since any one of n molecules may be placed in the first position, $n - 1$ in the second, $n - 2$ in the third, etc., down to the last position, which is to be filled with the one remaining molecule. This point is illustrated in Table I in Chapter 19.

Thus the number of microscopic states Ω which are accessible to n molecules in m cells is given by

$$\Omega = \frac{m^n}{n!} \qquad (27)$$

Now we are in a position to calculate the change in entropy of the gas in the expansion from volume V_1 (which contains V_1/v cells) to volume V_2 (which contains V_2/v cells).

$$\Delta S = k \ln \Omega_2 - k \ln \Omega_1 \qquad (28)$$

$$= k \ln \frac{(V_2/v)^n}{n!} - k \ln \frac{(V_1/v)^n}{n!} \qquad (29)$$

$$= nk \ln \frac{V_2}{V_1} \qquad (30)$$

It may be noted that the volume v of the cells cancels in this derivation. If a mole of gas is taken, n is equal to Avogadro's number N_0, and $N_0 k$ is the gas constant R, so that equation 30 becomes

$$\Delta \bar{S} = R \ln \frac{\bar{V}_2}{\bar{V}_1} \qquad (31)$$

which is identical with equation 19 derived from thermodynamics.

Third Law of Thermodynamics. The association of entropy with the probability of a system (as expressed by the number of equally probable microscopic states) suggests that the lowest value of the entropy would be that of a crystalline substance at absolute zero. For a perfect crystal at absolute zero there is only one microscopic state, and so Ω in equation 26 is unity and the entropy is zero. Since it is not actually possible to reach absolute zero, the third law of thermodynamics may be stated: *The entropy of a perfect crystal approaches zero as the temperature approaches absolute zero.** The entropy of an imperfect crystal or of a glass, with its greater disorder, would be greater than zero at absolute zero. The idea on which the third law is based was first proposed by T. W. Richards in 1902. The law was propounded by W. Nernst and was fully developed and applied to chemical problems by G. N. Lewis and his associates.

---

* The contributions to the entropy due to nuclear spin and due to the entropy of mixing of various isotopic species are ignored. This is permissible for ordinary chemical purposes, since the nuclei are not changed in chemical processes and isotopes are not ordinarily separated.

The absolute entropy of a substance at a higher temperature can be calculated from heat-capacity measurements down to the neighborhood of absolute zero and extrapolation of the heat-capacity curve to absolute zero by use of the Debye function (p. 53). The third law is important because it makes possible the determination of the absolute entropies of chemical compounds and the prediction of chemical equilibria, as is explained on p. 210.

The entropy at any higher temperature may be calculated from measurements of heat capacity and of heats of transition. If there are no transitions, the entropy of 1 mole of a solid at temperature T is given by

$$\bar{S}^\circ = \int_0^T \frac{\bar{C}\, dT}{T} = \int_{-\infty}^{\ln T} \bar{C}\, d\ln T = 2.303 \int_{-\infty}^{\log T} \bar{C}\, d\log T \quad (32)$$

Usually the relation between $\bar{C}$ and T is too complicated to be conveniently expressed mathematically, and the integration has to be carried out graphically.

Thus, the absolute entropy may be obtained by plotting $\bar{C}/T$ versus T or $\bar{C}$ versus $\log T$ and determining the area under the curve from absolute zero to any specified temperature. The area under the curve may be determined by counting squares or by using the trapezoid formula or a planimeter. If base 10 logarithms are used for the log plot, this area is multiplied by 2.303 to give the entropy in calories per degree per mole, as indicated by the last form of equation 32. Whenever there is a change in state or a transition between two crystalline forms, the entropy change is calculated from the heat of transition by use of equation 12 and must be added to that obtained from equation 32.

As an illustration of the determination of the absolute entropy of a substance, the measured heat capacities for SO_2 are shown as a function of T and of $\log T$ in *Fig. 5-4a* * and *b*. Solid SO_2 melts at $197.64°K$, and the heat of fusion is 1769.1 cal mole^{-1}. The liquid vaporizes at $263.08°K$, and the heat of vaporization is 5960 cal mole^{-1}. The calculation of the entropy at $25°$ is summarized in Table I.

Heat-capacity measurements down to these very low temperatures are made with special calorimeters in which the substance is heated electrically in a carefully insulated system and the input of electrical energy and the temperature are measured accurately.

Table II gives the entropies, $\bar{S}°$, at $25°$ for a number of elements, compounds, and ions. The standard state for the ions is the hypothetical state of unit activity, and the absolute entropy of H^+ is arbi-

---

* W. F. Giauque and C. C. Stephenson, *J. Am. Chem. Soc.*, *60*, 1389 (1938).

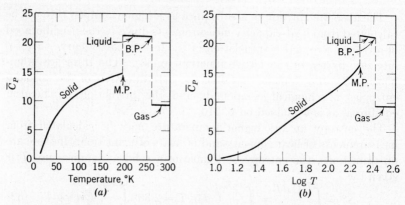

(a) Temperature,°K (b) Log T

Fig. 5-4. Heat capacity in calories per degree per mole of sulfur dioxide at constant pressure at different temperatures.

trarily assigned the value zero. Data of this type can be used in the calculation of equilibrium constants, as shown later in Chapter 9.

Example 6. Calculate the entropy change for the formation of water vapor at 25° from oxygen and hydrogen.

$$\tfrac{1}{2}O_2(g) + H_2(g) \rightarrow H_2O(g)$$

$$\Delta S° = 45.106 - 31.211 - \tfrac{1}{2}(49.003)$$

$$= -10.606 \text{ cal deg}^{-1}\text{mole}^{-1}$$

Absolute entropies may be calculated for simple molecules from spectroscopic data by use of statistical mechanics (Chapter 19). It is of considerable interest to compare the entropies calculated theoretically with those obtained from heat-capacity measurements on

Table I. The Entropy of Sulfur Dioxide

Temperature, °K	Method of Calculation	$\Delta\bar{S}$, cal deg^{-1} mole^{-1}
0–15	Debye function ($\bar{C}_P$ = constant T^3)	0.30
15–197.64	Graphical, solid	20.12
197.64	Fusion, 1769.1/197.64	8.95
197.64–263.08	Graphical, liquid	5.96
263.08	Vaporization, 5960/263.08	22.66
263.08–298.1	From $\bar{C}_P$ of gas	1.25

$$\bar{S}°_{298.1} = 59.24$$

Table II.[1]   Entropies at $25°$

$(\bar{S}°$ in cal deg^{-1} mole$^{-1})$

Elements and Inorganic Compounds

$O_2(g)$	49.003	$NO(g)$	50.339	$AgCl(s)$	22.97
$O_3(g)$	56.8	$NO_2(g)$	57.47	$Fe(s)$	6.49
$H_2(g)$	31.211	$NH_3(g)$	46.01	$Fe_2O_3(s)$	21.5
$H_2O(g)$	45.106	$HNO_3(l)$	37.19	$Fe_3O_4(s)$	35.0
$H_2O(l)$	16.716	$P(g)$	38.98	$Al(s)$	6.769
$He(g)$	30.126	$P(s,$ white$)$	10.6	$Al_2O_3(s)$	12.186
$Cl_2(g)$	53.286	$PCl_3(g)$	74.49	$UF_6(g)$	90.76
$HCl(g)$	44.617	$PCl_5(g)$	84.3	$UF_6(s)$	54.45
$Br_2(g)$	58.639	$C(s,$ diamond$)$	0.5829	$Ca(s)$	9.95
$Br_2(l)$	36.4	$C(s,$ graphite$)$	1.3609	$CaO(s)$	9.5
$HBr(g)$	47.437	$CO(g)$	47.301	$CaCO_3(s)$	22.2
$HI(g)$	49.314	$CO_2(g)$	51.061	$Na(s)$	12.2
S(rhombic)	7.62	$Pb(s)$	15.51	$NaF(s)$	14.0
S(monoclinic)	7.78	$PbO_2(s)$	18.3	$NaCl(s)$	17.3
$SO_2(g)$	59.40	$PbSO_4(s)$	35.2	$K(s)$	15.2
$SO_3(g)$	61.24	$Hg(g)$	41.80	$KF(s)$	15.91
$H_2S(g)$	49.15	$Hg(l)$	18.5	$KCl(s)$	19,76
$N_2(g)$	45.767	$Ag(s)$	10.206		

Organic Compounds

Methane, $CH_4(g)$	44.50	Propylene, $C_3H_6(g)$	63.80
Ethane, $C_2H_6(g)$	54.85	1-Butene, $C_4H_8(g)$	73.48
Propane, $C_3H_8(g)$	64.51	Acetylene, $C_2H_2(g)$	47.997
n-Butane, $C_4H_{10}(g)$	74.10	Formaldehyde, $CH_2O(g)$	52.26
Isobutane, $C_4H_{10}(g)$	70.42	Acetaldehyde, $C_2H_4O(g)$	63.5
n-Pentane, $C_5H_{12}(g)$	83.27	Methanol, $CH_3OH(l)$	30.3
n-Hexane, $C_6H_{14}(g)$	92.45	Ethanol, $CH_3CH_2OH(l)$	38.4
n-Heptane, $C_7H_{16}(g)$	101.64	Formic acid, $HCO_2H(l)$	30.82
n-Octane, $C_8H_{18}(g)$	110.82	Acetic acid, $CH_3CO_2H(l)$	38.2
Benzene, $C_6H_6(g)$	64.34	Oxalic acid, $(CO_2H)_2(s)$	28.7
Benzene, $C_6H_6(l)$	41.30	Carbon tetrachloride, $CCl_4(l)$	51.25
Ethylene, $C_2H_4(g)$	52.45	Glycine, $C_2H_5O_2N(s)$	26.1

Ions in H_2O

H^+	0.000	$SO_4{}^{2-}$	4.1	Cu^{2+}	-23.6
OH^-	-2.519	HS^-	14.6	Ag^+	17.67
F^-	-2.3	$NO_3{}^-$	35.0	Mg^{2+}	-28.2
Cl^-	13.17	$NH_4{}^+$	26.97	Ca^{2+}	-13.2
$ClO_4{}^-$	43.5	$PO_4{}^{3-}$	-52	Li^+	3.4
Br^-	19.29	$CO_3{}^{2-}$	-12.7	Na^+	14.4
I^-	26.14	Zn^{2+}	-25.45	K^+	24.5
S^{2-}	5.3	Cd^{2+}	-14.6		

Gaseous Atoms

H	27.3927	Br	41.8052	N	36.6147
F	37.917	I	43.184	C	37.76
Cl	39.4569				

[1] These data have been obtained from F. D. Rossini, D. D. Wagman, W. H. Evans, S. Levine, and I. Jaffe, "Selected Values of Chemical Thermodynamic Properties," *Natl. Bur. Standards Circ.* 500, U. S. Government Printing Office, Washington, D. C., 1952, and F. D. Rossini, K. S. Pitzer, W. J. Taylor, J. P. Ebert, J. E. Kilpatrick, C. W. Beckett, M. G. Williams, and H. G. Werner, "Selected Values of Properties of Hydrocarbons," *Natl. Bur. Standards Circ.* C 461, U. S. Government Printing Office, Washington, D. C., 1947.

the basis of the third law of thermodynamics. It is found that the agreement is within the experimental error for a large number of compounds, but H_2, CO, H_2O, N_2O, and certain other compounds are exceptions. For these substances the calorimetric values are 1.1–1.5 cal deg^{-1} $mole^{-1}$ smaller than the values calculated from spectroscopic data. The discrepancy for H_2 has been accounted for on the basis of the existence of ortho and para forms (p. 349). The discrepancies for CO and NNO are apparently due to disorder in the crystal lattice arising from end-over-end randomness in the arrangement of adjacent molecules. Thus in solid CO the molecules are arranged CO, OC, CO, CO, OC rather than CO, CO, CO, CO, CO.

Free Energy. The introduction of the necessary thermodynamic functions was completed with entropy, but it is convenient to introduce three more functions G, A, and μ which have very useful properties. The entropy provides a criterion for equilibrium in an isolated system, but the Gibbs free energy G provides a criterion for equilibrium at constant temperature and pressure, the work function or Helmholtz free energy A provides a criterion for equilibrium at constant temperature and volume, and the chemical potential μ is an intensive property (p. 114) determining the direction of chemical or physical change.

The Gibbs free energy * G is defined in terms of the other thermodynamic functions by

$$G = H - TS = E + PV - TS \qquad (33)$$

The Gibbs free-energy change in going from state 1 to state 2 is

$$G_2 - G_1 = (E_2 - E_1) + (P_2V_2 - P_1V_1) - (T_2S_2 - T_1S_1)$$

$$\Delta G = \Delta E + \Delta(PV) - \Delta(TS) = \Delta H - \Delta(TS) \qquad (34)$$

At constant pressure and temperature

$$\Delta G = \Delta E + P\,\Delta V - T\,\Delta S \qquad (35)$$

Substituting $\Delta E = q - w$,

$$\Delta G = q - w + P\,\Delta V - T\,\Delta S \qquad (36)$$

* This is sometimes referred to as the free energy or the Gibbs energy. The Gibbs free energy G is named in honor of Prof. J. Willard Gibbs of Yale University. His many important generalizations in thermodynamics have given him a position as one of the great geniuses of science. The symbol F has been generally used in American publications rather than G. It has been used in all previous editions of this book. In European publications F is used for the Helmholtz free energy, for which American chemists use A. A committee of the International Union of Pure and Applied Chemistry is endeavoring to effect a compromise and a standardization.

If a change is carried out by a reversible process and heat q is transferred from a reservoir at the same temperature T as the system, then $T \Delta S = q$ and $w = w_{rev}$. For this case equation 36 can be written

$$- \Delta G = w_{rev} - P \Delta V \tag{37}$$

Thus, when a change is carried out reversibly at constant temperature and pressure, the decrease in Gibbs free energy is equal to the maximum work w_{rev} that can be done in excess of the pressure-volume work, $P \Delta V$.

If a change is carried out by an irreversible process and heat q is transferred from a reservoir at the same temperature T as the system, then $T \Delta S > q$. Substitution into equation 36 shows that

$$- \Delta G > w_{rev} - P \Delta V \tag{38}$$

Thus for an irreversible process at constant temperature and pressure the decrease in Gibbs free energy is greater than the maximum work that can be done in excess of the pressure-volume work.

The work function or Helmholtz free energy A is defined in terms of the other thermodynamic functions by

$$A = E - TS \quad or \quad \Delta A = \Delta E - \Delta(TS) \tag{39}$$

Holding T constant and combining equation 39 with the first law of thermodynamics, it can be shown that

$$- \Delta A = w_{rev} \tag{40}$$

Thus the decrease in Helmholtz free energy is equal to the maximum amount of work which can be obtained from an isothermal process.

There is a definite change in the work function A for a given change, whether it is carried out reversibly or irreversibly. However, in order to determine the work-function decrease for a given change it is necessary to measure the work done when the process is carried out reversibly.

Criteria of Chemical Equilibrium. Early attempts by Berthelot to discover a thermodynamic criterion of spontaneous chemical reactions led him in 1879 to the false conclusion that reactions which evolve heat are spontaneous. The discovery of spontaneous reactions which absorb heat proved that this idea was wrong. It will be shown that an isothermal process at constant pressure is spontaneous if G decreases and that an isothermal process at constant volume is spontaneous if A decreases.

It is of considerable practical importance to know whether a system is in equilibrium or just in a metastable state. By equilibrium we mean that a system is in such a state that it can undergo no spontaneous change. Thus at equilibrium any infinitesimal change which might take place in the system must be *reversible*, since any *irreversible* change would result in a displacement of the original equilibrium.

Let us consider a system in contact with a reservoir at temperature T in which an infinitesimal *irreversible* process occurs and only pressure-volume work is done. The quantity of heat δq is exchanged with the reservoir, and since the process is irreversible the entropy change dS for the system is greater than $\delta q/T$:

$$dS > \frac{\delta q}{T} \tag{41}$$

as already shown. Since $T\, dS$ is greater than δq, $q - T\, \delta S$ is negative:

$$\delta q - T\, dS < 0 \tag{42}$$

Since the only work done is pressure-volume work, $\delta q = dE + P\, dV$. Substituting this into equation 42,

$$dE + P\, dV - T\, dS < 0 \tag{43}$$

This inequality is always applicable if the only work involved is pressure-volume work. If the volume and entropy of the system are held constant,

$$(dE)_{V,S} < 0 \tag{44}$$

Thus, for any irreversible process in a system of constant volume which does not change its entropy, the internal energy decreases. This is the familiar condition that for a conservative mechanical system the stable state is the one of lowest energy.

If the volume and internal energy of the system are held constant during the infinitesimal irreversible process, equation 43 indicates that

$$(dS)_{V,E} > 0 \tag{45}$$

The volume and internal energy of a system may be kept constant by isolating the system, and so this is just the condition illustrated earlier (p. 93) that the entropy increases in an irreversible process in an isolated system. It must be remembered that inequalities 43, 44, and 45 apply only to systems where the only work done is of the pressure-volume type.

If the system is not isolated, there are entropy changes in the adjacent systems which must also be considered. These additional entropy changes are taken into account automatically when the functions A and G are used under appropriate conditions. If the volume is constant during the infinitesimal irreversible process, inequality 43 becomes

$$(dE - T\,dS)_V < 0 \tag{46}$$

which may also be written

$$d(E - TS)_{T,V} < 0 \tag{47}$$

Substituting $A = E - TS$,

$$(dA)_{T,V} < 0 \tag{48}$$

Thus, in an irreversible process at constant T and V, the work function or Helmholtz free energy A *decreases*.

Physical processes or chemical reactions are usually carried out in the laboratory at constant pressure and temperature. When P and T are constant, inequality 43 may be written

$$d(E + PV - TS)_{T,P} < 0 \tag{49}$$

Introducing $G = E + PV - TS$,

$$(dG)_{T,P} < 0 \tag{50}$$

Thus, in an irreversible process at constant T and P which involves only pressure-volume work, the Gibbs free energy G decreases.

If the processes discussed above were reversible, the inequalities would all be replaced with equal signs because of equation 8. The conditions for irreversibility and reversibility for processes involving only pressure-volume work are summarized in Table III. Each line of this table represents a mathematical way of stating the second law of thermodynamics. Since the Gibbs free energy decreases in an irreversible process at constant T and P, it becomes a minimum at the final equilibrium state, where $dG = 0$ for any infinitesimal change. We can *imagine* a process occurring at equilibrium; for example, we may imagine the evaporation of an infinitesimal amount of water from

Table III. Criteria for Irreversibility and Reversibility for Processes Involving No Work or Only Pressure-Volume Work

For Irreversible Processes	For Reversible Processes
$(dS)_{V,E} > 0$	$(dS)_{V,E} = 0$
$(dE)_{V,S} < 0$	$(dE)_{V,S} = 0$
$(dA)_{T,V} < 0$	$(dA)_{T,V} = 0$
$(dG)_{T,P} < 0$	$(dG)_{T,P} = 0$

the liquid into the vapor phase which is saturated with water vapor at constant temperature and pressure. For such a process $dG = 0$.

These same relations may be applied to finite changes as well as infinitesimal changes, replacing the d's by Δ's. However, it must be remembered that spontaneous changes always go to the minimum (as in the case of free energy at constant T and P) or to the maximum (as in the case of the entropy of an isolated system) and not to some other condition, even though the change to some other condition satisfies the required inequality.

The above discussion has been restricted to systems which do not have the capability of doing useful work other than pressure-volume work. If the system contained an electrochemical cell, then electrical work could be done and the criteria for equilibrium would be altered.

Although these criteria show whether a certain change is a spontaneous one, it does not necessarily follow that the change will take place with an appreciable speed. Thus, a mixture of 1 mole of carbon and 1 mole of oxygen at 1 atm pressure and 25° has a Gibbs free energy greater than that of 1 mole of carbon dioxide at 1 atm and 25°, and so it is possible for the carbon and oxygen to combine to form carbon dioxide at this constant temperature and pressure. Although carbon may exist for a very long time in contact with oxygen, the reaction is theoretically possible. The reverse of a thermodynamically spontaneous process is of course a nonspontaneous process. Thus the decomposition of carbon dioxide at room temperature, which involves an increase in Gibbs free energy, is nonspontaneous. It can occur only with the aid of an outside agency or by heating to a very high temperature where the free-energy change has the opposite sign.

The Gibbs Free Energy as the Criterion of Equilibrium. These considerations of Gibbs free energy as a criterion for equilibrium or spontaneous change at constant temperature and pressure can be illustrated with a mixture of ice and water. Both ice and water have the same Gibbs free energy per mole at 0° and 1 atm pressure, and there is no tendency for the ice to melt or the water to freeze in a mixture at 0° and 1 atm. On the other hand, the Gibbs free energy of water supercooled to $-10°$ is higher per mole than that of ice at $-10°$, both being under a pressure of 1 atm. The change of water to ice at this temperature and pressure is accompanied by a decrease in Gibbs free energy, and hence it is a spontaneous change. The change in the reverse direction, that is, ice changing to water at $-10°$, cannot take place spontaneously because there would then be an increase in Gibbs free energy, that is, $\Delta G > 0$.

For an isothermal process the change in Gibbs free energy is obtained from equation 34:

$$\Delta G = \Delta H - T\,\Delta S \tag{51}$$

This is a very important equation, as will be seen in later chapters. The quantities ΔH and ΔS can be determined by direct calorimetric measurements, and ΔG can then be calculated. The Gibbs free-energy change is useful in calculating the voltages of electrochemical cells and the equilibrium constants of chemical reactions.

At constant temperature and pressure there are two opposing tendencies which determine the position of equilibrium; one is the tendency for the energy to be reduced as much as possible and the other is the tendency for the entropy to increase as much as possible. Since G is a minimum at equilibrium at constant temperature and pressure, the quantity $H - TS$ must also be a minimum at equilibrium.

For the mixing of a total of a mole of two ideal gases $\Delta \bar{H} = 0$, and the change in Gibbs free energy may be calculated by combining equation 51 with equation 24:

$$\Delta \bar{G} = RT(X_1 \ln X_1 + X_2 \ln X_2) \tag{52}$$

Since $X_1 < 1$ and $X_2 < 1$, it is apparent that ΔG of mixing ideal gases at constant temperature and pressure is always negative.

Differentials and Derivatives of the Thermodynamic Functions. Some applications of thermodynamics to chemistry are concerned with *reversible* processes in which *the only work done is pressure-volume work*. The corresponding expressions for the differentials of E, H, and G are fairly simple.

$$dE = \delta q - \delta w = T\,dS - P\,dV \tag{53}$$

$$dH = dE + d(PV) = dE + P\,dV + V\,dP \tag{54}$$

$$dG = dH - d(TS) = dH - T\,dS - S\,dT \tag{55}$$

It is possible to express E, H, and G in terms of P, V, T, and S.

Repeating equation 53,

$$dE = T\,dS - P\,dV \tag{56}$$

By substitution of equation 56 into 54, and 56 with 54 into 55:

$$dH = T\,dS + V\,dP \tag{57}$$

and

$$dG = -S\,dT + V\,dP \tag{58}$$

Equations 56, 57, and 58 are now compared with the mathematical expression for an exact differential (p. 716):

$$du = \left(\frac{\partial u}{\partial x}\right)_y dx + \left(\frac{\partial u}{\partial y}\right)_x dy \tag{59}$$

For example, taking E as a function of S and V, the differential of E is represented by

$$dE = \left(\frac{\partial E}{\partial S}\right)_V dS + \left(\frac{\partial E}{\partial V}\right)_S dV \tag{60}$$

By comparing equation 56 with equation 60 we see that

$$\left(\frac{\partial E}{\partial S}\right)_V = T \tag{61}$$

$$\left(\frac{\partial E}{\partial V}\right)_S = -P \tag{62}$$

Similarly from equation 57 for dH

$$\left(\frac{\partial H}{\partial S}\right)_P = T \tag{63}$$

$$\left(\frac{\partial H}{\partial P}\right)_S = V \tag{64}$$

From equation 58 for dG

$$\left(\frac{\partial G}{\partial T}\right)_P = -S \tag{65}$$

$$\left(\frac{\partial G}{\partial P}\right)_T = V \tag{66}$$

These expressions for derivatives of thermodynamic functions are very useful.

Equations 61–66 may also be written in terms of the change in the thermodynamic function for a physical change or a chemical reaction. For example, applying equation 65 to a transformation from state 1 to state 2:

$$\left(\frac{\partial G_2}{\partial T}\right)_P - \left(\frac{\partial G_1}{\partial T}\right)_P = -(S_2 - S_1) \tag{67}$$

$$\left(\frac{\partial \Delta G}{\partial T}\right)_P = -\Delta S \tag{68}$$

The application of equations 61–66 will be illustrated by considering equations 66 and 65 in some detail.

Influence of Pressure on Gibbs Free Energy. If the molar volume $\bar{V}$ is known as a function of pressure, the change of Gibbs free energy per mole with pressure may be calculated, since $(\partial \bar{G}/\partial P)_T = \bar{V}$. This will be illustrated for (a) a liquid or solid for which the volume remains constant over a moderate change in pressure and (b) an ideal gas.

If volume is independent of pressure,

$$\int_{\bar{G}_1}^{\bar{G}_2} dG = \bar{V} \int_{P_1}^{P_2} dP$$

$$\Delta \bar{G} = \bar{G}_2 - \bar{G}_1 = \bar{V}(P_2 - P_1) \tag{69}$$

For 1 mole of an ideal gas, at constant temperature,

$$\left(\frac{\partial \bar{G}}{\partial P}\right)_T = \bar{V} = \frac{RT}{P} \tag{70}$$

$$\int_{\bar{G}_1}^{\bar{G}_2} d\bar{G} = \int_{P_1}^{P_2} \frac{RT\, dP}{P}$$

$$\Delta \bar{G} = \bar{G}_2 - \bar{G}_1 = RT \ln \frac{P_2}{P_1} \tag{71}$$

This equation applies only to a change at constant temperature and for an ideal gas, but it gives the change in Gibbs free energy whether the process is carried out reversibly or irreversibly. The Gibbs free energy, like E, H, A, and S, depends only upon the state of the system and is independent of the manner in which that state was reached.

Example 7. Calculate the Gibbs free-energy change for the expansion of 2 moles of ideal gas from 1 atm to $\frac{1}{10}$ atm at 25°.

$$\Delta G = (2 \text{ moles})(1.987 \text{ cal deg}^{-1} \text{ mole}^{-1})(298 \text{ deg})(2.303) \log \tfrac{1}{10}$$

$$= -2730 \text{ cal}$$

Example 8. Calculate the change in Gibbs free energy for the process

$$H_2O(l, -10°) = H_2O(s, -10°)$$

The vapor pressure of water at $-10°$ is 2.149 mm of mercury, and the vapor pressure of ice at $-10°$ is 1.950 mm. The process may be carried out by the following reversible steps:

1. A mole of water is transferred at $-10°$ from liquid to saturated vapor ($P = 2.149$ mm). $\Delta \bar{G} = 0$, since the two phases are in equilibrium.

2. The water vapor is allowed to expand from 2.149 to 1.950 mm at $-10°$.

$$\Delta \bar{G} = RT \ln \frac{P_2}{P_1} = (1.987)(263)(2.303) \log \frac{1.950}{2.149}$$

$$= -52 \text{ cal mole}^{-1}$$

3. A mole of water is transferred at $-10°$ from vapor at $P = 1.950$ mm to ice at $-10°$. $\Delta \bar{G} = 0$, since the two phases are in equilibrium.

Thus the Gibbs free energy of the system decreases 52 cal mole^{-1} as water freezes at $-10°$. At $0°$ there is no change in Gibbs free energy, since ice and water have the same vapor pressure at this temperature.

Influence of Temperature on Gibbs Free Energy. The change in Gibbs free energy with temperature is related to the enthalpy change in a simple way which was first derived independently by Gibbs and by Helmholtz. Substitution of equation 65 into equation 33 yields

$$G = H + T \left(\frac{\partial G}{\partial T} \right)_P \tag{72}$$

or

$$\Delta G = \Delta H + T \left(\frac{\partial \Delta G}{\partial T} \right)_P$$

This equation involves both the Gibbs free energy and the temperature derivative of the Gibbs free energy, and it is more convenient to transform it so that only a temperature derivative appears. This may be accomplished by first differentiating G/T with respect to temperature at constant pressure:

$$\left[\frac{\partial (G/T)}{\partial T} \right]_P = \frac{T(\partial G/\partial T)_P - G}{T^2}$$

Eliminating G from the right-hand side by use of equation 72, we have

$$\left[\frac{\partial (G/T)}{\partial T} \right]_P = \frac{-H}{T^2} \tag{73}$$

Since $\partial (1/T)/\partial T = -T^{-2}$,

$$\left[\frac{\partial (G/T)}{\partial (1/T)} \right]_P = \left[\frac{\partial (G/T)}{\partial T} \right]_P \frac{\partial T}{\partial (1/T)} = H \tag{74}$$

This equation may also be written in terms of ΔG and ΔH to obtain

$$\left[\frac{\partial (\Delta G/T)}{\partial (1/T)} \right]_P = \Delta H$$

Thus ΔH for a reaction may be obtained from a plot of $\Delta G/T$ versus $1/T$ as well as by calorimetric measurements. This equation is important for the calculation of ΔG at another temperature if it is known at one temperature and ΔH is known (p. 218).

Thermodynamic Calculations. In this section simple physical processes are considered. Applications to chemical reactions will be found later throughout the book. In considering the application of thermodynamic equations to a given problem, the various restrictions under which the equations were derived must be borne in mind, and it is well to consider: (a) What are the initial and final states? (b) Is the process reversible or not? (c) Is it isothermal or not? (d) Is it isobaric or not; that is, is it carried out at constant pressure?

Example 9. One mole of steam is compressed reversibly to liquid water at the boiling point 100°. The heat of vaporization of water at 100° and 760 mm is 539.7 cal g^{-1}. Calculate w and q and each of the thermodynamic quantities $\Delta \bar{H}$, $\Delta \bar{E}$, $\Delta \bar{G}$, $\Delta \bar{A}$, and $\Delta \bar{S}$. The process is reversible, isothermal, and isobaric:

$$w = P \, \Delta \bar{V} = P(\bar{V}_l - \bar{V}_v) \cong^* -P\bar{V}_v = -RT$$

where $\bar{V}_l$ and $\bar{V}_v$ are the molar volumes of the liquid and vapor respectively.

$$= -(1.987 \text{ cal deg}^{-1} \text{ mole}^{-1})(373 \text{ deg}) = -741 \text{ cal mole}^{-1}$$

$$q_P = \Delta \bar{H} = -(539.7 \text{ cal g}^{-1})(18.0 \text{ g mole}^{-1}) = -9720 \text{ cal mole}^{-1}$$

$$\Delta \bar{E} = \Delta \bar{H} - P \, \Delta \bar{V} = -9720 + 741 = -8979 \text{ cal mole}^{-1}$$

$$\Delta \bar{G} = \int \bar{V} \, dP = 0$$

$$\Delta \bar{A} = -w_{\max} = 741 \text{ cal mole}^{-1}$$

$$\Delta \bar{S} = \frac{q_{\text{rev}}}{T} = \frac{-9720 \text{ cal mole}^{-1}}{373 \text{ deg}} = -26.0 \text{ cal deg}^{-1} \text{ mole}^{-1}$$

$\Delta \bar{G}$ may be calculated in another way.

$$\Delta \bar{G} = \Delta \bar{H} - T \, \Delta \bar{S} = -9720 \text{ cal mole}^{-1} - (373 \text{ deg})(-26.0 \text{ cal deg}^{-1} \text{ mole}^{-1}) = 0$$

Example 10. One mole of an ideal gas at 27.0° expands isothermally and reversibly from 10 atm to 1 atm against a pressure that is gradually reduced. Calculate q and w and each of the thermodynamic quantities $\Delta \bar{E}$, $\Delta \bar{H}$, $\Delta \bar{G}$, $\Delta \bar{A}$, and $\Delta \bar{S}$. Calculations with the ideal gas equation show that the volume expands from 2.462 to 24.62 liters.

Since the process is carried out isothermally and reversibly,

$$w_{\max} = RT \ln \frac{\bar{V}_2}{\bar{V}_1} = (1.987 \text{ cal deg}^{-1} \text{ mole}^{-1})(300.1 \text{ deg})(2.303) \log \frac{24.62}{2.462}$$

$$= 1373 \text{ cal mole}^{-1}$$

$$\Delta \bar{A} = -w_{\max} = -1373 \text{ cal mole}^{-1}$$

Since the internal energy of an ideal gas is not affected by a change in volume,

$$\Delta \bar{E} = 0$$

$$q = \Delta \bar{E} + w = 0 + 1373 = 1373 \text{ cal}$$

$$\Delta \bar{H} = \Delta \bar{E} + \Delta(P\bar{V}) = 0 + 0 = 0$$

* The symbol $\cong$ is used to indicate an approximate equality.

since $P\overline{V}$ is constant for an ideal gas at constant temperature.

$$\Delta \overline{G} = \int_{10}^{1} \overline{V}\, dP = RT[\ln P]_{10}^{1} = (1.987\text{ cal deg}^{-1}\text{ mole}^{-1})(300.1\text{ deg})(2.303)(-1)$$

$$= -1373\text{ cal mole}^{-1}$$

$$\Delta \overline{S} = \frac{q_{rev}}{T} = \frac{1373\text{ cal mole}^{-1}}{300.1\text{ deg}} = 4.58\text{ cal deg}^{-1}\text{ mole}^{-1}$$

Also,

$$\Delta \overline{S} = \frac{\Delta \overline{H} - \Delta \overline{G}}{T} = \frac{0 - (-1373\text{ cal mole}^{-1})}{300.1\text{ deg}} = 4.58\text{ cal deg}^{-1}\text{ mole}^{-1}$$

Example 11. One mole of an ideal gas expands isothermally at 27° into an evacuated vessel so that the pressure drops from 10 to 1 atm; that is, it expands from a vessel of 2.462 liters into a connecting vessel such that the total volume is 24.62 liters. Calculate the change in thermodynamic quantities.

This process is isothermal, but it is not reversible.

$w = 0$ because the system as a whole is closed and no external work can be done.

$\Delta \overline{E} = 0$ because the gas is ideal (p. 43).

$q = \Delta \overline{E} + w = 0 + 0 = 0$.

$\Delta \overline{E}$, $\Delta \overline{H}$, $\Delta \overline{G}$, $\Delta \overline{A}$, and $\Delta \overline{S}$ are the same as in example 10 because the initial and final states are the same.

Although the entropy change of the gas is 4.58 in both example 10 and example 11, it is important to consider the entropy change of the whole system, including both vessel and reservoir. In example 10 it should be noted that the entropy change for the constant-temperature reservoir is $(-1373)/300.1 = -4.58$ cal deg^{-1} mole^{-1} so that the entropy change for the whole system is zero, as it must be for a reversible process. In the process for example 11 no heat is absorbed from the reservoir, and so the entropy change for the whole system is 4.58 cal deg^{-1} mole^{-1}, which is positive, as it must be for an irreversible process in an isolated system.

Thermodynamics of a Chemical Reaction. The determination of the thermodynamic quantities ΔG and ΔS for a chemical reaction may be illustrated by considering the reaction

$$Zn(s) + 2HCl(aq) = ZnCl_2(aq) + H_2(g)$$

This reaction may be carried out either irreversibly or reversibly. The reaction occurs irreversibly if the zinc metal is simply added to an acid solution, as it would be in an open calorimeter. The calculation of ΔE and ΔH from calorimetric measurements was described in Chapter 4.

In order to determine ΔG for the reaction it is necessary to devise a method for determining the maximum amount of work which can be obtained per mole of zinc reacted at constant temperature and pressure, exclusive of the pressure-volume work which could be obtained from the evolution of hydrogen. This maximum work is obtained by carrying out the reaction reversibly in an electrochemical cell and measuring the electrical work done. Under these conditions $-\Delta G$ = electrical work. In order to carry out the reaction reversibly we may utilize an electrochemical cell consisting of a zinc electrode immersed in a solution of zinc chloride and a hydrogen electrode (p. 385) immersed in a solution of hydrochloric acid, the two solutions being connected through the conducting solution in the channels of a porous plate. The maximum work is obtained from such a cell by drawing current reversibly. By use of a potentiometer the voltage is measured under conditions such that the direction of current flow may be reversed by an infinitesimal change in the voltage applied by the potentiometer. If the voltage applied by the potentiometer is less than the electromotive force of the cell, the reaction proceeds spontaneously to the right. If the applied voltage is greater than the electromotive force of the cell, the reaction proceeds spontaneously to the left. The ΔG for the reaction may be calculated from the electromotive force of the reversible cell as described later (p. 388).

The ΔS for the reaction could be calculated by dividing the heat absorbed when the reaction is carried out reversibly by the absolute temperature. However, when the reaction is carried out reversibly in an electrochemical cell, the heat change per unit time is infinitesimally small, so this method is not practical. The value of ΔS cannot be calculated from the heat of reaction determined calorimetrically by adding zinc to hydrochloric acid because the reaction is not reversible when carried out in this way. However, ΔS may be calculated from ΔH and ΔG using $\Delta G = \Delta H - T \Delta S$.

The reaction may be carried out so as to obtain some electrical work but not the maximum work. Thus, q may vary between q_{rev} and ΔH, and w may vary between w_{max} and 0. But ΔE, ΔH, ΔA, ΔG, and ΔS are always the same, no matter how the reaction is carried out.

Partial Molal Quantities. The volume of an ideal solution is simply the sum of the volumes of the components. However, this is not true for many real solutions. For example, if 100 ml of sulfuric acid is added to 100 ml of water, the final volume is 182 ml, and there is an evolution of a considerable quantity of heat. The sulfuric acid and the water interact, and the sulfuric acid ionizes, with the result that the sulfuric acid and the water in the solution do not have the same properties they had as pure liquids. Also, when a mole of methanol is added to water, the increase in volume is less than the molar volume of liquid methanol and depends upon the concentration of the final solution. In order to treat such solutions thermodynamically it is necessary to introduce the concept of the partial molal property.

Let V represent the volume of a homogeneous solution. Since the volume depends upon the numbers of moles n_1 and n_2 of the components of a binary solution and upon the pressure and temperature, we can write

$$dV = \left(\frac{\partial V}{\partial n_1}\right)_{T,P,n_2} dn_1 + \left(\frac{\partial V}{\partial n_2}\right)_{T,P,n_1} dn_2$$
$$+ \left(\frac{\partial V}{\partial P}\right)_{T,n_1,n_2} dP + \left(\frac{\partial V}{\partial T}\right)_{P,n_1,n_2} dT \quad (75)$$

The partial derivative of V with respect to the number of moles of component i when temperature, pressure, and the numbers of moles of all other components are kept constant is called the *partial molal volume* and is represented by $\overline{V}_i$.

$$\overline{V}_i = \left(\frac{\partial V}{\partial n_i}\right)_{T,P,n_j} \quad (76)$$

The subscript n_j means that the number of moles of each component is held constant except for component i. This definition may be stated in words by saying that $\overline{V}_i$ is the change in V per mole of i added, when an infinitesimal amount of this component is added to the solution at constant temperature and pressure. Alternatively it may be said that $\overline{V}_i$ is the change in V when 1 mole of i is added to an infinite amount of the solution at constant temperature and pressure.

Introducing the partial molal volumes defined by equation 76 into equation 75 and limiting the discussion to constant temperature and pressure, we obtain

$$dV = \overline{V}_1 \, dn_1 + \overline{V}_2 \, dn_2 \quad (77)$$

This equation may be integrated at constant composition. At constant composition the mole fractions X_1 and X_2 are constant, and $\overline{V}_1$ and $\overline{V}_2$ are also constant, being independent of the volume of the solution at constant composition. Since $n_i = X_i n$, where n is the total number of moles,

$$dn_i = X_i \, dn \quad (87)$$

Substituting these relations into equation 77 yields

$$dV = (\overline{V}_1 X_1 + \overline{V}_2 X_2) \, dn \quad (79)$$

Since the quantity in parentheses is constant, integration yields

$$V = (\overline{V}_1 X_1 + \overline{V}_2 X_2)n + C \tag{80}$$

but the integration constant C is zero since $V = 0$ when $n = 0$. Thus equation 80 may be written

$$V = \overline{V}_1 n_1 + \overline{V}_2 n_2 \tag{81}$$

The volume V of the solution may be calculated for a given concentration, using this equation, if the partial molal volumes $\overline{V}_1$ and $\overline{V}_2$ at the given concentration are known.

In order to determine the partial molal volumes it is necessary to measure the densities of solutions over a range of concentrations. An obvious method for determining the partial molal volume of a solute consists in plotting the volume of the solution containing 1000 grams of solvent against the number of moles of solute per 1000 grams of the solvent (that is, against the molality, p. 719), and determining the slope of the curve as shown in *Fig. 5-5*. The slope of the curve $\partial V/\partial n_2$ at any molality gives the rate of change of volume with the number of moles of solute added, the amount of solvent being held constant; this is by definition the partial molal volume of the solute at this molality. In Fig. 5-5 the dashed line is tangent to the experimental curve at 2 molal. The slope is 38.4 ml mole^{-1} = $\overline{V}_{\text{MeOH}}$ at 2 molal methanol in water at 20°. This value may be compared with 40.47 ml mole^{-1}, which is the molal volume of pure methanol at 20°.

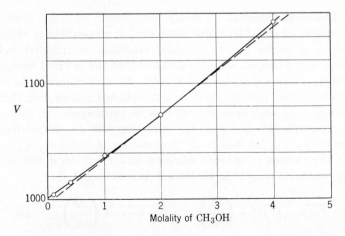

Fig. 5-5. Determination of partial molal volumes by the method of tangents. The volume (in milliliters) of solution at 20° containing 1000 grams of water is represented by V.

The partial molar volume of water may be determined in a similar manner by drawing tangents to the curve obtained by plotting the volume of the solution against the molality of the water in the methanol-water solution. After the partial molal volumes have been determined, the volume V of the whole solution can be calculated at any concentration, by use of equation 81.

More accurate methods for calculating partial molal quantities, such as $\overline{V}$ and $\overline{G}$, have been devised * and would be used in actual practice.

Extensive and Intensive Properties. Extensive properties are those which depend upon the quantity of homogeneous or uniform substance considered. They can be added together. Examples of extensive properties are V, E, S, and G.

Intensive properties do not depend upon the quantity of homogeneous substance considered. Examples of intensive properties are P, T, $\overline{V}$, $\overline{E}$, $\overline{S}$, and $\overline{G}$. Density is weight per unit volume, and 200 grams of material has the same density as 100 grams; hence density is also an intensive property.

We have discussed criteria of equilibrium states in terms of extensive properties S, A, and G. Criteria of equilibrium can also be stated in terms of intensive properties. We are already familiar with the fact that for two phases to be in equilibrium they must be at the same temperature and pressure, but now we will add another important condition involving the *chemical potential*.

The Chemical Potential. The thermodynamic relations which have been discussed so far have not taken explicit recognition of changes in numbers of moles due to chemical reactions or transfers between phases. For example, we have assumed that the internal energy E of a system is a function of S and V only. In other words we have been discussing *closed systems* which do not exchange matter with their surroundings, although heat or work may be exchanged. An *open system* is one that permits the exchange of matter with its surroundings. In order to provide for changes in the numbers of moles n_1, n_2, n_3, $\cdots$, n_n of the various substances, equation 56 is rewritten in the following form, where n_j represents all the substances except j:

$$dE = T\, dS - P\, dV + \left(\frac{\partial E}{\partial n_1}\right)_{V,S,n_j} dn_1 + \cdots + \left(\frac{\partial E}{\partial n_n}\right)_{V,S,n_j} dn_n \qquad (82)$$

* I. M. Klotz, *Chemical Thermodynamics*, Prentice-Hall, Englewood Cliffs, N. J., 1950, p. 193.

Following Gibbs, the coefficient of dn_i in this equation is called the *chemical potential* μ_i of component i.

$$\mu_i = \left(\frac{\partial E}{\partial n_i}\right)_{V,S,n_j} \tag{83}$$

By use of equation 83, equation 82 may be written

$$dE = T\,dS - P\,dV + \Sigma\,\mu_i\,dn_i \tag{84}$$

where the summation includes all the different components.

The chemical potential may also be defined in other ways. For example, introduction of equation 82 into equation 54 and substitution of equation 54 into equation 55 leads to

$$dG = V\,dP - S\,dT + \Sigma\,\mu_i\,dn_i \tag{85}$$

Therefore by equation 59

$$\mu_i = \left(\frac{\partial G}{\partial n_i}\right)_{T,P,n_j} = \bar{G}_i \tag{86}$$

Thus the chemical potential of a substance i is equal to the rate of change in the Gibbs free energy of the system with number of moles n_i of this component when the temperature, the pressure, and the number of moles of all other components are held constant. Stated in another way, the chemical potential of a component is the amount by which the capacity of the system for doing work *other than pressure-volume work* is increased per mole of substance added, for an infinitesimal addition at constant temperature and pressure. The chemical potential is equal to the partial molal Gibbs free energy. It is important to realize that the partial molal Gibbs free energy is an intensive property, whereas the Gibbs free energy is an extensive property.

By reference to equation 86 it may be seen that the chemical potential of a component is equal to its partial molal Gibbs free energy in the phase considered. If a phase consists of a pure substance, the chemical potential of that substance is equal to its Gibbs free energy per mole. The chemical potential is of special importance because it is an *intensive* property of the phase, like temperature and pressure. Thus the difference in chemical potential of a substance in two phases determines the direction in which the substance will diffuse spontaneously, just as the difference in temperature determines the direction in which heat will flow. The usefulness of the chemical potential will be illustrated frequently later in the book.

Criteria of Equilibrium in Terms of Intensive Properties. Criteria of equilibrium can be stated in terms of the intensive properties T, P, and μ. We are familiar with the fact that for two phases, such as ice and water, to be in equilibrium they must be at the same temperature and pressure. This can be proved by considering that an infinitesimal quantity of heat is transferred from a phase α to a phase β with which it is in equilibrium. The condition for equilibrium is

$$dS = 0 \quad \text{or} \quad dS_\alpha + dS_\beta = 0$$

where the phases are designated by subscripts. Since the process is reversible

$$\frac{-q}{T_\alpha} + \frac{q}{T_\beta} = 0$$

or

$$T_\alpha = T_\beta \tag{87}$$

The fact that the pressure must be the same in two phases at equilibrium may be proved by considering that phase α increases in volume by an infinitesimal volume dV and phase β decreases by the same amount. If the temperature and volume of the whole system are held constant,

$$dA_\alpha + dA_\beta = 0 \quad \text{or} \quad -P_\alpha\, dV + P_\beta\, dV = 0$$

and so

$$P_\alpha = P_\beta \tag{88}$$

An additional restriction may be derived by considering the transfer of a small quantity of substance i from phase α to phase β, which are in equilibrium. If the temperature of the whole system and the pressures of the various phases are kept constant, then, since $dG = 0$,

$$dG_\alpha + dG_\beta = 0$$

or using equation 86,

$$-\mu_{i\alpha}\, dn_i + \mu_{i\beta}\, dn_i = 0$$

or

$$\mu_{i\alpha} = \mu_{i\beta} \tag{89}$$

Thus, the chemical potential of a component is the same in all phases at equilibrium.

If phases α and β are not in equilibrium and a small quantity dn_i of species i is transferred from phase α to phase β in the direction of approaching equilibrium, we have at constant temperature and pressure

$$dG_\alpha + dG_\beta < 0$$

$$-\mu_{i\alpha}\, dn_i + \mu_{i\beta}\, dn_i < 0$$

If dn_i is positive

$$\mu_{i\alpha} > \mu_{i\beta} \tag{90}$$

Thus, a substance will tend to pass spontaneously from the phase where it has the higher chemical potential to the phase where it has the lower chemical potential. Also a substance will diffuse spontaneously from a region where its concentration and chemical potential are higher into a more dilute solution where its chemical potential is lower. In this respect the chemical potential is like other kinds of potential, electrical, gravitational, etc., in that the spontaneous change is always in the direction from high to low potential. It is really to this property that the chemical potential owes its name.

The Chemical Potential for an Ideal Gas. According to equation 86, the chemical potential μ of a component of a phase is equal to the partial molal Gibbs free energy $\overline{G}$. If the phase consists of a single component, $\overline{G}$ is simply the free energy per mole of pure substance. Thus equation 66 becomes

$$\left(\frac{\partial \overline{G}}{\partial P}\right)_T = \left(\frac{\partial \mu}{\partial P}\right)_T = \overline{V} \tag{91}$$

where $\overline{V}$ is the molar volume. For an ideal gas $\overline{V} = RT/P$. Substitution of this expression into equation 91 and integration yields

$$\int_{\mu^\circ}^{\mu} d\mu = \int_{P^\circ}^{P} \frac{RT}{P} dP \tag{92}$$

$$\mu - \mu^\circ = RT \ln \frac{P}{P^\circ} \tag{93}$$

where μ and μ° are the chemical potentials of the pure gas at the pressures P and P° at temperature T. It is convenient to choose P° as 1 atm so that μ° is the chemical potential of 1 mole of pure gas at 1 atm pressure and temperature T. Equation 93 is usually written

$$\mu = \mu^\circ + RT \ln P \tag{94}$$

since $P^\circ = 1$ atm. In using such an equation it should always be remembered that it is not possible to take the logarithm of a quantity with units (that is, pressure) and that P really represents the ratio of the actual pressure to some other pressure at which the chemical potential is μ°. Equation 94 gives the chemical potential of a component of an ideal gaseous mixture if P is the partial pressure, just as if it were the only gas at the same pressure P. In order to make this equation applicable to nonideal gases the pressure must be replaced by the fugacity.* The fugacity of a gas may be calculated if its equation of state is known.

REFERENCES

E. F. Caldin, *An Introduction to Chemical Thermodynamics*, Oxford University Press, Oxford, 1958.

K. G. Denbigh, *The Principles of Chemical Equilibrium*, Cambridge University Press, Cambridge, 1955.

J. W. Gibbs, *The Collected Works of J. Willard Gibbs*, Yale University Press, New Haven, 1948.

S. Glasstone, *Thermodynamics for Chemists*, D. Van Nostrand Co., Princeton, N. J., 1947.

E. A. Guggenheim, *Modern Thermodynamics by the Methods of Willard Gibbs*, Methuen & Co., London, 1933.

O. A. Hougen, K. M. Watson, and R. A. Ragatz, *Chemical Process Principles*, Part II: *Thermodynamics*, John Wiley & Sons, New York, 1959.

I. M. Klotz, *Chemical Thermodynamics*, Prentice-Hall, Englewood Cliffs, N. J., 1950.

G. N. Lewis, M. Randall, K. S. Pitzer, and L. Brewer, *Thermodynamics*, McGraw-Hill Book Co., New York, 1961.

I. Prigogine, *Introduction to Thermodynamics of Irreversible Processes*, Thomas, Springfield, 1955.

I. Prigogine and R. Defay, *Chemical Thermodynamics*, Longmans, Green and Co., New York, 1954.

F. D. Rossini, *Chemical Thermodynamics*, John Wiley & Sons, New York, 1950.

F. T. Wall, *Chemical Thermodynamics*, W. H. Freeman & Co., San Francisco, 1958.

M. W. Zemansky, *Heat and Thermodynamics*, McGraw-Hill Book Co., New York, 1957.

PROBLEMS

1. Calculate the entropy changes for the following processes: (a) melting of 1 mole of aluminum at its melting point, $660°$ ($\Delta \bar{H}_{fus} = 1.91$ kcal g atom^{-1}); (b) evaporation of 2 moles of liquid oxygen at its boiling point, $-182.97°$ ($\Delta \bar{H}_{vap} = 1.630$ kcal mole^{-1}); (c) heating of 10 grams of hydrogen sulfide from 50 to $100°$ ($\bar{C}_P = 7.15 + 0.00332T$).   *Ans.* (a) 2.05, (b) 36.2, (c) 0.351 cal deg^{-1}.

2. A mole of steam is condensed at $100°$, and the water is cooled to $0°$ and frozen to ice. What is the entropy change of the water? Consider that the average specific heat of liquid water is 1.0 cal deg^{-1} g^{-1}. The heat of vaporization at the boiling point and the heat of fusion at the freezing point are 539.7 and 79.7 cal g^{-1}, respectively.   *Ans.* $\Delta \bar{S} = -36.9$ cal deg^{-1} mole^{-1}.

3. Calculate the change in entropy if 350 grams of water at $5°$ is mixed with 500 grams of water at $70°$, assuming that the specific heat is 1.00 cal deg^{-1} g^{-1}.
          Ans. 4.485 cal deg^{-1}.

---

* G. N. Lewis, M. Randall, K. S. Pitzer, and L. Brewer, *Thermodynamics*, McGraw-Hill Book Co., New York, 1961, and O. A. Hougen, K. M. Watson, and R. A. Ragatz, *Chemical Process Principles*, Part II: *Thermodynamics*, John Wiley & Sons, New York, 1959.

4. Calculate the entropy change for a hundredfold expansion of a mole of ideal gas. $Ans.$ 9.17 cal deg^{-1} mole^{-1}.

5. In the reversible isothermal expansion of an ideal gas at 300°K from 1 to 10 liters, where the gas has an initial pressure of 20 atm, calculate (a) ΔS for the gas and (b) ΔS for all systems involved in the expansion.

$Ans.$ (a) 4.58, (b) 0 cal deg^{-1}.

6. A thermostat was maintained at a temperature of 96.9°. The air in the room was at 26.9°. During a certain length of time 1000 cal of heat leaked through the thermostat insulation into the room. (a) What was the entropy change of the material in the thermostat? (b) What was the entropy change of the air in the room? (c) Was the process reversible or irreversible?

$Ans.$ (a) -2.70, (b) 3.33 cal deg^{-1}. (c) Total entropy change $= 0.63$ cal deg^{-1} mole^{-1}, therefore irreversible.

7. Calculate $\Delta \bar{S}$ for the formation of a quantity of air containing 1 mole of gas by mixing nitrogen and oxygen. Air may be taken to be 80 per cent nitrogen and 20 per cent oxygen by volume. $Ans.$ 0.995 cal deg^{-1} mole^{-1}.

8. Theoretically, how high could a gallon of gasoline lift an automobile weighing 2800 lb against the force of gravity, if it is assumed that the cylinder temperature is 2200°K and the exit temperature 1200°K? (Density of gasoline $= 0.80$ g cm^{-3}; 1 lb $= 453.6$ grams; 1 ft $= 30.48$ cm; 1 liter $= 0.2642$ gal. Heat of combustion of gasoline $= 11,200$ cal g^{-1}.) $Ans.$ 17,000 ft.

9. Calculate the molal entropy of liquid chlorine at its melting point, 172.12°K, from the following data obtained by W. F. Giauque and T. M. Powell:

T, °K	15	20	25	30	35	40	50	60
$\bar{C}_P$, cal deg^{-1} mole^{-1}	0.89	1.85	2.89	3.99	4.97	5.73	6.99	8.00

T, °K	70	90	110	130	150	170	172.12
$\bar{C}_P$, cal deg^{-1} mole^{-1}	8.68	9.71	10.47	11.29	12.20	13.17	M.P.

The heat of fusion is 1531 cal mole^{-1}. Below 15°K it may be assumed that $\bar{C}_P$ is proportional to T^3. $Ans.$ 25.8 cal deg^{-1} mole^{-1}.

10. Using atomic and molecular entropies from Table II, calculate $\Delta S°$ for the following reactions at 25°:

(a) $\quad$ H$_2(g) + \frac{1}{2}$O$_2(g) =$ H$_2$O(l)

(b) $\quad$ H$_2(g) +$ Cl$_2(g) = 2$HCl(g)

(c) $\quad$ Propane$(g) +$ ethane$(g) = n$-pentane$(g) +$ H$_2(g)$

(d) $\quad$ Methane$(g) + \frac{1}{2}$O$_2(g) =$ methanol(l)

$Ans.$ (a) -38.996, (b) 4.737, (c) -4.88, (d) -38.7 cal deg^{-1}.

11. Calculate the Gibbs free-energy changes at 25° for the reactions in problem 10 when the reactants are in their standard states by use of enthlapy-of-formation data in Table II of Chapter 4. $Ans.$ (a) -56.690, (b) -45.536, (c) 11.51, (d) -27.59 kcal.

12. When rubber is allowed to contract, the mechanical work obtained is equal to the force times the displacement in the direction of the force and is given by

$dw = -f\,dL$, where f is force and L is the length of the piece of rubber. If the contraction is carried out reversibly, the first law may be written

$$dE = \left(\frac{\partial E}{\partial T}\right)_L dT + \left(\frac{\partial E}{\partial L}\right)_T dL = T\,dS + f\,dL$$

if pressure-volume work is neglected. (a) Show that

$$\left(\frac{\partial S}{\partial T}\right)_L = \frac{1}{T}\left(\frac{\partial E}{\partial T}\right)_L \qquad \left(\frac{\partial S}{\partial L}\right)_T = \frac{1}{T}\left[\left(\frac{\partial E}{\partial L}\right)_T - f\right]$$

(b) By using the fact that the order of differentiation used to obtain $\partial^2 S/\partial L\,\partial T$ is immaterial, show that

$$\left(\frac{\partial E}{\partial L}\right)_T = f - T\left(\frac{\partial f}{\partial T}\right)_V$$

13. One mole of an ideal gas is allowed to expand reversibly and isothermally (25°) from a pressure of 1 atm to a pressure of 0.1 atm. (a) What is the change in Gibbs free energy? (b) What would be the change in Gibbs free energy if the process occurred irreversibly? *Ans. (a) −1364, (b) −1364 cal.*

14. The vapor pressures of water and ice at −5° are 3.163 and 3.013 mm, respectively. Calculate $\Delta\bar{G}$ for the transformation of water to ice at −5°.

Ans. −27 cal mole⁻¹.

15. (a) Calculate the work done against the atmosphere when 1 mole of toluene is vaporized at its boiling point, 111°. The heat of vaporization at this temperature is 86.5 cal g⁻¹. For the vaporization of 1 mole, calculate (b) q, (c) $\Delta\bar{H}$, (d) $\Delta\bar{E}$, (e) $\Delta\bar{G}$, (f) $\Delta\bar{S}$. *Ans. (a) 763, (b) 7969, (c) 7969, (d) 7206, (e) 0 cal mole⁻¹, (f) 20.7 cal deg⁻¹ mole⁻¹.*

16. One liter of an ideal gas at 300°K has an initial pressure of 15 atm and is allowed to expand isothermally to a volume of 10 liters. Calculate (a) the maximum work which can be obtained from the expansion, (b) $\Delta\bar{E}$, (c) $\Delta\bar{H}$, (d) $\Delta\bar{G}$, (e) $\Delta\bar{A}$. *Ans. (a) 836, (b) 0, (c) 0, (d) −836, (e) −836 cal.*

17. One mole of ammonia (considered to be an ideal gas) initially at 25° and 1 atm pressure is heated at constant pressure until the volume has trebled. Calculate (a) q, (b) w, (c) $\Delta\bar{H}$, (d) $\Delta\bar{E}$, (e) $\Delta\bar{S}$. See Table VI in Chapter 4.
Ans. (a) 6320, (b) 1185, (c) 6320, (d) 5135 cal mole⁻¹; (e) 11.23 cal deg⁻¹ mole⁻¹.

18. Calculate the partial molal volume of zinc chloride in 1-molal $ZnCl_2$ solution using the following data:

% by weight of $ZnCl_2$	2	6	10	14	18	20
Density, g ml⁻¹	1.0167	1.0532	1.0891	1.1275	1.1665	1.1866

Ans. 29.3 ml mole⁻¹.

19. Calculate the increase in entropy of nitrogen when it is heated from 25 to 1000° (a) at constant pressure and (b) at constant volume.

20. Compute the entropy difference between 1 mole of liquid water at 25° and 1 mole of water vapor at 100° and 1 atm. The average specific heat of liquid water may be taken as 1 cal deg⁻¹ g⁻¹, and the heat of vaporization is 540 cal g⁻¹.

21. One hundred and fifty grams of ice is added to a kilogram of water at $25°$ in an isolated system. Calculate the change in entropy if the heat of fusion is 1435 cal mole^{-1} and $\bar{C}_P = 18$ cal deg^{-1} mole^{-1} for liquid water.

22. Calculate the entropy change of a mole of helium which undergoes a reversible adiabatic expansion from $25°$ and 1 atm to a final pressure of $\frac{1}{2}$ atm.

23. Show that the process

$$H_2O(l, 5°) = H_2O(s, 5°)$$

is not a spontaneous process in an isolated system containing in addition to the water a thermostat at $5°$. The heat of fusion of water is 79.7 cal g^{-1} at $0°$, and the specific heats for water and ice may be taken as 1 cal deg^{-1} g^{-1} and 0.5 cal deg^{-1} g^{-1}, respectively.

24. A 1-liter bulb containing nitrogen at 1 atm pressure and $25°$ is connected by a tube with a stopcock to a 3-liter bulb containing carbon dioxide at 2 atm pressure. The stopcock is opened, and the gases are allowed to mix until equilibrium is reached. Assuming that the gases are both ideal, what is ΔS for this spontaneous change?

25. Calculate the theoretical maximum efficiency with which heat can be converted into work in the following hypothetical turbines: (a) steam at $100°$ with exit at $40°$; (b) mercury vapor at $360°$ with exit at $140°$; (c) steam at $400°$ and exit at $150°$; (d) air at $800°$ and exit at $400°$; (e) air at $1000°$ and exit at $400°$, special alloys being used; (f) helium at $1500°$ and exit at $400°$, heat from atomic energy being used.

26. Calculations with the Debye formula show the molal entropy of silver iodide to be 1.5 cal deg^{-1} mole^{-1} at $15°$K. From the following data for the molar heat capacity at constant pressure, calculate the molar entropy of silver iodide at $298.1°$K.

T, °K	$\bar{C}_P$	T, °K	$\bar{C}_P$	T, °K	$\bar{C}_P$	T, °K	$\bar{C}_P$
21.00	3.82	64.44	9.36	145.67	11.92	258.79	13.05
30.53	5.23	88.58	10.60	170.86	12.15	273.23	13.26
42.70	7.09	105.79	11.19	198.89	12.49	287.42	13.48
52.15	8.20	126.53	11.60	228.34	12.76	301.37	13.64

27. Calculate the molal entropy of carbon disulfide at $25°$ from the following heat-capacity data and the heat of fusion, 1049.0 cal mole^{-1}, at the melting point ($161.11°$K):

T, °K	15.05	20.15	29.76	42.22	57.52	75.54	89.37
$\bar{C}_P$, cal deg^{-1} mole^{-1}	1.65	2.87	4.96	6.97	8.50	9.57	10.31

T, °K	99.00	108.93	119.91	131.54	156.83	161–298
$\bar{C}_P$, cal deg^{-1} mole^{-1}	10.98	11.59	12.07	12.58	13.53	18.04

28. Calculate the entropy changes for the following reactions at $25°$:

　(a)　S(rhombic) = S(monoclinic)

　(b)　Ethanol(l) $+ \frac{1}{2}O_2(g)$ = acetaldehyde(g) $+ H_2O(l)$

　(c)　n-Hexane(g) = benzene(g) $+ 4H_2(g)$

29. Using the combined first and second laws of thermodynamics, show that $P\bar{V} = RT$ implies $(\partial \bar{E}/\partial \bar{V})_T = 0$. (a) Show that for a reversible process at constant temperature

$$\left(\frac{\partial \bar{E}}{\partial \bar{V}}\right)_T = T\left(\frac{\partial \bar{S}}{\partial \bar{V}}\right)_T - P$$

(b) Complete the proof using one of Maxwell's relations, $(\partial \bar{S}/\partial \bar{V})_T = (\partial P/\partial T)_{\bar{V}}$.

30. Show that

$$\left(\frac{\partial E}{\partial S}\right)_V = \left(\frac{\partial H}{\partial S}\right)_P$$

$$\left(\frac{\partial H}{\partial P}\right)_S = \left(\frac{\partial G}{\partial P}\right)_T$$

31. Two moles of ideal gas are compressed isothermally from 1 to 5 atm at 100°. (a) What is the Gibbs free-energy change? (b) What would have been the Gibbs free-energy change if the compression had been carried out at 0°?

32. At 50° the partial pressure of $H_2O(g)$ over $CuSO_4 \cdot H_2O(s)$ is 4.5 mm and over $CuSO_4 \cdot 5H_2O(s)$ is 47 mm. Calculate the Gibbs free-energy change for the reaction:

$$CuSO_4 \cdot 5H_2O(s) = CuSO_4 \cdot H_2O(s) + 4H_2O(g)$$

33. The heat of vaporization of liquid oxygen at 1 atm is 1630 cal mole^{-1} at its boiling point, $-183°$. For the reversible evaporation of 1 mole of liquid oxygen calculate (a) q, (b) $\Delta \bar{E}$, (c) $\Delta \bar{G}$, and (d) $\Delta \bar{S}$.

34. One mole of an ideal gas in 22.4 liters is expanded isothermally and reversibly at 0° to a volume of 224 liters and $\frac{1}{10}$ atm. Calculate (a) w, (b) q, (c) $\Delta \bar{H}$, (d) $\Delta \bar{G}$, (e) $\Delta \bar{S}$ for the gas.

One mole of an ideal gas in 22.4 liters is allowed to expand irreversibly into an evacuated vessel such that the final total volume is 224 liters. Calculate (f) w, (g) q, (h) $\Delta \bar{H}$, (i) $\Delta \bar{G}$, (j) $\Delta \bar{S}$ for the gas.

Calculate (k) $\Delta \bar{S}$ for the system and its surroundings involved in the reversible isothermal expansion and calculate (l) $\Delta \bar{S}$ for the system and its surroundings involved in the irreversible isothermal expansion.

35. One-half mole of an ideal monatomic gas initially at 25° and occupying a volume of 2 liters is expanded adiabatically and reversibly to a pressure of 1 atm. The gas is then compressed isothermally and reversibly until its volume is 2 liters at the lower temperature. Calculate (a) q, (b) w, (c) ΔE, (d) ΔH, and (e) ΔS.

36. If the partial specific volume v in milliliters per gram is independent of concentration, it is equal to the volume of the solution minus the volume of pure solvent it contains divided by the weight of solute:

$$v = \frac{100 - \left(\dfrac{100\rho_s - g}{\rho_0}\right)}{g}$$

where g is the number of grams of solute in 100 ml of solution, ρ_s is the density of the solution, and ρ_0 is the density of the solvent. The density of a solution of serum albumin containing 1.54 grams of protein per 100 ml is 1.0004 g cm^{-3} at 25° ($\rho_0 = 0.99707$ g cm^{-3}). Calculate the apparent specific volume.

37. A solution of magnesium chloride, $MgCl_2$, in water containing 41.24 g liter^{-1} has a density of 1.0311 g cm^{-3} at 20°. The density of water at this temperature is 0.99823 g cm^{-3}. Calculate (a) the partial specific volume (see the equation in problem 36) and (b) the partial molal volume of $MgCl_2$ in this solution.

---

38. What is the change in entropy when 1 mole of water vapor is heated from 300 to 600° at constant pressure?

39. Calculate the change in entropy of a mole of aluminum which is heated from 600 to 700°. The melting point of aluminum is 660°, the heat of fusion is 94 cal g^{-1}, and the heat capacities of the solid and liquid may be taken as 7.6 and 8.2 cal deg^{-1} mole^{-1}, respectively.

40. Calculate the differences between the molal entropies of Hg(l) and Hg(s) at −50°. The melting point of mercury is −39°, and the heat of fusion is 560 cal g-atom^{-1}. The heat capacity per gram atom of Hg(l) may be taken as 7.1 − $0.0016T$, and that of Hg(s) as 6.4 cal deg^{-1}.

41. Derive the expression for the entropy change of a van der Waals' gas which is allowed to expand from volume $\bar{V}_1$ to $\bar{V}_2$ at constant temperature.

42. Calculate the entropy change of aluminum when it crystallizes 100° below its melting point. The required data are given in problem 39. What is the entropy change for the aluminum plus its surroundings at 560°?

43. Two blocks of the same metal are of the same size but are at different temperatures, T_1 and T_2. These blocks of metal are brought together and allowed to come to the same temperature. Show that the entropy change is given by

$$\Delta S = C_P \ln \left[\frac{(T_2 - T_1)^2}{4T_1 T_2} + 1 \right]$$

if C_P is constant. How does this equation show that the change is spontaneous?

44. A mole of helium at 100° is mixed with 0.5 mole of neon which is at 0°. What is ΔS for this change if the initial and final pressures are all 1 atm and the gases are ideal?

45. (a) Calculate the least work that would have to be performed in order to extract 100 cal of heat from an ice bath at 0°, when the surroundings are at 25°. (b) How much heat at 25° could be obtained from the ice bath on the expenditure of 10 cal of work in a reversible process?

46. Using the following data, calculate the molal entropy of gaseous isobutene at 25° [S. S. Todd and G. S. Parks, *J. Am. Chem. Soc.*, *58*, 134 (1936)]:

$$\bar{S}_{90°K} = 10.81 \text{ cal deg}^{-1} \text{ mole}^{-1}$$

$$\text{F.P.} = -140.7°$$

$$\Delta\bar{H}_{fus} = 25.22 \text{ cal}^{-1} \text{ g}^{-1}$$

$$\text{B.P.} = -7.1°$$

$$\Delta\bar{H}_{vap} = 96.5 \text{ cal}^{-1} \text{ g}^{-1}$$

$$\bar{C}_P(\text{gas}) \text{ in range } 226\text{--}298°K = 20 \text{ cal deg}^{-1} \text{ mole}^{-1}$$

Specific Heat

T, °K	93.3	105.5	118.9	139.2	166.1	179.8	210.2	253.1
$\bar{C}_P$	0.2498	0.2749	0.3056	0.4547	0.4621	0.4681	0.4860	0.5173

47. Calculate the entropy changes for the following reactions at $25°$:

$$(a) \quad H^+(aq) + OH^-(aq) = H_2O(l)$$

$$(b) \quad Ag^+(aq) + Cl^-(aq) = AgCl(s)$$

$$(c) \quad HS^-(aq) = H^+(aq) + S^{2-}(aq)$$

48. Calculate $\Delta G°$ at $25°$ for the following reactions:

$$(a) \quad Fe_2O_3(s) + Fe(s) + \tfrac{1}{2}O_2(g) = Fe_3O_4(s)$$

$$(b) \quad n\text{-}C_6H_{14}(g) = C_6H_6(g) + 4H_2(g)$$

$$(c) \quad NaCl(s) + KF(s) = NaF(s) + KCl(s)$$

49. An equation for the pressure P as a function of height h in the atmosphere may be derived easily if it is assumed that the temperature T, acceleration g of gravity, and molecular weight M of air are constant. The molal Gibbs free energy of the gas is a function of pressure and height and must be the same throughout the atmosphere. Thus

$$d\bar{G} = \left(\frac{\partial \bar{G}}{\partial P}\right)_h dP + \left(\frac{\partial \bar{G}}{\partial h}\right)_P dh = 0$$

Show that $(\partial \bar{G}/\partial h)_P = Mg$, and then that

$$P = P_0 e^{-Mgh/RT}$$

50. Calculate ΔG for

$$H_2O(g, 25°) = H_2O(l, 25°)$$

The vapor pressure of water at $25°$ is 23.76 mm.

51. Calculate (a) w and (b) $\Delta \bar{G}$ when 1 mole of liquid water is evaporated at its boiling point $100°$ at 1 atm and then expanded in its vapor state to 50 liters at $100°$.

52. Ten grams of helium is compressed isothermally and reversibly at $100°$ from a pressure of 2 atm to 10 atm. Calculate (a) q, (b) w, (c) ΔG, (d) ΔA, (e) ΔH, (f) ΔE, (g) ΔS.

53. A 2-liter container at $0°$ contains hydrogen sulfide (assumed to be an ideal gas) at 1 atm pressure. The gas is heated to $100°$, the external pressure remaining 1 atm. Calculate (a) the heat absorbed, (b) the work done, (c) ΔE, (d) ΔH, and (d) ΔS. For hydrogen sulfide, $\bar{C}_P = 7.15 + 0.00332T$.

54. When 1 mole of water was added to an infinitely large amount of an aqueous methanol solution having a mole fraction of methanol of 0.40, the volume of the solution increased 17.35 ml. When 1 mole of methanol was added to such a solution, the volume increased 39.01 ml. Calculate the volume of solution containing 0.40 mole of methanol and 0.60 mole of water.

55. Calculate the equilibrium pressure for the conversion of graphite to diamond at $25°$. The densities of graphite and diamond may be taken to be 2.55 and 3.51 g cm^{-3}, respectively, independent of pressure, in calculating the change of ΔG with pressure. The necessary enthalpy data and entropy data are to be found in tables in this book.

ONE-COMPONENT SYSTEMS

6

A pure substance may exist as a solid, liquid, or gas. A solid substance may have several crystalline forms. In going from solid to liquid to gas, heat is absorbed so that the enthalpy increases in passing from one of these phases to the next. The enthalpy of the liquid is greater than that of the solid because heat is absorbed on melting. Similarly the enthalpy of the gas is greater than that of the liquid because heat is absorbed on vaporization.

The entropy increases in going from solid to liquid to gas because of the increase in randomness. Whether or not a given change, for example, the vaporization of a liquid at 1 atm pressure, is spontaneous at constant temperature and pressure depends upon ΔG. Since $\Delta G = \Delta H - T \Delta S$ and ΔH and ΔS for vaporization are always positive, it is evident that at some temperature ΔG is zero for the transition

$$\text{liquid (1 atm)} \rightarrow \text{gas (1 atm)},$$

and these phases will be in equilibrium. At higher temperatures ΔG is negative and this change will take place spontaneously.

Vapor Pressure. According to the kinetic theory, there is a continuous flight of molecules from the surface of a liquid into the free space above it. At the same time molecules of vapor * return to the surface of the liquid at a rate depending on the concentration of the vapor. As the concentration of vapor molecules increases, a condition of equilibrium is established between the liquid and its vapor, when the rate of escape is exactly equal to the rate of condensation of vapor. The vapor is then said to be saturated. The pressure exerted by vapor in equilibrium with the liquid is known as the vapor pressure. The equilibrium vapor pres-

* A vapor is generally defined as gas below its critical point.

125

sure is dependent on the temperature but is independent of the relative or absolute amounts of liquid and vapor. Since heat is absorbed in the vaporization process, the vapor pressure increases with temperature, as predicted by Le Châtelier's principle (p. 217), because the system at equilibrium shifts so as to counteract the applied force; that is, the vaporization of liquid absorbs the heat. As the temperature is raised, the density of the saturated vapor increases and the density of the liquid decreases. At the critical temperature these densities become equal, and above this temperature there can be no liquid phase. The temperature at which the vapor pressure is 760 mm is called the standard boiling point. Table I gives the vapor pressures of several liquids and their standard boiling points.

Solids, like liquids, have a vapor pressure which depends upon the temperature. If a solid is converted directly into vapor it is said to sublime. The sublimation pressures of several solids are also given in Table I.

Table I.[1] Vapor Pressures of Liquids and Sublimation Pressures of Solids

			Pressure, mm Hg				
	1	5	20	60	200	760	Melting Point, °C
Compound				Temperature, °C			
Aluminum	1284	1421	1555	1684	1844	2056	660
Ammonia	−109.1	−97.5	−85.8	−74.3	−57.0	−33.6	−77.7
Bromine	−48.7	−32.8	−16.8	−0.6	24.3	58.2	−7.3
Carbon (graphite)	3586	3828	4069	4273	4516	4827	
Carbon dioxide	−134.3	−124.4	−114.4	−104.8	−93.0	−78.2	−57.5
Copper	1628	1795	1970	2127	2325	2595	1083
Hydrogen (para)	−263.3	−261.9	−260.4	−258.9	−256.3	−252.5	−259.1
Water	−17.3	1.2	22.1	41.5	66.5	100.0	0.0
Iodine	38.7	62.2	84.7	105.4	137.3	183.0	112.9
Tungsten	3990	4337	4690	5007	5403	5927	3370
Uranium hexafluoride	−38.8	−22.0	−5.2	10.4	30.0	55.7	69.2
Acetone	−59.4	−40.5	−20.8	−2.0	22.7	56.5	−94.6
Acetylene	−142.9	−133.0	−122.8	−112.8	−100.3	−84.0	−81.5
Aniline	34.8	57.9	82.0	106.0	140.1	184.4	−6.2
Benzene	−36.7	−19.6	−2.6	15.4	42.2	80.1	5.5
Bromobenzene	2.9	27.8	53.8	78.1	110.1	156.2	−30.7
Decane	16.5	42.3	69.8	95.5	128.4	174.1	−29.7
Diethyl ether	−74.3	−56.9	−38.5	−21.8	2.2	34.6	−116.3
Ethane	−159.5	−148.5	−136.7	−125.4	−110.2	−88.6	−183.2
Ethanol	−31.3	−2.3	12.5	46.7	48.2	78.4	−112
n-Hexane	−53.9	−34.5	−14.1	5.4	31.6	68.7	−95.3
Methane	−205.9	−199.0	−191.8	−185.1	−175.5	−161.5	−182.5
Methyl iodide	...	−55.0	−35.6	−16.9	8.0	42.4	−64.4
Naphthalene	52.6	74.2	101.7	130.2	167.7	217.9	80.2
n-Octane	−14.0	19.2	38.5	58.5	82	125.6	−56.5

[1] Compiled from J. H. Perry, *Chemical Engineers Handbook*, McGraw-Hill Book Co., New York, 1950.

Measurement of Vapor Pressure or Sublimation Pressure. In the *static method* the liquid or solid is enclosed in a thermostated container at various temperatures, and the equilibrium pressure is measured directly using a manometer. In this method it is absolutely necessary to remove air which would contribute to the measured pressure. The substance studied is degassed by freezing and melting under vacuum.

In the *Ramsay-Young method* for measuring the vapor pressure of a liquid with a manometer the liquid is allowed to drip slowly over the bulb of a thermometer. There is no danger of superheating the thermometer, since it is heated by condensing vapor. If the thermometer is placed directly in a boiling liquid, the temperature may read too high because of superheating.

In the *gas-saturation method* a measured current of pure dry air or other gas is bubbled slowly through a weighed amount of the liquid or solid whose vapor pressure is to be determined, so that the gas stream becomes saturated. The liquid or solid is maintained at constant temperature, and its loss in weight is measured, or the vapor may be removed from the gas stream in an absorption tube or cold trap and weighed.

If V is the volume of gas which contains g grams of the vaporized liquid or solid with the molecular weight M, and p is the partial pressure of the vapor in equilibrium with the liquid at the temperature T, then the vapor pressure p of the liquid or solid may be calculated approximately, using the ideal gas law:

$$p = \frac{g}{MV} RT \tag{1}$$

For approximate calculations the volume V occupied by the vapor may be taken as the volume of the dry air measured before it is saturated with the vapor. For more accurate calculations or for high vapor pressures, allowance must be made for the fact that the total volume of the gases is increased by the introduction of the vapor. The volume v, of both air and vapor through which the vapor molecules are distributed, is $v'P/(P - p)$, where v' is the volume of the pure air before saturation, P is the barometric pressure, and p is the vapor pressure of the liquid or solid. Then,

$$p = \frac{g}{M} \frac{RT}{v} = \frac{g}{M} \frac{RT(P - p)}{v'P} \tag{2}$$

$$p \left(1 + \frac{g}{M} \frac{RT}{v'P} \right) = \frac{g}{M} \frac{RT}{v'}$$

Or, solving for p,

$$p = \frac{gRT/Mv'}{1 + (gRT/Mv'P)} \tag{3}$$

Example 1. Twenty liters of dry air was bubbled slowly through liquid CCl_4, which was held at 30.0°. The barometric pressure was 760 mm, and 28.6 grams of CCl_4 ($M = 153.8$) was vaporized. Calculate the vapor pressure of CCl_4 (a) using the ideal gas law, and (b) using equation 3.

(a) $p = \dfrac{gRT}{Mv'} = \dfrac{(28.6 \text{ g})(0.08205 \text{ l-atm deg}^{-1} \text{ mole}^{-1})(303.1 \text{ deg})(760 \text{ mm atm}^{-1})}{(153.8 \text{ g mole}^{-1})(20.0 \text{ l})}$

$= 176 \text{ mm}$

(b) $p = \dfrac{176 \text{ mm}}{1 + (176 \text{ mm}/760 \text{ mm})} = 143 \text{ mm}$

In the *Knudsen method* an enclosed volume above a solid or liquid is saturated with vapor and the rate of effusion of vapor through a small hole into a vacuum is measured. The pressure outside the container must be sufficiently low so that the mean free path is long compared with the diameter of the hole. Under these conditions the number of molecules passing through the hole is equal to the number of molecules which would collide with the corresponding area of wall. The necessary equations are discussed later (p. 278). This method is especially useful for determining pressures in the range 10^{-9} to 10^{-3} atm.

Dependence of Vapor Pressure on Temperature. The dependence of vapor pressure on temperature may be represented graphically or by means of an equation. Some of the data in Table I are plotted in *Fig. 6-1* on rectangular coordinates. In *Fig. 6-2* the logarithms of the vapor pressures and sublimation pressures in Table I are plotted against the reciprocals of the absolute temperatures. The reciprocals of the absolute temperatures have been multiplied by 10^3 for convenience in plotting. Thus, 0°C or 273.1°K gives a value for $1/T$ of 0.00366 or 3.66×10^{-3}.

If the temperature range is not too wide, these plots follow the equation

$$\log P = A + \frac{B}{T} \tag{4}$$

where P is the vapor pressure and A and B are constants. The symbol P rather than p is used because the vapor pressure is the total pressure for a one-component system. The theoretical justification for this empirical equation will be given shortly.

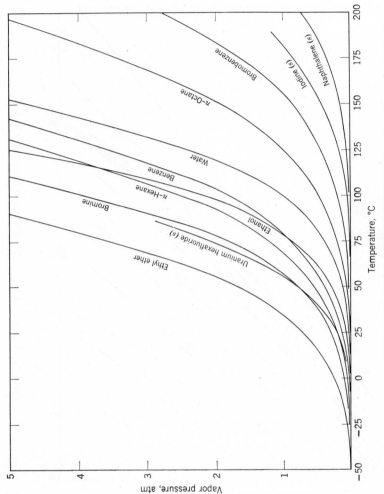

Fig. 6-1. Vapor pressure–temperature curves.

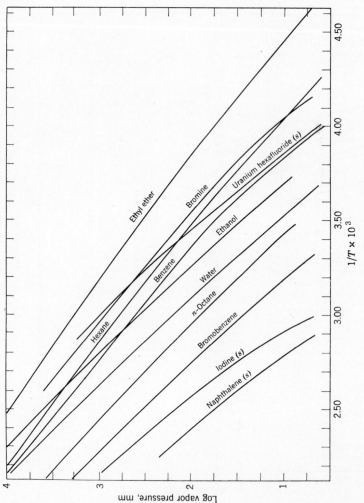

Fig. 6-2. Log p vs. $1/T$ for the substances shown in Fig. 6-1.

Pressure-Temperature Diagram for Water. The relationship between the vapor-pressure curve, sublimation curve, and solid-liquid equilibrium curve is illustrated for water in *Fig. 6-3*. This figure is not drawn to scale because of the very wide range of pressures involved. Along the line AB liquid water and vapor are in equilibrium. At pressures and temperatures represented by points below this line the liquid will vaporize completely, and so this region is labeled vapor. At pressures

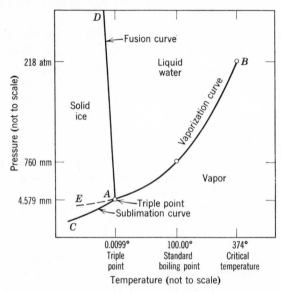

Fig. 6-3. Schematic pressure-temperature diagram for water, showing the conditions for various phases.

and temperatures represented by points above AB the vapor is completely condensed to liquid. The upper limit of the vaporization curve is at B, which is the critical point, 374° and 218 atm for water. Above this temperature the vapor and liquid phases become indistinguishable.

The line AC is the sublimation curve of ice. Above it lies ice and below it lies vapor. Only at temperatures and pressures represented by points along this line can ice and water vapor exist in equilibrium. Line AC theoretically goes down to absolute zero.

The dashed line AE, which is a continuation of AB, is the vapor-pressure curve for supercooled water. Since the vapor pressure of supercooled water is greater than the sublimation pressure of ice at the same temperature, ice and water cannot be in equilibrium at temperatures below point A. If liquid is added, its molecules will pass from the liquid to the solid, which has a lower vapor pressure.

The line AD shows how the melting point of ice depends upon the pressure. At all points on this line the pressure is greater than the vapor pressure given by line CAB, and so no vapor is present. For most substances line AD tilts away from the vertical axis rather than toward it, but water is an unusual substance which expands when it freezes. Since liquid water occupies a smaller volume than ice, we can predict with the aid of Le Châtelier's principle that raising the pressure will cause the system at equilibrium to shift toward the liquid form; that is, the freezing point will be lowered.

Investigations conducted by Bridgman to determine the course of the fusion curve AD have revealed the existence of seven different crystalline modifications of ice, all of which, with the exception of ordinary ice, are denser than water. The first of these new forms of ice makes its appearance at a pressure of 2115 kg cm^{-2}, and the last at a pressure of 22,400 kg cm^{-2}.

Where the three lines, representing pairs of phases, intersect at A, the three areas touch, and all three phases can exist together at equilibrium. Only one such point is possible * with three phases and is called the *triple point*. The triple point of water in the absence of air is at 0.0099° and 4.579 mm. In the presence of air at 1 atm the three phases are in equilibrium at 0°, which is one of the defined points on the centigrade scale. The total pressure in this case is 1 atm, but the partial pressure of water vapor is only 4.58 mm. The lowering of the triple point by air is due to two effects: (a) the solubility of air in liquid water at 1 atm pressure is sufficient to lower the freezing point 0.0024° (p. 181), and (b) the increase of pressure from 4.58 mm to 1 atm lowers the freezing point 0.0075°, as will be shown shortly.

Ice will be removed by sublimation if the partial pressure of water vapor is maintained at a value less than 4.6 mm and the temperature is raised.

The slopes of the lines in Fig. 6-3 are determined by the Clapeyron equation, which is to be discussed shortly, but first another figure will be discussed in order to give a fuller appreciation of the significance of Fig. 6-3.

The relationship between P, $\overline{V}$, and T for a mole of a substance may be represented as a surface in a three-dimensional diagram as illustrated in *Fig. 6-4* for water. Again the diagram is not drawn to scale. The two-phase regions on this surface are marked with horizontal lines on the three-dimensional space model. These three surfaces intersect at the triple point A. When this space model is projected on the $P\text{-}T$

---

* The proof will be given on p. 239.

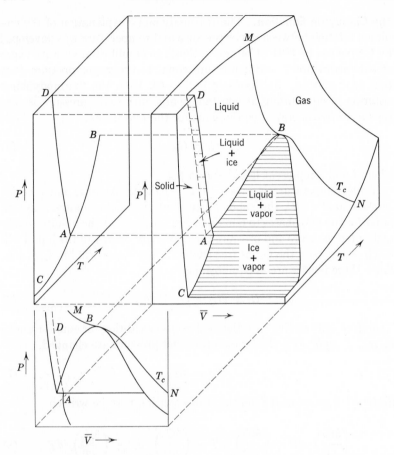

Fig. 6-4. Plot of the pressure-volume-temperature relation for a pure substance like water.

plane as shown to the left, Fig. 6-3 is obtained; when this space model is projected on the P-V plane as shown in front, a plot similar to Fig. 2-5 is obtained. The horizontal line at A indicates the equilibrium between liquid, solid, and vapor. At temperatures below the triple point A, water vapor condenses to give ice rather than liquid water as the volume of the vapor is reduced. At temperatures between the triple point and the critical point, liquid water is formed as the volume of the vapor is reduced. The vapor pressure of the liquid is given by the height of the liquid + vapor surface above the base of the three-dimensional figure at a particular temperature. Similarly the sublimation pressure of the solid is given by the height of the ice + vapor surface.

The Clapeyron Equation. The thermodynamic explanation of the empirical relation between vapor pressure and temperature was developed by Clapeyron in 1834. Consider a liquid in equilibrium with its vapor at a temperature T and a pressure equal to the vapor pressure P at that temperature. As discussed earlier (p. 104), the thermodynamic criterion of equilibrium at constant temperature and pressure is that the Gibbs free energy G be the same for the two states:

$$G_l = G_v \tag{5}$$

where l and v represent liquid and vapor.

If the temperature is raised to $T + dT$, the pressure must be increased to $P + dP$, the vapor pressure at this higher temperature, in order for the two phases to remain in equilibrium. At the infinitesimally higher temperature and pressure the Gibbs free energy of the liquid will be $G_l + dG_l$, and the Gibbs free energy of the vapor will be $G_v + dG_v$. Since these phases are in equilibrium,

$$G_l + dG_l = G_v + dG_v \tag{6}$$

Therefore, subtracting equation 5 gives the condition for equilibrium to be maintained when the temperature and pressure are changed.

$$dG_l = dG_v \tag{7}$$

Since dG is an exact differential, this equation may be written

$$\left(\frac{\partial G_l}{\partial P}\right)_T dP + \left(\frac{\partial G_l}{\partial T}\right)_P dT = \left(\frac{\partial G_v}{\partial P}\right)_T dP + \left(\frac{\partial G_v}{\partial T}\right)_P dT \tag{8}$$

According to equations 65 and 66 in Chapter 5, equation 8 can be written

$$V_l\, dP - S_l\, dT = V_v\, dP - S_v\, dT \tag{9}$$

On rearranging,

$$\frac{dP}{dT} = \frac{S_v - S_l}{V_v - V_l} \tag{10}$$

Since by equation 12 in Chapter 5,

$$S_v - S_l = \frac{\Delta H_{\text{vap}}}{T} \tag{11}$$

where ΔH_{vap} is the enthalpy of vaporization of the liquid at temperature T, equation 10 may be written

$$\frac{dP}{dT} = \frac{\Delta H_{vap}}{T(V_v - V_l)} \tag{12}$$

This important equation is referred to as the *Clapeyron equation*. It gives the rate of change of the vapor pressure with temperature, dP/dT, in terms of the enthalpy of vaporization ΔH_{vap}, volume of the liquid V_l, and volume of the vapor V_v, at temperature T and at a pressure equal to the vapor pressure.

Since the above derivation does not depend upon any assumptions concerning the nature of the two phases, similar equations may readily be derived for the equilibrium between a solid and the gas phase in equilibrium with it, for the equilibrium between solid and liquid, and for the equilibrium between two different crystalline forms of a solid. Equation 12 may be written for these cases as follows:

$$\frac{dP}{dT} = \frac{\Delta H_{sub}}{T(V_v - V_s)} \tag{13}$$

$$\frac{dP}{dT} = \frac{\Delta H_{fus}}{T(V_l - V_s)} \tag{14}$$

$$\frac{dP}{dT} = \frac{\Delta H_{tr}}{T(V_{s2} - V_{s1})} \tag{15}$$

where ΔH_{sub}, ΔH_{fus}, and ΔH_{tr} are the enthalpies of sublimation, fusion, and transition (between solid states 1 and 2), respectively. The heats of sublimation, fusion, and vaporization *at a given temperature* are related by

$$\Delta H_{sub} = \Delta H_{fus} + \Delta H_{vap} \tag{16}$$

since the heat required to vaporize a given amount of the solid is the same whether this process is carried out directly or by first melting the solid and then vaporizing the liquid. Each of these equations may also be written in terms of molar quantities.

In using equations 12–15 it is necessary to express the enthalpy change of the process in the same units as the product of pressure and volume change. For this purpose it is useful to calculate the factor for converting calories to liter-atmospheres: $(0.08205 \text{ l-atm deg}^{-1} \text{ mole}^{-1})/(1.987 \text{ cal deg}^{-1} \text{ mole}^{-1}) = 0.04129 \text{ l-atm cal}^{-1}$.

Example 2. What is the change in the boiling point of water at 100° per mm change in atmospheric pressure? The heat of vaporization is 539.7 cal g^{-1}, the molar volume of liquid water is 18.78 ml, and the molar volume of steam is 30.199 liters, all at 100° and 1 atm.

$$\frac{dP}{dT} = \frac{\Delta \bar{H}_{vap}}{T(\bar{V}_v - \bar{V}_l)} = \frac{(539.7 \text{ cal g}^{-1})(18.01 \text{ g mole}^{-1})(0.04129 \text{ l-atm cal}^{-1})}{(373.1 \text{ deg})(30.199 \text{ l mole}^{-1} - 0.01878 \text{ l mole}^{-1})}$$

$$= 0.0356 \text{ atm deg}^{-1}$$

$$= (0.0356 \text{ atm deg}^{-1})(760 \text{ mm atm}^{-1}) = 27.1 \text{ mm deg}^{-1}$$

Thus $dT/dP = 0.037$ deg mm^{-1}.

Example 3. Calculate the change in pressure required to change the freezing point of water 1°. At 0° the heat of fusion of ice is 79.7 cal g^{-1}, the density of water is 0.9998 g ml^{-1}, and the density of ice is 0.9168. The reciprocals of the densities, 1.0002 and 1.0908, are the volumes in milliliters of 1 gram. The volume change upon freezing $(V_l - V_s)$ is therefore -9.06×10^{-5} liter g^{-1}. For small changes ΔH_{fus}, T, and $(V_l - V_s)$ are virtually constant, so that

$$\frac{\Delta P}{\Delta T} = \frac{\Delta H_{fus}}{T(V_l - V_s)}$$

$$= \frac{(79.7 \text{ cal g}^{-1})(0.04129 \text{ l-atm cal}^{-1})}{(273.1 \text{ deg})(-9.06 \times 10^{-5} \text{ l g}^{-1})}$$

$$= -133 \text{ atm deg}^{-1}$$

In other words a pressure of 133 atm is required to lower the freezing point of water 1°; and the reciprocal,

$$\frac{\Delta T}{\Delta P} = \frac{-1}{133} = -0.0075 \text{ deg atm}^{-1}$$

shows that an increase in pressure of 1 atm lowers the freezing point 0.0075°. The negative sign indicates that an increase in pressure causes a decrease in temperature.

The Clausius-Clapeyron Equation. For vaporization and sublimation Clausius showed how the Clapeyron equation may be simplified by assuming that the vapor obeys the ideal gas law and by neglecting the volume of a mole of liquid $\bar{V}_l$ in comparison with a mole of vapor $\bar{V}_v$. For example, with water at 100°, $\bar{V}_v$ is 30.2 liters and $\bar{V}_l$ is 0.0188 liter. Substituting RT/P for $\bar{V}_v$,

$$\frac{dP}{dT} = \frac{\Delta \bar{H}_{vap}}{T\bar{V}_v} = \frac{P \Delta \bar{H}_{vap}}{RT^2} \tag{17}$$

On rearrangement this becomes

$$\frac{1}{dT}\frac{dP}{P} = \frac{\Delta \bar{H}_{vap}}{RT^2} \tag{18}$$

or

$$\frac{d \ln P}{dT} = \frac{\Delta \bar{H}_{vap}}{RT^2} \tag{19}$$

Integrating on the assumption that $\Delta \bar{H}_{vap}$ is independent of temperature yields

$$\int d \ln P = \frac{\Delta \bar{H}_{vap}}{R} \int T^{-2} \, dT \tag{20}$$

$$\ln P = -\frac{\Delta \bar{H}_{vap}}{RT} + C \tag{21}$$

$$\log P = \frac{-\Delta \bar{H}_{vap}}{2.303RT} + C' \tag{22}$$

where C is the integration constant. The theoretical basis for the empirical relation given in equation 4 is now apparent. Equation 21 is the equation of a straight line when $\ln P$ is plotted against $1/T$ and the slope is $-\Delta \bar{H}_{vap}/R$. When logarithms to the base 10 are used, the slope is $-\Delta \bar{H}_{vap}/2.303R$. Thus the heat of vaporization can be calculated, using

$$\Delta \bar{H}_{vap} \text{ (in cal mole}^{-1}) = -(\text{slope})(2.303)(1.987) \tag{23}$$

Example 4. Calculate the heat of vaporization of water at 25° from the slope of the line tangent to the plot in Fig. 6-2 at this temperature. At $1/T = 34.71 \times 10^{-4}$, $\log P = 1.107$, and at $1/T = 32.47 \times 10^{-4}$, $\log P = 1.625$, and so the slope is

$$\text{Slope} = \frac{1.107 - 1.625}{(34.71 - 32.47) \times 10^{-4}} = -2.31 \times 10^3$$

$$\Delta \bar{H}_{vap} = -(-2.31 \times 10^3)(2.303)(1.987)$$

$$= 10,590 \text{ cal mole}^{-1}$$

Frequently, it is more convenient to use the equation obtained by integrating between limits, P_2 at T_2 and P_1 at T_1, as follows:

$$\int_{P_1}^{P_2} d \ln P = \frac{\Delta \bar{H}_{vap}}{R} \int_{T_1}^{T_2} T^{-2} \, dT \tag{24}$$

$$\ln P_2 - \ln P_1 = \frac{\Delta \bar{H}_{\text{vap}}}{R} \left[-\frac{1}{T_2} - \left(-\frac{1}{T_1} \right) \right] \tag{25}$$

$$\log \frac{P_2}{P_1} = \frac{\Delta \bar{H}_{\text{vap}} (T_2 - T_1)}{2.303 R T_2 T_1} \tag{26}$$

Using this equation, it is possible to calculate the heat of vaporization from the vapor pressures at two different temperatures; and, if the heat of vaporization and the vapor pressure at one temperature are known, the vapor pressure at any other temperature in the range where $\Delta \bar{H}$ is constant can be calculated. Any units of pressure may be chosen as long as the same units are used for both pressures, and any units of heat may be used as long as $\Delta \bar{H}_{\text{vap}}$ and R are expressed in the same units of energy.

The variation of sublimation pressure with temperature may also be expressed by use of equation 26, provided that the temperature range is not too great. Since the heat of sublimation of a solid is greater than the heat of vaporization of the corresponding liquid, the sublimation pressure of the solid changes more rapidly with temperature than the vapor pressure of the corresponding liquid, and the curve is steeper.

The differential expression (equation 17) may be employed if the changes in temperature and pressure are small. For example, it is convenient to use the following form in correcting boiling points for barometric fluctuations:

$$\frac{\Delta T}{\Delta P} = \frac{R T^2}{\Delta \bar{H}_{\text{vap}} P} \tag{27}$$

Since equation 26 for calculating the heat of vaporization was derived on the assumption that the vapor is an ideal gas, the results obtained by its use are no more accurate than the calculations involving the equation $P \bar{V} = RT$.

Another approximation is involved in the assumption that the heat of vaporization is independent of temperature. Over wide temperature ranges plots of $\log P$ versus $1/T$ are somewhat curved because $\Delta \bar{H}_{\text{vap}}$ varies with the temperature. It is possible to calculate the heat of vaporization at any particular temperature from the slope of the curve by drawing a tangent to the curve at that temperature.

A vapor-pressure equation which provides for a linear change of $\Delta \bar{H}_{\text{vap}}$ with temperature may be derived as follows. According to equation 9 in Chapter 4, the molar heat of vaporization $\Delta \bar{H}_{\text{vap}}$ depends upon temperature according to

$$\Delta \bar{H}_{vap} = \Delta \bar{H}_{0,vap} + \int_0^T (\bar{C}_{P,vap} - \bar{C}_{P,liq})\, dT = \Delta \bar{H}_{0,vap} + \int_0^T \Delta \bar{C}_P\, dT \tag{28}$$

where $\Delta \bar{H}_{0,vap}$ is the hypothetical heat of vaporization at absolute zero. Assuming that $\Delta \bar{C}_P$ is independent of temperature,

$$\Delta \bar{H}_{vap} = \Delta \bar{H}_{0,vap} + T \Delta \bar{C}_P$$

Since $\Delta \bar{C}_P$ is negative, $\Delta \bar{H}_{vap}$ decreases as the temperature increases. On the molecular basis this is expected because the liquid expands as the temperature rises, and since the molecules are further apart, less energy is required to separate them in forming the vapor.

Substituting into equation 19 yields

$$\frac{d \ln P}{dT} = \frac{\Delta \bar{H}_{0,vap} + T\, \Delta \bar{C}_P}{RT^2} = \frac{\Delta \bar{H}_{0,vap}}{RT^2} + \frac{\Delta \bar{C}_P}{RT} \tag{29}$$

Thus the indefinite integral is

$$\log P = \frac{-\Delta \bar{H}_{0,vap}}{2.303RT} + \frac{\Delta \bar{C}_P}{R} \log T + \text{constant} \tag{30}$$

$$= \frac{A}{T} + B \log T + C \tag{31}$$

The evaluation of the three constants, A, B, and C, in this equation from data at three temperatures by solving the three simultaneous equations requires accurate data. This equation is applicable over a wider temperature range than equation 21, but it is not exact because deviations from the ideal gas law introduce an appreciable error which is not corrected by this derivation.

Entropy of Vaporization. For many liquids the molal entropy of vaporization at the standard boiling point (the boiling point at 1 atm pressure) is a constant, about 21 cal deg^{-1} mole^{-1}.

$$\Delta \bar{S}_{vap} = \frac{\Delta \bar{H}_{vap}}{T_b} \cong 21 \text{ cal deg}^{-1} \text{ mole}^{-1} \tag{32}$$

This is known as Trouton's rule and is useful for estimating the molar heat of vaporization of a liquid of known boiling point. The applicability of this rule is illustrated by the data of Table II.

The theoretical significance of Trouton's rule is that $\Delta \bar{H}_{vap}/T_b$ is the entropy of vaporization at the standard boiling point. The relative constancy of the entropy of vaporization from liquid to liquid is readily understood in terms of the Boltzmann hypothesis relating entropy to disorder.

Table II. Enthalpies and Entropies of Vaporization at the Standard Boiling Point

Substance	Boiling Temperature, °C at 760 mm	$\Delta \bar{H}_{vap}$, kcal mole^{-1}	$\Delta \bar{S}_{vap}$, cal deg^{-1} mole^{-1}
O_2	-182.97	1.630	18.07
H_2	-252.77	0.216	10.6
H_2O	100.00	9.7171	26.040
He	-268.944	0.020	4.7
HF	19.9	1.8	6.1
Cl_2	-34.06	4.878	20.40
HCl	-85.05	3.86	20.5
SO_2	-10.02	5.955	22.63
H_2S	-60.34	4.463	20.97
N_2	-195.82	1.333	17.24
NH_3	-33.43	5.581	23.28
CH_3OH	64.7	8.43	24.95
CCl_4	76.7	7.17	20.5
$CHCl_3$	61.2	7.02	20.99
CS_2	46.25	6.40	20.0
C_2H_5OH	78.5	9.22	26.22
PbI_2	872	24.8	21.7
Methane, CH_4	-161.49	1.955	17.51
Ethane, C_2H_6	-88.63	3.517	19.06
n-Butane, C_4H_{10}	-0.50	5.352	19.63
n-Hexane, C_6H_{14}	68.742	6.896	20.17
n-Octane, C_8H_{18}	125.66	8.360	20.96
Benzene, C_6H_6	80.10	7.353	20.81
Toluene, C_7H_8	110.62	8.00	20.85
Cyclohexane, C_6H_{12}	80.74	7.19	20.30
Methylcyclohexane, C_7H_{14}	100.94	7.58	20.26
Acetic acid, CH_3CO_2H	118.3	5.82	14.8

The change from liquid to vapor leads to increased disorder. The entropy of vaporization is zero at the critical temperature because the liquid and gas are indistinguishable and the enthalpy of vaporization is zero. Most liquids behave alike not only at their critical temperatures but also at equal fractions of their critical temperatures, and we have seen (p. 23) that the standard boiling points of many liquids are roughly equal fractions of the critical temperatures. Hence, different liquids should have about the same entropy of vaporization at their boiling point, provided that there is no association or dissociation upon vaporization. For substances like water and alcohols which form hydrogen bonds (p. 494) the entropy of vaporization is greater than 21 cal $\deg^{-1}$ mole^{-1}. Hydrogen and helium, which boil at only a little above absolute zero, might well be expected to show large departures from this rule. Acetic acid and carboxylic acids, in general, have abnormally low heats of vaporization, since the vapor consists of double molecules and still more energy would be required to break them up into single molecules comparable with those of other gases.

For nonpolar liquids Trouton's rule provides a means of estimating the vapor pressure at a given temperature, provided that the standard boiling point is known.

Example 5. The boiling point of n-hexane is $69.0°$. Estimate (a) its molar heat of vaporization and (b) its vapor pressure at $60°$.

$$(a) \quad \Delta \bar{H}_{\text{vap}} \cong (21)(342) = 7190 \text{ cal mole}^{-1}$$

The experimental value is 6896 cal mole^{-1}.
Using equation 26,

$$(b) \quad \log \frac{1}{P_1} = \frac{(7190)(9)}{(2.303)(1.987)(333)(342)}$$

$$P_1 = 571 \text{ mm}$$

The experimental value is 555.9 mm.

Entropy of Fusion. The entropy of fusion is not so constant from substance to substance as the entropy of vaporization. The enthalpies and entropies of fusion of a number of substances at their melting points are given in Table III. The entropies of fusion of elongated molecules are especially large. This is connected with the fact that there is a large increase in the number of configurations and motions when such a molecule passes from the crystal into solution.

Table III. Enthalpies and Entropies of Fusion at the Melting Point

Substance	Melting Point, °C	$\Delta \bar{H}_{fus}$, kcal mole^{-1}	$\Delta \bar{S}_{fus}$, cal deg^{-1} mole^{-1}
O_2	-218.76	0.106	1.95
H_2	-259.20	0.028	2.0
H_2O	0	1.4363	5.2581
He	-269.7	0.005	1.5
HF	-83.07	1.094	5.756
Cl_2	-101.00	1.531	8.89
HCl	-114.22	0.476	2.99
SO_2	-75.48	1.769	8.95
H_2S	-85.53	0.568	3.03
N_2	-210.01	0.172	2.72
NH_3	-77.76	1.351	6.914
CH_3OH	-97.90	0.757	4.32
CCl_4	-22.9	0.60	2.4
$CHCl_3$	-63.5	2.2	10.5
CS_2	-112.1	1.05	6.52
C_2H_5OH	-114.6	1.200	7.57
PbI_2	412	5.2	7.6
Methane, CH_4	-182.48	0.225	2.48
Ethane, C_2H_6	-183.27	0.6834	7.603
n-Butane, C_4H_{10}	-138.350	1.114	8.263
n-Hexane, C_6H_{14}	-95.348	3.114	17.51
n-Octane, C_8H_{18}	-56.795	4.957	22.91
Benzene, C_6H_6	5.533	2.351	8.436
Toluene, C_7H_8	-94.991	1.582	8.879
Cyclohexane, C_6H_{12}	6.554	0.6398	2.287
Methylcyclohexane, C_7H_{14}	-126.593	1.6134	11.008
Acetic acid, CH_3CO_2H	16.61	2.80	9.66

REFERENCES

R. R. Dreisbach, *Physical Properties of Chemical Compounds*, American Chemical Society, Washington, D. C., 1955.

J. H. Hildebrand and R. L. Scott, *Solubility of Non-Electrolytes*, Reinhold Publishing Corp., New York, 1950.

T. E. Jordan, *Vapor Pressure of Organic Compounds*, Interscience Publishers, New York, 1954.

J. Timmermans, *Physico-Chemical Constants of Pure Organic Compounds*, Elsevier Publishing Co., New York, 1956.

A. Weissberger, *Technique of Organic Chemistry*, Interscience Publishers, New York, 1949.

M. W. Zemansky, *Heat and Thermodynamics*, McGraw-Hill Book Co., New York, 1957.

PROBLEMS

1. In an industrial operation 10,000 cu ft of dry air is blown through a chamber per min. The air picks up moisture and has a relative humidity of 40 per cent at 25°. The moist air is dried by removal of the water in an adsorbing agent. Calculate how many kilocalories of heat will be required per hour to regenerate the adsorbing agent by evaporating the water (assuming that the heat of desorption is 582 cal g^{-1}). The vapor pressure of water at 25° is 23.7 mm; 1 cu ft = 28.316 liters. *Ans.* 90,600 kcal.

2. Ten liters of air was bubbled through carbon tetrachloride at 20°. The loss in weight of the liquid was 8.698 grams. Calculate the vapor pressure of CCl_4 by (*a*) neglecting the volume of the CCl_4 vapor and by (*b*) not neglecting the volume of the vapor. *Ans.* (*a*) 0.136, (*b*) 0.120 atm.

3. Propene has the following vapor pressures:

T, °K	150	200	250	300
P, mm	3.82	198.0	2074	10,040

From these data calculate (*a*) the heat of vaporization and (*b*) the vapor pressure at 225°K by a graphical method. *Ans.* (*a*) 4670 cal $mole^{-1}$, (*b*) 741 mm.

4. Liquid mercury has a density of 13.690 g ml^{-1}, and solid mercury has a density of 14.193 g ml^{-1}, both being measured at the melting point, −38.87°, under 1 atm pressure. The heat of fusion is 2.33 cal g^{-1}. Calculate the melting points of mercury under a pressure of (*a*) 10 atm and (*b*) 3540 atm. The observed melting point under 3540 atm is −19.9°. *Ans.* (*a*) −38.81°, (*b*) −16°.

5. *n*-Propyl alcohol has the following vapor pressures:

t, °C	40	60	80	100
P, mm	50.2	147.0	376	842.5

Plot these data so as to obtain a nearly straight line, and calculate (*a*) the heat of vaporization and (*b*) the boiling point at 760 mm.

Ans. (*a*) 10.7 kcal $mole^{-1}$, (*b*) 98°.

6. The heat of vaporization of ether is 88.39 cal g^{-1} at its boiling point, 34.5°. (a) Calculate the rate of change of vapor pressure with temperature dP/dT, at the boiling point. (b) What is the boiling point at 750 mm? (c) Estimate the vapor pressure at 36.0°.　　　　　*Ans.* (a) 26.5 mm deg^{-1}, (b) 34.1°, (c) 800 mm.

7. The heats of vaporization and of fusion of water are 595 cal g^{-1} and 79.7 cal g^{-1} at 0°. The vapor pressure of water at 0° is 4.58 mm. Calculate the sublimation pressure of ice at −15°, assuming that the enthalpy changes are independent of temperature.　　　　　*Ans.* 1.245 mm.

8. For uranium hexafluoride the vapor pressures (in millimeters) for the solid and liquid are given by

$$\log P_s = 10.648 - 2559.5/T$$

$$\log P_l = 7.540 - 1511.3/T$$

Calculate the temperature and pressure of the triple point.　　*Ans.* 64°, 1122 mm.

9. The vapor pressure of 2,2-dimethyl-1-butanol is given by the expression

$$\log P = (-4849.3/T) - 14.701 \log T + 53.1187$$

where P is expressed in millimeters of mercury. Calculate the heat of vaporization (a) at 25°, and (b) at the boiling point, 136.7°.

Ans. (a) 13,480, (b) 10,200 cal $mole^{-1}$.

10. Trouton's rule is useful in estimating the vapor pressure of a substance for which only the standard boiling point is known. For example, at what temperature would you expect aniline to boil in a vacuum-still at 20 mm pressure? The standard boiling point is 185°.　　　　　*Ans.* 68°.

---

11. A room 5 by 10 by 4 meters is filled with air containing some water vapor. The temperature is 20°, and the relative humidity is 60 per cent. The vapor pressure of water at 20° is 17.36 mm. (The relative humidity is the partial pressure of water vapor divided by the vapor pressure of liquid water at that temperature.) How many grams of water are contained in the air of this room?

12. Calculate the loss in weight of a sample of water held at 25° when 10 liters of dry air is bubbled through slowly. The vapor pressure of water at this temperature is 23.76 mm.

13. From the data of Table I calculate the temperature at which benzene has a vapor pressure of 400 mm.

14. The vapor pressure of toluene is 60 mm at 40.3° and 20 mm at 18.4°. Calculate (a) the heat of vaporization and (b) the vapor pressure at 25°.

15. Using the vapor pressures of bromobenzene at 2.9° and 53.8° in Table I, calculate the boiling point. What are the possible reasons for the difference from the experimental value of 156.2°?

16. Using the data of Table II, calculate the change in boiling point per millimeter change in barometric pressure at the standard boiling point for (a) n-hexane, (b) N_2, and (c) NH_3.

17. Estimate the vapor pressure of ice at the temperature of solid carbon dioxide (−78° at 1 atm pressure of CO_2), assuming that the heat of sublimation is constant. The heat of sublimation of ice is 676 cal g^{-1}, and the vapor pressure of ice is 4.58 mm at 0°.

18. Using the data in Table I, calculate the heat of sublimation of carbon dioxide.

19. The vapor pressure of solid benzene, C_6H_6, is 2.24 mm at $-30°$ and 24.5 mm at $0°$, and the vapor pressure of liquid C_6H_6 is 26.73 mm at $0°$ and 118.5 mm at $30°$. Calculate from these data (a) the triple point of C_6H_6 and (b) the heat of fusion of C_6H_6.

20. (a) Calculate the vapor pressure of water at $200°$ using the Clausius-Clapeyron equation and assuming that $\Delta \bar{H}_{vap}$ is 9.7171 kcal mole^{-1} independent of temperature. (b) Calculate the vapor pressure, allowing for the fact that $\Delta \bar{C}_P = -10$ cal deg^{-1} mole^{-1}. The directly measured value is 11661.2 mm.

21. The boiling point of n-butyl chloride is $77.96°$. (a) Using this as the only experimental datum available, estimate the vapor pressure at $50°$, and compare this estimate with that calculated from the empirical equation (in which P is expressed in millimeters):

$$\log P = -(1763/T) + 7.912$$

(b) Calculate the heat of vaporization per gram from this equation.

---

22. (a) How many tons of water can be evaporated from a square mile of moist land on a clear summer day, if it is assumed that the limiting factor is the supply of solar heat, which amounts to about 1.0 cal min^{-1} cm^{-2} for an 8-hr day? The temperature is $25°$, the vapor pressure of water is 23.7 mm, and the heat of vaporization is 582 cal g^{-1}. One mile = 1.609 kilometers. (b) How many liters of air are required to hold this much water if the temperature is $25°$?

23. It is proposed to operate a large calcium oxide-lined furnace at a temperature of $2100°$. The volatility of the calcium oxide, CaO, may be a difficulty. Air is blown continuously through the furnace at a rate of 1000 ft^3 (28,320 liters) min^{-1} (calculated for $0°$ and 760 mm pressure). Assuming that, if the sublimation pressure of the CaO is large enough to give a loss of more than 5 kg per day, the process will be impractical, calculate the maximum permissible sublimation pressure in millimeters of the CaO, if the process is to be practical. Assume that the air becomes saturated with CaO vapor.

24. From the data of Table I calculate the vapor pressure of diethyl ether at $60°$.

25. A block of ice is placed in a lake of pure water, forced 100 ft below the surface, and maintained in a quiet, steady position. What will be the temperature of the surface of the ice? Assume that the densities of the ice and water are not changed by the pressure and are 0.9106 and 1.000 g cm^{-3}, respectively.

26. The standard boiling point of cyclohexane is $80.7°$, and the heat of vaporization is 7.19 kcal mole^{-1}. Calculate (a) the boiling point at 650 mm pressure and (b) the vapor pressure at $25°$.

27. What is the boiling point of water on a mountain where the barometer reading is 660 mm? The heat of vaporization of water may be taken to be 9.72 kcal mole^{-1}.

28. At $0°$ ice absorbs 79.7 cal g^{-1} in melting; water absorbs 595 cal g^{-1} in vaporizing. (a) What is the heat of sublimation of ice at this temperature? (b) At $0°$ the vapor pressure of both ice and water is 4.58 mm. What is the rate of change of vapor pressure with temperature dP/dT for ice and liquid water at this temperature? (c) Estimate the vapor pressures of ice and of liquid water at $-5°$.

29. Using data from Tables II and III, calculate the sublimation pressure of lead iodide at 350°.

30. The heat of vaporization of water at 0° is 10,720 cal mole^{-1}, and the heat of sublimation of ice is 12,120 cal mole^{-1}. Given the fact that the triple point is at 0.0099° and a pressure of 4.58 mm of mercury, calculate the vapor pressure of water at 15° and of ice at $-15°$ using the Clausius-Clapeyron equation. These three points are used to construct a plot of log P versus $1/T$. The fusion curve may be drawn in as a vertical line above the triple point, since the effect of pressures in this range is negligible. The regions in the diagram are then labeled.

31. The sublimation pressures of solid Cl_2 are 2.64 mm at $-112°$ and 0.26 mm at $-126.5°$. The vapor pressures of liquid Cl_2 are 11.9 mm at $-100°$ and 58.7 mm at $-80°$. Calculate (a) $\Delta \bar{H}_{sub}$, (b) $\Delta \bar{H}_{vap}$, (c) $\Delta \bar{H}_{fus}$, and (d) the triple point.

32. Plot the logarithm of the vapor pressure of mercury against $1/T$ for values of T from 273° to 633° (from reference tables). Does the heat of vaporization change with the temperature? If mercury vapor is monatomic, what can be stated regarding the specific heat of liquid mercury?

33. A certain liquid boils under atmospheric pressure at $t°$. Estimate (a) the critical temperature of the substance, (b) its molar heat of vaporization, and (c) its boiling point at 720 mm pressure. How accurate would you expect these estimates to be?

34. Show that the observed boiling point T_{obs}, °K, at a barometric pressure of P mm may be corrected approximately to the corrected boiling point T_{corr}, °K, at 760 mm by the following equation:

$$T_{corr} = T_{obs} + (T_{obs}/8000)(760 - P)$$

SOLUTIONS

7

A *solution* is a system of different substances which has the same chemical composition and physical properties in every part. Solutions may exist in a gaseous, liquid, or solid phase. If the system is composed of only two substances, it is called a *binary solution*, as, for example, a solution of alcohol in water. That substance which is present in larger quantity is usually called the *solvent* and the other the *solute*, but the designation is quite arbitrary. For example, if a little alcohol is dissolved in a large quantity of water, the water is called the solvent and the alcohol is the solute; but if a little water is dissolved in an excess of alcohol, the water is called the solute and the alcohol the solvent.

The Composition of Solutions. The composition of a solution can be expressed in a variety of different ways, each of which has advantages for a particular purpose: molar concentration M (1 mole of solute per liter of solution) is used for volumetric analysis, and per cent by weight of solute in the solution is employed for some technical work and in cases where the molecular weight is not known. Mole fraction X (p. 14) and molal concentration m (1 mole of solute per 1000 grams of solvent) are preferred in physical chemistry. They do not change with temperature. Calculations illustrating these different methods for expressing concentrations are given in the Appendix (p. 719).

Vapor Pressure of Solutions. Determination of the vapor pressure of a solution is similar to that for a pure liquid, but precautions must be taken to avoid any significant change in concentration during the measurement. The partial pressures of the components in the vapor may be calculated from the composition of the equilibrium vapor and the total vapor pressure. Air or other gas may be passed slowly through the solution to become saturated with vapor at a given temperature. The vapor is then condensed in a cold trap and analyzed by the use of refractive index measurements, for example. The partial pressure of a component of the vapor is defined as its mole fraction in the vapor times the total vapor pressure, assuming ideal gas behavior.

Raoult's Law. The components of a binary solution may be referred to as 1 and 2, so that p_1 represents the partial pressure of component 1 above the solution and p_2 the partial pressure of component 2. Ideal solutions are those for which

$$p_1 = X_1 p_1{}^\circ \tag{1}$$

$$p_2 = X_2 p_2{}^\circ \tag{2}$$

where $p_1{}^\circ$ and $p_2{}^\circ$ are the vapor pressures of pure component 1 and pure component 2, respectively, at the temperature of the solution. Thus for an ideal solution the partial pressure of a component is directly proportional to its mole fraction X in the liquid, and the proportionality constant is the vapor pressure of the pure substance. This relation was discovered empirically by Raoult in 1884 and is referred to as *Raoult's law*. It will be evident from data given later that even for nonideal solutions this law always applies to a component in the limit as its mole fraction approaches 1.

It is evident from *Fig. 7-1* that the partial vapor pressure of benzene over solutions of benzene and toluene is directly proportional to the mole fraction of benzene in agreement with Raoult's law. Also the partial pressure of toluene over the solution is directly proportional to the mole fraction of toluene. The uppermost line in Fig. 7-1 gives the total vapor pressure of the solution at each mole fraction of the liquid solution.

Vapor Composition of Ideal Binary Solutions. For an ideal solution composed of two liquids with identical vapor pressures at a given temperature, the composition of the vapor would be the same as the composition of the solution. Examples of liquids which practically meet these conditions are found among solutions of isotopically different compounds, such as $C^{12}HCl_3$ and $C^{13}HCl_3$ and certain pairs of D-L isomers. However, in most solutions the vapor pressures of the pure components are not equal, and that liquid which has the higher vapor pressure at a given temperature will have relatively more of its molecules in the gas phase.

The mole fraction of a component in the vapor is equal to its pressure fraction in the vapor. Since for ideal solutions the partial pressures of the components in the vapor may be readily calculated using equations

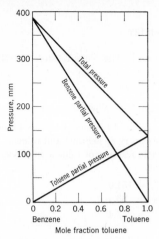

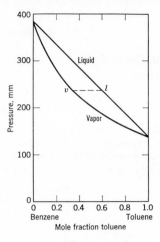

Fig. 7-1. Benzene-toluene; partial and total pressures at 60°.

Fig. 7-2. Benzene-toluene; liquid and vapor compositions at 60°.

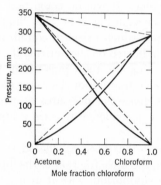

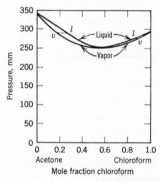

Fig. 7-3. Acetone-chloroform; partial and total pressures at 35.2°.

Fig. 7-4. Acetone-chloroform; liquid and vapor compositions at 35.2°.

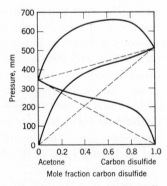

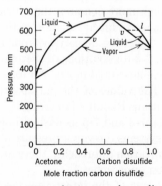

Fig. 7-5. Acetone-carbon disulfide; partial and total pressures at 35.2°.

Fig. 7-6. Acetone-carbon disulfide; liquid and vapor compositions at 35.2°.

1 and 2, the mole fraction of a component in the vapor may be calculated using

$$X_{1.vap} = \frac{p_1}{p_1 + p_2} = \frac{X_1 p_1°}{X_1 p_1° + X_2 p_2°} \tag{3}$$

Example 1. The vapor pressures of pure benzene and toluene at 60° are 385 and 139 mm, respectively. Calculate the partial pressures of benzene and toluene, the total vapor pressure of the solution, and the mole fraction of toluene in the vapor above a solution with 0.60 mole fraction toluene.

$$p_{benzene} = (0.40)(385) = 154.0$$
$$p_{toluene} = (0.60)(139) = \underline{83.4}$$
$$P_{total} = 237.4$$

$$X_{toluene,vap} = \frac{83.4}{237.4} = 0.351$$

In *Fig. 7-2* the total pressure and the composition of the vapor are plotted versus the mole fraction of benzene. It will be noted that the top or "liquid" line in Fig. 7-2 is the same as in Fig. 7-1. This "liquid" line gives the total pressure of the vapor which exists in equilibrium with the *liquid* having the composition indicated on the horizontal axis. The "vapor" curve is obtained by plotting the total pressure of the vapor along the vertical axis and the mole fraction of the *vapor* along the horizontal axis. The vapor curve gives the pressures at which vapors of a given composition first show a tendency to form a liquid phase when the pressure is increased.

The point labeled *v* on the vapor curve has been calculated in example 1. The horizontal line connecting the mole fraction of the liquid with the mole fraction of the vapor in equilibrium with it at a given total pressure is referred to as a *tie line*.

Vapor Pressure of Nonideal Solutions. For nonideal solutions, which are much more common than ideal solutions, the total vapor pressure is no longer a linear function of the composition expressed in mole fractions. Negative deviations from Raoult's law are found as illustrated in *Fig. 7-3* for solutions of acetone and chloroform, and positive deviations as illustrated in *Fig. 7-5* for solutions of acetone and carbon disulfide. The values of the partial pressures and the total pressure calculated using Raoult's law are given in Tables I and II and are plotted in Figs. 7-3 and 7-5 as dashed lines. It should be noted that for both these systems the vapor pressure of the component present at the higher concentration approaches the values given by Raoult's law as its mole fraction approaches 1.

In terms of the interaction between molecules of a solution we can describe an ideal solution of A and B as one in which the interaction

Table I.[1] Partial Pressures of Acetone and Chloroform in the Vapor
in Equilibrium with Liquid Solutions at 35.2°

(Pressures in mm)

Mole Fraction Chloroform in Liquid Solution	Chloroform		Acetone		Total	
	p_{obs}	p_{calc}	p_{obs}	p_{calc}	p_{obs}	p_{calc}
0	0	0	344	344	344	344
0.2	34	59	270	275	304	334
0.4	82	117	183	207	265	324
0.6	148	177	102	137	250	314
0.8	225	234	42	69	267	303
1.00	293	293	0	0	293	293

[1] J. von Zawidzki, Z. physik. Chem., 35, 129 (1900).

Table II.[1] Partial Pressures of Acetone and Carbon Disulfide in the Vapor
in Equilibrium with Liquid Solutions at 35.2°

(Pressures in mm)

Mole Fraction Carbon Disulfide in Liquid Solution	Carbon Disulfide		Acetone		Total	
	p_{obs}	p_{calc}	p_{obs}	p_{calc}	p_{obs}	p_{calc}
0	0	0	344	344	344	344
0.2	280	102	290	275	570	377
0.4	378	206	255	204	633	410
0.6	425	306	230	138	655	444
0.8	460	410	190	67	650	477
1.00	512	512	0	0	512	512

[1] J. von Zawidzki, Z. physik. Chem., 35, 129 (1900).

between A and B molecules is the same as between A molecules and other A molecules or B molecules and other B molecules. In a nonideal solution the intermolecular attractive energy between A and B molecules is different from that between A molecules and other A molecules or between B molecules and other B molecules. If the $A-B$ interaction energy is larger than the $A-A$ and $B-B$ interaction energies, the tendency of each of the components to pass into the vapor phase is reduced and there are negative deviations from Raoult's law, as shown by acetone-chloroform solutions; that is, the vapor pressures are lower than the values calculated with equations 1 and 2.

If the $A-B$ interaction energy is smaller than the $A-A$ and $B-B$ interaction energies, the tendency of each of the components to pass into the vapor phase is increased and there are positive deviations from Raoult's law, as shown by acetone-carbon disulfide solutions.

The interaction between acetone and chloroform which leads to negative deviations from Raoult's law is due to the formation of a weak hydrogen bond between the oxygen of the acetone and the hydrogen of the chloroform. A hydrogen bond is a bond between two molecules, or two parts of one molecule, resulting from the sharing of a proton between two atoms, one of which is usually fluorine, oxygen, or nitrogen (p. 494). Thus:

$$\begin{array}{ccc} \text{Cl} & & \text{CH}_3 \\ | & & | \\ \text{Cl}-\text{C}-\text{H}\cdots\text{O}=\text{C} \\ | & & | \\ \text{Cl} & & \text{CH}_3 \end{array}$$

This attractive energy due to the formation of a hydrogen bond occurs not only in solutions of acetone and chloroform but also in many other solutions containing ketones, esters, or carboxylic acids and partially halogenated hydrocarbons or other compounds containing hydrogen. Since carbon disulfide cannot form a hydrogen bond with acetone, negative deviations would not be expected in this system and are not found, as illustrated in Fig. 7-5. In fact, in this system there are large positive deviations, indicating that the attraction between the two components is less than that between the molecules in pure carbon disulfide or pure acetone.

The vapor curves in *Figs. 7-4* and *7-6* give the compositions of the vapor in equilibrium with the various solutions. These compositions had to be determined experimentally. Figure 7-6 shows that the vapor in equilibrium with a solution of 0.65 mole fraction carbon disulfide has the same composition as the liquid. For solutions containing less than 0.65 mole fraction carbon disulfide the vapor phase is richer in carbon disulfide, but for solutions containing more than 0.65 mole fraction carbon disulfide the vapor phase is richer in acetone. In plotting vapor and liquid compositions, it is convenient to remember that the vapor is always richer in the more volatile liquid (or solution of liquids which gives a maximum or minimum).

Henry's Law. Although the acetone-chloroform and acetone-carbon disulfide solutions do not obey Raoult's law, it is evident from Figs. 7-3 and 7-5 that the partial pressure of the component present at lower concentration is directly proportional to its mole fraction *for dilute solutions.*

$$p_2 = X_2 K_2 \tag{4}$$

The subscript 2 indicates that the solute is being considered. This equation is referred to as Henry's law. For ideal solutions $K_2 = p_2^\circ$, and Henry's law becomes identical with Raoult's law. In dilute solutions the environment of the minor component is constant, and its escaping tendency is proportional to its mole fraction. Thus Henry's law holds for the solute in the same range where Raoult's law holds for the solvent.

The value of the Henry's-law constant K_2 is obtained by plotting the ratio p_2/X_2 versus X_2 and extrapolating to $X_2 = 0$. Such a plot is shown later in Fig. 7-8.

Solubility of Gases in Liquids. A gas dissolves in a liquid until the rate of escape of gas molecules from the surface is just equal to the rate at which gas molecules enter the liquid phase. For dilute solutions the solubility of a gas in a liquid expressed as its mole fraction X_2 depends upon the pressure of the gas p_2 according to Henry's law. Therefore it is convenient to express the solubilities of gases in liquids by use of Henry's-law constants.

$$K_2 = \frac{p_2}{X_2}$$

A few gas solubilities at 25° are summarized in this way in Table III. Up to a pressure of 1 atm Henry's law holds within 1–3 per cent for many gases.

Example 2. Calculate the solubility of carbon dioxide in water at 1 atm pressure and 25° in terms of n moles per liter, assuming that a liter of solution contains practically 1000 grams of water.

$$K = 1.25 \times 10^6 = \frac{760}{n_{CO_2}}\left(n_{CO_2} + \frac{1000}{18.02}\right)$$

The number of moles of carbon dioxide n_{CO_2} may be considered negligible in comparison with the number of moles of water, 1000/18.02. Then,

$$n_{CO_2} = \frac{(760)(55.55)}{1.25 \times 10^6} = 3.38 \times 10^{-2} \text{ mole liter}^{-1}$$

Table III.　Henry's-Law Constants [1] for Gases at 25°

Solvent

Gas	Water	Benzene
H_2	5.34×10^7	2.75×10^6
N_2	6.51×10^7	1.79×10^6
O_2	3.30×10^7	
CO	4.34×10^7	1.22×10^6
CO_2	1.25×10^6	8.57×10^4
CH_4	$31.4 \ \times 10^6$	4.27×10^5
C_2H_2	1.01×10^6	
C_2H_4	8.67×10^6	
C_2H_6	$23.0 \ \times 10^6$	

[1] The partial pressure of the gas is given in millimeters, and the concentration units are mole fractions.

Dalton showed that the solubility of the individual gases in a mixture of gases is directly proportional to their partial pressures, the solubility of each gas being nearly independent of the presence of the others. The solubility of oxygen in water is nearly twice as great as that of nitrogen and so the dissolved air is considerably richer in oxygen than the air above water.

The solubility of gases in liquids is usually decreased by an increase in temperature, since heat is generally evolved in the solution process. There are numerous exceptions, however, especially with the solvents liquid ammonia, molten silver, and many organic liquids. It is a common observation that a glass of cold water, when warmed to room temperature, shows the presence of many small air bubbles. The rate of escape of the molecules of dissolved gas from the liquid is increased more by an increase in temperature than is the rate at which molecules of the gas phase strike the surface and dissolve in the liquid. From an energy standpoint, the forces of attraction that cause the gas molecules to dissolve in the liquid are partially offset by the increased kinetic energy at the higher temperatures.

The solubility of unreactive gases is due to intermolecular attractive forces between solute and solvent. There is a good correlation between the solubilities of gases in solvents at room temperature and their boiling points. Substances with low boiling points (He, H_2, N_2, Ne, etc.) have weak intermolecular attractions and are therefore not very soluble in liquids.

The attractive force between the solute molecules and the solvent molecules is referred to as van der Waals' attraction because it has the same origin as the attractive force which causes deviations from the ideal gas law. This force arises from the induction of instantaneous dipole moments in one molecule by an instantaneous dipole moment in another. The dipole moment (p. 501) of a molecule is equal to the product of the distance between the average centers of positive and negative charge and the magnitude of the positive charge. Even though a molecule is electrically neutral as a whole, parts of the molecule are positively charged and other parts are negatively charged at any instant because of the motion of electrons. Even helium molecules have instantaneous dipole moments, but the attractive force due to dipole moments which they induce in each other is so weak that it is overcome by the slight thermal agitation which exists at 4°K, the boiling point of helium. Water molecules, on the other hand, have a considerable dipole moment, and, although the molecule as a whole is neutral, the charged parts induce an opposite charge in a neighboring helium molecule. Thus a force of attraction is set up between the two, causing some helium to be dissolved in water.

The solubility of gases in water is usually decreased by the addition of other solutes, particularly electrolytes. The extent of this "salting out" varies considerably with different salts, but with a given salt the relative decrease in solubility is nearly the same for different gases. For example, if a certain salt reduces the solubility of oxygen in water to 80 per cent of its value, it will also reduce the solubility of nitrogen in water to about 80 per cent of its value. Sometimes the salting-out effect can be explained on the hypothesis that it is caused by the hydration of the salt. A portion of the water combines with the salt, and the water thus removed from the role of solvent is no longer free to dissolve gas. More specifically, the water molecules with their electric dipoles can be considered to be partially oriented around ions of the dissolved salt and to be less free to induce dipoles in the molecules of gas. Sometimes the salts interact with solute as, for example, in the salting in of hydrochloric acid, which leads to a greater solubility. The solubility of liquids and solids in water also shows this salting-out phenomenon.

The Chemical Potential and Ideal Solutions. The thermodynamic condition for the equilibrium of a component i between the solution and vapor phases at a given temperature and total pressure is that the chemical potential for this component be the same in the two phases.

$$\mu_{i,\text{soln}} = \mu_{i,\text{vap}} \tag{5}$$

For an ideal gaseous mixture the chemical potential of component i in the gas phase is given by equation 94 in Chapter 5.

$$\mu_i = \mu_i^\circ + RT \ln p_i \tag{6}$$

where p_i is the partial pressure of i, and μ_i° is a function of temperature only and is the chemical potential of i when $p_i = 1$ atm.

If the solution is ideal, Raoult's law is obeyed and the chemical potential of the ith component of the vapor may be expressed in terms of its mole fraction X_i in the liquid by substituting Raoult's law into equation 6.

$$\mu_i = \mu_i^\circ + RT \ln X_i p_i^\circ$$

$$= \mu_i^* + RT \ln X_i \tag{7}$$

where $\mu_i^* = \mu_i^\circ + RT \ln p_i^\circ$ is a constant at a constant temperature. Equation 7 gives the chemical potential of the ith component of an ideal liquid solution. Since $\mu_i = \mu_i^*$ when $X_i = 1$, μ_i^* is the chemical potential of the ith component in the pure liquid state under standard conditions of temperature and total pressure.

Activity Coefficient. The concept of ideal solutions forms such a useful basis for comparison that it is advantageous in dealing with nonideal solutions to use equations of the same form as for ideal solutions by introducing the *activity* a_i and the *activity coefficient* γ_i, which are defined by

$$\mu_i = \mu_i^* + RT \ln a_i \tag{8}$$

$$= \mu_i^* + RT \ln \gamma_i X_i$$

where μ_i is the chemical potential of a component of a solution. The activity a_i for a nonelectrolyte is simply equal to the product of an activity coefficient and a concentration.

$$a_i = \gamma_i X_i \tag{9}$$

A more complicated relation is needed for electrolytes, as will be seen later in Chapter 14.

Equation 8 is equivalent to writing Raoult's law in the form

$$p_i = \gamma_i (X_i p_i^\circ) \tag{10}$$

or Henry's law in the form

$$p_i = \gamma_i (X_i K_i) \tag{11}$$

It is evident from equation 10 that for solutions which show positive deviations from Raoult's law γ_i is greater than unity, and for solutions which show negative deviations from Raoult's law γ_i is less than unity.

The chemical potential μ_i^*, in the reference state where $a_i = 1$, is a function of temperature and pressure only, while γ_i is a function of concentration as well as temperature and pressure. In order to complete the definition of the activity coefficient it is customary to adopt *one* of the following conventions.

Convention I. If the components of the solution are liquids, the activity coefficient of each component may be taken to approach unity as its mole fraction approaches unity.

$$\gamma_i \to 1 \text{ as } X_i \to 1 \tag{12}$$

As the logarithmic term in equation 8 vanishes under these limiting conditions, μ_i^* is equal to the free energy of a mole of pure i at the temperature and pressure under consideration. If both components follow Raoult's law over the whole range of concentration (as they do in an ideal solution), their activity coefficients will be equal to unity over the whole range of concentration.

Convention II. It is sometimes convenient to distinguish between solvent and solute and to introduce a different convention for the activity coefficient of the solute. The activity of the solvent is defined as given by convention I.

$$\gamma_{\text{solvent}} \to 1 \text{ as } X_{\text{solvent}} \to 1$$

The activity coefficient for the solute is taken to approach unity as its mole fraction approaches zero,

$$\gamma_{\text{solute}} \to 1 \text{ as } X_{\text{solute}} \to 0 \tag{13}$$

If the activity coefficient of the solute is to approach unity at infinite dilution, μ_i^* for the solute in equation 8 must be the chemical potential of pure solute in a hypothetical standard state in which the solute at unit concentration has the properties which it would have at infinite dilution.

Calculation of Activity Coefficients for Binary Liquid Systems. The activity coefficients of ether and acetone in ether-acetone solutions may be calculated from the data of *Fig. 7-7.** If these substances formed ideal solutions, the partial pressure of acetone above a solution containing 0.5 mole fraction acetone would be given by the length AB, which is $0.5p_2^\circ$, acetone being referred to as component 2. The actual

* J. Sameshima, *J. Am. Chem. Soc.*, *40*, 1498 (1918).

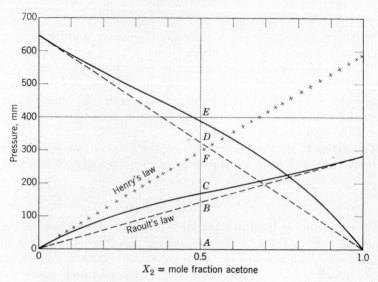

Fig. 7-7. Partial pressures of ether-acetone solutions at 30°.

partial pressure is represented by the length AC. Solving equation 10 for the activity coefficient of acetone,

$$\gamma_2 = \frac{p_2}{X_2 p_2^\circ} = \frac{AC}{AB} = 1.19 \qquad (14)$$

Similarly the activity coefficient of ether (component 1) at 0.5 mole fraction is given by

$$\gamma_1 = \frac{p_1}{X_1 p_1^\circ} = \frac{AE}{AD} = 1.21 \qquad (15)$$

The activity coefficients of both components, calculated in this way at other concentrations by use of convention I, are summarized in Table IV. It will be noticed that, as the mole fraction of either component approaches unity, its activity coefficient approaches unity, since the vapor pressure asymptotically approaches that given by Raoult's law.

The calculation of the activity coefficients of acetone on the basis of convention II is accomplished by use of the line passing through F in Fig. 7-7. This line is tangent to the vapor-pressure curve for acetone as the mole fraction of acetone approaches zero, and its slope is equal to the value of the Henry's-law constant for acetone in ether, obtained by extrapolating the *apparent* Henry's-law constant defined by

$$K_2' = \frac{p_2}{X_2} \qquad (16)$$

Table IV.   Activity Coefficients for Acetone-Ether Solutions at $30°$

Mole Fraction Acetone X_2	Convention I						Convention II [1]	
	Ether			Acetone			Acetone	
	p_1	$X_1p_1°$	γ_1	p_2	$X_2p_2°$	γ_2	K_2X_2	γ_2
0	646	646	1.00	0	0	...	0	(1.000)
0.2	535	517	1.03	90	56.6	1.59	117.6	0.766
0.4	440	388	1.13	148	113.2	1.31	235.2	0.630
0.5	391	323	1.21	168	141.5	1.19	294	0.575
0.6	332	258.4	1.28	190	170.0	1.12	353	0.538
0.8	202	129.2	1.56	235	226	1.04	471	0.499
1.0	0	0	...	283	283	1.00	588	(0.481)

[1] The activity coefficients for ether are the same as those calculated by convention I.

to infinite dilution of the acetone. The extrapolation of this ratio for the data of Fig. 7-7 is illustrated in *Fig. 7-8*, where values of p_2/X_2 are plotted versus X_2. It is found that the Henry's-law constant at infinite dilution (K_2) has a value of 588 mm at this temperature of $30°$.

If acetone obeyed Henry's law with this value of the constant over the entire concentration range, its vapor pressure at 0.5 mole fraction would be represented by the length AF in Fig. 7-7. The actual partial pressure is represented by the length AC, so that according to equation

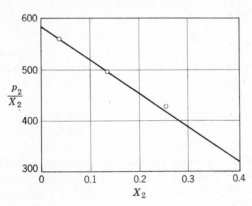

Fig. 7-8. Evaluation of the Henry's-law constant, K_2, for acetone in ether-acetone solutions at $30°$.

11 the activity coefficient of acetone at 0.5 mole fraction is given by

$$\gamma_2 = \frac{p_2}{K_2 X_2} = \frac{AC}{AF} = 0.575$$

Thus, when convention II is used, the extent to which the activity coefficient differs from unity is a measure of the deviation from Henry's law. The activity coefficients of acetone calculated in this way are also summarized in Table IV. The activity coefficients for the "solvent" ether remain the same as calculated before with convention I.

Although the numerical values of the activity coefficients of acetone depend upon which convention is employed, the same result is obtained in any thermodynamic calculation using these activity coefficients, independent of whether convention I or convention II is chosen. These thermodynamic calculations involve two different concentrations, and the standard reference state cancels out. The magnitude of the activity coefficient also depends upon the concentration scale used; for example, the molal scale would require a different standard state from that needed with the mole-fraction scale.

Boiling-Point Diagrams of Binary Solutions. The preceding discussions have been concerned with vapor-pressure isotherms. If the equilibrium vapor has a different composition from the liquid, it is possible to achieve a separation of the components by isothermal distillation. However, it is more practical to carry out distillations at constant pressure than at constant temperature. The temperature of the solution is raised until the solution boils at the applied pressure. The solution boils when the sum of the partial pressures of the two components becomes equal to the applied pressure. *Figure 7-9* is a boiling-point diagram for benzene and toluene, which form nearly ideal solutions; *Fig. 7-10* is for acetone-chloroform, which gives a maximum in the boiling-point curve; and *Fig. 7-11* is for ethanol-benzene, which gives a minimum in the boiling-point curve. The vapor is always richer in the more volatile component or solution with a minimum boiling point. Figure 7-12 will be discussed later on page 167.

The relation between the vapor-pressure diagram for benzene-toluene (Fig. 7-2) and the boiling-point diagram (Fig. 7-9) is shown in *Fig. 7-13* as a three-dimensional diagram. The front face of this diagram is identical with Fig. 7-2, and the top face with Fig. 7-9. The right-hand side is simply a plot of vapor pressure versus temperature for toluene, and the left-hand side is a plot of vapor pressure versus temperature for benzene. The upper curved surface inside the parallelepiped gives the total vapor pressure as a function of temperature and

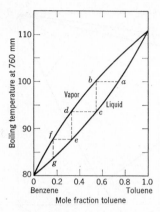

Fig. 7-9. Benzene-toluene boiling points; liquid and vapor compositions.

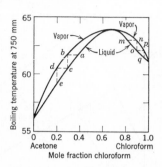

Fig. 7-10. Acetone-chloroform boiling points; liquid and vapor compositions.

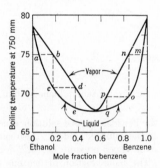

Fig. 7-11. Ethanol-benzene boiling points; liquid and vapor compositions.

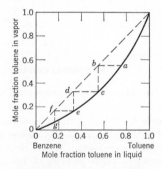

Fig. 7-12. Benzene-toluene; composition vapor versus composition liquid (cf. p. 167).

mole fraction of toluene in the *liquid;* it is therefore labeled *l.* The lower curved surface, which is mostly hidden and has dashed lines drawn on it, gives the compositions of the *vapor* phases in equilibrium with the liquid phases; it is therefore labeled *v.* The dashed lines are the vapor-pressure curves for solutions containing 0.2, 0.4, 0.6, and 0.8 mole fraction of toluene. It is readily seen that the vapor curve always lies below the liquid curve in plots of vapor pressure versus composition, and above the liquid curve in plots of boiling point versus composition.

The boiling-point diagram can be calculated for two liquids that form ideal solutions provided the vapor pressures are known for the two pure liquids at temperatures between their boiling points. This is illustrated in example 3.

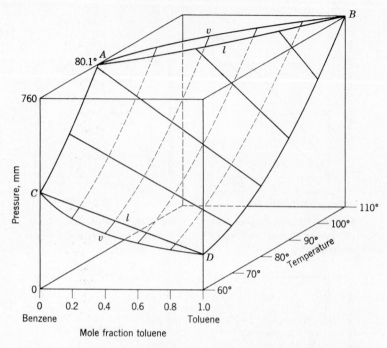

Fig. 7-13. Three-dimensional diagram for the benzene-toluene system.

Example 3. Calculate the composition of the benzene-toluene solution which will boil at 1 atm pressure at 90°, assuming that the solution is ideal. Also calculate the vapor composition. At 90° benzene has a vapor pressure of 1022 mm, and toluene has a vapor pressure of 406 mm. The mole fraction of benzene in the liquid which will boil at 90° is obtained from

$$760 = 1022X_B + 406(1 - X_B)$$

$$X_B = 0.574$$

The mole fraction of benzene in the vapor is equal to its pressure fraction in the vapor, which is given by

$$X_{B,\mathrm{vap}} = \frac{1022X_B}{760} = 0.772$$

Other points on the liquid and vapor curves in Fig. 7-9 may be calculated in the same way. For nonideal solutions the points have to be obtained experimentally.

Azeotropic Solutions. When a boiling-point curve has a maximum or a minimum, the solutions having the maximum or minimum boiling points are called *azeotropes*. These solutions distill without change in composition because the liquid and the vapor have the same composition.

Many examples of azeotropic solutions are known.* Ethanol and water form a minimum-boiling azeotrope which boils at 78.174° and contains 4.0 per cent water. Hydrochloric acid and water form a maximum-boiling azeotrope.

The boiling points and compositions of some binary azeotropic solutions are summarized in Table V.

Table V. Binary Azeotropic Solutions at 1 Atm Pressure [1]

Component A	B.P. of A, °C	Component B	B.P. of B, °C	B.P. of Azeotrope, °C	Weight Per Cent, A
Maximum-Boiling Azeotropes					
HCl	−80	H_2O	100	108.584	20.222
$CHCl_3$	61.2	CH_3COCH_3	56.10	64.43	78.5
$CHCl_3$	61.2	$CH_3CO_2CH_3$	57.05	64.8	77
$CHCl_3$	61.2	$HCO_2C_2H_5$	54.15	62.7	87
CH_3CO_2H	118.5	$(CH_2)_4O_2$	101.35	119.5	77
CH_3CO_2H	118.5	C_5H_5N	115.5	140	53
Minimum-Boiling Azeotropes					
H_2O	100	$CHCl_3$	61.2	56.12	2.8
H_2O	100	CH_3CH_2OH	78.3	78.174	4.0
H_2O	100	$CH_3CH_2CH_2OH$	82.3	80.3	12.6
H_2O	100	C_6H_6	80.2	69.25	8.83
CCl_4	76.75	CH_3CH_2OH	78.3	65.08	84.15
$CHCl_3$	61.2	CH_3OH	64.7	53.43	87.4

[1] L. H. Horsley, *Azeotropic Data*, Advances in Chemistry Series, American Chemical Society, Washington, D. C., 1952.

The system hydrochloric acid-water has been studied extensively, and the composition of the constant-boiling mixture is so reproducible that it has been used as a standard in quantitative analysis. If any solution of hydrochloric acid is boiled for a sufficient time under a pressure of 760 mm, the temperature will gradually rise to 108.58°, and the solution boiling at this constant temperature will contain 20.222 per cent hydrochloric acid by weight. The position of the maximum

* L. H. Horsley and coworkers, *Azeotropic Data*, Advances in Chemistry Series, American Chemical Society, Washington, D. C., 1952.

changes somewhat with pressure. At 700 mm the maximum temperature is 106.42° at a composition of 20.360 per cent hydrochloric acid, and at 600 mm it is 102.21° at a composition of 20.638 per cent.

For hydrochloric acid and water, the minimum in the vapor-pressure curve, or maximum in the boiling-point curve, is due to the ionization of hydrochloric acid. Water and pure hydrochloric acid have high vapor pressures, but the hydrogen and chloride ions which exist in aqueous solutions cannot escape from the solution. It is shown in Chapter 8 that they lower the vapor pressure of the water. In small amounts, hydrochloric acid added to water lowers the total vapor pressure; but in large amounts, it increases the total vapor pressure.

Maxima and minima are not confined to vapor-pressure and boiling-point curves; they are sometimes found when freezing points, densities, viscosities, and other properties are plotted against composition. *They are not found in ideal solutions.* Whenever a maximum exists, there must be at least two opposing factors, one tending to increase the magnitude of the property and the other tending to decrease it as the concentration is changed.

It was thought at one time that maxima or minima of this type corresponded to definite chemical compounds, and indeed a maximum in a freezing-point curve may indicate the formation of a chemical compound, as explained in Chapter 10. The composition of 20.22 per cent hydrochloric acid in the constant-boiling mixture corresponds very closely to the formula $HCl \cdot 8H_2O$, but the relation is accidental. Such mixtures are not definite chemical compounds, since the composition of the azeotropic mixture changes with pressure.

Fractional Distillation. When a solution of two liquids is partially vaporized, that component which has the higher vapor pressure is concentrated in the vapor phase, thus producing a difference in composition between the liquid and the equilibrium vapor. This vapor may be condensed, and the vapor obtained by partially vaporizing this condensate is still further enriched in the more volatile component. In *fractional distillation* this process of successive vaporization and condensation is carried out in a fractionating column.

In Fig. 7-9 it is seen that a solution of 0.75 mole fraction of toluene and 0.25 mole fraction of benzene reaches the boiling point at 100° under 1 atm pressure as indicated by point a. The equilibrium vapor is richer in the more volatile compound, benzene, and has the composition b. This vapor may be condensed by lowering the temperature along the line bc. If a small amount of this condensed liquid is vaporized, the first vapor formed will have the composition corresponding to d.

This process of vaporization and condensation may be repeated many times, with the result that a vapor fraction which is rich in benzene is obtained. As the liquid loses weight by vaporization, the vapor has more of the more volatile benzene and less toluene and so the liquid becomes richer in toluene. In this way it is possible by continued distillation to separate the two liquids which give a boiling-point diagram of the type illustrated in Fig. 7-9.

The binary solutions may exhibit a maximum in their boiling points as shown in Fig. 7-10. A series of fractional distillations of a solution rich in acetone will give pure liquid acetone in the distillate and the constant-boiling mixture or azeotrope in the residue. At 1 atm pressure this azeotrope boils at 64.43° and has a composition of 0.64 mole fraction of chloroform. The steps along $abcde$ indicate a hypothetical distillation as discussed above. From solutions rich in chloroform it is possible to obtain pure chloroform in the distillate and the azeotrope in the residue as indicated by the lines $mnopq$. When the azeotropic concentration is reached, the temperature and the composition remain constant because the vapor and the liquid have the same composition. Although the constancy of boiling point of an organic liquid is often used as a criterion of purity, it is well to supplement this test with other tests, such as freezing-point constancy.

The efficiency with which two liquids can be separated by fractional distillation is a matter of practical importance. Each vaporization and condensation represented by the lines $abcde$ and $mnopq$ on Figs. 7-9 to 7-11 corresponds to an idealized process in that only a small amount of vapor is condensed and only a small amount of it is revaporized. It is more practical to effect the separation by means of a distillation column, such as the bubble-cap column illustrated in $Fig.\ 7\text{-}14$.

Each layer of liquid on the plates of the column is equivalent to the boiling liquid in a distilling flask, and the liquid on the plate above it is equivalent to the condenser. The vapor passes upward through the bubble caps, where it is partially condensed in the liquid and mixed with it. Part of the resulting solution is vaporized in this process and is condensed in the next higher layer, while part of the liquid overflows and runs down the tube to the next lower plate. In this way there is a continuous flow of redistilled vapor coming out the top and a continuous flow of recondensed liquid returning to the boiler at the bottom. To make up for this loss of material from the distilling column fresh solution is fed into the column, usually at the middle. The column is well insulated, or it is surrounded by a controlled heating jacket so that there will not be too much condensation on the walls. The whole system reaches a steady state in which the composition of the solution

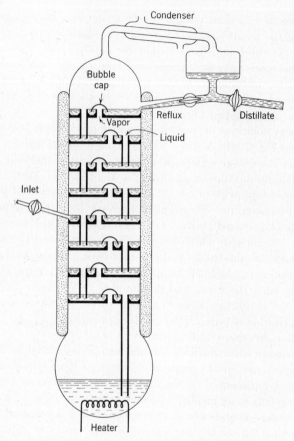

Fig. 7-14. Bubble-cap fractionating column.

on each plate remains unchanged as long as the composition of the liquid in the distilling pot remains unchanged.

A distillation column may also be packed with material which will provide efficient contact between liquid and vapor and will occupy only a small volume so that there is free space to permit a large throughput of vapor. Helices of glass, spirals of screen, and different types of packing * are used with varying degrees of efficiency.

The efficiency of a column is expressed in terms of the number of theoretical plates to which it is equivalent. The number of *theoretical plates* in a column is equal to the number of successive infinitesimal vaporizations at equilibrium to give the separation which is actually

* F. Daniels, J. H. Mathews, J. W. Williams, P. Bender, and R. A. Alberty, *Experimental Physical Chemistry*, McGraw-Hill Book Co., New York, 1956; T. P. Carney, *Laboratory Fractional Distillation*, The Macmillan Co., New York, 1949.

achieved. The number of theoretical plates depends somewhat upon the reflux ratio, the ratio of the rate of return of liquid to the top of the column to the rate of distilling liquid off.

The number of theoretical plates in a distillation column under actual operating conditions may be determined by the method of McCabe and Thiele, as illustrated in *Fig. 7-12.* In this graph the mole fraction of the less volatile component in the vapor is plotted against its mole fraction in the liquid at a total pressure of 1 atm and the boiling temperature of the solution. Any point on the solid line such as a, c, or e gives on the vertical axis the actual composition of vapor which is in equilibrium with liquid of the composition specified on the horizontal axis.

Suppose that in distilling a solution of benzene and toluene with a certain distillation column it is found that distillate of composition g is obtained when the composition of the liquid in the boiler is given by a. Such a distillation is equivalent to three simple vaporizations and condensations, as indicated by steps abc, cde, and efg. Since three such steps can be drawn between a and g, and since the distilling pot itself corresponds to one theoretical plate, the column has two theoretical plates.

A distilling column operating at total reflux obviously would not be practical for separating liquids. An ordinary distilling flask and unpacked column may be equivalent to one or two theoretical plates, but, when the column is packed with special packing which presents a large area of the flowing liquid to the vapor, it is possible to have the equivalent of a theoretical plate every inch or so. The demands of the petroleum industry have given impetus to the development of the theory and practice of fractional distillation.

Immiscible Liquids. If two liquids are insoluble in each other, they exert their vapor pressures independently. Thus the total vapor pressure of the mixture is equal to the sum of the vapor pressures of the two pure liquids.

$$P = p_A{}^\circ + p_B{}^\circ \tag{17}$$

Consequently the mixture boils at a temperature below the boiling point of either liquid.

The vapor-pressure curves for water and bromobenzene, which are immiscible, are shown in *Fig. 7-15.* The total vapor pressure of the mixture reaches atmospheric pressure at 95°, and both liquids distill together at this temperature. When either one of the liquids has completely distilled away at 95°, the vapor pressure drops to that of the remaining liquid, $p_A{}^\circ$ or $p_B{}^\circ$, and with continued heating the temperature will rise until this liquid begins to boil.

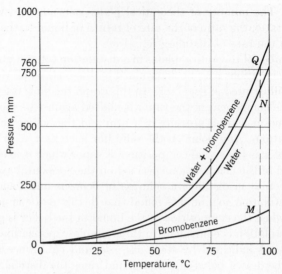

Fig. 7-15. Pressure-temperature graph for immiscible liquids, water and bromobenzene.

The ratio of the partial pressures of A and B is the same as the ratio of the number n of moles in the vapor.

$$\frac{p_A{}^\circ}{p_B{}^\circ} = \frac{n_A}{n_B} \tag{18}$$

The number of moles can be calculated by dividing the weight w in grams by the molecular weight M, giving

$$\frac{p_A{}^\circ}{p_B{}^\circ} = \frac{w_A/M_A}{w_B/M_B}$$

or

$$\frac{w_A}{w_B} = \frac{p_A{}^\circ M_A}{p_B{}^\circ M_B} \tag{19}$$

The equation is useful in calculating the relative weights w_A and w_B of the two liquids which are condensed out in the distillation of a pair of immiscible liquids.

A common laboratory and industrial operation which makes use of this relation is *steam distillation*. The steam is blown through a liquid which is immiscible with water, and the vapors coming off are condensed. In this way it is possible to distill many high-boiling liquids below 100°.

If a substance is immiscible with water and unaffected chemically by steam, a purification can be effected by steam distillation even though the vapor pressure of the substance is relatively low.

Example 4. Calculate the molecular weight of nitrobenzene from the fact that, when a mixture of nitrobenzene and water is distilled at a pressure of 731.9 mm, the distillation temperature is 98.2° and the weight ratio of nitrobenzene to water in the distillate is 0.188. The vapor pressure of water at this temperature is 712.4 mm. Thus the vapor pressure of nitrobenzene is $731.9 - 712.4 = 19.5$ mm. The molecular weight of nitrobenzene is given by

$$M_A = \frac{w_A p_B{}^\circ}{w_B p_A{}^\circ} M_B$$

$$= \frac{(0.188)(712.4)(18.0)}{(19.5)} = 123 \text{ g mole}^{-1}$$

REFERENCES

T. P. Carney, *Laboratory Fractional Distillation*, The Macmillan Co., New York, 1949.

K. G. Denbigh, *The Principles of Chemical Equilibrium*, Cambridge University Press, Cambridge, 1955.

E. Hála, J. Pick, V. Fried, and O. Vilím, *Vapor-Liquid Equilibrium* (translated by G. Standart), Pergamon Press, New York, 1958.

J. H. Hildebrand and R. L. Scott, *Solubility of Non-Electrolytes*, Reinhold Publishing Corp., New York, 1950.

I. M. Klotz, *Chemical Thermodynamics*, Prentice-Hall, Englewood Cliffs, N. J., 1950.

C. S. Robinson and E. R. Gilliland, *The Elements of Fractional Distillation*, McGraw-Hill Book Co., New York, 1939.

J. Timmermans, *The Physico-Chemical Constants of Binary Systems in Concentrated Solutions*, Vols. 1, 2, and 3, Interscience Publishers, New York, 1959.

PROBLEMS

1. The density of an aqueous solution of sodium chloride containing 8.000 grams of salt per 100 grams of solution is 1.0541 g ml^{-1} at 25°. Calculate the concentration of this sodium chloride solution on the (a) molar and (b) molal scales. *Ans.* (a) 1.44. (b) 1.49.

2. Ethanol and methanol form very nearly ideal solutions. The vapor pressure of ethanol is 44.5 mm, and that of methanol is 88.7 mm, at 20°. (a) Calculate the mole fractions of methanol and ethanol in a solution obtained by mixing 100 grams of each. (b) Calculate the partial pressures and the total vapor pressure of the solution. (c) Calculate the mole fraction of methanol in the vapor.

Ans. (a) $X_{C_2H_5OH} = 0.410$; $X_{CH_3OH} = 0.590$.
(b) $p_{C_2H_5OH} = 18.2$, $p_{CH_3OH} = 52.3$, $P_{total} = 70.5$ mm.
(c) 0.741.

3. Show that, for ideal solutions of two volatile liquids A and B,

$$P = p_A + p_B = p_A{}^\circ + X_B(p_B{}^\circ - p_A{}^\circ)$$

Check this equation against a graph for the total vapor pressure of an ideal solution.

4. For solutions of n-propanol and water the following partial pressures in millimeters of mercury are measured at 25°. Draw a complete pressure-composition diagram, including the total pressure. What is the composition of the vapor in equilibrium with a solution containing 0.5 mole fraction of n-propanol?

$X_{n\text{-propanol}}$	p_{H_2O}	$p_{n\text{-propanol}}$	$X_{n\text{-propanol}}$	p_{H_2O}	$p_{n\text{-propanol}}$
0	23.76	0	0.600	19.9	15.5
0.020	23.5	5.05	0.800	13.4	17.8
0.050	23.2	10.8	0.900	8.13	19.4
0.100	22.7	13.2	0.950	4.20	20.8
0.200	21.8	13.6	1.000	0.00	21.76
0.400	21.7	14.2			

Ans. $X_{n\text{-propanol,vap}} = 0.406$.

5. Solutions of hydrogen chloride in chlorobenzene obey Henry's law. In dilute solutions at 25°

$$K = p/m = 0.438$$

where p is given in atmospheres and m is concentration on the molal scale. What is the partial pressure of HCl in millimeters over a 1 per cent by weight solution of HCl in chlorobenzene? *Ans.* 92.1 mm.

6. Using the Henry-law constants in Table III, calculate the percentage (by volume) of oxygen and nitrogen in air dissolved in water at 25°. The air in equilibrium with the water at 1 atm pressure may be considered to be 20 per cent oxygen and 80 per cent nitrogen by volume. *Ans.* 33% oxygen, 67% nitrogen.

7. The following data on ethanol-chloroform solutions at 35° were obtained by G. Scatchard and C. L. Raymond [*J. Am. Chem. Soc.*, *60*, 1278 (1938)]:

$X_{EtOH,liq}$	0	0.2	0.4	0.6	0.8	1.0
$X_{EtOH,vap}$	0.0000	0.1382	0.1864	0.2554	0.4246	1.0000
Total pressure, mm	295.11	304.22	290.20	257.17	190.19	102.78

Calculate the activity coefficients of ethanol in these solutions according to convention I. *Ans.* 2.04, 1.315, 1.067, 0.983, 1.000.

8. Using the data in problem 4, calculate the activity coefficients of water and n-propanol at 0.20, 0.40, 0.60, and 0.80 mole fraction n-propanol, using convention II and considering n-propanol to be the solvent.

$$Ans. \quad X_1 = 0.20, 0.40, 0.60, 0.80;$$
$$\gamma_1 = 3.12, 1.63, 1.19, 1.02;$$
$$\gamma_2 = 0.314, 0.417, 0.574, 0.773.$$

9. At 100° benzene has a vapor pressure of 1357 mm and toluene has a vapor pressure of 558 mm. Assuming that these substances form ideal binary solutions with each other, calculate the composition of the solution that will boil at 1 atm at 100° and the vapor composition. *Ans.* $X_{benzene,liq} = 0.253$, $X_{benzene,vap} = 0.451$.

10. In the system isopropyl ether-isopropanol the vapor and liquid have the following compositions at the boiling point:

Mole Fraction Isopropyl Ether

In liquid	0	0.084	0.19	0.44	0.66	0.75	0.78	0.88	0.95	1.00
In vapor	0	0.30	0.45	0.64	0.73	0.76	0.78	0.84	0.91	1.00

Plot the data, and state whether this system exhibits a minimum or maximum boiling point. If so, which? What is the composition at the maximum or minimum boiling point? With a rough sketch show what the temperature-composition diagram would look like. *Ans.* Minimum boiling point at 0.78 mole fraction ether.

11. The following table gives mole per cent acetic acid in aqueous solutions and in the equilibrium vapor at the boiling point of the solution at 1 atm:

B.P., °C		118.1	113.8	107.5	104.4	102.1	100.0
Mole %	Liquid	100	90.0	70.0	50.0	30.0	0
acetic acid	Vapor	100	83.3	57.5	37.4	18.5	0

Calculate the minimum number of theoretical plates for the column required to produce an initial distillate of 28 mole per cent acetic acid from a solution of 80 mole per cent acetic acid. *Ans.* 3.

12. The boiling point of the immiscible liquid system naphthalene-water is 98° under a pressure of 733 mm. The vapor pressure of water at 98° is 707 mm. Calculate the weight per cent of naphthalene in the distillate. *Ans.* 20.7%.

---

13. A solution of potassium nitrate contains 192.6 grams of salt per liter of solution. The density of the solution is 1.1432 g cm^{-3}. Calculate the concentration in terms of (*a*) molality, (*b*) molarity, (*c*) weight per cent, (*d*) mole fraction.

14. At 25° the vapor pressures of chloroform and carbon tetrachloride are 199.1 and 114.5 mm, respectively. If the two liquids form an ideal solution, (*a*) what is the composition of the vapor in equilibrium with a solution containing 1 mole of each; (*b*) what is the total vapor pressure of the mixture?

15. Ethylene dibromide and propylene dibromide form very nearly ideal solutions. Plot the partial vapor pressure of ethylene dibromide ($p° = 172$ mm), the partial vapor pressure of propylene dibromide ($p° = 127$ mm), and the total vapor pressure of the solution versus the mole fraction of ethylene dibromide at 80°. (*a*) What will be the composition of the vapor in equilibrium with a solution containing 0.75 mole fraction of ethylene dibromide? (*b*) What will be the composition of the liquid phase in equilibrium with ethylene dibromide-propylene dibromide vapor containing 0.50 mole fraction of each?

16. A 10-liter tank of methane at 740 mm total pressure and 25° contains 1 liter of water. How many grams of methane are dissolved in the water?

17. The total vapor pressure of a solution containing 3 per cent by weight of ethanol, C_2H_5OH, in water is 760 mm at 97.11°. The vapor pressure of pure water at this temperature is 685 mm. Using Raoult's law and Henry's law, calculate the partial pressures at 97.11° of C_2H_5OH and water over a solution containing 0.02 mole fraction of C_2H_5OH.

18. Using the data of Table I, calculate the activity coefficients of acetone and chloroform at 35.2°, following convention I, for mole fractions of chloroform of 0.20, 0.40, 0.60, and 0.80.

19. Using the data in problem 4, calculate the activity coefficients of water and *n*-propanol at 0.20, 0.40, 0.60, and 0.80 mole fraction of *n*-propanol, using convention II and considering water to be the solvent.

20. At 1 atm pressure propane boils at −42.1° and *n*-butane boils at −0.5°; the following vapor-pressure data are available:

Temperature, °C	−31.2	−16.3
Vapor pressure, propane	1200	2240
Vapor pressure, *n*-butane	200	400

Assuming that these substances form ideal binary solutions with each other, (a) calculate the mole fractions of propane at which the solution will boil at 1 atm pressure at $-31.2°$ and $-16.3°$. (b) Calculate the mole fractions of propane in the equilibrium vapor at these temperatures. (c) Plot the temperature-mole fraction diagram at 1 atm, using these data.

21. Plot the following boiling-point data for benzene-ethanol solutions and estimate the azeotropic composition:

B.P., °C	78	75	70	70	75	80
Mole fraction of benzene						
In liquid	0	0.04	0.21	0.86	0.96	1.00
In vapor	0	0.18	0.42	0.66	0.83	1.00

State the range of mole fractions of benzene for which pure benzene could be obtained by fractional distillation at 1 atm.

22. The following table gives the mole per cent of n-propanol ($M = 60.1$) in aqueous solutions and in the vapor at the boiling point of the solution at 760 mm pressure.

Mole % n-Propanol

Liquid	Vapor	B.P., °C
0	0	100.0
2.0	21.6	92.0
6.0	35.1	89.3
20.0	39.2	88.1
43.2	43.2	87.8
60.0	49.2	88.3
80.0	64.1	90.5
100.0	100.0	97.3

With the aid of a graph of these data calculate the mole fraction of n-propanol in the first drop of distillate when the following solutions are distilled with a simple distilling flask which gives one theoretical plate: (a) 87 grams of n-propanol and 211 grams of water; (b) 50 grams of n-propanol and 5.02 grams of water.

23. The vapor pressure of the immiscible liquid system diethylaniline-water is 760 mm at $99.4°$. The vapor pressure of water at that temperature is 744 mm. How many grams of steam are necessary to distill 100 grams of diethylaniline?

24. Ten grams of acetic acid, $HC_2H_3O_2$, is dissolved in 100 grams of water. The density of the solution at $20°$ is 1.0123 g cm^{-3}. Calculate the concentration of $HC_2H_3O_2$ in terms of (a) per cent by weight, (b) molality, (c) molarity, and (d) mole fraction.

25. Benzene and toluene form very nearly ideal solutions. At $80°$ the vapor pressures of benzene and toluene are as follows: benzene, $p° = 753$ mm; toluene, $p° = 290$ mm. (a) For a solution containing 0.5 mole fraction of benzene and 0.5 mole fraction of toluene, what is the composition of the vapor and the total vapor pressure at $80°$? (b) What is the composition of the liquid phase in equilibrium at $80°$ with benzene-toluene vapor having 0.75 mole fraction benzene?

26. At $25°$ the vapor pressure of carbon tetrachloride, CCl_4, is 143 mm and that of chloroform, $CHCl_3$, is 199 mm. These liquids form very nearly ideal solutions with each other. If 1 mole of CCl_4 and 3 moles of $CHCl_3$ are mixed, what will be the mole fraction of CCl_4 in the vapor phase and the total vapor pressure of the solution?

27. The solubilities of carbon monoxide and nitrous oxide in water are 0.757 and 0.539, respectively, where solubilities are expressed in volume of gas under standard conditions per volume of solution. The solubility of carbon monoxide in 1.0 molal $Mg(NO_3)_2$ is 0.559. Calculate the solubility of nitrous oxide in 1.0 molal $Mg(NO_3)_2$. The experimental value is 0.385.

28. Two 2-liter vessels are connected with a tube and stopcock of negligible volume. Initially the first bulb contains 10 grams of water and is at 10°. The other bulb contains ammonia at a pressure of 5 atm and is at 0°. Calculate the total pressure in the system when the stopcock is opened and the whole apparatus is brought to equilibrium at 25°. The solubility of ammonia in water at 25° is 27.011 moles per 1000 grams of water at 1 atm. Second-order effects may be neglected.

29. By use of the data in Table II calculate the activity coefficients (following convention I) for acetone and carbon disulfide at 35.2° for a solution containing 0.6 mole fraction of carbon disulfide.

30. Using the data in problem 4, calculate the activity coefficients of water and n-propanol at 0.20, 0.40, 0.60, and 0.80 mole fraction of n-propanol using convention I.

31. The boiling points of o-xylene and p-xylene at 760 mm pressure are 144.4° and 138.4°, respectively. Assuming that these substances form ideal binary solutions and that for each the change in boiling point per millimeter change in pressure is 0.05° in this temperature range, calculate several points on the boiling-point line and several points on the corresponding vapor line.

32. From the data given below construct a complete temperature-composition diagram for the system ethanol-ethyl acetate for 760 mm pressure. A solution containing 0.8 mole fraction of ethanol, EtOH, is distilled completely at 760 mm. (a) What is the composition of the first vapor to come off? (b) That of the last drop of liquid to evaporate? (c) What would be the values of the above quantities if the distillation were carried out in a cylinder provided with a piston so that none of the vapor could escape?

$X_{EtOH,liq}$	$X_{EtOH,vap}$	B.P., °C	$X_{EtOH,liq}$	$X_{EtOH,vap}$	B.P., °C
0	0	77.15	0.563	0.507	72.0
0.025	0.070	76.7	0.710	0.600	72.8
0.100	0.164	75.0	0.833	0.735	74.2
0.240	0.295	72.6	0.942	0.880	76.4
0.360	0.398	71.8	0.982	0.965	77.7
0.462	0.462	71.6	1.000	1.000	78.3

33. The vapor pressures of n-decane ($M = 142.3$) at 95° and 100° are 105.1 and 125.9 mm, respectively. Calculate the temperature at which a steam distillation will occur at 745 mm pressure and the weight per cent of n-decane in the distillate.

PROPERTIES OF DILUTE SOLUTIONS

8

In Chapter 7 we considered binary solutions of volatile components. In this chapter we will consider the lowering of the vapor pressure and the elevation of the boiling point by nonvolatile solutes. The lowering of the freezing point and the osmotic pressure are considered for solutions in general. These four properties are related, and they are especially useful for calculating molecular weights of dissolved substances. The relations derived will be generally applicable only to dilute solutions.

Lowering of the Vapor Pressure by a Nonvolatile Solute. If the solute is nonvolatile, the vapor pressure of the solution is simply that of the solvent. For ideal solutions the vapor pressure p_1 is given by Raoult's law

$$p_1 = X_1 p_1{}^\circ = (1 - X_2)p_1{}^\circ \tag{1}$$

where the subscript 1 refers to the solvent and the subscript 2 to the nonvolatile solute. For nonideal solutions this equation applies when X_2, the mole fraction of the solute, is sufficiently small so that the effect of the solute on the character of the solvent is negligible. Equation 1 may be rearranged to give

$$\frac{p_1{}^\circ - p_1}{p_1{}^\circ} = X_2 \tag{2}$$

The difference between two quantities such as $p_1{}^\circ$ and p_1 often can be determined experimentally more accurately and more easily than the absolute value of one of them.

Example 1. Calculate the lowering of the vapor pressure of water at 20° by the addition of 54.1 grams of mannitol ($M = 182.2$) per 1000 grams of water. The vapor pressure of water at this temperature is 17.54 mm.

$$p_1{}^\circ - p_1 = X_2 p_1{}^\circ$$

$$= \frac{(54.1/182.2)(17.54)}{(54.1/182.2) + (1000/18.0)}$$

$$= 0.0935 \text{ mm}$$

The experimental value is 0.0922 mm [J. C. W. Frazer, B. F. Lovelace, and T. H. Rogers, *J. Am. Chem. Soc.*, *42*, 1793 (1920)]. A much larger number of figures would have to be carried in order to do this calculation with equation 1 rather than equation 2.

The vapor pressure of a solution may be determined by a static method in which the pressure is read directly with a manometer. However, a differential experimental measurement is simpler and more accurate. In this method one arm of the differential manometer is connected to the solution and the other to the pure solvent. In another method, vessels containing two different solutions are placed side by side in a closed container, and vapor is allowed to distill from the solution having the higher vapor pressure to the one having the lower vapor pressure. In this process the concentrated solution is diluted and the dilute solution is concentrated until, at equilibrium, the two solutions have the same vapor pressure. This *isopiestic* method is simple but can yield very precise results.* It is important that the vessels be in good thermal contact so that both are held at the same temperature. The attainment of equilibrium is accelerated by the removal of air from the containing vessel, which increases the rate of diffusion of the vapor.

This method depends upon knowing the vapor pressure of one of the solutions from other studies. Thus the reference solution may contain potassium chloride, since the vapor pressures of potassium chloride solutions are accurately known as a function of concentration. A determination of the concentration of potassium chloride at equilibrium permits a calculation of the vapor pressure of the reference solution of potassium chloride and hence that of the solution being studied.

The gas-saturation method described on p. 127 may also be used to determine the vapor pressure of a solution. The loss in weight of the solution is determined after bubbling through a known volume of an inert gas, or the vaporized solvent is caught in an absorption tube and weighed or titrated.†

* R. A. Robinson and D. A. Sinclair, *J. Am. Chem. Soc.*, *56*, 1830 (1934); G. Scatchard, W. J. Hamer, and S. E. Wood, *J. Am. Chem. Soc.*, *60*, 3061 (1938).

† M. F. Bechtold and R. F. Newton, *J. Am. Chem. Soc.*, *62*, 1390 (1940).

Elevation of the Boiling Point. If a nonvolatile solute is added to a solvent, the vapor pressure is reduced as shown schematically in *Fig. 8-1*. As a result the solution has to be heated to a higher temperature than the solvent before the vapor pressure of the solution will be equal to the applied pressure so that boiling can take place. It can also be seen from the diagram that, if *pure solvent* crystallizes out, the solution will have to be cooled to a temperature below the freezing point of the pure liquid before the solution and the solid solvent will have the same vapor pressure and can therefore be in equilibrium. The fusion curves are actually nearly vertical, but in the diagram their slopes are exaggerated so that it can be emphasized that the freezing-point depression ΔT_f is measured at a total pressure of 1 atm.

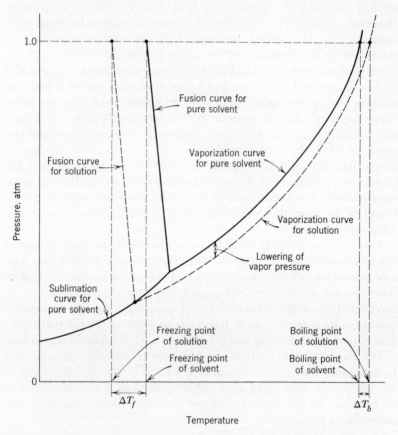

Fig. 8-1. Schematic diagram showing the relation between the elevation of the boiling point, lowering of the freezing point, and lowering of the vapor pressure caused by the addition of a nonvolatile solute. The diagram is not to scale.

The elevation of the boiling point ΔT_b caused by a nonvolatile solute may by derived from the Clausius-Clapeyron equation, which may be written as follows for small changes in temperature and pressure for a pure liquid:

$$\frac{\Delta P}{P \Delta T} = \frac{\Delta \bar{H}_{vap}}{RT^2}$$

Applying this equation to the lowering of the vapor pressure of a solvent at its boilng point T_0 by a nonvolatile solvent,

$$\frac{\Delta p}{\Delta T_b} = \frac{\Delta \bar{H}_{vap} \, p^{\circ}_1}{RT_0^2} \tag{3}$$

The lowering of the vapor pressure for an ideal solution is given by

$$\Delta p = X_2 p_1^{\circ} \tag{4}$$

Eliminating Δp between equations 3 and 4, we obtain the elevation of the boiling temperature which corresponds to the lowering of the vapor pressure of the solvent

$$\Delta T_b = \frac{RT_0^2}{\Delta \bar{H}_{vap}} X_2 \tag{5}$$

This equation is applicable only to calculations for dilute solutions.

In discussing the elevation of the boiling point the concentration of the solute is generally given in terms of molal concentration m (that is, moles of solute per 1000 grams of solvent) rather than of mole fraction. The relation between these concentrations is

$$X_2 = \frac{n_2}{n_1 + n_2} = \frac{m}{1000/M_1 + m} \xrightarrow{m \to 0} \frac{m}{1000/M_1} \tag{6}$$

where M_1 is the molecular weight of the solvent. The last form is applicable to dilute solutions for which the number of moles of solute is negligible in comparison with the number of moles of solvent.

Exercise 1. Show that in a 1-molal aqueous solution an error of 1.8 per cent is caused by neglecting n_2 in the denominator of equation 6.

Substituting the last form of equation 6 into equation 5 and rearranging, we obtain

$$\Delta T_b = \frac{RT_0^2 M_1 m}{1000 \Delta \bar{H}_{vap}} = K_b m \tag{7}$$

where K_b is called the molal boiling-point constant.

$$K_b = \frac{RT_0^2 M_1}{1000 \Delta \bar{H}_{vap}} \tag{8}$$

Example 2. Calculate the molal boiling-point constant for water, which has a boiling point of $100.00°$, a heat of vaporization of 539.7 cal g^{-1}, and a molecular weight of 18.02.

$$K_b = \frac{RT^2 M_1}{1000 \Delta \overline{H}_{vap}} = \frac{(1.987)(373.1)^2(18.02)}{(1000)(18.02)(539.7)} = 0.513 \text{ deg molal}^{-1}$$

The molal boiling-point constants for several liquids are given in Table I together with the molal freezing-point constants, which will be considered in a later section. The constant K_b is not the actual

Table I. Molal Boiling-Point Constants and Freezing-Point Constants

Solvent	Boiling Point	K_b, deg molal^{-1}	Freezing Point	K_f, deg molal^{-1}
Acetic acid	118.1	2.93	17	3.9
Acetone	56.0	1.71	. . .	. . .
Benzene	80.2	2.53	5.4	5.12
Chloroform	61.2	3.63	. . .	. . .
Ethanol	78.3	1.22	. . .	. . .
Ethylene bromide	. . .	. . .	10	12.5
Ethyl ether	34.4	2.02	. . .	. . .
Heptachloropropane	. . .	. . .	29.5	12.0
Naphthalene	. . .	. . .	80	6.8
Tribromophenol	. . .	. . .	95	20.4
Water	100	0.51	0	1.860

elevation of boiling point for a 1-molal solution, because the assumptions involved in the derivation of equation 7 limit its validity to dilute solutions. The value of K_b may also be determined experimentally by measuring the elevation of the boiling point ΔT_b at several concentrations, and plotting $\Delta T_b/m$ versus concentration and extrapolating to zero concentration. As in many other experiments which will be encountered later, it is difficult to make accurate measurements with solutions that are dilute enough to give exact values of theoretical significance. Therefore, the experiments are carried out in several solutions as dilute as convenient for accurate measurements, and then the values of $\Delta T_b/m$ are plotted and extrapolated to zero concentration. The values of K_b obtained in this way with nondissociating or nonassociating solutes agree closely with the values calculated using equation 8.

In order to determine the molecular weight of a solute it is convenient to write equation 7 in a different way. If w_2 grams of solute having a molecular weight M_2 is dissolved in w_1 grams of solvent, the number of moles of solute is w_2/M_2 and the molality m is $1000w_2/M_2w_1$. Then

$$\Delta T_b = K_b m = K_b \frac{w_2}{M_2} \frac{1000}{w_1} \tag{9}$$

Example 3. What is the molecular weight of dinitrobenzene if the addition of 1.00 gram to 50.00 grams of benzene raises the boiling point of the benzene 0.30°?

$$M_2 = K_b \frac{w_2}{\Delta T_b} \frac{1000}{w_1} = 2.53 \left(\frac{1.00}{0.30}\right)\left(\frac{1000}{50.00}\right) = 170 \text{ g mole}^{-1}$$

Example 4. Calculate the boiling point of a solution containing 5.00 grams of urea in 75.00 grams of water. The molecular weight of urea is 60.06.

$$\Delta T_b = 0.513m = (0.513)\left(\frac{5.00}{60.06}\right)\left(\frac{1000}{75.00}\right) = 0.569°$$

The boiling point of the solution at 1 atm is $100.000° + 0.569° = 100.569°$.

Derivation of Equation 5 Using the Chemical Potential. In order for solvent vapor at 1 atm pressure (or other applied pressure) to be in equilibrium with solvent in solution at a certain temperature, the chemical potential μ of the solvent must be the same in the vapor phase (μ_v) as in the liquid phase (μ_l).

$$\mu_v = \mu_l \tag{10}$$

If the vapor pressure of the solvent obeys Raoult's law, the chemical potential of the solvent in the solution is expressed by

$$\mu_l = \mu_1^* + RT \ln X_1 \tag{11}$$

where μ_1^* is the chemical potential of pure solvent at the temperature and pressure of the solution.

Substituting equation 11 into equation 10 and rearranging, we obtain

$$\frac{\mu_v}{T} - \frac{\mu_1^*}{T} = R \ln X_1 \tag{12}$$

Differentiating equation 12 with respect to absolute temperature at constant pressure,

$$\left[\frac{\partial(\mu_v/T)}{\partial T}\right]_P - \left[\frac{\partial(\mu_1^*/T)}{\partial T}\right]_P = R \frac{\partial \ln X_1}{\partial T} \tag{13}$$

It has been shown earlier (p. 108) that

$$\left[\frac{\partial(G/T)}{\partial T}\right]_P = \frac{-H}{T^2} \tag{14}$$

If this equation is applied to 1 mole, it may be written

$$\left[\frac{\partial(\mu/T)}{\partial T}\right]_P = \frac{-\bar{H}}{T^2} \tag{15}$$

Substituting this equation into equation 13 yields

$$-\frac{\bar{H}_v - \bar{H}_1{}^*}{T^2} = R\frac{\partial \ln X_1}{\partial T} \tag{16}$$

where $\bar{H}_v$ is the molal enthalpy of the vapor and $\bar{H}_1{}^*$ is the molal enthalpy of the pure liquid, so that $\bar{H}_v - \bar{H}_1{}^*$ is simply the molal enthalpy of vaporization $\Delta\bar{H}_{vap}$. Thus

$$\frac{\partial \ln X_1}{\partial T} = \frac{-\Delta\bar{H}_{vap}}{RT^2} \tag{17}$$

For small boiling-point elevations $\Delta\bar{H}_{vap}$ may be considered independent of temperature, and equation 17 may be integrated from the boiling point T_0 of pure solvent, in which $X_1 = 1$ and $\ln X_1 = 0$, to the boiling point T of the solution of mole fraction solvent X_1:

$$-\int_{\ln 1=0}^{\ln X_1} d \ln X_1 = \int_{T_0}^{T} \frac{\Delta\bar{H}_{vap}}{RT^2} dT \tag{18}$$

$$-\ln X_1 = \frac{\Delta\bar{H}_{vap}(T - T_0)}{RTT_0} \cong \frac{\Delta\bar{H}_{vap}\Delta T_b}{RT_0{}^2} \tag{19}$$

This equation has been derived for ideal solutions but is applicable to nonideal solutions, provided that the mole fraction of the solvent is very close to unity. For dilute solutions $-\ln X_1$ can be represented by the first several terms of a power series (p. 718) in X_2, which is the mole fraction of the solute:

$$-\ln X_1 = -\ln (1 - X_2) = X_2 + \tfrac{1}{2}X_2{}^2 + \tfrac{1}{3}X_2{}^3 + \cdots \tag{20}$$

For sufficiently low concentrations of solute the second and higher terms of this series are negligible,* and so equation 19 reduces to equation 5.

Experimental Determination of Boiling Points.† In determining the boiling point of a solution the thermometer must be placed in the liquid,

---

* For example, if $X_2 = 0.01$, the series becomes $0.01 + \tfrac{1}{2}(0.0001) + \tfrac{1}{3}(0.000001)$, which is equal to 0.01 within 0.5 per cent.

† W. Swietoslawski and J. R. Anderson, in *Technique of Organic Chemistry,* Part I, ed. by A. Weissberger, Interscience Publishers, New York, 1949, Chapter 4.

because if it were placed in the vapor the liquid condensing on the thermometer would be pure solvent and the temperature recorded would be the boiling point of the condensing solvent rather than that of the solution. When placed in the liquid, however, the thermometer is likely to read too high because the liquid can become superheated by conduction from the heater.

In order to prevent superheating and obtain the true boiling point of the solution, the vapor from the boiling liquid is passed into an inverted funnel below the surface so that it pumps a mixture of liquid and vapor upward in a tube which discharges the mixture onto the thermometer bulb placed above the liquid. During the passage of the vapor and liquid through this tube the two have opportunity to come to equilibrium, and any superheated liquid is cooled to the boiling point by further evaporation.

Since the boiling point is affected by changes in atmospheric pressure, the determinations on the solution and solvent should be made simultaneously in two pieces of apparatus, or over such short periods of time that the barometer changes are negligible. The need for these precautions is evident from the fact that a barometric change of 0.3 or 0.4 mm changes the boiling point of most solvents by 0.01°.

Freezing-Point Lowering. The equation for the freezing-point lowering is derived on the assumption that pure solid solvent separates from the solution, uncontaminated with solute, when the temperature is lowered. At the freezing point of the solution there is equilibrium between the solid solvent and the solution. Therefore, the chemical potentials of the solvent in the solid phase (μ_s) and solution phase (μ_l) are equal.

$$\mu_s = \mu_l \tag{21}$$

Substituting equation 11 into equation 21 and rearranging, we obtain

$$\frac{\mu_s}{T} - \frac{\mu_1{}^*}{T} = R \ln X_1 \tag{22}$$

Exercise II. From this point the derivation for the freezing-point lowering is exactly analogous to that for the elevation of the boiling point starting with equation 12. Show that, if $\Delta \bar{H}_{\text{fus}}$ may be considered independent of temperature,

$$- \ln X_1 = \frac{\Delta \bar{H}_{\text{fus}}(T_0 - T)}{RTT_0} \cong \frac{\Delta \bar{H}_{\text{fus}} \Delta T_f}{RT_0{}^2} \tag{23}$$

where T_0 is the freezing point of the pure solvent and ΔT_f is the lowering of the freezing point.

Equation 23 gives the dependence of the freezing point of an ideal solution on the solvent concentration. It may equally well be interpreted as giving the *solubility of solid solute* in the solvent when ideal solutions are formed. Thus for solvent-solute combinations which yield ideal solutions, equation 23 may be used to calculate the solubility of one component in the other, provided that the heat of fusion of the solid is known.* Such a calculation is illustrated in problem 5 at the end of this chapter.

With the help of mathematical operations discussed previously for the boiling-point elevation, the following useful equations are obtained:

$$\Delta T_f = \frac{RT_0^2 M_1 m}{1000 \Delta \overline{H}_{fus}} = K_f m \tag{24}$$

and

$$K_f = \frac{RT_0^2 M_1}{1000 \Delta \overline{H}_{fus}} \tag{25}$$

$$\Delta T_f = K_f \frac{w_2}{M_2} \frac{1000}{w_1} \tag{26}$$

Example 5. For water K_f has the value $1.86°$, calculated as follows:

$$K_f = \frac{RT_0^2 M_1}{1000 \Delta \overline{H}_{fus}} = \frac{(1.987)(273.1)^2(18.02)}{(1000)(18.02)(79.7)} = 1.86 \text{ deg molal}^{-1}$$

According to this equation, solute added to 1000 grams of water will lower the freezing point $1.86°$ per mole added, but the relation holds only for dilute solutions. Even a 1-molal solution is too concentrated, and the depression will be something less than $1.86°$.

Determination of Freezing-Point Depressions. A tube containing the solution is jacketed and immersed in a bath having a slightly lower temperature than the freezing point of the solution. The solution is stirred, and the temperature gradually falls until the solid appears. Often supercooling occurs; this leads to the freezing out of a considerable quantity of solvent with a consequent change in the concentration of the solution. The amount of supercooling may be reduced by adding seed crystals before the supercooling becomes too great.

The most accurate values of the freezing-point depression are determined by a differential method in which the difference in temperature between the solution in equilibrium with solid solvent and pure solvent in equilibrium with solid solvent is measured, using a multiple-junction

---

* J. H. Hildebrand and R. L. Scott, *Solubility of Non-Electrolytes*, Reinhold Publishing Corp., New York, 1950.

thermocouple and a sensitive potentiometer. Such an arrangement is illustrated in *Fig. 8-2* for an aqueous solution. The concentration of solution in equilibrium with solid solvent is determined accurately by chemical analysis or by physical measurements, for example, by a measurement of refractive index.

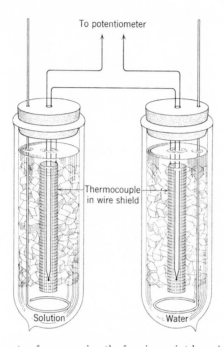

Fig. 8-2. Apparatus for measuring the freezing-point lowering by a solute.

Table II gives the freezing-point lowerings for aqueous solutions of urea. The ratio $\Delta T_f/m$ would have the value 1.860 in very dilute solutions. Table II indicates the kind of deviations from ideality that are encountered in more concentrated solutions of nonelectrolytes.

Osmotic Pressure. When a solution is separated from the solvent by a membrane which is permeable by solvent but not by solute, the solvent flows through the membrane into the solution, where the chemical potential of the solvent is lower. This process is known as osmosis. An excess of pressure must be applied to the solution to prevent this flow of solvent through the membrane. The osmotic pressure π is the pressure difference across the membrane required to prevent spontaneous flow in either direction across the membrane.

184   PHYSICAL CHEMISTRY

Table II. Lowering of Freezing Point of Water by Urea[1,2]

$m,$ moles per 1000 g H_2O	ΔT_f	$\Delta T_f/m$
0.324_1	0.595_3	1.837
0.431_5	0.789_3	1.829
0.645_8	1.169_8	1.811
1.521_3	2.673_2	1.757
3.360_1	5.489_7	1.635

[1] H. M. Caldwell and F. W. Politi, *J. Am. Chem. Soc.*, *60*, 1291 (1938).
[2] When the last figure is uncertain it is sometimes set slightly below the line.

The phenomenon of osmotic pressure was described by Abbé Nollet in 1748, and Pfeffer, a botanist, made the first direct measurements in 1877. Van't Hoff analyzed Pfeffer's data on the osmotic pressure of sugar solutions and found empirically that an equation quite analogous to the ideal gas law gave approximately the behavior of dilute solutions, namely, $\pi\overline{V} = RT$, where $\overline{V}$ is the volume of solution containing a mole of solute. However, the origin of the pressure is quite different from that for a gas, and the equation of the form of the ideal gas equation is applicable only in the limit of low concentrations.

At equilibrium the chemical potential of pure solvent at 1 atm pressure (μ_1°) is equal to the chemical potential of solvent in the compressed solution (μ_1').

$$\mu_1^\circ = \mu_1' \tag{27}$$

The chemical potential of the solvent in the solution is less than that of the pure solvent at the same pressure and temperature, but the chemical potential of the solvent in the solution can be raised by applying pressure. When the applied pressure is equal to the osmotic pressure, these two effects exactly counterbalance one another, so that equation 27 is obeyed.

The effect on the chemical potential of the solvent of adding solute and changing the pressure is given by

$$d\mu_1 = \left(\frac{\partial\mu_1}{\partial P}\right)_{T,X_2} dP + \left(\frac{\partial\mu_1}{\partial X_2}\right)_{T,P} dX_2 \tag{28}$$

where $d\mu_1$ is the total change in the chemical potential of the solvent when the pressure is changed by dP and the mole fraction of the solute is changed by dX_2. From equation 66 in Chapter 5

$$\left(\frac{\partial \overline{G}_1}{\partial P}\right)_{T,X_2} = \left(\frac{\partial \mu_1}{\partial P}\right)_{T,X_2} = \overline{V}_1 \tag{29}$$

where $\overline{V}_1$ is the partial molal volume of the solvent.

Substitution of $(1 - X_2)$ for X_1 in equation 11 and differentiation with respect to X_2 yields

$$\left(\frac{\partial \mu_1}{\partial X_2}\right)_{T,P} = \frac{-RT}{1 - X_2} \tag{30}$$

Substituting equations 29 and 30 into 28 yields

$$d\mu_1 = \overline{V}_1 \, dP - \frac{RT \, dX_2}{1 - X_2} \tag{31}$$

Since the pressure and concentration are changed in such a way that the chemical potential is constant, $d\mu_1 = 0$ and

$$\overline{V}_1 \, dP = \frac{RT \, dX_2}{1 - X_2} = \frac{-RT \, dX_1}{X_1} \tag{32}$$

Integrating from 1 atm to $1 + \pi$ atm, and from X_1 or $\ln X_1 = 0$ to $\ln X_1$, assuming that $\overline{V}_1$ is independent of pressure and concentration,

$$\int_1^{1+\pi} \overline{V}_1 \, dP = -RT \int_{\ln X_1 = 0}^{\ln X_1} d \ln X_1 \tag{33}$$

$$\overline{V}_1 \pi = -RT \ln X_1 \tag{34}$$

Introducing Raoult's law $p_1 = X_1 p_1°$, we obtain

$$\overline{V}_1 \pi = RT \ln \frac{p_1°}{p_1} \tag{35}$$

With this equation it is possible to calculate the osmotic pressure of a solution from the vapor pressures of the solvent and the solution, and the partial molar volume of the solvent.

Example 6. Calculate the osmotic pressure of a 1-molar sucrose solution in water from the fact that at $30°$ the vapor pressure of the solution is 31.207 mm. The vapor pressure of water at $30°$ is 31.824 mm. The density of pure water at this temperature (0.99564 g cm^{-3}) may be used to estimate $\overline{V}_1$ for a dilute solution.

$$\pi = (RT/\overline{V}_1) \ln (p_1°/p_1)$$

$$\overline{V}_1 = \frac{18.02 \text{ g mole}^{-1}}{0.99564 \text{ g cm}^{-3}} = 18.10 \text{ cm}^3 \text{ mole}^{-1} \text{ or } 0.01810 \text{ l mole}^{-1}$$

$$\pi = \frac{(0.08205 \text{ l-atm deg}^{-1} \text{ mole}^{-1})(2.303)(303.1 \text{ deg})}{(0.01810 \text{ l mole}^{-1})} \log \frac{31.824}{31.207}$$

$$= 26.9 \text{ atm } *$$

We have limited consideration to ideal solutions, and in integrating equation 33 we have assumed that the partial molar volume of the solvent $\overline{V}_1$ is independent of pressure and concentration. At sufficiently high dilution the logarithmic term of equation 34 may be expanded as shown in equation 20. When only the first term in the series is retained, equation 34 becomes

$$\overline{V}_1\pi = RTX_2 \tag{36}$$

Since the solution is dilute, $X_2 = n_2/n_1$ and $\overline{V}_1 = V/n_1$, where V is the volume of the solution. Thus equation 36 may be written

$$\pi V = n_2 RT \tag{37}$$

which is the approximate equation which van't Hoff found empirically. It is evident from the approximations introduced why this equation cannot hold for concentrated solutions.

Example 7. Calculate the osmotic pressure of a 1-molar sucrose solution in water at 30°, using the approximate form of the osmotic-pressure equation.

$$\pi = \frac{nRT}{V} = \frac{(0.082)(303)}{1.000} = 24.8 \text{ atm}$$

This may be compared with the more accurate value of 26.9 atm calculated in example 6.

The osmotic pressure is determined experimentally by measuring the pressure applied to the solution which will prevent flow of solvent

---

* This problem may be solved to a sufficiently high degree of accuracy with a slide rule rather than logarithm tables by writing the logarithmic term as a series. For small values of x it may be seen on p. 718 of the Appendix that

$$\ln (1 + x) \cong x$$

Thus,

$$\ln \frac{31.824}{31.207} = \ln \left(1 + \frac{31.824 - 31.207}{31.207} \right)$$

$$= \ln (1 + 0.0198)$$

$$\cong 0.0198$$

$$\pi = 27.1 \text{ atm}$$

through the semipermeable membrane. The membrane may be semipermeable because the passages through it are too small to allow solute to pass through. Measurements of osmotic pressure are used in the studies of macromolecules (p. 577). Osmosis is very important in the flow of water in the cells of plants and animals.

Comparison of Experimental Methods. The four properties of solutions which have just been studied, vapor-pressure lowering, boiling-point elevation, freezing-point depression, and osmotic pressure, are closely related. The freezing-point depression can be measured most accurately and most easily, but the method is limited to low temperatures where the solubility is often small. The freezing-point method cannot be used unless pure solvent crystallizes out. Boiling points are seriously affected by fluctuations in the barometric pressure, and in water the molal elevation is only about one-third as great as the freezing-point depression. The solute must have quite a low vapor pressure. The vapor-pressure method has the advantage that the measurements can be carried out at any desired temperature between the freezing point and boiling point, but it is more difficult to make accurate measurements. Osmotic pressure played an important role in the early development of the theory of solutions but now finds its greatest application in the measurement of molecular weights of high polymers. These four properties are sometimes called *colligative* properties.

Dissociation of Solutes. The preceding discussion has been based on solutes which do not dissociate or associate in solution. If there is dissociation, the vapor-pressure lowering, boiling-point elevation, freezing-point lowering, and osmotic pressure will be increased over the values expected for a nondissociating solute; and for an associating solute these quantities will be decreased. As the concentration approaches zero, $\Delta p/X_2$, $\Delta T_b/m$, $\Delta T_f/m$, and π/m for dissociating solutes approach values which are greater than those for nondissociating solutes by factors of 2, 3, etc. The factor is the same no matter which colligative property is measured. The abnormal colligative properties and the electrical conductivities of these solutions were explained in 1887 by Arrhenius * as being due to dissociation into ions. The multiples of the normal colligative properties observed in very dilute solutions are identical with the number of ions into which a molecule of the solute can dissociate, 2, 3, $\cdots$.

As the concentration of a dissociating solute is increased, the factor by which the colligative properties are greater than those for nondis-

* S. Arrhenius, *Z. physik. Chem.*, *1*, 631 (1887).

sociating solutes *decreases*. Although it was originally thought by Arrhenius that this change with concentration was due to the change of the degree of dissociation of the salt, it is now known that the explanation lies in the fact that there is considerable electrostatic interaction between the ions in solution, so that the solutions are not ideal except in the limit of infinitely dilute solutions. The application of the Debye-Hückel theory in accounting for this nonideality will be discussed later (p. 392).

REFERENCES

H. S. Harned and B. B. Owen, *The Physical Chemistry of Electrolytic Solutions*, Reinhold Publishing Corp., New York, 1958.

J. H. Hildebrand and R. L. Scott, *Solubility of Non-Electrolytes*, Reinhold Publishing Corp., New York, 1950.

A. Weissberger, *Technique of Organic Chemistry*, Vol. I, Part I, Interscience Publishers, New York, 1959.

PROBLEMS

1. The vapor pressure of a solution containing 13 grams of a nonvolatile solute in 100 grams of water at 28° is 27.371 mm. Calculate the molecular weight of the solute, assuming that the solution is ideal. The vapor pressure of water at this temperature is 28.065 mm. *Ans.* 92.3 g mole^{-1}.

2. Ten grams of benzene, 10 grams of toluene, and 10 grams of naphthalene are mixed together to give a homogeneous solution. If it is assumed that the solution is ideal, how many grams of toluene will be vaporized by passing through 10 liters of air at 30° if the vapor pressure of toluene at this temperature is 36.7 mm, that of benzene is 118.5 mm, and that of naphthalene is negligible?

Ans. 0.617 g.

3. The boiling point of chloroform can be measured with a particular apparatus with an accuracy of 0.01°. Calculate the number of grams of an impurity of $M = 100$ which would be required to raise the boiling point of 50 grams of chloroform by this amount. *Ans.* 0.0138 g.

4. A hydrocarbon of the type $H(CH_2)_n H$ is dissolved in ethylene bromide, which freezes at 10.00°. A solution which contains 0.81 gram of hydrocarbon per 190 grams of ethylene bromide freezes at 9.47°. Calculate the value of n. *Ans.* 7.

5. Calculate the solubility of naphthalene in benzene at 25°, assuming an ideal solution is formed. The melting point of naphthalene is 80°, and the heat of fusion is 4610 cal mole^{-1}. The actual measured solubility of naphthalene in benzene is $X_1 = 0.296$. *Ans.* $X_1 = 0.297$.

6. The osmotic pressure of an aqueous solution of 1 gram of sucrose ($M = 342$) per 100 ml of solution is 0.649 atm at 0°. Calculate the expected osmotic pressure, using the simple form of the osmotic-pressure equation. *Ans.* 0.655 atm.

7. Calculate the osmotic pressure of 0.16 M sodium chloride at 0° and 37°, assuming complete dissociation. *Ans.* 7.16, 8.14 atm.

8. If 68.4 grams of sucrose $(M = 342)$ is dissolved in 1000 grams of water, what are (a) the vapor pressure, and (b) the osmotic pressure, at 20°? (c) What is the freezing point? (d) What is the boiling point? The density of the solution at 20° is 1.024 g cm^{-3}. The vapor pressure of water at 20° is 17.363 mm.

$Ans.$ (a) 7.30 mm. (b) 4.61 atm. (c) $-0.372°$. (d) 100.103°.

9. A certain number of grams of a given substance in 100 grams of benzene lowers the freezing point by 1.28°. The same weight of solute in 100 grams of water lowers the freezing point by 1.395°. If the substance has its normal molecular weight in benzene and is completely dissociated in water, into how many ions does a molecule of this substance dissociate when placed in water? $Ans.$ 3.

10. The vapor pressure of water at 25° (23.756 mm) is lowered 0.071 mm by the addition of 1.53 grams of a nonvolatile substance to 100 grams of water. Calculate the molecular weight of the solute, using Raoult's law. (See the discussion in example 1 concerning the most convenient form of Raoult's law for this calculation.)

11. The vapor pressure of water at 25° is 23.756 mm. Calculate the vapor pressure of solutions containing (a) 6.01 grams of urea, NH_2CONH_2, (b) 9.4 grams of phenol, C_6H_5OH, and (c) 6.01 grams of urea $+$ 9.4 grams of phenol per 1000 grams of water, assuming no chemical action between the two substances. (d) Calculate (c), assuming that a stable compound is formed containing 1 mole of the urea to 1 mole of phenol.

12. Calculate the molal boiling-point constant for chloroform $(M = 119.4)$ from the fact that its boiling point is 61.2° and its heat of vaporization is 59.0 cal g^{-1}.

13. The Henry-law constants for oxygen and nitrogen in water at 0° are 1.91×10^7 mm and 4.09×10^7 mm, respectively. Calculate the lowering of the freezing point of water by dissolved air with 80 per cent N_2 and 20 per cent O_2 by volume at 1 atm pressure.

14. Calculate the solubility of anthracene $(M = 178.2)$ in toluene $(M = 92.1)$ at 100°. The heat of fusion of anthracene is 6900 cal mole^{-1}, and the melting point of anthracene is 217°. The actual solubility is 0.0592 on the mole-fraction scale. How do you explain the discrepancy?

15. An aqueous solution of maltose at 25° has a vapor pressure of 23.476 mm, whereas pure water has a vapor pressure of 23.756 mm. What is the osmotic pressure of the solution?

16. When cells of the skeletal muscle of a frog were placed in a series of sodium chloride solutions of different concentrations, it was observed microscopically that the cells remained unchanged in 0.7 per cent sodium chloride solution but shrank in more concentrated solutions and swelled in more dilute solutions. Calculate the equilibrium pressure across the cell walls if the cells were placed in water.

17. Given a 0.01-molal solution of urea $(M = 60.06)$ in water at 25°, calculate: (a) the boiling point of the solution; (b) the vapor pressure of the solution if the vapor pressure of pure water is 23.756 mm; (c) the osmotic pressure (assuming that the density of the solution is practically 1.0 g cm^{-3}).

18. When 1.4511 grams of dichloroacetic acid is dissolved in 56.87 grams of carbon tetrachloride, the boiling point is increased 0.518°. The boiling point of carbon tetrachloride is 76.75°, and its heat of vaporization is 46.5 cal g^{-1} at the boiling point. What is the apparent molecular weight of the acid? How can the discrepancy be explained?

---

19. Calculate the vapor pressure at $25°$ of an aqueous solution of urea ($M = 60.06$) containing 5 grams of urea per 1000 grams of water. The vapor pressure of water at this temperature is 23.756 mm, and ideal-solution behavior may be assumed.

20. Calculate the boiling-point constants for $O_2(l)$ and $PbI_2(l)$. (See Table II in Chapter 6.)

21. What mole per cent impurity is required to lower the freezing point of benzene $0.05°$, provided that pure benzene crystallizes out?

22. Assuming that ideal solutions are formed, (a) how many grams of methanol, CH_3OH, must be added to a 10-liter tank of water to prevent freezing at $-5°$? (b) How many grams of calcium chloride, $CaCl_2$, assuming complete dissociation? (c) How many grams of glycol, $(CH_2OH)_2$?

23. (a) Assuming ideal solutions, what molal concentration of solutes at $20°$ is required to raise by osmosis a column of solution having a density of approximately 1.0 g cm^{-3} to a height of 100 ft? * (b) What is the vapor pressure of the solution at $20°$? The vapor pressure of pure water at $20°$ is 17.363 mm.

24. Human blood plasma freezes at $-0.56°$. What is its osmotic pressure at $37°$ measured with a membrane permeable only by water?

25. The freezing point of a 0.01-molal solution of barium chloride is $-0.050°$. What is the approximate vapor pressure of the solution at $25°$ if the vapor pressure of pure water is 23.756 mm?

26. Purified nitrogen gas is slowly bubbled through a solution of 3.000 grams of a nonvolatile organic compound dissolved in 200 grams of benzene and then bubbled through pure benzene. The solution is found to be 2.1540 grams lighter, while the pure benzene suffered a loss in weight of 0.0160 gram. What is the apparent molecular weight of the dissolved substance?

27. Derive the equation for the Gibbs free-energy change when a mole of substance is transferred from a large amount of an ideal solution where its mole fraction is X_1 to another where its mole fraction is X_2. The Gibbs free-energy change is calculated for each of the steps: (a) transfer to the vapor in equilibrium with solution 1, (b) change in pressure of the vapor to the equilibrium vapor pressure of solution 2, and (c) transfer from the equilibrium vapor to the liquid phase of mole fraction X_2.

* The rise of the sap in a tall tree is not to be attributed *entirely* to osmosis.

CHEMICAL EQUILIBRIA

9

The idea of the reversibility of chemical reactions was first stated clearly in 1799 by C. Berthollet, while he was acting as scientific adviser to Napoleon in Egypt. He noted the deposits of sodium carbonate in certain salt lakes and concluded that they were produced by the high concentration of sodium chloride and dissolved calcium carbonate, the reverse of the laboratory experiment in which sodium carbonate reacts with calcium chloride to precipitate calcium carbonate. In 1863 the influence which the concentrations of ethyl alcohol and acetic acid have on the concentration of ethyl acetate formed was reported by M. Berthelot and Saint-Gilles.

In 1864 Guldberg and Waage showed experimentally that in chemical reactions a definite equilibrium is reached which can be approached from either direction. They were apparently the first to realize that there is a mathematical relation between the concentrations of reactants and products at equilibrium. In 1877 van't Hoff suggested that in the equilibrium expression for the hydrolysis of ethyl acetate the concentrations of each reactant should appear to the first power, each reactant having a coefficient of unity in the balanced chemical equation. Since Guldberg and Waage used the term "active masses" to mean concentration, the term "mass action expression" is still used, although we now realize that chemical equilibria can be expressed accurately only in terms of activities.

This chapter will be concerned with chemical equilibria. The following chapter deals with equilibria between different phases.

Derivation of the General Equilibrium Expression. For the general reaction in which a moles of A and b moles of B react to give the products g moles of G and h moles of H

$$aA + bB = gG + hH \qquad (1)$$

the expression for the differential change in Gibbs free energy (p. 115) is

$$dG = V\,dP - S\,dT + \mu_A\,dn_A + \mu_B\,dn_B + \mu_G\,dn_G + \mu_H\,dn_H \quad (2)$$

If no new material is added to the system, the stoichiometry of the reaction requires that any change in the number of moles of one of the reactants or products be accompanied by an equivalent change in all the other reactants and products. Then

$$\frac{dn_A}{a} = \frac{dn_B}{b} = \frac{-dn_G}{g} = \frac{-dn_H}{h} \quad (3)$$

Substitution of these relations into equation 2 and restriction to conditions of constant temperature and pressure yields

$$dG = \mu_A\,dn_A + \frac{b\mu_B\,dn_A}{a} - \frac{g\mu_G\,dn_A}{a} - \frac{h\mu_H\,dn_A}{a}$$

$$= (a\mu_A + b\mu_B - g\mu_G - h\mu_H)\frac{dn_A}{a} \quad (4)$$

This equation gives the infinitesimal change in Gibbs free energy when an infinitesimal quantity of the reactants is converted to products, the various reactants and products having certain concentrations or partial pressures. At equilibrium the Gibbs free energy of the reaction mixture must be a minimum (p. 103). At the extent of reaction which gives the minimum free energy, $(\partial G/\partial n_A)_{T,P} = 0$. When this is true, it is evident from equation 4 that

$$a\mu_A + b\mu_B = g\mu_G + h\mu_H \quad (5)$$

This is the *general condition for chemical equilibrium* and does not contain any assumptions of ideality. This relation is applicable whether the reactants and products are solids, liquids, or gases.

To obtain the equilibrium expression in terms of the activities a of the reactants and products the relationship between the chemical potential and the activity must be introduced. This relation (p. 156) is

$$\mu_i = \mu_i^\circ + RT \ln a_i \quad (6)$$

where μ_i°, the chemical potential for the substance at unit activity, is a function of temperature and pressure only. The equilibrium value of the chemical potential is given by equation 6 when a_i is the activity at equilibrium. Substituting equation 6 with activities at equilibrium into equation 5 and rearranging terms leads to

$$g\mu_G^\circ + h\mu_H^\circ - a\mu_A^\circ - b\mu_B^\circ = -RT \ln \frac{a_G{}^g a_H{}^h}{a_A{}^a a_B{}^b}$$

$$= -RT \ln K \qquad (7)$$

where K is the thermodynamic equilibrium constant defined in terms of the activities of the reactants and products at equilibrium;

$$K = \frac{a_G{}^g a_H{}^h}{a_A{}^a a_B{}^b} \qquad (8)$$

The derivation shows that this function of the equilibrium activities is a constant at a given temperature. This derivation of the equilibrium expression from thermodynamics demonstrates that the position of equilibrium depends only upon thermodynamic quantities and is independent of any considerations of kinetics or mechanism. The equilibrium expression permits the calculation of the maximum yield of products to be obtained from the reactants at specified concentrations.

The convention in writing equilibrium expressions is that the numerator contains the activities of those substances which are on the right-hand side (products) of the chemical equation; and that the denominator contains the activities of those substances on the left-hand side (reactants). Since the exponents in the equilibrium expression correspond to the coefficients in the balanced chemical equation, *it is absolutely necessary to know the way in which the reaction is written in order to interpret a numerical value of an equilibrium constant.*

The Equilibrium Expression for Gas Reactions. The equilibrium expression for a nonideal gas mixture may be derived as above, using a function called the fugacity f (p. 118), which is defined by

$$\mu_i = \mu_i^\circ + RT \ln f_i \qquad (9)$$

Substitution of equation 9 into equation 5 and rearranging terms as was done for activities leads to

$$K_f = \frac{f_G{}^g f_H{}^h}{f_A{}^a f_B{}^b} \qquad (10)$$

where K_f is a constant at constant temperature. Exact calculations for nonideal gas mixtures may be made using equation 10 and fugacities calculated from the deviations of the gases from ideality.*

* G. N. Lewis, M. Randall, K. S. Pitzer, and L. Brewer, *Thermodynamics,* McGraw-Hill Book Co., New York, 1961; and O. A. Hougen, K. M. Watson, and R. A. Ragatz, *Chemical Process Principles,* Part II: *Thermodynamics,* John Wiley & Sons, New York, 1959.

To obtain the equilibrium expression in terms of the partial pressures of ideal reacting gases, the relationship between the chemical potential and the partial pressure of an ideal gas must be used. This relationship was given in equation 94 in Chapter 5.

$$\mu_i = \mu_i^{\circ} + RT \ln p_i \tag{11}$$

where μ_i°, the chemical potential of the gas at 1 atm pressure, is a function of the temperature only. Repeating the steps in the above derivation, we obtain

$$K_p = \frac{p_G{}^g p_H{}^h}{p_A{}^a p_B{}^b} \tag{12}$$

The necessity of knowing the balanced chemical equation in order to interpret the numerical value of an equilibrium constant is illustrated by the following equations for the ammonia-synthesis reaction at 400°, assuming ideal gas behavior:

$$N_2 + 3H_2 = 2NH_3$$

$$K_p = \frac{p_{NH_3}{}^2}{p_{N_2} p_{H_2}{}^3} = 1.64 \times 10^{-4}$$

If the reaction is written

$$\tfrac{1}{2}N_2 + \tfrac{3}{2}H_2 = NH_3$$

$$K_p = \frac{p_{NH_3}}{p_{N_2}{}^{1/2} p_{H_2}{}^{3/2}} = (1.64 \times 10^{-4})^{1/2} = 1.28 \times 10^{-2}$$

and if the reaction is written

$$2NH_3 = N_2 + 3H_2$$

$$K_p = \frac{p_{N_2} p_{H_2}{}^3}{p_{NH_3}{}^2} = \frac{1}{1.64 \times 10^{-4}} = 0.61 \times 10^4$$

If the number of moles of gaseous products is different from the number of moles of gaseous reactants, the value of K_p will depend upon the pressure units used. Unless otherwise specified, the pressures are given in atmospheres.

K_p, K_c, and K_X. The equilibrium expression for a gas reaction may also be written in terms of the concentrations of the reactants and products at equilibrium.

$$K_c = \frac{c_G{}^g c_H{}^h}{c_A{}^a c_B{}^b} \tag{13}$$

The values of K_c for reactions of ideal gases may be calculated from the values of K_p. Substituting $c = 1/\overline{V} = p/RT$ into equation 13, where c is expressed in moles per liter (the reciprocal of the number of liters $\overline{V}$ containing 1 mole) and p is expressed in atmospheres, we have

$$K_c = \frac{(p_G/RT)^g(p_H/RT)^h}{(p_A/RT)^a(p_B/RT)^b} = \left(\frac{1}{RT}\right)^{(g+h)-(a+b)} \frac{p_G{}^g p_H{}^h}{p_A{}^a p_B{}^b} = \left(\frac{1}{RT}\right)^{\Delta n} K_p$$

$$(14)$$

where R is given in liter-atmospheres per degree per mole, and Δn is the change in the number of moles of gas during the reaction, that is, $(g + h) - (a + b)$. Then

$$K_p = K_c(RT)^{\Delta n} \tag{15}$$

In reactions where there is no change in the number of moles of gas, $\Delta n = 0$ and $K_p = K_c$.

Sometimes it is advantageous to express the equilibrium constant in terms of mole fractions rather than pressures or concentrations.

$$K_X = \frac{X_G{}^g X_H{}^h}{X_A{}^a X_B{}^b} \tag{16}$$

This equilibrium constant is related to K_p in the following way:

$$K_p = \frac{(X_G P)^g(X_H P)^h}{(X_A P)^a(X_B P)^b} = \frac{X_G{}^g X_H{}^h}{X_A{}^a X_B{}^b} P^{g+h-(a+b)}$$

$$= K_X P^{\Delta n} \tag{17}$$

where P is the total pressure of the reacting gases. The value of K_p (or K_c) for a reaction of ideal gases does not depend upon the pressure. But if $\Delta n \neq 0$, the value of the equilibrium constant K_X expressed in terms of mole fractions does *depend upon the pressure*, since $K_X = K_p P^{-\Delta n}$.

Example 1. For the reaction $N_2 + 3H_2 = 2NH_3$ at $400°$

$$K_p = \frac{p_{NH_3}{}^2}{p_{N_2} p_{H_2}{}^3} = 1.64 \times 10^{-4}$$

Calculate K_c.

$$K_c = K_p(RT)^{-\Delta n} = (1.64 \times 10^{-4})[(0.08205)(673.1)]^2$$

$$= 0.500 \; l^2 \; mole^{-2}$$

Calculate K_X at 10 atm.

$$K_X = K_p P^{-\Delta n} = (1.64 \times 10^{-4})(10)^2 = 1.64 \times 10^{-2}$$

Determination of Equilibrium Constants. If the initial concentrations of the reactants are known, it is necessary to determine the concentration of only one reactant or product at equilibrium in order to be able to calculate the concentrations or pressures of the others by means of the balanced chemical equation. Chemical methods can be used for such analyses only when the reaction may be stopped at equilibrium, as by a very sudden chilling to a temperature where the rate of further chemical change is negligible, or by destruction of a catalyst. Otherwise, the equilibrium will shift during the chemical analysis.

Measurements of physical quantities, such as density, pressure, light absorption, refractive index, and electrical conductivity, are especially useful for the determination of the concentrations of reactants at equilibrium, since it is unnecessary to "stop" the reaction. The way of relating the physical property of the equilibrium mixture to the concentrations of the reactants will be discussed for a few typical cases.

It is essential to know that equilibrium has been reached before the analysis of the mixture can be used for calculating the equilibrium constant. Some reactions are very slow, and the mixture may be far from equilibrium even though the composition does not appear to change. The following are useful criteria for the attainment of equilibrium.

1. The same equilibrium constant should be obtained when the equilibrium is approached from either side. For reaction 1 the same value should be obtained for K when A and B are mixed as when G and H are mixed.

2. The same equilibrium constant should be obtained when the concentrations of reacting materials are varied over a wide range. For reaction 1 the same value should be obtained for K when the initial ratio of A and B is $10:1$ as when the initial ratio is $1:10$.

Flow methods are sometimes used for determining equilibrium constants. For example, known mixtures of nitrogen and hydrogen may be forced through a heated chamber (containing a catalyst), and the issuing gas passed quickly through a capillary tube to an absorption bottle where the ammonia is titrated. The partial pressures of all three gases can then be calculated. The gas is passed through at various rates of flow, and the equilibrium constant is calculated when the flow rate is so slow that making it still slower does not increase the concentration of ammonia.

Dissociation of Gases. The determination of the density of a partially dissociated gas provides one of the simplest methods for measuring the extent to which the gas is dissociated. When a gas dissociates, more molecules are produced, and at constant temperature and pressure the volume increases. The density at constant pressure then decreases, and the difference between the density of the undissociated gas and that of the partially dissociated gas is directly related to the degree of dissociation.

If we start with 1 mole of gas and let α represent the fraction dissociated, then $1 - \alpha$ denotes the fraction remaining undissociated. If 1 mole of gas yields ν moles of gaseous products, where $\nu = 1\frac{1}{2}$, 2, 3, etc., the total number of moles present at equilibrium will be

$$(1 - \alpha) + \nu\alpha \quad \text{or} \quad 1 + (\nu - 1)\alpha$$

Since the density of a gas at constant pressure and temperature is *inversely* proportional to the number of moles for a given weight, the ratio of the density ρ_1 of the undissociated gas to the density ρ_2 of the partially dissociated gas is given by the expression

$$\frac{\rho_1}{\rho_2} = \frac{1 + (\nu - 1)\alpha}{1} \tag{18}$$

$$\alpha = \frac{(\rho_1/\rho_2) - 1}{\nu - 1} = \frac{\rho_1 - \rho_2}{\rho_2(\nu - 1)} \tag{19}$$

It is always advantageous to check an equation with some simple calculations. With reference to equation 19, if there is no dissociation, $\alpha = 0$ and $\rho_1 = \rho_2$; if dissociation is complete, $\alpha = 1$, $\rho_2(\nu - 1) = \rho_1 - \rho_2$ and $\rho_1 = \nu\rho_2$.

Molecular weights may be substituted in equation 19 for the densities of gases to which they are proportional at constant temperature and pressure, giving

$$\alpha = \frac{M_1 - M_2}{M_2(\nu - 1)} \tag{20}$$

where M_1 is the molecular weight of the undissociated gas, and M_2 is the average molecular weight of the gases when the gas is partially dissociated. The use of equation 20 is illustrated in Table I for the reaction

$$N_2O_4 = 2NO_2$$

for which $\nu = 2$.

The average molecular weight M_2 of the partially dissociated gas is determined experimentally, and M_1 is taken as the molecular weight of undissociated nitrogen tetroxide (N_2O_4), that is, 92.02. The degree of dissociation of N_2O_4 may be conveniently determined by an independent method, since the NO_2 formed by dissociation is brown and the undissociated N_2O_4 is colorless. It is noticed that the color be-

198 PHYSICAL CHEMISTRY

Table I. Average Molecular Weight M_2 of Partially Dissociated Nitrogen Tetroxide (N_2O_4) at 1 Atm Pressure

Temperature, °C	M_2	$\alpha = \dfrac{92.02 - M_2}{M_2}$
15	82.00	0.122
25	77.64	0.185
35	72.45	0.270
45	66.80	0.378
55	61.24	0.502
65	56.51	0.628
75	52.85	0.741

comes darker brown as the temperature is raised at constant pressure and the gas density becomes less. The intensity of the brown color may be measured quantitatively with a spectrophotometer.

Example 2. If 1.588 grams of nitrogen tetroxide gives a total pressure of 760 mm when partially dissociated in a 500-ml glass vessel at 25°, what is the degree of dissociation α?

$$M_2 = \frac{RT}{P}\frac{g}{V} = \frac{(0.08205 \text{ l-atm deg}^{-1}\text{mole}^{-1})(298.1 \text{ deg})(1.588 \text{ g})}{(1 \text{ atm})(0.500 \text{ l})}$$

$$= 77.68 \text{ g mole}^{-1}$$

$$\alpha = \frac{92.02 - 77.68}{77.68} = 0.1846$$

Equilibrium Constants for Gaseous Reactions. The dissociation of nitrogen tetroxide is represented by the equation

$$N_2O_4 = 2NO_2$$

and

$$K_p = \frac{p_{NO_2}^2}{p_{N_2O_4}} \tag{21}$$

If α represents the degree of dissociation, $(1 - \alpha)$ is proportional to the number of moles of undissociated N_2O_4; 2α is proportional to the number of moles of NO_2; and $(1 - \alpha) + 2\alpha$ or $1 + \alpha$ is proportional to the total number of moles.

If the total pressure is P, the partial pressures are:

$$p_{N_2O_4} = \frac{1 - \alpha}{1 + \alpha}P \quad \text{and} \quad p_{NO_2} = \frac{2\alpha}{1 + \alpha}P$$

Then,

$$K_p = \frac{\left(\dfrac{2\alpha}{1+\alpha}P\right)^2}{\dfrac{1-\alpha}{1+\alpha}P} = \frac{4\alpha^2 P}{1-\alpha^2} \tag{22}$$

In this reaction there is an increase in volume at constant pressure; each mole of gas that dissociates produces 2 moles of gas. According to the principle of Le Châtelier (p. 217), it is possible to predict that an increase of pressure will cause the reaction to shift toward N_2O_4 since the equilibrium shifts in the direction that tends to minimize the effect of the applied change. Equation 22 makes it possible to calculate the equilibrium constant from the degree of dissociation of N_2O_4 at any one pressure and then to calculate the degree of dissociation at the same temperature at any other pressure.

Example 3. At 25.0° and 1 atm, nitrogen tetroxide has been found by gas-density measurements to be 18.46 per cent dissociated. Find K_p.

$$K_p = \frac{4\alpha^2 P}{1-\alpha^2} = \frac{(4)(0.1846)^2(1)}{1-(0.1846)^2} = 0.141$$

Calculate the degree of dissociation of nitrogen tetroxide at 0.5 atm and 25°.

$$K_p = 0.141 = \frac{4\alpha^2(0.5)}{1-\alpha^2}$$

and

$$0.141(1 - \alpha^2) = 2\alpha^2$$

$$\alpha = 0.257$$

A gaseous equilibrium only slightly more complicated than the dissociation of nitrogen tetroxide is the dissociation of phosphorus pentachloride. The following reaction takes place:

$$PCl_5 = PCl_3 + Cl_2$$

When 1 mole of PCl_5 dissociates, there will be at equilibrium $1 - \alpha$ mole of PCl_5, α mole of PCl_3, and α mole of Cl_2, where α is the degree of dissociation. The total number of moles is

$$[1 - \alpha] + \alpha + \alpha = 1 + \alpha$$

and the mole fractions are

$$X_{PCl_5} = \frac{1-\alpha}{1+\alpha} \qquad X_{PCl_3} = \frac{\alpha}{1+\alpha} \qquad X_{Cl_2} = \frac{\alpha}{1+\alpha}$$

If P is the total pressure due to PCl_5, PCl_3, and Cl_2, the partial pressures are

$$p_{PCl_5} = \frac{1-\alpha}{1+\alpha}P \qquad p_{PCl_3} = \frac{\alpha}{1+\alpha}P \qquad p_{Cl_2} = \frac{\alpha}{1+\alpha}P$$

and

$$K_p = \frac{p_{PCl_3}p_{Cl_2}}{p_{PCl_5}} = \frac{\left(\dfrac{\alpha}{1+\alpha}P\right)\left(\dfrac{\alpha}{1+\alpha}P\right)}{[(1-\alpha)/(1+\alpha)]P} = \frac{\alpha^2 P}{1-\alpha^2} \tag{23}$$

It should be noted that this equation differs from equation 22 by the omission of the number 4. If these gases are contained at equilibrium in a vessel of V liters which originally contained 1 mole of PCl_5, the concentrations in moles per liter are

$$c_{PCl_5} = \frac{1-\alpha}{V} \qquad c_{PCl_3} = \frac{\alpha}{V} \qquad c_{Cl_2} = \frac{\alpha}{V}$$

Thus K_c is given by

$$K_c = \frac{c_{PCl_3}c_{Cl_2}}{c_{PCl_5}} = \frac{(\alpha/V)(\alpha/V)}{(1-\alpha)/V} = \frac{\alpha^2}{(1-\alpha)V} \tag{24}$$

Exercise I. Show that equations 23 and 24 are in agreement with equation 15.

Several examples will be given to illustrate the calculation and use of equilibrium constants.

Example 4. At 250°, 1 liter of partially dissociated phosphorus pentachloride gas, at 1 atm, weighs 2.690 grams. Calculate the degree of dissociation α from the measured density of the gas, and calculate the equilibrium constant K_p.

$$M_1 = 208.3$$

$$M_2 = \frac{gRT}{PV} = \frac{(2.690 \text{ g})(0.08205 \text{ l-atm deg}^{-1}\text{ mole}^{-1})(523.1 \text{ deg})}{(1 \text{ atm})(1 \text{ l})} = 115.7 \text{ g mole}^{-1}$$

$$\alpha = \frac{M_1 - M_2}{M_2} = \frac{208.3 - 115.7}{115.7} = 0.800$$

According to equation 23,

$$K_p = \frac{0.800^2 \times 1}{1 - 0.800^2} = 1.78$$

This reaction is an interesting one to discuss in more detail. Qualitatively, it can be seen that increasing the total pressure will decrease the degree of dissociation, because the undissociated PCl_5 occupies the smaller volume. If chlorine is added, p_{Cl_2} increases, and, since K_p remains constant, p_{PCl_3} must diminish and p_{PCl_5} must increase. The degree of dissociation is decreased also by the addition of PCl_3. In general the dissociation of any substance is repressed by the addition of its dissociation products. The addition of an inert gas at constant volume has no effect on the dissociation because the partial pressures of the gases involved in the reaction are not affected by the presence of another gas provided that the gases behave ideally.

Example 5. What will be the degree of dissociation of phosphorus pentachloride at $250°$ when 0.1 mole is placed in a 3-liter vessel containing chlorine at 0.5 atm pressure? Let x = the number of moles of PCl_3 formed or additional moles of Cl_2 formed by the dissociation of the PCl_5.

$$K_p = 1.78 = \frac{p_{PCl_3}p_{Cl_2}}{p_{PCl_5}} = \frac{\dfrac{xRT}{V}\left(0.5 + \dfrac{xRT}{V}\right)}{(0.1 - x)RT/V} = \frac{x\left[0.5 + \dfrac{(0.08205)(523.1)x}{3}\right]}{0.1 - x}$$

$$x = 0.0574 \text{ mole}$$

$\alpha = 0.0574/0.1 = 0.574$.

Example 6. How many moles of phosphorus pentachloride must be added to a liter vessel at $250°$ in order to obtain a concentration of 0.1 mole of chlorine per liter?

$$x = \text{number of moles of } PCl_5 \text{ added to vessel}$$

$$K_p = 1.78 = \frac{p_{PCl_3}p_{Cl_2}}{p_{PCl_5}} = \frac{\left(0.1\dfrac{RT}{V}\right)\left(0.1\dfrac{RT}{V}\right)}{(x - 0.1)(RT/V)} = \frac{0.1^2}{(x - 0.1)}\left(\frac{RT}{V}\right)$$

$$= \frac{(0.01)(0.08205)(523.1)}{(x - 0.1)}$$

$$x = 0.341 \text{ mole}$$

Example 7. Under what total pressure must an equimolar mixture of chlorine and phosphorus trichloride be placed in order to obtain 1 atm of phosphorus pentachloride at $250°$? If we let $x = p_{PCl_3} = p_{Cl_2}$ at equilibrium,

$$K_p = 1.78 = \frac{p_{PCl_3}p_{Cl_2}}{p_{PCl_5}} = \frac{x^2}{1}$$

$$x = 1.33 \text{ atm}$$

The total pressure at equilibrium is the sum of the partial pressures of the gases.

$$p_{PCl_3} + p_{Cl_2} + p_{PCl_5} = 1.33 + 1.33 + 1 = 3.66 \text{ atm}$$

Example 8. Under what pressure must an equimolar mixture of chlorine and phosphorus trichloride be placed at $250°$ in order to obtain an 80 per cent conversion of the phosphorus trichloride into phosphorus pentachloride?

$$K_p = 1.78 = \frac{\alpha^2 P}{1 - \alpha^2} = \frac{(0.20)^2 P}{1 - (0.20)^2}$$

$$P = 42.7 \text{ atm}$$

Another classical example of an equilibrium in gases is the dissociation of hydrogen iodide gas,

$$2HI = H_2 + I_2$$

Very careful measurements were made * in which quartz vessels of known volume were filled with hydrogen iodide at a measured pressure and heated in an electric thermostat at 425.1° for several hours until equilibrium was established. The vessels were then chilled quickly and analyzed for iodine by titration with sodium thiosulfate. The concentration of hydrogen at equilibrium is equal to that of the iodine. The concentration of hydrogen iodide at equilibrium was obtained by subtracting twice the iodine concentration from the initial hydrogen iodide concentration. The equilibrium concentrations in moles per liter are shown in Table II. The first three sets of data were

Table II. Equilibrium between Hydrogen, Iodine, and Hydrogen Iodide at 698.2°K

$c_{I_2} \times 10^3$, mole/l	$c_{H_2} \times 10^3$, mole/l	$c_{HI} \times 10^3$, mole/l	$K_c = \dfrac{c_{H_2}c_{I_2}}{c_{HI}^2}$
0.4789	0.4789	3.531	1.840×10^{-2}
1.1409	1.1409	8.410	1.840
0.4953	0.4953	3.655	1.832
1.7069	2.9070	16.482	1.827
1.2500	3.5600	15.588	1.831
0.7378	4.5647	13.544	1.835
2.3360	2.2523	16.850	1.853
3.1292	1.8313	17.671	1.835

obtained by starting with hydrogen iodide. The last five were obtained by starting from the other side of the equilibrium, weighing the initial quantity of iodine, measuring the pressure of hydrogen, and titrating the iodine after equilibrium was reached. The close check between the two sets of data shows that equilibrium was reached in every case.

When many routine calculations are needed, it is advantageous to express the concentrations with letters and obtain a general formula. Thus, if a moles of hydrogen is mixed with b moles of iodine, and $2x$ moles of hydrogen iodide is formed, when equilibrium is established, $a - x$ is the number of moles of hydrogen, and $b - x$ is the number of moles of iodine present.

* A. H. Taylor, Jr., and R. H. Crist, *J. Am. Chem. Soc.*, *63*, 1381 (1941).

Exercise II. Show that for the hydrogen iodide dissociation equilibrium

$$K_c = \frac{(a - x)(b - x)}{4x^2} \quad \text{and} \quad x = \frac{a + b - \sqrt{(a - b)^2 + 16abK_c}}{2(1 - 4K_c)}$$

It is of interest to note that a change in pressure does not alter the equilibrium in this gaseous reaction. In terms of the partial pressures of the components of the gaseous system, instead of the concentrations, we have

$$\frac{p_{H_2}p_{I_2}}{p_{HI}^2} = K_p$$

Now, if the total pressure on the system is increased to n times its original value, all the partial pressures are increased in the same proportion, and

$$\frac{(np_{H_2})(np_{I_2})}{n^2 p_{HI}^2} = K_p$$

which is equivalent to the original expression, since n cancels out. The equilibrium is thus seen to be independent of the pressure. This independence applies only to those reactions for which the number of moles of gaseous reactants is equal to the number of moles of gaseous products. In this case $K_p = K_c = K_X$.

Illustrations of the calculations of more complicated gaseous equilibria will now be given.

Example 9. Ammonia is formed from a mixture of 3 parts of hydrogen and 1 part of nitrogen (p. 194). At lower temperatures the yield is higher, but the time required for equilibrium to be reached would be too great to be practical, except for the addition of a catalyst. The pressure is kept as high and the temperature as low as practical.

Under equilibrium conditions at 400° and 10 atm pressure, 3.85 per cent of ammonia by volume is obtained.

Calculate K_p for the reaction $N_2 + 3H_2 = 2NH_3$. The ratio of 3 volumes of hydrogen to 1 volume of nitrogen is maintained, regardless of the amount of ammonia formed. Of the 96.15 per cent by volume which is not ammonia, one-fourth is nitrogen and three-fourths is hydrogen.

$$K_p = \frac{p_{NH_3}^2}{p_{N_2}p_{H_2}^3} = \frac{(0.0385 \times 10)^2}{[(\frac{1}{4})(0.9615)(10)][(\frac{3}{4})(0.9615)(10)]^3} = 1.64 \times 10^{-4}$$

Calculate the total pressure P necessary to give a mixture containing 5 per cent by volume ammonia at this temperature.

$$p_{NH_3} = 0.05P \quad\quad p_{N_2} = \tfrac{1}{4} \times 0.95P \quad\quad p_{H_2} = \tfrac{3}{4} \times 0.95P$$

$$K_p = 1.64 \times 10^{-4} = \frac{(0.05P)^2}{(0.2375P)(0.7125P)^3} = \frac{0.0025P^2}{0.0859P^4}$$

$$P^2 = \frac{0.0025}{0.000164 \times 0.0859} = 177.5 \quad\quad P = 13.3 \, \text{atm}$$

Calculate the percentage by volume of ammonia when the 3 to 1 mixture is subjected to a pressure of 50 atm. at 400°.

$$p_{H_2} = 3p_{N_2} \qquad p_{N_2} + p_{H_2} + p_{NH_3} = 50 \text{ atm} \qquad p_{NH_3} = 50 - 4p_{N_2}$$

$$K_p = 1.64 \times 10^{-4} = \frac{p_{NH_3}^2}{p_{N_2}p_{H_2}^3} = \frac{(50 - 4p_{N_2})^2}{(p_{N_2})(3p_{N_2})^3} = \frac{(50 - 4p_{N_2})^2}{27p_{N_2}^4}$$

$$\frac{50 - 4p_{N_2}}{p_{N_2}^2} = \sqrt{0.000164 \times 27} = 6.65 \times 10^{-2}$$

$$p_{N_2} = 10.62 \qquad p_{H_2} = (3)(10.62) = 31.86$$

$$p_{NH_3} = 50 - (10.62 + 31.86) = 7.52$$

$$\text{Per cent ammonia} = (7.52/50.0)(100) = 15.0$$

Reaction Equilibrium in Solution. As shown earlier (p. 156), the chemical potential of a component of a solution is given by

$$\mu_i = \mu_i^* + RT \ln \gamma_i X_i \tag{25}$$

where γ_i is the activity coefficient. If expressions of this type are substituted into equation 5, it is readily shown that the equilibrium constant for reaction 1 is given by

$$K = \frac{\gamma_G{}^g \gamma_H{}^h}{\gamma_A{}^a \gamma_B{}^b} \frac{X_G{}^g X_H{}^h}{X_A{}^a X_B{}^b} \tag{26}$$

Activity coefficients determined from the thermodynamic properties of solutions (p. 157) may be used. In some cases the activity coefficients remain quite constant over a range of reactant concentrations so that it is possible to transfer the activity-coefficient term to the other side of the equation, combine it with the equilibrium constant, and speak of the *apparent* equilibrium constant K' for the reaction

$$K' = \frac{X_G{}^g X_H{}^h}{X_A{}^a X_B{}^b} \tag{27}$$

The equilibrium constants for reactions in solution may be markedly affected by the solvent, even if the solvent is not a direct participant in the reaction, because the solvent may affect the activity coefficients of the reactants and products quite differently. A number of equilibria in solution will be discussed in Chapter 15 on ionic equilibrium.

Example 10. One mole of acetic acid is mixed with 1 mole of ethanol at 25°, and after equilibrium is reached a titration with standard alkali solution shows that 0.667 mole of acetic acid has reacted.

$$CH_3CO_2H + C_2H_5OH = CH_3CO_2C_2H_5 + H_2O$$

Calculate the apparent equilibrium constant in terms of mole fraction.

$$K' = \frac{X_{CH_3CO_2C_2H_5}X_{H_2O}}{X_{CH_3CO_2H}X_{C_2H_5OH}} = \frac{(0.667/2)(0.667/2)}{[(1.000 - 0.667)/2][(1.000 - 0.667)/2]}$$
$$= 4.00$$

The total number of moles appears in the denominator of each term and therefore cancels. When 0.500 mole of ethanol is added to 1.000 mole of acetic acid at 25°, how much ester x will be formed at equilibrium?

$$K' = 4.00 = \frac{x^2}{(1.000 - x)(0.500 - x)} \qquad x = 0.422 \quad \text{or} \quad 1.577 \text{ mole}$$

Two solutions of a quadratic equation are possible, but in such problems one solution may be shown to be incompatible with the physical-chemical facts. In this example it is impossible to produce more moles of ester than the original number of moles of ethanol, and so the value 1.577 is impossible. Actually 0.422 mole of ester and 0.422 mole of water are formed, and $(0.500 - 0.422)$ or 0.078 mole of ethanol and $(1.000 - 0.422)$ or 0.578 mole of acetic acid remain unreacted. An experimental value of 0.414 mole of ester was obtained in the laboratory. Additional determinations are as follows:

Moles ethanol added to 1 mole of acetic acid	0.080	0.280	2.240	8.000
Moles of ethyl acetate calculated from K'	0.078	0.232	0.864	0.945
Moles of ethyl acetate found experimentally	0.078	0.226	0.876	0.966

In example 10 the number of moles of reactants and of products is the same, and the calculation is simplified. In reactions where Δn is not 0 the total number of moles will not cancel out.

In some cases it is convenient to write the equilibrium expression in terms of molal or molar concentrations, but even for *ideal* solutions such equilibrium constants will be independent of concentration only in dilute solutions. The reason for this is that molar or molal concentrations are proportional to mole fractions only in dilute solutions. This may be seen from the following relations for a solution containing n_2 moles of solute and n_1 moles of solvent of molecular weight M_1:

$$X_2 = \frac{n_2}{n_1 + n_2}$$

$$m_2 = \frac{1000 n_2}{M_1 n_1}$$

$$m_2 = \frac{1000 X_2}{M_1}\left(1 + \frac{n_2}{n_1}\right)$$

Only when n_2/n_1 is small is the molal concentration m_2 proportional to X_2.

Equilibria Involving Solids. If pure solids (or pure immiscible liquids) are involved in a reaction with one or more gases, the equilibrium constant may be written in terms of the partial pressures in the gas phase. For example, for the reaction

$$CaCO_3(s) = CaO(s) + CO_2(g) \qquad (28)$$

the equilibrium constant may be expressed using equation 8:

$$K = \frac{a_{CaO}a_{CO_2}}{a_{CaCO_3}} \qquad (29)$$

If carbon dioxide behaves nearly as an ideal gas, its activity is measured by its pressure. If calcium oxide and calcium carbonate are pure solids, their activities are constant and independent of the extent of reaction. Thus it is convenient to incorporate the activities of the solids into the equilibrium constant to obtain

$$K_p = \frac{Ka_{CaCO_3}}{a_{CaO}} = p_{CO_2} \qquad (30)$$

The equilibrium constant of such a reaction is independent of the amount of pure solid (or liquid) phase, provided only that it is present at equilibrium. Table III gives the equilibrium pressures of CO_2 above $CaCO_3 + CaO$ at various temperatures.

Table III. Dissociation Pressures of Calcium Carbonate

Temperature, °C	Pressure, atm	Temperature, °C	Pressure, atm
500	0.000096	897	1.000
600	0.00242	1000	3.871
700	0.0292	1100	11.50
800	0.220	1200	28.68

If the partial pressure of CO_2 over $CaCO_3$ is maintained lower than K_p at a constant temperature, all the $CaCO_3$ is converted into CaO and CO_2. On the other hand, if the partial pressure of CO_2 is maintained higher than K_p, all the CaO is converted into $CaCO_3$. In this respect equilibria involving pure solids (or liquids) are different from other chemical equilibria which would simply go to a new equilibrium position, and not to completion, if the partial pressure of one of the reactants or products is maintained constant.

If solid or liquid solutions are formed (for example, if CaO and $CaCO_3$ were somewhat mutually soluble), the position of the equilibrium would depend upon the concentration or, more specifically, the activities of the components in the equilibrium solution.

Two or more gaseous species may be formed. For example, solid ammonium hydrosulfide is in equilibrium with hydrogen sulfide and ammonia in the gas phase:

$$NH_4HS(s) = NH_3(g) + H_2S(g)$$

If only NH_4HS is initially present, the partial pressures of NH_3 and H_2S are equal and are each half the total pressure P, the partial pressure of gaseous NH_4HS being negligibly small. Thus

$$K_p = p_{NH_3}p_{H_2S} = \left(\frac{P}{2}\right)^2 = \frac{P^2}{4} \tag{31}$$

At 25.1°, $P = 0.66$ atm and $K_p = (0.66)^2/4 = 0.109$. The equilibrium constant may also be determined by mixing various amounts of NH_3 and H_2S and determining the equilibrium partial pressures of both gases. Some data of this type are shown in Table IV.

Table IV. Equilibrium Constants for the Dissociation of Ammonium Hydrosulfide at 25.1°

Pressure of Ammonia, atm	Pressure of Hydrogen Sulfide, atm	$p_{NH_3}p_{H_2S} = K_p$
0.330	0.330	0.109
0.274	0.387	0.106
0.182	0.603	0.110
0.549	0.192	0.105
0.596	0.188	0.112

Exercise III. The dissociation of ammonium carbamate * takes place according to the reaction

$$(NH_2)CO(ONH_4)(s) = 2NH_3(g) + CO_2(g)$$

When an excess of ammonium carbamate is placed in a previously evacuated vessel, the partial pressure generated by NH_3 is twice the partial pressure of the CO_2,

* T. R. Briggs and V. Migrdichian, *J. Phys. Chem.*, *28*, 1121 (1924).

and the partial pressure of $(NH_2)CO(ONH_4)$ is negligible in comparison. Show that

$$K_p = (p_{NH_3})^2 p_{CO_2} = \frac{4}{27}P^3$$

where P is the total pressure.

Relation between Gibbs Free-Energy Changes and Equilibrium Constants.

The expression for the equilibrium constant has been derived earlier in terms of the chemical potential. It is now convenient to discuss chemical equilibrium in terms of the Gibbs free energy, since tabulated thermodynamic data are generally given in these terms. The Gibbs free-energy change for the reaction $aA + bB = gG + hH$ is given by

$$\Delta G = g\bar{G}_G + h\bar{G}_H - a\bar{G}_A - b\bar{G}_B \tag{32}$$

The absolute values of the Gibbs free energies are not known, but the differences in Gibbs free energy measured with respect to some standard state can be determined. Therefore it is convenient to subtract the Gibbs free-energy change $\Delta G°$ for a hypothetical reaction in which reactants in their standard states are converted to products in their standard states.

$$\Delta G° = g\bar{G}°_G + h\bar{G}°_H - a\bar{G}°_A - b\bar{G}°_B \tag{33}$$

For gases the standard Gibbs free energies are the Gibbs free energies per mole at 1 atm pressure. For liquids and solids the standard Gibbs free energies are for 1 mole of pure liquid or 1 mole of a particular crystalline form of the pure solid at 1 atm pressure. Subtracting equation 33 from equation 32,

$$\Delta G - \Delta G° = g(\bar{G}_G - \bar{G}°_G) + h(\bar{G}_H - \bar{G}°_H)$$
$$- a(\bar{G}_A - \bar{G}°_A) - b(\bar{G}_B - \bar{G}°_B) \tag{34}$$

The difference in Gibbs free energy for two states of an ideal gas at the same temperature and at pressures p_A and 1 atm is given by equation 71 in Chapter 5. This relation may be written

$$\bar{G}_A - \bar{G}°_A = RT \ln \frac{p_A}{1} = RT \ln p_A \tag{35}$$

The pressure must be in units of atmospheres if the standard state is at 1 atm pressure. Substituting relations of this type into equation 34,

$$\Delta G - \Delta G° = RT \ln \frac{p_G{}^g p_H{}^h}{p_A{}^a p_B{}^b} \tag{36}$$

The pressures in this equation may be any arbitrary pressures. In the special case that the system is at equilibrium, $\Delta G = 0$ and the pressures p_A, p_B, etc., become equilibrium pressures. Then equation 36 becomes

$$\Delta G^\circ = -RT \ln \frac{p_G{}^g p_H{}^h}{p_A{}^a p_B{}^b} \tag{37}$$

$$\Delta G^\circ = -RT \ln K_p \tag{38}$$

Equation 37 is a very important equation because it connects the standard Gibbs free-energy change for a reaction with the value of the equilibrium constant. The standard Gibbs free energies can be calculated from calorimetric and thermodynamic data alone, and thus it is possible to obtain equilibrium constants without direct experimental determination of the chemical equilibrium.

When reactants in their standard states are converted to the products in their standard states, there is a change in Gibbs free energy equal to $-RT$ times the natural logarithm of the equilibrium constant. This relation has been derived for ideal gases, but there are corresponding expressions for K_a, K_f, etc.

If ΔG° has a negative value, the equilibrium constant has a value greater than 1 and the reactants in their standard states will react spontaneously to give the products in their standard states.

Example 11.　What is ΔG° at $25°$ for the reaction

$$N_2O_4(g) = 2NO_2(g)$$

$$K_p = p_{NO_2}{}^2/p_{N_2O_4} = 0.141$$

$$\Delta G^\circ = -RT \ln K_p = -(1.987)(298.1)(2.303) \log 0.141 = +1161 \text{ cal}$$

Example 12.　What is ΔG° at $25°$ for the reaction

$$2NO_2(g) = N_2O_4(g)$$

$$K_p = p_{N_2O_4}/p_{NO_2}{}^2 = 1/0.141 = 7.09$$

$$\Delta G^\circ = -RT \ln K_p = -(1.987)(298.1)(2.303) \log 7.09 = -1161 \text{ cal}$$

It is clear that if a reaction is reversed the equilibrium constant becomes the reciprocal of that for the first reaction, and the Gibbs free-energy change has the same magnitude but the opposite sign.

If $\Delta G^\circ = 0$, the reactants in their standard states are in equilibrium with the products in their standard states and $K_p = 1$. Even when ΔG° is positive there is some reaction, but K_p is less than unity. Thus it is not necessary for ΔG° to be negative in order for a reaction to be of practical use in manufacturing a substance. For example, a product may be removed and recovered at low pressures, or the reactants may be introduced into the reaction chamber at high pressures. However, as $\Delta G°$ becomes more positive the yield at equilibrium becomes quite small.

If a reaction is carried out so that the reactants are provided at some specified concentration or pressure other than that of the standard state and the products are withdrawn at some specified concentration or pressure other than that of the standard state, the Gibbs free-energy change will be different from $\Delta G°$ and may be calculated as described later on p. 214.

The value of $\Delta G°$ calculated from $-RT \ln K$ for a reaction in solution is the Gibbs free-energy change for the transformation of the reactants at unit activity to products at unit activity. Thus the numerical value of $\Delta G°$ depends upon the activity scale which is being used.

Example 13. The equilibrium constant for the association of benzoic acid to a dimer in dilute benzene solutions at 43.9° is 2.7×10^2 in terms of molar concentrations. Calculate $\Delta G°$, and state its meaning.

$$2C_6H_5COOH = (C_6H_5COOH)_2$$

$$K_c = \frac{[(C_6H_5COOH)_2]}{(C_6H_5COOH)^2} = 2.7 \times 10^2$$

$$\Delta G° = -RT \ln K_c = -(1.987)(317.0)(2.303) \log 2.7 \times 10^2$$

$$= -3530 \text{ cal}$$

Hence, there is a Gibbs free-energy decrease of 3530 cal when 2 moles of benzoic acid monomer, C_6H_5COOH, at unit activity on the molar scale, is converted to 1 mole of benzoic acid dimer at unit activity in benzene at 43.9°.

Calculation of $\Delta G°$ from Thermochemical Data. The standard Gibbs free-energy changes for many reactions have been calculated from experimental measurements of equilibrium constants. The Gibbs free-energy changes for many other reactions have been calculated from enthalpies of formation and absolute entropies, using the equation

$$\Delta G° = \Delta H° - T \Delta S° \tag{39}$$

This latter method is very important for reactions which cannot be measured directly, particularly those which proceed so slowly that direct measurements of the equilibrium cannot be made. For example, methane appears to be a stable substance at room temperature, and carbon and hydrogen appear to be unreactive toward each other. It is not possible then to measure the equilibrium among the three at room temperature, but the equilibrium constant may be calculated from the absolute entropies and the heat of reaction.

Example 14. Calculate the equilibrium constant for the following reaction at 25°:

$$C(\text{graphite}) + 2H_2(g) = CH_4(g)$$

From Table II in Chapter 4, $\Delta H^\circ = -17,889$ cal. From Table II of Chapter 5, the entropy change for this reaction is

$$\Delta S^\circ = 44.50 - 2(31.211) - 1.3609$$

$$= -19.28 \text{ cal deg}^{-1}$$

$$\Delta G^\circ = \Delta H^\circ - T \Delta S^\circ = -17.889 - (298.1)(-19.28)$$

$$= -12,140 \text{ cal}$$

The Gibbs free-energy change obtained in this way is identical with that obtained directly from Table V.

The equilibrium constant may be calculated from

$$-12,140 = -(1.987)(298.1)(2.303) \log K_p$$

$$\log K_p = 8.91$$

$$K_p = 8.1 \times 10^8$$

Although the equilibrium constant for this reaction is very large at room temperature, it is not possible to carry the reaction out in a reasonable time since no catalyst is known. At high temperatures where a catalyst would probably not be required the equilibrium constant for the reaction is unfavorable for the synthesis of methane.

The limitation in many calculations of this type is the accuracy with which the enthalpy of reaction is known. The enthalpy values are usually obtained from differences between large quantities, and a small error in them makes a large error in the value of ΔH° and hence of ΔG°. In the calculation of the equilibrium constant for the formation of methanol from its elements, for example, an error of 0.1 per cent in one of the values for the heat of combustion makes an error of 35 per cent in the equilibrium constant.

From equation 39 we can see what it takes to make a chemical reaction spontaneous. If ΔH° is negative and ΔS° is positive, the reaction will certainly be spontaneous. However, the usual situation is for the two terms in equation 39 to have opposite signs. For example, in a reaction in which bonds are broken ΔH° is positive, and, since the dissociated products have a greater degree of randomness, ΔS° is positive. At low temperatures ΔG° will be positive for such reactions and $K_p < 1$ because the ΔH° term predominates. However, as the temperature is raised, the $T \Delta S^\circ$ term increases and at a sufficiently high temperature ΔG° will become negative and $K_p > 1$. Conversely, for the reverse reaction (that is, one in which bonds are formed), for which

$\Delta H°$ is negative and $\Delta S°$ is negative, $K_p > 1$ at sufficiently low temperatures and $K_p < 1$ at sufficiently high temperatures.

In addition to being calculated from calorimetric data, equilibrium constants may be calculated from spectroscopic data, provided that the reactants and products are not too complicated. Such calculations are discussed in Chapter 19 on statistical mechanics. This determination of chemical equilibria from nonchemical data was a goal which was eagerly sought by many early investigators.

Gibbs Free Energy of Formation. By adding and subtracting the reactions for which $\Delta G°$ is known, the Gibbs free-energy changes may be obtained for many other reactions, but the most convenient way to tabulate the rather extensive data on Gibbs free-energy changes is by means of the *Gibbs free energy of formation* $\Delta \bar{G}°_f$, which is defined similarly to the enthalpy of formation (p. 65). The Gibbs free energy of formation of a chemical compound is the Gibbs free-energy change for the reaction in which the substance in its standard state at 25° is formed from its elements in their standard states at 25°.

Table V gives some Gibbs free energies of formation taken from the larger table of the National Bureau of Standards. The Gibbs free-energy change for a reaction may be calculated from the Gibbs free energies of formation by use of an equation of the form

$$\Delta G° = g\,\Delta \bar{G}°_{f,G} + h\,\Delta \bar{G}°_{f,H} - a\,\Delta \bar{G}°_{f,A} - b\,\Delta \bar{G}°_{f,B} \qquad (40)$$

The equilibrium constant for the reaction may then be calculated by use of an equation of the form of equation 38.

The way in which Gibbs free-energy changes for reactions at other temperatures are calculated from the values at 25° is discussed in a later section.

The use of Table V in calculating Gibbs free-energy changes and equilibrium constants is illustrated by example 15.

Example 15. Calculate $\Delta G°$ and K_p at 25° for

$$CO(g) + H_2O(g) = CO_2(g) + H_2(g)$$

$$\Delta G° = (-94.2598 + 0) - (-32.8079 - 54.6357)$$

$$= -6.8162\ \text{kcal}$$

$$\Delta G° = -(1.987)(298.1)(2.303)\log K_p$$

$$K_p = \frac{p_{H_2}p_{CO_2}}{p_{CO}p_{H_2O}} = 1.02 \times 10^5$$

In the absence of data on Gibbs free energies of formation or of sufficient information to permit theoretical calculations of thermo-

Table V.[1]   Gibbs Free Energy of Formation at $25°$

$(\Delta \bar{G}°_f$ in kcal mole$^{-1})$

Elements and Inorganic Compounds

$O_3(g)$	39.06	$C(s, \text{diamond})$	0.6850
$H_2O(g)$	-54.6357	$CO(g)$	-32.8079
$H_2O(l)$	-56.6902	$CO_2(g)$	-94.2598
$HCl(g)$	-22.769	$PbO_2(s)$	-52.34
$Br_2(g)$	0.751	$PbSO_4(s)$	-193.89
$HBr(g)$	-12.72	$Hg(g)$	7.59
$HI(g)$	0.31	$AgCl(s)$	-26.224
$S(\text{monoclinic})$	0.023	$Fe_2O_3(s)$	-177.1
$SO_2(g)$	-71.79	$Fe_3O_4(s)$	-242.4
$SO_3(g)$	-88.52	$Al_2O_3(s)$	-376.77
$H_2S(g)$	-7.892	$UF_6(g)$	-485
$NO(g)$	20.719	$UF_6(s)$	-486
$NO_2(g)$	12.390	$CaO(s)$	-144.4
$NH_3(g)$	-3.976	$CaCO_3(s)$	-269.78
$HNO_3(l)$	-19.100	$NaF(s)$	-129.3
$P(g)$	66.77	$NaCl(s)$	-91.785
$PCl_3(g)$	-68.42	$KF(s)$	-127.42
$PCl_5(g)$	-77.59	$KCl(s)$	-97.592

Organic Compounds

Methane, $CH_4(g)$	-12.140	Propylene, $C_3H_6(g)$	14.990
Ethane, $C_2H_6(g)$	-7.860	1-Butene, $C_4H_8(g)$	17.217
Propane, $C_3H_8(g)$	-5.614	Acetylene, $C_2H_2(g)$	50.000
n-Butane, $C_4H_{10}(g)$	-3.754	Formaldehyde, $CH_2O(g)$	-26.3
Isobutane, $C_4H_{10}(g)$	-4.296	Acetaldehyde, $CH_3CHO(g)$	-31.96
n-Pentane, $C_5H_{12}(g)$	-1.96	Methanol, $CH_3OH(l)$	-39.73
n-Hexane, $C_6H_{14}(g)$	0.05	Ethanol, $CH_3CH_2OH(l)$	-41.77
n-Heptane, $C_7H_{16}(g)$	2.09	Formic acid, $HCO_2H(l)$	-82.7
n-Octane, $C_8H_{18}(g)$	4.14	Acetic acid, $CH_3CO_2H(l)$	-93.8
Benzene, $C_6H_6(g)$	30.989	Oxalic acid, $(CO_2H)_2(s)$	-166.8
Benzene, $C_6H_6(l)$	29.756	Carbon tetrachloride, $CCl_4(l)$	-16.4
Ethylene, $C_2H_4(g)$	16.282	Glycine, $H_2NCH_2CO_2H(s)$	-88.61

Ions in Water

H^+	0.000	$SO_4{}^{2-}$	-177.34	Cu^{2+}	15.53
OH^-	-37.595	HS^-	3.01	Ag^+	18.430
F^-	-66.08	$NO_3{}^-$	-26.41	Mg^{2+}	-108.99
Cl^-	-31.350	$NH_4{}^+$	-19.00	Ca^{2+}	-132.18
$ClO_4{}^-$	-2.57	$PO_4{}^{3-}$	-245.1	Li^+	-70.22
Br^-	-24.574	$CO_3{}^{2-}$	-126.22	Na^+	-62.589
I^-	-12.35	Zn^{2+}	-35.184	K^+	-67.466
S^{2-}	20.0	Cd^{2+}	-18.58		

Gaseous Atoms

H	48.575	Br	19.69	N	81.471
F	14.2	I	16.766	C	160.845
Cl	25.192				

[1] These data have been obtained from F. D. Rossini, D. D. Wagman, W. H. Evans, S. Levine, and I. Jaffe, "Selected Values of Chemical Thermodynamic Properties," *Natl. Bur. of Standards Circ.* 500, U. S. Government Printing Office, Washington, D. C., 1952, and F. D. Rossini, K. S. Pitzer, W. J. Taylor, J. P. Ebert, J. E. Kilpatrick, C. W. Beckett, M. G. Williams, and H. G. Werner, "Selected Values of Properties of Hydrocarbons," *Natl. Bur. Standards Circ.* C461, U. S. Government Printing Office, Washington, D. C., 1947.

dynamic quantities as described on pp. 561 and 568 certain empirical relations may be used.* For example, when CH_3 is substituted for a hydrogen atom in an aliphatic compound, the Gibbs free energy of formation at 25° becomes more positive by about 1900 cal; when C_2H_5 is substituted, it becomes more positive by 3000 cal. In a similar way the substitution of a hydrogen atom by an OH group to form a primary alcohol gives a change in $\Delta G°_{f,298°K}$ of $-34,000$; Cl for H, a change of -1600; NH_2 for H, a change of 6000; and NO_2 for H, a change of 7000.

Calculations of ΔG. Equation 36 may be used to calculate the Gibbs free-energy change for a reaction in which the reactants are not in their standard states at the beginning of the reaction and the products are not removed in their standard states.

If $\Delta G°$ has a positive value, the reactants in their standard states will not react spontaneously to give products in their standard states. However, by increasing the pressures or concentrations of the reactants, it may often be possible to make the reaction proceed even if $\Delta G°$ has a positive value, as long as ΔG has a negative value.

Example 16. Calculate the change in Gibbs free energy for the production of $2NO_2(g)$ at 1 atm from $N_2O_4(g)$ at 10 atm at 25°. As shown in example 11, the change in Gibbs free energy for the reaction

$$N_2O_4(g) = 2NO_2(g)$$

is $+1161$ cal, so that this reaction is not spontaneous at 25°. Equation 36 becomes

$$\Delta G = \Delta G° + RT \ln \frac{p_{NO_2}^2}{p_{N_2O_4}}$$
$$= +1161 + (1.987)(298)(2.303) \log \frac{1^2}{10}$$
$$= -212 \text{ cal}$$

Thus the production of $NO_2(g)$ at 1 atm from $N_2O_4(g)$ at 10 atm is a spontaneous process. Thus a continuous process would be thermodynamically feasible if N_2O_4 was maintained at 10 atm and NO_2 was withdrawn by some method so that its partial pressure was maintained at 1 atm.

Influence of Temperature on Chemical Equilibrium. The effect of temperature on the equilibrium constant may be calculated by use of the Gibbs-Helmholtz equation which has been derived earlier (p. 108).

$$\frac{\partial(\Delta G°/T)}{\partial T} = - \frac{\Delta H°}{T^2} \tag{41}$$

* O. A. Hougen, K. M. Watson, and R. A. Ragatz, *Chemical Process Principles*, Part II: *Thermodynamics*, John Wiley & Sons, New York, 1959.

or

$$\frac{\partial(\Delta G^\circ / T)}{\partial(1/T)} = \Delta H^\circ \tag{42}$$

Substituting $\Delta G^\circ = -RT \ln K_p$, we obtain

$$\frac{\partial \ln K_p}{\partial T} = \frac{\Delta H^\circ}{RT^2} \tag{43}$$

or

$$\frac{\partial \ln K_p}{\partial(1/T)} = \frac{-\Delta H^\circ}{R} \tag{44}$$

Assuming that ΔH° is independent of temperature, the indefinite integral of these equations is

$$\ln K_p = 2.303 \log K_p = \frac{-\Delta H^\circ}{RT} + C \tag{45}$$

where C is the integration constant. According to this equation, a plot of $\log K_p$ versus $1/T$ has a slope of $-\Delta H^\circ/2.303\ R$, and if ΔH° is independent of temperature a straight line is obtained.

Integrating equation 43 between temperatures T_1 and T_2, we obtain

$$\log \frac{K_2}{K_1} = \frac{\Delta H^\circ (T_2 - T_1)}{2.303\ RT_1 T_2} \tag{46}$$

These equations are useful for calculating ΔH° from the variation of the equilibrium constant with temperature, and for calculating equilibrium constants at other temperatures. The similarity of this equation to the Clausius-Clapeyron equation, derived on p. 136, should be noted. The vapor pressure is a special case of equilibrium.

Exercise IV. Show that for gaseous equilibria where $K_p = K_c(RT)^{\Delta n}$

$$\frac{\partial \ln K_c}{\partial T} = \frac{\Delta E^\circ}{RT^2} \tag{47}$$

Exercise V. Show that for solution reactions where $\Delta V = 0$

$$\frac{\partial \ln K_c}{\partial T} = \frac{\Delta E^\circ}{RT^2} = \frac{\Delta H^\circ}{RT^2} \tag{48}$$

If the enthalpy change for a reaction is zero, the equilibrium constant is independent of temperature. The reaction of ethanol with acetic acid to form ethyl acetate is a reaction for which this is very nearly true.

Table VI. Equilibrium Constants for the Reaction N₂(g) + O₂(g) = 2NO(g)

Temp, °K	1900	2000	2100	2200	2300	2400	2500	2600
$K_p \times 10^4$	2.31	4.08	6.86	11.0	16.9	25.1	36.0	50.3

Data are given in Table VI for the equilibrium constants at different temperatures for the reaction $N_2(g) + O_2(g) = 2NO(g)$.

In *Fig. 9-1* the values of log K_p are plotted against $1/T$, and it is evident that a straight line is produced. The enthalpy of reaction $\Delta H°$ can be calculated from the slope of the line, as follows:

$$\Delta H° = - \text{slope} \times 2.303R$$
$$= - (-9510)(2.303)(1.987) = 43,500 \text{ cal} \qquad (49)$$

The value of the integration constant C in equation 45 can be calculated from the experimental value of K_p at some temperature, and

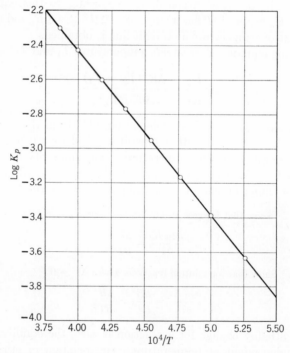

Fig. 9-1. Log K_p plotted against reciprocal absolute temperature for the reaction $N_2(g) + O_2(g) = 2NO(g)$. The standard enthalpy change for the reaction is calculated from the slope of the straight line.

equation 45 for this reaction becomes

$$\log K_p = \frac{-43,500}{(2.303)(1.987)T} + 5.365 \tag{50}$$

Example 17. Calculate the enthalpy change for the reaction $N_2(g) + O_2(g) = 2NO(g)$ from the equilibrium constants given in Table VI for 2000°K and 2500°K.

$$\log \frac{K_{2500°}}{K_{2000°}} = \log \frac{3.60 \times 10^{-3}}{4.08 \times 10^{-4}} = \frac{\Delta H°(2500 - 2000)}{(2.303)(1.987)(2500)(2000)}$$

and
$$\Delta H° = 43,300 \text{ cal}$$

Example 18. For the reaction

$$CO(g) + H_2O(g) = CO_2(g) + H_2(g)$$

$K_p = 10.0$ at 690°K, and the enthalpy change $\Delta H°$ is $-10,200$ cal. Calculate the partial pressures of each of the gases in an equilibrium mixture obtained from 0.400 mole of CO and 0.200 mole of H_2O in a volume of 5 liters at 800°K.

$$\log \frac{K_{800}}{K_{690}} = \frac{(-10,200)(110)}{(2.303)(1.987)(690)(800)} = -0.445$$

$$K_{800} = 0.359 K_{690} = 3.59$$

Since the number of moles of gaseous products is equal to the number of moles of gaseous reactants, the volume may be ignored in calculating the number of moles which react. If x represents the number of moles of CO_2, or H_2, produced,

$$K_{800} = 3.59 = \frac{x^2}{(0.4 - x)(0.2 - x)} \qquad x = 0.167 \text{ mole}$$

$$p_{CO_2} = p_{H_2} = \frac{xRT}{V} = \frac{(0.167)(0.08205)(800)}{5} = 2.19 \text{ atm}$$

$$p_{CO} = \frac{(0.234)(0.08205)(800)}{5} = 3.07 \text{ atm}$$

$$p_{H_2O} = \frac{(0.034)(0.08205)(800)}{5} = 0.045 \text{ atm}$$

It is evident from equation 43 or 44 that an increase in temperature at constant pressure causes an equilibrium to be displaced in the direction in which it absorbs heat. According to Le Châtelier's principle, an equilibrium will always be displaced in such a way as to minimize a change from the outside. When the temperature of a reaction mixture is raised, this change cannot be prevented by the system, but what happens is that the equilibrium shifts in such a way that more heat is required to heat the reaction mixture to the higher temperature than if the gas mixture were inert. In order to state Le Châtelier's principle in a completely unambiguous way it is necessary to introduce more advanced thermodynamic concepts. The correct formulations and the difficulties with simpler formulations have been discussed by de Heer.*

The present section has dealt with reactions over ranges of temperature where ΔH can be considered independent of temperature. We must now discuss the equations which result when the change of ΔH with temperature must be considered.

Influence of Temperature on Gibbs Free-Energy Changes. Often the Gibbs free energies of formation $\Delta \bar{G}°_f$ and enthalpies of formation $\Delta \bar{H}°_f$ are available for 25°, and the values $\bar{C}_P$ for the reactants and products are known over a range of temperature. With this information it is possible to calculate $\Delta G°$ at any temperature in the range where the $\bar{C}_P$ data are valid, and of course from $\Delta G°$ the equilibrium constant may be calculated using $\Delta G° = -RT \ln K$.

The enthalpy of reaction at temperature T is given by

$$\Delta H_T = \Delta H_0 + \int_0^T \Delta \bar{C}_P dT \tag{51}$$

where ΔH_0 is the hypothetical enthalpy of reaction at absolute zero. Since the equations used to represent $\bar{C}_P$ as a function of temperature are not valid down to absolute zero, ΔH_0 would not be the actual enthalpy change at absolute zero. However, if this equation is used only to calculate ΔH in the temperature range where the empirical equations for $\bar{C}_P$ are valid, no error is introduced. Since $\Delta \bar{C}_P = \Delta a + (\Delta b)T + (\Delta c)T^2 + \cdots$, it is readily shown that

$$\Delta H = \Delta H_0 + (\Delta a)T + \tfrac{1}{2}(\Delta b)T^2 + \tfrac{1}{3}(\Delta c)T^3 + \cdots \tag{52}$$

Substituting this value of ΔH into equation 41 and integrating, it is readily shown that

$$\Delta G = \Delta H_0 - (\Delta a)T \ln T - \tfrac{1}{2}(\Delta b)T^2 - \tfrac{1}{6}(\Delta c)T^3 + \cdots + IT \tag{53}$$

where I is an integration constant.

The Gibbs free-energy change for a reaction may be calculated from equation 53 if (1) the heat capacity of each reactant and product is known as a function of temperature from 25° to the desired temperature (that is, the values of the constants a, b, and c have been determined for each reactant and product); (2) the heat of reaction ΔH is

---

* J. de Heer, *J. Chem. Educ.*, *34*, 375 (1957); *35*, 133 (1958).

known at one temperature so that ΔH_0 may be evaluated; and (3) the value of ΔG is known at one temperature so that the integration constant I may be calculated.

Example 19. Calculate $\Delta G°$ and the equilibrium constant at 1000°K for the water-gas reaction

$$C(\text{graphite}) + H_2O(g) = CO(g) + H_2(g)$$

$$\Delta G°_{298°K} = -32.8079 - (-54.6357)$$

$$= 21.8278 \text{ kcal}$$

From Table II in Chapter 4,

$$\Delta H°_{298°K} = -26.4157 - (-57.7979)$$

$$= 31.3822 \text{ kcal}$$

According to the empirical equations for the heat capacities of gases, Table IV in Chapter 4, and $\bar{C}_{P,\text{graphite}} = 3.81 + 1.56 \times 10^{-3}T$,

$$\Delta \bar{C}_P = \bar{C}_{P,H_2} + \bar{C}_{P,CO} - \bar{C}_{P,H_2O} - \bar{C}_{P,\text{graphite}}$$

$$= 2.29 - 2.30 \times 10^{-3}T - 0.077 \times 10^{-7}T^2$$

$$\Delta H_0 = \Delta H - 2.29T - \tfrac{1}{2}(-2.30 \times 10^{-3})T^2 - \tfrac{1}{3}(-0.077 \times 10^{-7})T^3$$

$$= 31,382.2 - (2.29)(298.1) + (1.15 \times 10^{-3})(298.1)^2$$

$$+ (0.026 \times 10^{-7})(298.1)^3$$

$$= 30,801 \text{ cal}$$

Substituting in equation 53,

$$21,827.8 = 30,801 - (2.29)(298.1)(2.303)(2.474) - \tfrac{1}{2}(-2.30 \times 10^{-3})(298.1)^2$$

$$- \tfrac{1}{6}(-0.077 \times 10^{-7})(298.1)^3 + 298.1I$$

$$I = -17.4$$

and

$$\Delta G° = 30,801 - 5.26T \log T + 1.15 \times 10^{-3}T^2 + 0.013 \times 10^{-7}T^3 - 17.4T$$

This general equation may now be used to calculate the Gibbs free-energy change for the reaction at any temperature in the range for which the heat-capacity equations are valid (300–1500°K). At 1000°K this general equation yields

$$\Delta G°_{1000°K} = -1330 \text{ cal}$$

The equilibrium constant for the reaction at 1000°K may be calculated from

$$\Delta G°_{1000°K} = -RT \ln K_p = -1330 = -(1.987)(1000)(2.303) \log K_p$$

$$K_p = 1.96$$

It should be noted that the equilibrium constant is greater than unity at 1000°K, although it is far smaller than unity at room temperature.

The Effect of Pressure on Equilibrium. The value of K_p for a reaction is not affected by pressure if the reactants and products are ideal gases. Therefore for ideal gases no shift in equilibrium is produced by the addition of an inert gas provided that the volume is held constant. However, when an inert gas is added at constant total pressure, the volume increases and there is a decrease in the partial pressures of reactants and products and a consequent shift in equilibrium, provided that $\Delta n \neq 0$, just as if the equilibrium mixture of gases had been allowed to expand into a larger volume. If $\Delta n = 0$, alterations in volume have no effect if the gases are ideal.

For ideal gases the effect of pressure on the equilibrium constant expressed in terms of mole fractions is given by $K_X = K_p P^{-\Delta n}$ (p. 195). Taking the natural logarithms of both sides of this equation and then differentiating with respect to total pressure at constant temperature,

$$\ln K_X = \ln K_p - \Delta n \ln P \tag{54}$$

$$\left(\frac{\partial \ln K_X}{\partial P} \right)_T = \frac{-\Delta n}{P} = \frac{-\Delta V}{RT} \tag{55}$$

Thus for a reaction with $\Delta n > 0$ (that is, the number of moles of gaseous products is greater than the number of moles of gaseous reactants), an increase in pressure at constant temperature leads to a decrease in K_X. Thus when the pressure is raised the equilibrium is displaced in the direction of volume contraction. This is an illustration of Le Châtelier's principle.

Example 20. At 250° PCl_5 is 80 per cent dissociated at a pressure of 1 atm, and so $K_p = 1.78$. What is the percentage dissociation at equilibrium after sufficient nitrogen has been added at constant pressure to produce a nitrogen partial pressure of 0.9 atm? The total pressure is maintained at 1 atm. The sum of the partial pressures of the reacting gases is 0.1 atm.

$$K_p = \frac{\alpha^2 P}{1 - \alpha^2} = 1.78 = \frac{\alpha^2 0.10}{1 - \alpha^2}$$

$$\alpha = 0.973 \quad \text{or} \quad 97.3\%$$

Free-Energy Function.* As discussed on p. 210, it is possible to calculate the equilibrium constant for a reaction from the enthalpies of formation of the reactants and products and their absolute entropies, obtained from heat-capacity data down to close to absolute zero. It will be shown later (p. 568) that all the thermodynamic properties of

---

* W. F. Giauque, *J. Am. Chem. Soc.*, *52*, 4808 (1930); J. L. Margrave, *J. Chem. Educ.*, *32*, 520 (1955).

gases may be computed from spectroscopic data. Thus the equilibrium constants for a number of reactions involving fairly simple gas molecules have been calculated from spectroscopic data alone. In order to make such data available in the most useful form it is convenient to use the *free-energy function* $[(\overline{G}° - \overline{H}°_0)/T]$,* which is readily computed for gases from spectroscopic data, and for solids and liquids from experimental heat-capacity data. Remembering that $\overline{G}° = \overline{H}° - T\overline{S}°$, subtracting $\overline{H}°_0$, the enthalpy at absolute zero from both sides of the equation, and dividing by T, we obtain

$$\frac{\overline{G}° - \overline{H}°_0}{T} = \frac{\overline{H}° - \overline{H}°_0}{T} - \overline{S}° \tag{56}$$

which shows that the free-energy function can be calculated from $\overline{H}°$ and $\overline{S}°_0$.

Values of $(\overline{G}° - \overline{H}°_0)/T$ for many chemical compounds at several temperatures are listed in tables,† and so it is easy to calculate $\Delta\left(\dfrac{\overline{G}° - \overline{H}°_0}{T}\right)_{reaction}$ by subtracting $\Sigma\left(\dfrac{\overline{G}° - \overline{H}°_0}{T}\right)_{reactants}$ from $\Sigma\left(\dfrac{\overline{G}° - \overline{H}°_0}{T}\right)_{products}$. Fortunately the values of the free-energy function do not change much with temperature, and tables giving values every 100° or 500° are sufficient for interpolation and extrapolation, as may be seen in Table VII. The difference between the free-energy function of the products and reactants may be written

$$\Delta\left(\frac{\overline{G}° - \overline{H}°_0}{T}\right) = \frac{\Delta G°}{T} - \frac{\Delta H°_0}{T} \tag{57}$$

In accordance with previous conventions $\Delta G°$ and $\Delta H_0°$ are used to represent changes of the thermodynamic quantities for the overall reaction, whereas the bars are used for the molal quantities. Then

$$\frac{\Delta G°}{T} = \frac{\Delta H°_0}{T} + \Delta\left(\frac{\overline{G}° - \overline{H}°_0}{T}\right) \tag{58}$$

---

* The reference temperature is taken here to be 0°K, but 298°K is sometimes used, and the free-energy function is written $[(\overline{G}° - \overline{H}°_{298})/T]$.

† F. D. Rossini *et al.*, "Selected Values of Properties of Hydrocarbons," *Natl. Bur. Standards Circ.* C461, 1947, and *Selected Values of Physical and Thermodynamic Properties of Hydrocarbons and Related Compounds*, Carnegie Press, 1953; L. Brewer, L. A. Bromley, P. W. Gilles, and N. L. Lofgren, in *Chemistry and Metallurgy of Miscellaneous Materials: Thermodynamics*, ed. by L. L. Quill, McGraw-Hill Book Co., New York, 1950, Papers 3, 5, and 6.

Table VII.   Free-Energy Function and $\Delta \bar{H}^\circ{}_0$ [1]

$$-(\bar{G}^\circ - \bar{H}^\circ{}_0)/T, \text{ cal mole}^{-1} \text{ deg}^{-1}$$

Gas	298.16°K	500°K	1000°K	1500°K	2000°K	$\Delta\bar{H}^\circ{}_0$, kcal mole^{-1}
$H_2(g)$	24.44	27.96	32.75	35.60	37.68	0
$O_2(g)$	42.08	45.69	50.71	53.83	56.12	0
$Cl_2(g)$	45.95	49.86	55.45	58.88	61.36	0
$N_2(g)$	38.83	42.43	47.32	50.30	52.50	0
$HCl(g)$	37.73	41.32	46.17	49.10	51.25	-21.84
$CO(g)$	40.31	43.96	48.89	51.88	54.09	-27.18
$CO_2(g)$	43.57	47.68	54.14	58.51	61.88	-98.95
$H_2O(g)$	37.20	41.32	47.05	50.66	53.41	-57.11
$NH_3(g)$	37.99	42.25	48.63	53.03	56.56	-9.36
$CH_4(g)$	36.46	40.75	47.65	52.84		
$C_2H_6(g)$	45.27	50.77	61.11	69.46		
$C_3H_8(g)$	52.73	59.81	74.10	85.86		
$C_4H_{10}(g)$	58.52	67.93	86.73	102.04		
$C_6H_6(g)$	52.93	60.24	76.57	90.45		
$C_2H_4(g)$	43.98	48.74	57.29	63.94		
$H(g)$	22.42	24.99	28.44	30.45	31.88	51.62
$N(g)$	31.65	34.21	37.66	39.67	41.10	$(112.55)^2$
$O(g)$	33.08	35.84	39.46	41.54	43.00	58.586
$Cl(g)$	34.44	37.07	40.69	42.84	44.35	28.45

[1] Data from L. Brewer in L. L. Quill, *Chemistry and Metallurgy of Miscellaneous Materials: Thermodynamics*, McGraw-Hill Book Co., New York, 1950, page 61, and F. D. Rossini *et al.*, *Natl. Bur. Standards Circ.* C461, Washington, D. C., 1947.

[2] A. G. Gaydon, *Dissociation Energies*, Chapman & Hall, London, 1953.

But, since $\Delta\bar{G}^\circ = -RT \ln K$,

$$\ln K = 2.303 \log K = -\frac{1}{R}\left[\frac{\Delta H^\circ{}_0}{T} + \Delta\left(\frac{\bar{G}^\circ - \bar{H}^\circ{}_0}{T}\right)\right] \qquad (59)$$

In order to calculate the value of an equilibrium constant at a given temperature, it is necessary to know the value of $\Delta H^\circ{}_0$ as well as the values of the free-energy function. The enthalpy of reaction at absolute zero $\Delta H^\circ{}_0$ is calculated from measurements of the heat of reaction at constant pressure at one temperature and the heat capacities down to nearly absolute zero.

Example 21. Calculate the equilibrium constant for the dissociation of gaseous oxygen at 2000°K.

$$O_2(g) = 2O(g)$$

The enthalpy of dissociation of the oxygen molecule into atoms at 0°K is 117,172 cal mole^{-1}, as may be calculated from the data given in Table VII. The free-energy functions are also given in Table VII. Thus

$$\log K = -\frac{1}{2.303R}\left[\frac{\Delta H^\circ_0}{T} + \Delta\left(\frac{\bar{G}^\circ - \bar{H}^\circ_0}{T}\right)\right]$$

$$= -\frac{1}{(2.303)(1.987)}\left[\frac{117,172}{2000} + (2)(-43.00) - (-56.12)\right]$$

$$= -6.26$$

Thus, $K = 5.50 \times 10^{-7}$.

Example 22. Calculate the equilibrium constant for the formation of HCl(g) at 25°.

$$H_2(g) + Cl_2(g) = 2HCl(g)$$

Using equation 59,

$$\log K = \frac{-1}{(2.303)(1.987)}\left[\frac{-(21.840)(2)}{298.15} + 2(-37.73) - (-24.44) - (-45.95)\right]$$

$$= 3.25$$

$$K = 1.6 \times 10^{53}$$

The calculation of the free-energy functions of $H_2(g)$, $Cl_2(g)$, and $HCl(g)$ from the molecular weights, moments of inertia, and vibrational frequencies is shown on p. 568.

Another important use of free-energy functions is in evaluating enthalpies of reaction from equilibrium data in a more accurate manner than by taking the slope of log K versus $1/T$ plot. From equation 59 it is easily seen that one ΔH_0 value can be obtained from *each* measurement of an equilibrium constant or ΔG°, provided that the change in the free-energy function for the reaction is known. The free-energy-function approach often allows accurate evaluation of heats of reactions even for reactions at very high temperatures.

Calculations of equilibrium constants at high temperatures using the free-energy function are of great value in predicting the temperature at which a reaction must be carried out in order for the equilibrium to be favorable.

The amount of "isoöctane" available for antiknock fuel has been greatly increased by use of the reaction

$$C_4H_{10}(g, \text{isobutane}) + C_4H_8(g, \text{isobutene}) = C_8H_{18}(g, \text{isoöctane})$$

The variation of log K for this reaction with temperature, as calculated from various thermodynamic data by Rossini,* is shown by line A in *Fig. 9-2*. This reaction cannot be carried out at high temperatures because of the unfavorable equilibrium constant. Its use at temperatures as low as room temperature, where the equilibrium is quite

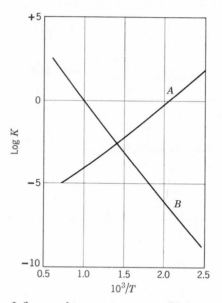

Fig. 9-2. Influence of temperature on equilibrium constants.

A. $\quad$ $C_4H_{10}(g) + C_4H_8(g) = C_8H_{18}(g)$
B. $\quad$ $C_4H_8(g) = C_4H_6(g) + H_2(g)$

favorable, was made possible by the discovery of commercially usable catalysts (sulfuric acid and hydrofluoric acid).

An example of a reaction for which the equilibrium is favorable only at rather high temperatures is the dehydrogenation of 1-butene to yield 1,3-butadiene.

$$\underset{\substack{|\;\;|\\ H\;\; H}}{\overset{\substack{H\;H\;H\;H\\|\;|\;|\;|}}{H-C=C-C-C-H}}(g) \;=\; \overset{\substack{H\;H\;H\;H\\|\;|\;|\;|}}{H-C=C-C=C-H}(g) + H_2(g)$$

The variation of log K for this reaction with temperature, as calculated from various thermodynamic data by Rossini,* is shown by line B in Fig. 9-2.

* F. D. Rossini, *J. Wash. Acad. Sci.*, *39*, 249 (1949).

REFERENCES

K. G. Denbigh, *The Principles of Chemical Equilibrium*, Cambridge University Press, Cambridge, 1955.

S. Glasstone, *Thermodynamics for Chemists*, D. Van Nostrand Co., Princeton, N. J., 1947.

O. A. Hougen, K. M. Watson, and R. A. Ragatz, *Chemical Process Principles*, Part II: *Thermodynamics*, John Wiley & Sons, New York, 1959.

I. M. Klotz, *Chemical Thermodynamics*, Prentice-Hall, Englewood Cliffs, N. J., 1950.

G. N. Lewis, M. Randall, K. S. Pitzer, and L. Brewer, *Thermodynamics*, Chapter 24, McGraw-Hill Book Co., New York, 1961.

F. D. Rossini, *Chemical Thermodynamics*, John Wiley & Sons, New York, 1950.

F. D. Rossini, K. S. Pitzer, W. J. Taylor, J. P. Ebert, J. E. Kilpatrick, C. W. Beckett, M. G. Williams, and H. G. Werner, "Selected Values of Properties of Hydrocarbons," *Circ. Natl. Bur. Standards* C461, U. S. Government Printing Office, Washington, D. C., 1947.

F. D. Rossini, D. D. Wagman, W. H. Evans, S. Levine, and I. Jaffe, "Selected Values of Chemical Thermodynamic Properties," *Circ. Natl. Bur. Standards* 500, U. S. Government Printing Office, Washington, D. C., 1952.

F. T. Wall, *Chemical Thermodynamics*, W. H. Freeman & Co., San Francisco, 1958.

PROBLEMS

1. At $25°$ $K_p = 1.7 \times 10^{12}$ for the reaction

$$SO_2(g) + \tfrac{1}{2}O_2(g) = SO_3(g)$$

Calculate (a) K_p and (b) K_c at this temperature for the reaction

$$2SO_3(g) = 2SO_2(g) + O_2(g)$$

Ans. (a) 0.35×10^{-24}. (b) 1.4×10^{-26}.

2. At $55°$ and 1 atm the average molecular weight of partially dissociated N_2O_4 is 61.2 g mole^{-1}. Calculate (a) α and (b) K_p for the reaction $N_2O_4(g) = 2NO_2(g)$. (c) Calculate α at $55°$ if the total pressure is reduced to 0.1 atm.

Ans. (a) 0.503. (b) 1.36. (c) 0.876.

3. For the reaction $N_2O_4(g) = 2NO_2(g)$, K_p at $25°$ is 0.141. What pressure would be expected if 1 gram of liquid N_2O_4 were allowed to evaporate into a liter vessel at this temperature? Assume that N_2O_4 and NO_2 are ideal gases.

Ans. 0.351 atm.

4. Under what pressure must PCl_5 be placed at $250°$ in order to obtain a 30 per cent conversion into PCl_3 and Cl_2? For the reaction $PCl_5(g) = PCl_3(g) + Cl_2(g)$, $K_p = 1.78$.

Ans. 18.0 atm.

5. For the gaseous reaction $COCl_2(g) = CO(g) + Cl_2(g)$ at $100°$, K_p is 6.7×10^{-9}. Calculate the partial pressure of carbon monoxide in equilibrium with phosgene at this temperature under a total pressure of 2 atm if only phosgene is initially present. The dissociation is so slight that the partial pressure of phosgene may be taken as equal to the total pressure. *Ans.* 1.16×10^{-4} atm.

6. The equilibrium constant for the reaction $SO_2(g) + \frac{1}{2}O_2(g) = SO_3(g)$ at $727°$ is given by

$$K_p = \frac{p_{SO_3}}{p_{SO_2}p_{O_2}^{1/2}} = 1.85$$

What is the ratio p_{SO_3}/p_{SO_2} (*a*) when the partial pressure of oxygen at equilibrium is 0.3 atm, (*b*) when the partial pressure of oxygen at equilibrium is 0.6 atm? (*c*) What is the effect on the equilibrium if the total pressure of the mixture of gases is increased by forcing in nitrogen at constant volume?

Ans. (*a*) 1.01. (*b*) 1.44. (*c*) No effect if the gases behave ideally.

7. A 1:3 mixture of nitrogen and hydrogen was passed over a catalyst at $450°$. It was found that 2.04 per cent by volume of ammonia was formed when the total pressure was maintained at 10 atm [A. T. Larson and R. L. Dodge, *J. Am. Chem. Soc.*, *45*, 2918 (1923)]. Calculate the value of K_p for $\frac{3}{2}H_2 + \frac{1}{2}N_2 = NH_3$ at this temperature. *Ans.* $K_p = 6.55 \times 10^{-3}$.

8. The reaction $CO_2(g) + H_2(g) = CO(g) + H_2O(g)$ was investigated by passing mixtures of CO_2 and H_2 over a catalyst at $900°$ at 1 atm pressure. The resulting gas was chilled quickly to room temperature by passage through a capillary and was analyzed. In one experiment the partial pressures of CO_2, H_2, CO, and H_2O were 0.2142, 0.2549, 0.2654, and 0.2654 atm, respectively. Calculate the number of moles of H_2 present in another mixture containing 0.2272 mole of CO, 0.2272 mole of H_2O, and 0.4850 mole of CO_2 at equilibrium. *Ans.* 0.0825 mole.

9. The equilibrium constant for the reaction $N_2O_4 = 2NO_2$ in chloroform solution at $0°$ is 4.5×10^{-7} when the equilibrium constant is expressed in mole fractions and the concentration of N_2O_4 is below 0.1 mole fraction. If 0.02 mole of N_2O_4 is dissolved in 1 mole of chloroform, how many moles of NO_2 will be produced at equilibrium? *Ans.* 9.6×10^{-5} mole.

10. Amylene, C_5H_{10}, and acetic acid react to give the ester according to the reaction

$$C_5H_{10} + CH_3COOH = CH_3COOC_5H_{11}$$

What is the value of K_c if 0.00645 mole of amylene and 0.001 mole of acetic acid dissolved in 845 ml of a certain inert solvent react to give 0.000784 mole of ester? *Ans.* $K_c = 540$.

11. At $1273°K$ and at a total pressure of 30 atm the equilibrium in the reaction $CO_2(g) + C(s) = 2CO(g)$ is such that 17 molar per cent of the gas is CO_2. (*a*) What percentage would be CO_2 if the total pressure were 20 atm? (*b*) What would be the effect on the equilibrium of adding N_2 to the reaction mixture in a closed vessel until the partial pressure of N_2 is 10 atm? (*c*) At what pressure will 25 per cent of the gas be CO_2?

Ans. (*a*) 12.5%. (*b*) No effect. (*c*) 54 atm.

12. For the reaction at $750°$

$$\tfrac{1}{2}SnO_2(s) + H_2(g) = \tfrac{1}{2}Sn(s) + H_2O(g)$$

the total pressure of the system is 32.0 mm, and the partial pressure of water is 23.7 mm. (*a*) Calculate K_p for this reaction. For the reaction

$$H_2(g) + CO_2(g) = CO(g) + H_2O(g)$$

K_p has a value of 0.771 at 750°.   (b) Calculate K_p for the reaction

$$\tfrac{1}{2}SnO_2(s) + CO(g) = \tfrac{1}{2}Sn(s) + C_2(g)$$

Ans. (a) 2.85.   (b) 3.71.

13. The reaction

$$2NOCl(g) = 2NO(g) + Cl_2(g)$$

comes to equilibrium at 1 atm total pressure and 227° when the partial pressure of the nitrosyl chloride, NOCl, is 0.64 atm. Only NOCl was present initially. (a) Calculate $\Delta G°$ for this reaction.   (b) At what total pressure will the partial pressure of Cl_2 be 0.1 atm?   *Ans.* (a) 4060 cal.   (b) 0.785 atm.

14. Calculate the equilibrium constant for the isomerization of *n*-butane to isobutane at 25°:

$$n\text{-Butane}(g) = \text{isobutane}(g)$$

using data on the Gibbs free energies of formation.   *Ans.* $K_p = 2.54$.

15. For the reaction $A(g) + B(g) = AB(g)$, $\Delta G° = -2000$ cal at 27°. Under what total pressure must an equimolecular gaseous mixture of A and B be placed in order to produce a 40 per cent conversion into AB?   *Ans.* 0.063 atm.

16. The equilibrium constant for the gas reaction $A = B$ is 0.10 at 27°. Calculate (a) $\Delta G°$ and (b) ΔG for the production of 1 mole of B at a pressure of 1 atm from A at a pressure of 20 atm.   (c) Is the reaction spontaneous under the latter conditions?   *Ans.* (a) +1373, (b) −413 cal.   (c) Yes.

17. The following reaction takes place in the presence of aluminum chloride:

$$\text{Cyclohexane}(l) = \text{Methylcyclopentane}(l)$$

At 25° $K_c = 0.143$, and at 45° $K_c = 0.193$. From these data calculate: (a) $\Delta G°$ at 25°, (b) $\Delta H°$.   *Ans.* (a) 1152, (b) 3200 cal mole^{-1}.

18. The following data apply to the reaction $Br_2(g) = 2Br(g)$:

T, °K	1123	1173	1223	1273
$K_p \times 10^3$	0.403	1.40	3.28	7.1

Determine by graphical means the enthalpy change when 1 mole of Br_2 dissociates completely at 1200°K.   *Ans.* 55 kcal mole^{-1}.

19. Mercuric oxide dissociates according to the reaction $2HgO(s) = 2Hg(g) + O_2(g)$. At 420° the dissociation pressure is 387 mm, and at 450° it is 810 mm. Calculate (a) the equilibrium constants, and (b) the enthalpy of dissociation per mole of HgO.   *Ans.* (a) 0.0196, 0.1794 atm^3.   (b) 36,750 cal mole^{-1}.

20. The vapor pressure of water above mixtures of $CuCl_2 \cdot H_2O(s)$ and $CuCl_2 \cdot 2H_2O(s)$ is given as a function of temperature in the following table:

t, °C	17.9	39.8	60.0	80.0
P, atm	0.0049	0.0247	0.120	0.322

(a) Calculate $\Delta H°$ for the reaction

$$CuCl_2 \cdot 2H_2O(s) = CuCl_2 \cdot H_2O(s) + H_2O(g)$$

(b) Calculate $\Delta G°$ for the reaction at 60.0°.   (c) Calculate $\Delta S°$ for the reaction at 60.0°.   *Ans.* (a) 13,700 cal mole^{-1}.   (b) 1410 cal mole^{-1}.
                (c) 36.9 cal deg^{-1} mole^{-1}.

21. When platinum is heated in the presence of chlorine gas, the following reaction takes place:

$$Pt(s) + Cl_2(g) = PtCl_2(g)$$

At $1000°K$, $\Delta G°_{1000°} = 14$ kcal.   If the pressure of Cl_2 is 1 atm, what will be the partial pressure of $PtCl_2$?   *Ans.* 8.7×10^{-4} atm.

22. (*a*) Calculate the Gibbs free energy of formation of urea, $CO(NH_2)_2(s)$, from the following data:

$$CO_2(g) + 2NH_3(g) = H_2O(g) + CO(NH_2)_2(s) \qquad \Delta G°_{298} = 456 \text{ cal}$$

$$H_2O(g) = H_2(g) + \tfrac{1}{2}O_2(g) \qquad \Delta G°_{298} = 54{,}636 \text{ cal}$$

$$C(\text{graphite}) + O_2(g) = CO_2(g) \qquad \Delta G°_{298} = -94{,}260 \text{ cal}$$

$$N_2(g) + 3H_2(g) = 2NH_3(g) \qquad \Delta G°_{298} = -7752 \text{ cal}$$

(*b*) Calculate $\Delta \bar{G}_f°$ for urea at $298.1°K$ from $\Delta \bar{S}°_f$, which is -109.05 cal $\deg^{-1}$ mole^{-1}, and $\Delta \bar{H}°_f$, which is $-79{,}634$ cal mole^{-1}.

Ans. (*a*) $-47{,}120$, (*b*) $-47{,}126$ cal mole^{-1}.

23. At $2000°$ water is 2 per cent dissociated into oxygen and hydrogen at a total pressure of 1 atm. (*a*) Calculate K_p. (*b*) Will the degree of dissociation increase or decrease if the pressure is reduced? (*c*) Will the degree of dissociation increase or decrease if argon gas is added, holding the total pressure equal to 1 atm? (*d*) Will the degree of dissociation change if the pressure is raised by addition of argon to the closed system containing partially dissociated water vapor? (*e*) Will the degree of dissociation increase or decrease if oxygen gas is added while holding the total pressure constant at 1 atm?

Ans. (*a*) 2.03×10^{-3}. (*b*) Increase. (*c*) Increase. (*d*) No change. (*e*) Decrease.

24. Chlorine gas is partially dissociated to chlorine atoms at elevated temperatures. Calculate the degree of dissociation of Cl_2 gas at (*a*) $1250°K$ and (*b*) $1750°K$ when the total pressure is 0.1 atm. *Ans.* (*a*) 1.33×10^{-2}. (*b*) 0.379.

---

25. For the reaction

$$CH_4(g) + 2H_2S(g) = CS_2(g) + 4H_2(g)$$

$K_p = 2.05 \times 10^9$ at $25°$. Calculate (*a*) K_p and (*b*) K_c at this temperature for

$$2H_2(g) + \tfrac{1}{2}CS_2(g) = H_2S(g) + \tfrac{1}{2}CH_4(g)$$

26. The dissociation of N_2O_4 is represented by $N_2O_4(g) = 2NO_2(g)$. If the density of the equilibrium gas mixture is 3.174 g liter^{-1} at a total pressure of 1 atm at $24°$, what minimum pressure would be required to keep the degree of dissociation of N_2O_4 below 0.1 at this temperature?

27. A reaction vessel containing PCl_5 is brought to equilibrium at $250°$, and only gaseous PCl_5, PCl_3, and Cl_2 are present with a total pressure of 5 atm. Calculate the equilibrium partial pressure of PCl_5 if K_p in atmospheres for the following reaction:

$$PCl_5(g) = PCl_3(g) + Cl_2(g)$$

is 1.78.

28. Show that for a reaction of the type

$$AB(g) = A(g) + B(g)$$

at any temperature, the total pressure at which AB is 50 per cent dissociated will be numerically equal to 3 times the equilibrium constant K_p.

29. For the reaction

$$2HI(g) = H_2(g) + I_2(g)$$

at $698.6°K$, $K_p = 1.83 \times 10^{-2}$. (a) How many grams of hydrogen iodide will be formed when 10 grams of iodine and 0.2 gram of hydrogen are heated to this temperature in a 3-liter vessel? (b) What will be the partial pressures of H_2, I_2, and HI?

30. At $400°$ $K_p = 78.1$ for the reaction

$$NH_3(g) = \tfrac{1}{2}N_2(g) + \tfrac{3}{2}H_2(g)$$

Show that the fraction (α) of NH_3 dissociated at a total pressure P is given by

$$\alpha = \frac{1}{\sqrt{1 + kP}}$$

and calculate the value of k in this equation.

31. When 4.0×10^{-4} mole of amylene and 3.0×10^{-4} mole of acetic acid are dissolved in 845 ml of an inert solvent, 1.28×10^{-4} mole of ester is formed according to the reaction

$$CH_3COOH + C_5H_{10} = CH_3COOC_5H_{11}$$

How much ester will be formed when 0.002 mole of amylene and 0.001 mole of acetic acid are dissolved in 500 ml?

32. For the reaction

$$C(s) + 2H_2(g) = CH_4(g)$$

at $1000°$, $K_p = 0.263$. Calculate the total pressure at equilibrium when 0.100 mole of CH_4 is placed in a volume of 2 liters at $1000°$.

33. Ten grams of calcium carbonate is placed in a container of 1-liter capacity and heated to $800°$. (a) How many grams of $CaCO_3$ remain undecomposed? (b) If the amount of $CaCO_3$ were 20 grams, how much would remain undecomposed?

34. The equilibrium pressure of solid NH_4HS is 500 mm at $25°$. Assuming that the vapor is completely decomposed into NH_3 and H_2S, calculate the maximum pressure of H_2S which can be added to a system containing NH_3 at 50 mm without precipitating NH_4HS.

35. Using the fact that $K_p = 0.141$ atm at $25°$ for $N_2O_4(g) = 2NO_2(g)$ and the Gibbs free energy of formation of NO_2 in Table V, calculate the Gibbs free energy of formation of N_2O_4.

36. Calculate the equilibrium constants at $25°$ for the following reactions:

$$CO(g) + 2H_2(g) = CH_3OH(g)$$
$$C_2H_4(g) + H_2O(g) = C_2H_5OH(g)$$

The vapor pressures of methanol and ethanol at $25°$ are 0.16 and 0.078 atm, respectively. These vapor pressures may be used to calculate the differences in Gibbs free energies of formation of the liquids and corresponding gases.

37. In determining equilibrium constants for reactions with large or small constants, the analytical method usually puts a limit on the magnitude of the constant which can be experimentally determined. For a reaction of the type $A = B$ it is found that there is less than 1 part per 1000 of B at equilibrium at $25°$. Calculate the *minimum* value for $\Delta G°_{298}$ for this reaction.

38. For the reaction

$$N_2(g) + 3H_2(g) = 2NH_3(g)$$

$K_p = 1.64 \times 10^{-4}$ at $400°$. Calculate (a) $\Delta G°$ and (b) ΔG when the pressures of N_2 and H_2 are maintained at 10 atm and 30 atm, respectively, and NH_3 is removed at a partial pressure of 3 atm. (c) Is the reaction spontaneous under the latter conditions?

39. The equilibrium constant K_p for $H_2(g) \rightleftharpoons 2H(g)$ is 1.52×10^{-7} at $1800°K$ and 3.10×10^{-6} at $2000°K$. Calculate $\Delta H°$ for this temperature range.

40. The average molecular weights M_{avg} of equilibrium mixtures of NO_2 and N_2O_4 at 1 atm total pressure are given in the following table at three temperatures:

t, °C	25	45	65
M_{avg}	77.64	66.80	56.51

(a) Calculate the degree of dissociation of N_2O_4 and the equilibrium constant at each of these temperatures. (b) Plot $\log K_p$ against $1/T$, and calculate $\Delta H°$ for the dissociation of N_2O_4. (c) Calculate the equilibrium constant at $35°$. (d) Calculate the degree of dissociation α for N_2O_4 at $35°$ when the total pressure is 0.5 atm.

41. Ammonium hydroselenide dissociates [F. F. Mikus and F. J. Poss, *J. Am. Chem. Soc.*, *71*, 429 (1949)] as follows:

$$NH_4HSe(s) = NH_3(g) + H_2Se(g)$$

(a) Express K_p in terms of total pressure. K_p increases with temperature as follows:

t, °C	15	18	21	24.8	29.3
$K_p \times 10^4$	0.20	0.31	0.45	0.85	1.9

(b) What is the value of $\Delta H°$ for this reaction at $18°$?

42. The partial pressure of oxygen in equilibrium with a mixture of silver oxide and silver is given by

$$\log p = 6.2853 - 2859/T$$

where p is expressed in atmospheres. Calculate the temperature at which silver oxide should begin to decompose when it is heated in air at 760 mm pressure.

43. The Gibbs free-energy change for the reaction

$$CO(g) + Cl_2(g) = COCl_2(g)$$

in calories per mole can be represented by the equation

$$\Delta G° = -24,100 + 4T \ln T + 3.5T$$

Calculate the partial pressure of chlorine in equilibrium with phosgene at $250°$ and a total pressure of 1 atm, assuming that the gases are ideal.

44. For the formation of nitric oxide

$$N_2(g) + O_2(g) = 2NO(g)$$

K_p at $2126.9°$ is 2.5×10^{-3}. (a) In an equilibrium mixture containing 0.1 atm partial pressure of N_2 and 0.1 atm partial pressure of O_2, what is the partial pressure of NO? (b) In an equilibrium mixture of N_2, O_2, NO, CO_2, and other inert gases at $2126.9°$ and 1 atm total pressure, 80 per cent by volume of the gas is N_2 and 16 per cent is O_2. What is the per cent by volume of NO? (c) What is the total partial pressure of the inert gases?

45. For the reaction:

$$PtCl(s) = Pt(s) + \tfrac{1}{2}Cl_2(g) \qquad \Delta G°_{500} = 6 \text{ kcal}$$

calculate the equilibrium pressure of chlorine at $500°K$.

46. A gas mixture containing 97 mole per cent water and 3 mole per cent hydrogen is heated to $1000\,°$K. Will the equilibrium mixture react with nickel at $1000\,°$K to produce nickel oxide?

$$\mathrm{Ni}(s) + \tfrac{1}{2}\mathrm{O}_2(g) = \mathrm{NiO}(s) \qquad \Delta G°_{1000} = -35,400 \text{ cal.}$$

$$\mathrm{H}_2(g) + \tfrac{1}{2}\mathrm{O}_2(g) = \mathrm{H}_2\mathrm{O}(g) \qquad \Delta G°_{1000} = -45,600 \text{ cal.}$$

47. Calculate (a) K_p and (b) $\Delta G°$ for the following reaction at $20°$:

$$\mathrm{CuSO}_4 \cdot 4\mathrm{NH}_3(s) = \mathrm{CuSO}_4 \cdot 2\mathrm{NH}_3(s) + 2\mathrm{NH}_3(g)$$

The equilibrium pressure of NH_3 is 62 mm.

48. Calculate the degree of dissociation of $\mathrm{H}_2\mathrm{O}(g)$ at $2000\,°$K and 1 atm pressure, using the free-energy function.

49. The equilibrium vapor pressure of tantalum has been determined as 6.216×10^{-9} atm at $2624\,°$K, as 9.692×10^{-8} atm at $2839\,°$K, and as 3.655×10^{-7} atm at $2948\,°$K. The free-energy functions for solid and gaseous Ta are:

T, °K	$-\left(\dfrac{\bar{G}° - \bar{H}°_0}{T}\right)_{\text{solid}}$, cal deg^{-1} mole^{-1}	$-\left(\dfrac{\bar{G}° - \bar{H}°_0}{T}\right)_{\text{gas}}$, cal deg^{-1} mole^{-1}
2624	18.12	51.38
2839	18.67	51.92
2948	18.94	52.18

Calculate the heat of sublimation of Ta at $0°$K. Compare this with the heat obtained from the slope of a $\log p$ versus $1/T$ plot. Why do these heats differ?

---

50. At $670\,°$K

$$\mathrm{H}_2(g) + \mathrm{D}_2(g) = 2\mathrm{HD}(g) \qquad K_p = 3.78$$

where D is deuterium. Calculate K_p and K_c at this temperature for the reaction

$$\mathrm{HD}(g) = \tfrac{1}{2}\mathrm{H}_2(g) + \tfrac{1}{2}\mathrm{D}_2(g)$$

51. At $55°$ $K_p = 1.36$ for $\mathrm{N}_2\mathrm{O}_4(g) = 2\mathrm{NO}_2(g)$. (a) How many moles of $\mathrm{N}_2\mathrm{O}_4$ must be added to a 10-liter vessel at $55°$ in order that the concentration of NO_2 will be 0.1 mole liter^{-1}? (b) How many moles of $\mathrm{N}_2\mathrm{O}_4$ must be added to a previously evacuated 10-liter vessel at $55°$ in order that the total pressure will be 2 atm?

52. An evacuated tube containing 5.96×10^{-3} moles liter^{-1} of solid iodine is heated to $973\,°$K. The experimentally determined pressure is 0.490 atm [M. L. Perlman and G. K. Rollefson, *J. Chem. Phys.*, *9*, 362 (1941)]. Assuming that the gases are ideal, calculate K_p for $\mathrm{I}_2(g) = 2\mathrm{I}(g)$.

53. Calculate the total pressure which must be applied to a mixture of 3 parts of hydrogen and 1 part of nitrogen to give a mixture containing 10 per cent ammonia at $400°$. At $400°$, $K_p = 1.64 \times 10^{-4}$ for the reaction $\mathrm{N}_2(g) + 3\mathrm{H}_2(g) = 2\mathrm{NH}_3(g)$.

54. Derive an equation for K_p in terms of α and the total pressure P for the reaction $2A(g) = 2B(g) + C(g)$. Show that α varies inversely as the cube root of P, when P/K_p is large.

55. At $500°$ $K_p = 5.5$ for the reaction

$$\mathrm{CO}(g) + \mathrm{H}_2\mathrm{O}(g) = \mathrm{CO}_2(g) + \mathrm{H}_2(g)$$

If a mixture of 1 mole of CO and 5 moles of H_2O is passed over a catalyst at this temperature, what will be the equilibrium mole fraction of H_2O?

56. A mixture of N_2 and H_2 is passed over a catalyst at $400°$ to obtain the equilibrium conversion to NH_3. The equilibrium constant at this temperature for $N_2(g) + 3H_2(g) = 2NH_3(g)$ is $K_p = 1.64 \times 10^{-4}$. (a) Calculate the total pressure required to produce 5.26 mole per cent NH_3 if an equimolar mixture of N_2 and H_2 is passed over the catalyst. (b) If a mixture of 2 moles of N_2 per mole of H_2 is passed over the catalyst, what total pressure will be required to produce 5.26 mole per cent NH_3 at equilibrium? The fact that a higher pressure is required when a larger proportion of N_2 is used may appear to be in violation of Le Châtelier's principle, but it is not in conflict with the correct statement of this principle [J. de Heer, *J. Chem. Educ.*, *34*, 375 (1957)].

57. Show that the equilibrium constant K_p for a reaction $A + B = 2C$ determined in the gas phase is related to the equilibrium constant K_X for the reaction in the solution phase by

$$\frac{K_p}{K_X} = \frac{K_C{}^2}{K_A K_B}$$

where K_A, K_B and K_C are the Henry's-law constants for the solubility of A, B, and C in the solvent.

58. Adkins and Adams studied the equilibria involved in the formation of acetals by titrating the equilibrium mixture and determining the aldehyde concentration. At $25°$, 1 mole of ethanol was mixed with 0.091 mole of acetaldehyde in a volume of 63.0 ml, and it was found that, when equilibrium was reached, 90.72 per cent of the acetaldehyde had reacted to give acetal. The reaction is

$$2C_2H_5OH + CH_3CHO = CH_3CH(OC_2H_5)_2 + H_2O$$

(a) Calculate the equilibrium constant, assuming an ideal solution. (b) If the mixture is diluted to 100 ml with an inert solvent, what per cent of acetaldehyde will have reacted?

59. Air (20 per cent O_2) will not oxidize silver at $200°$ and 1 atm pressure. Make a statement about the equilibrium constant for the reaction

$$2Ag(g) + \tfrac{1}{2}O_2(g) = Ag_2O(s)$$

60. The solubility of hydrogen in a molten iron alloy is found to be proportional to the square root of the partial pressure of hydrogen. How can this be explained?

61. For the reaction

$$2NaHCO_3(s) = Na_2CO_3(s) + CO_2(g) + H_2O(g)$$

$K_p = 0.23$ when the pressures are expressed in atmospheres at $100°$. On a day when the barometric pressure was 740 mm, the room temperature $27°$, and the relative humidity 0.70, 20 grams of solid $NaHCO_3$ was placed in a 5-liter flask and sealed with the air from the room. It was then brought up to $100°$. (a) What was the partial pressure of CO_2 at equilibrium in the flask (if the CO_2 of the air is neglected)? The vapor pressure of water at $27°$ is 26.8 mm. (b) What was the pressure in the flask?

62. Calculate the equilibrium constants K_p for the following reactions at $25°$:

    (a) $P(g) + 2\tfrac{1}{2}Cl_2(g) = PCl_5(g)$

    (b) $UF_6(g) = U(s) + 3F_2(g)$

    (c) $H_2S(g) + 2O_2(g) = H_2O(g) + SO_3(g)$

63. For the reaction forming the triphenyl methyl free radical ($\phi_3 C\cdot$)

$$\phi_3 CC\phi_3 = 2\phi_3 C\cdot$$

in $CHCl_3$ at $25°$, $\Delta H° = 11.60$ kcal mole^{-1} and $\Delta S° = 23.4$ cal deg^{-1} mole^{-1}. The dot represents the unpaired electron in the free radical. Calculate (a) K_c and (b) the molar concentration of $\phi_3 C$ if 1 mole of $\phi_3 CC\phi_3$ is added per liter.

64. The following thermodynamic quantities for α- and β-pinene have been obtained at $25°$ from heat-of-combustion measurements and low-temperature heat-capacity determinations (H. A. McGee, Jr.):

	$\Delta \overline{H}°_f$, kcal mole^{-1}	$\overline{S}°$, cal deg^{-1} mole^{-1}
DL-α-pinene(l)	-3.6 ± 0.3	70.95 ± 0.11
DL-β-pinene(l)	-1.5 ± 0.3	69.48 ± 1.5

Calculate the Gibbs free-energy change and equilibrium constant on the mole-fraction scale at $25°$ for the reaction

$$\text{DL-}\alpha\text{-pinene}(l) = \text{DL-}\beta\text{-pinene}(l)$$

Indicate the magnitude of the uncertainty in these values resulting from the indicated uncertainties in the thermodynamic values.

65. The equilibrium ratio of sodium fumarate to sodium L-malate at pH 7 is 0.22 at $25°$. If in a living tissue the concentration of fumarate is maintained at 0.001 M by other enzymatic reactions and the concentration of L-malate is maintained at 0.01 M, can L-malate be spontaneously dehydrated to fumarate?

66. The measured density of an equilibrium mixture of N_2O_4 and NO_2 at $15°$ and 1 atm is 3.62 g liter^{-1}, and the density at $75°$ and 1 atm is 1.84 g liter^{-1}. What is the enthalpy change of the reaction $N_2O_4(g) = 2NO_2(g)$?

67. For the reactions

$$M(s) = M(g) \qquad \Delta H_1$$

$$M(s) = \tfrac{1}{2}M_2(g) \qquad \Delta H_2$$

$$\tfrac{1}{2}M_2(g) = M(g) \qquad \Delta H_D$$

find the relation between ΔH_1, ΔH_2, and ΔH_D. If $\Delta H_2 > \Delta H_1$, will the pressure of monomer (M) or dimer (M_2) gas molecules above $M(s)$ increase more rapidly as the temperature is increased?

68. Calculate ΔH for the reaction

$$CaCO_3(s) = CaO(s) + CO_2(g)$$

in the range 1000–$1200°$ from the data of Table III of this chapter.

69. For the reaction

$$Fe_2O_3(s) + 3CO(g) = 2Fe(s) + 3CO_2(g)$$

the following values of K_p are known:

t, $°$	100	250	1000
K_p	1100	100	0.0721

At $1120°$ for the reaction $2CO_2(g) = 2CO(g) + O_2(g)$, $K_p = 1.4 \times 10^{-12}$ atm. What equilibrium partial pressure of O_2 would have to be supplied to a vessel at $1120°$ containing 1 mole of solid Fe_2O_3 in order just to prevent the formation of Fe?

234   PHYSICAL CHEMISTRY

70. A certain optically active organic compound slowly racemized in solution, and eventually the solution showed no optical rotation, the D and L forms being at equal concentrations. When the temperature of the solution was varied over wide limits, there was no return of optical activity. What facts can be deduced about $\Delta G°$ and $\Delta H°$ for the racemization reaction?

71. When N_2O_4 is allowed to dissociate to form NO_2 at 25° at a total pressure of 1 atm, it is 18.5 per cent dissociated at equilibrium, and so $K_p = 0.141$. (a) If N_2 is added to the system at constant volume, will the equilibrium shift? (b) If the system is allowed to expand as N_2 is added at a constant total pressure of 1 atm, what will be the equilibrium degree of dissociation when the N_2 partial pressure is 0.6 atm?

72. A liter reaction vessel containing 0.233 mole of N_2 and 0.341 mole of PCl_5 is heated to 250°. The total pressure at equilibrium is 28.95 atm. Assuming that all the gases are ideal, calculate K_p for the only reaction which occurs:

$$PCl_5(g) = PCl_3(g) + Cl_2(g)$$

73. From the entropy values and the heats of formation given in Chapters 4 and 5, together with the value 29.09 cal deg^{-1} mole^{-1} for the entropy of Ag_2O at 25°, calculate $\Delta G°$ and K for the reaction

$$2Ag_2O(s) = 4Ag(s) + O_2(g)$$

at 25°. What is the dissociation pressure of Ag_2O at 25°?

74. If 1 mole of CO_2 is mixed with 2 moles of NH_3, what total pressure must be applied to obtain 0.5 mole of urea at equilibrium at 298°K if H_2O remains in the vapor phase? The Gibbs free energy of formation of urea(s) is $-47,120$ cal mole^{-1}, and the Gibbs free energies of formation of the other substances may be obtained from Table V.

75. In the formation of 1 mole of AgI(s) from solid silver and solid iodine 14,815 cal is evolved at 25°. From specific heat measurements at low temperatures the molal entropy of AgI(s) at 25° has been found to be 27.6 cal deg^{-1} mole^{-1}, whereas the atomic entropy of silver at 25° is 10.2 and that of iodine is 13.3 cal deg^{-1} mole^{-1}. Calculate the Gibbs free energy of formation of AgI(s) at 25°.

76. Using the free-energy function, calculate the equilibrium constant at 1000°K for the reaction

$$CO(g) + H_2O(g) = CO_2(g) + H_2(g)$$

77. Which process will be most important in the vaporization of $NiCl_2$: (a) vaporization of gaseous $NiCl_2$ molecules or (b) decomposition to Ni(s) and $Cl_2(g)$? The equilibrium gas pressure over $NiCl_2(s)$ is 10^{-3} atm at 934°K. The following data are available:

	$\dfrac{-(\bar{G}° - \bar{H}°_{298})}{T}$, cal deg^{-1} mole^{-1}			$\Delta \bar{H}°_{298}$, kcal mole^{-1}
	298.1°K	500°K	1000°K	
$NiCl_2(s)$	25.6	27.1	34.5	-73
$Ni(s)$	7.12	7.82	10.68	0
$Cl_2(g)$	53.31	54.25	57.65	0
$Ni(g)$	43.53	44.17	46.46	101.75

PHASE EQUILIBRIA

10

Several simple phase equilibria have already been discussed. These include the liquid-vapor, solid-vapor, solid-liquid, and solid-solid transformations in one-component systems (Chapter 6), the vapor pressures and boiling temperatures of binary solutions (Chapter 7), the colligative properties of dilute solutions (Chapter 8), and solid-gas reactions (Chapter 9). In proceeding now to discuss more complicated phase equilibria it is essential to introduce a new point of view to classify systems and clarify their relationships. This point of view is based upon the phase rule derived by Gibbs * in 1876.

Phases, Components, and Degrees of Freedom (Variance). A *phase* is a part of a system, uniform throughout in chemical composition and physical properties, which is separated from other homogeneous parts of the system by boundary surfaces. By the term number of phases, designated by p, is meant the number of different phases; for example, a system containing liquid water and many pieces of ice, but no gas phase, has only two phases. Also the number of phases does not depend upon the relative amounts of the various phases. Since gases are completely miscible with each other, there can be only a single gaseous phase in a system. The phase rule permits the calculation of the maximum number of phases which can be in equilibrium with each other.

The *number of components* c in a system is the smallest number of substances in terms of which the compositions of each of the phases in the system may be described separately. The number of components c may be obtained by counting all the chemical substances and sub-

* J. W. Gibbs, *Trans. Conn. Acad. Arts Sci.*, 1876–78; *The Collected Works of J. Willard Gibbs*, Vol. 1, Yale University Press, New Haven, Conn., reprinted 1948.

tracting the number of quantitative relations between concentrations of different substances. There are often several possible choices of components which are equally satisfactory. The choice of components is arbitrary, but the *number* of components is an important characteristic of a system. In this chapter we will restrict our attention to one-, two-, and three-component systems. There are the following three types of relations.

Chemical reactions. For each different chemical reaction the number of independent concentrations is reduced by one by the equilibrium expression. For example, if calcium oxide, calcium carbonate, and carbon dioxide are in equilibrium, the number of independent components is reduced by one because of the equilibrium expression for

$$CaCO_3(s) = CaO(s) + CO_2(g)$$

Initial conditions. There may be relationships between components due to specified initial conditions. For example, if only calcium carbonate (and no calcium oxide or carbon dioxide) is added to a system, the number of moles of calcium oxide and carbon dioxide formed will be equal. Because of this restriction and the mass-action expression, there is just one component even though the calcium carbonate is partially dissociated. As another example, at higher temperatures water is partially dissociated into hydrogen and oxygen. If the hydrogen and oxygen are formed only from water, $p_{H_2} = 2p_{O_2}$, and in addition there is the equilibrium expression

$$K_p = \frac{p_{H_2}p_{O_2}^{1/2}}{p_{H_2O}}$$

so that the number of independent components is $c = 3 - 2 = 1$. If hydrogen and oxygen are added to the system separately, there are two components.

Electroneutrality. Since electrical neutrality must be maintained, the total concentration of cations per liter must be equal to the total concentration of anions.

In general we may write

$$c = s - n - m \tag{1}$$

where s is the number of substances, n is the number of independent chemical reactions, and m is the number of relations between concentrations due to initial conditions and electrical neutrality.

The *number of degrees of freedom* or *variance* v of a system is the smallest number of independent variables (pressure, temperature, and concentrations of the various phases) that must be specified in order to describe completely the state of the system. As we have seen before, in order to describe the state of a pure gas it is necessary to specify only two variables, T and P or P and V or V and T, because the third variable can be calculated from the equation of state. Thus a pure gas has two degrees of freedom or a variance $v = 2$. A pure liquid or solid also has a variance of 2. However, if liquid water and water vapor are in equilibrium, we know that the state of the system may be completely described by giving only the temperature *or* pressure, there being only one temperature at which the saturation vapor pressure has a given value. For this case, $v = 1$. In order to specify the concentration of a binary solution it is necessary to specify the mole fraction of only one of the components, the mole fraction of the other being given by $X_2 = 1 - X_1$. The phase rule gives the relation between the number of components, the number of phases, and the variance for a system which is in a state of equilibrium.

Derivation of the Phase Rule. Consider a system in equilibrium which consists of p phases and c components. If a phase contains c components, its composition may be specified by stating $(c - 1)$ concentrations; one less than the number of components because the concentration of one component can be obtained from $\Sigma X_i = 1$, where X_i represents the mole fraction of component i. Thus the total number of concentrations to be specified for the whole system is $(c - 1)$ for each of the p phases or $(c - 1)p$ concentrations. In general, there are two more variables which have to be considered, temperature and pressure, so that the total number of independent variables is $(c - 1)p + 2$. We do not have to talk about the temperatures and pressures of the different phases separately because they are in equilibrium and so they are all at the same pressure and temperature (p. 116). In order to avoid consideration of pressure differences in systems which result from hydrostatic pressures it is assumed that the system is removed from a gravitational field. If temperature or pressure was held constant, the number of independent variables would be $(c - 1)p + 1$. On the other hand, if the system was affected by another independent variable, such as magnetic field strength, the number of independent variables would be $(c - 1)p + 3$.

Next we consider the number of relationships which must be satisfied at equilibrium. The chemical potential μ (p. 114) for each component is the same in each phase α, β, γ, etc., and $\mu_{i,\alpha} = \mu_{i,\beta} = \mu_{i,\gamma} = \cdots$ for the component i. Altogether there are c components, each one of which can be involved in an equilibrium between phases. There are p phases but only $(p - 1)$ equilibrium relationships for each component. For example, if there are two phases, there is nevertheless only one equilibrium relationship for each component. Thus there is a total of $c(p-1)$ equilibrium relations.

The variance v is equal to the total number of variables minus the total number of equilibrium and stoichiometric relations between these variables; that is, v is the additional number of variables which must be specified in order to define the system completely. Thus, for systems in which pressure, temperature, and concentration are the only variables,

$$v = [p(c-1) + 2] - c(p-1)$$

or

$$v = c - p + 2 \tag{2}$$

This is the important phase rule of Gibbs.

It can be seen from this equation that, the greater the number of components in a system, the greater is the number of degrees of freedom or variance. On the other hand, the greater the number of phases the smaller is the number of variables such as temperature, pressure, and concentration that must be specified to describe the system completely.

In discussing various phase equilibria by use of phase diagrams it will be useful to consider the variance of the system under various conditions. All systems of the same variance will be found to have certain characteristics in common.

The phase rule is of great value in solving practical problems such as the preparation of alloys or salts from complicated mixtures and the adjustment of temperature, pressure, and composition to obtain a desired product. The extraction of potassium chloride from the Stassfurt salt deposits was one of the early examples. The guidance afforded by the phase rule has led to the discovery of many new substances.

The Phase Diagram for One-Component Systems. The application of the phase rule to water may be discussed with reference to Fig. 6-3. Three general areas are labeled in which ice, liquid water, or vapor can exist alone. The mere statement that a single phase is present does not completely describe the system, nor is it sufficient to state that a single phase is present at a particular temperature. In order to define the system completely in these one-phase regions, it is necessary to specify both the pressure and the temperature. In terms of the phase rule there is only one component, water, and in each area there is only one phase, and so $v = c - p + 2 = 1 - 1 + 2 = 2$. Since the variance is 2, both the temperature and pressure must be specified in order to define the system.

Two areas touch along the lines, and so along each line two phases exist in equilibrium. If two phases are present, it is necessary to specify only the temperature or the pressure in order to define the system. For example, if both liquid water and water vapor are present at $25°$, it is not necessary to specify the pressure because it has been found by experiment that liquid water and its vapor can exist together at $25°$ only under a pressure of 23.7 mm.

The pressure at any temperature may be read from the vapor-pressure curve. Likewise, if the pressure is stated, the temperature may be determined from the graph. A single variable, either temperature or pressure, is sufficient to completely describe the system along a line, since the variance $v = c - p + 2 = 1 - 2 + 2 = 1$.

Along lines AC and AD there are also two phases present, and so it is necessary to specify only one variable, either temperature or pressure, to describe the system completely.

When three phases are present, it is not necessary to specify either temperature or pressure, for there is only one temperature and one pressure which will permit all three phases to exist together in equilibrium. If the temperature is raised at constant pressure, the ice and liquid will vaporize, leaving only vapor; if the temperature is lowered, there will be only ice; if the pressure on the vapor is raised at constant temperature, the vapor will condense; and, finally, if the pressure is lowered, the liquid and ice will vaporize. The variance v is zero because there are three phases and $v = 1 - 3 + 2 = 0$, and this point is called a triple point.

A substance may exist in more than one solid form, and the reversible transition of one solid form into another may be represented in a P-T diagram in the same way as melting. If the two solid forms can exist in equilibrium with each other, the transformation is called an enantiotropic change. An example is provided by sulfur, for which the phase diagram is given in $Fig.$ 10-1. If rhombic sulfur is heated very slowly under its own vapor pressure, it is converted at $95.6°$ to the monoclinic form, which then melts at $120°$. However, if rhombic sulfur is heated rapidly, this transition to the monoclinic form does not have time to occur at $95.6°$ and the melting is observed at $115°$, the metastable triple point indicated by the intersection of the two dashed lines. The monoclinic form of sulfur may be avoided even with slow heating and maintenance of equilibrium conditions if the rhombic form is subjected to pressures above 1400 atm. At P, rhombic, monoclinic, and liquid sulfur are in equilibrium. Thus there are three triple points, D, B, and P, and a metastable triple point C. The phase behavior of sulfur is actually somewhat more complicated than shown

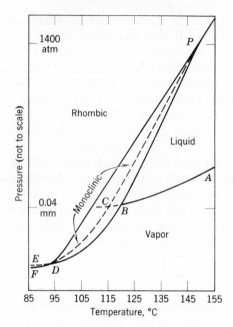

Fig. 10-1.   Pressure-temperature diagram for sulfur which has two different crystalline forms.

because of the existence of polymeric forms in the liquid state which are not rapidly interconvertible.

Exercise I.   List the phases present for each area, line, and point in Fig. 10-1 and calculate the variance at each.

BINARY SYSTEMS

The phase behavior of a binary system may be represented by a three-dimensional plot of temperature, pressure, and mole fraction. Such a plot has already been shown in Fig. 7-13 for a binary system in the region where only vapor and a single liquid phase exist. The complete diagram for such a system would include the region in which there is equilibrium between solid and liquid phases as well and perhaps a region of partial miscibility of the two liquids.

The phase rule for a binary system becomes $v = 2 - p + 2 = 4 - p$. Thus, if there is a single phase the system is trivariant, and the temperature, pressure, and mole fraction of one of the components must be specified in order to describe the system completely.   If two phases are present, the equilibrium condition is represented by a surface in a

P-T-X plot, and only two variables need be specified in order to describe the system completely. If three phases are present, the system is univariant. If four phases are present, the system is invariant.

In order to simplify the description of binary systems we will make extensive use of sections through the complete three-dimensional diagram. For example, if the pressure is sufficiently high, there will be a region in which there are only solid-liquid equilibria and pressure is not a significant variable. Then temperature is the only variable in addition to mole fraction, and the phase rule becomes $v = 2 - p + 1 = 3 - p$. As an illustration we will consider first diagrams involving only two liquids and then diagrams involving only liquids and solids.

Systems Consisting of Two Liquid Phases. The mutual solubilities of n-butanol and water are shown as a function of temperature in *Fig. 10-2*. This phase diagram is determined by preparing various mixtures of n-butanol and water, heating till the two liquids are completely soluble in each other and one homogeneous liquid phase is produced, and then cooling till two liquid phases appear. The temperature is recorded at which a slight cloudiness first appears, due to the formation of droplets of a second immiscible liquid phase with different refractive index. Temperatures for several mixtures are plotted, and the smooth curve ABC is drawn. The pressure is maintained sufficiently high so that no vapor is formed, and the solution does not boil.

Points in such a diagram may also be determined by titration. If one starts with pure water and adds increasing quantities of n-butanol,

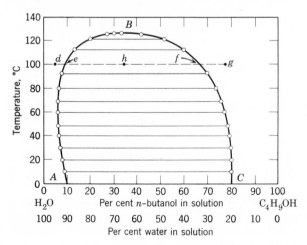

Fig. 10-2. Influence of temperature on the mutual solubilities of n-butanol and water.

a concentration eventually will be reached at which the solution separates into two layers. This concentration at $0°$ is represented by the point A. When the temperature is raised, the solubility of butanol in water decreases slightly at first and then increases, as shown by the curve AB. In like manner, if one starts with pure butanol and adds increasing amounts of water at $0°$, separation into two layers occurs at a concentration represented by the point C. As the temperature is raised, the solubility of water in butanol increases, as shown by the curve CB. When the temperature is raised above $126°$, corresponding to the height of the point B, butanol and water become soluble in all proportions. This temperature, above which there cannot be more than one liquid phase no matter what the composition, is called the *critical solution temperature*.

If one starts with a solution at a temperature and composition represented by the point d, the addition of increasing amounts of butanol at constant temperature is represented by the dashed line $defg$. When the point e is reached, the solution separates into two layers. As more butanol is added, the quantity of the butanol layer saturated with water increases, but the composition of each of the two layers remains constant and is given by e or f. Beyond f the solution again becomes homogeneous, and the addition of more butanol increases the concentration of butanol in the solution, as, for example, at g. In the area outside the line ABC there is only one liquid phase, $v = 3 - 1 = 2$, and so both the temperature and composition must be specified in order to define the system completely. In the area inside the line ABC there are two liquid phases, $v = 2 - 2 + 1 = 1$, and so if the temperature is specified the system is completely defined because the compositions of both liquid phases can be read from the intersections of the temperature line with the line ABC. Alternatively, if the composition of one phase is specified, the temperature can be determined from the line AB or BC, and the intersection of this temperature line with the other part of the curve gives the composition of the second phase. Such a line, which connects the compositions of two phases which are in equilibrium, is called a *tie line*. The relative amounts of the two phases can be calculated by measuring the distance along the tie line from the point representing the gross composition of the mixture to the points representing the two equilibrium solutions. For example, if a 35 per cent n-butanol solution is heated to $100°$, the gross composition is represented by point h and the two phases have compositions e and f. At an over-all composition a little richer in butanol than corresponds to e most of the material will be in the water phase saturated with butanol. As the over-all composition is moved to the right, the ratio of the f phase to the e phase increases. At the over-all composition corresponding to h the ratio of the e phase to the f phase will be the ratio hf/he.

There is a close connection between the mutual solubility of liquids and deviations from Raoult's law. If the positive deviations from Raoult's law are sufficiently large, the components will not be completely soluble in each other.

Some liquid mixtures show a minimum in the solubility curve rather than a maximum; this is a result of chemical interactions.

Systems Consisting of Two Liquid Phases and Vapor. Figure 10-2 represents the n-butanol–water system for the case that the pressure is sufficiently high so that there is no vapor phase. If the pressure is held constant at 1 atm, the liquids will be vaporized at a sufficiently high temperature; in this case the system boils below the critical solution temperature. The phase diagram at 1 atm shown in *Fig. 10-3* has a similarity to the phase diagram for a system with a minimum-boiling azeotrope (p. 161). The part of the figure $FDEG$, which gives the mutual solubilities of the two liquids, is the same as Fig. 10-2, but the system boils before it becomes homogeneous. Between compositions D and E two phases are present at the boiling point, and the boiling temperature is independent of the relative amounts of the two phases. At the boiling point of the two-phase mixture the composition of the water-rich phase is given by D, the composition of the butanol-rich

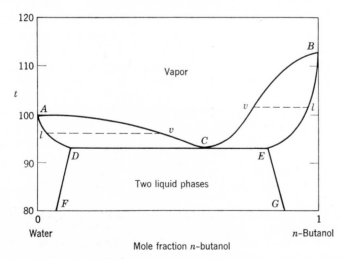

Fig. 10-3. Boiling-point diagram for water–n-butanol at 1 atm [data of J. S. Stockhardt and C. M. Hull, *Ind. Eng. Chem.*, *23*, 1438 (1931)].

phase by E, and the composition of the vapor by C. If the gross composition of the two-phase mixture lies between C and E, the vapor is richer in water than the mixture and so the relative amount of phase D decreases on continued boiling until only phase E remains. The temperature will then rise along the line EB, and the composition of the vapor at any liquid composition can be determined by drawing a tie line similar to vl. When the mixture is distilled at a lower pressure, the boiling point is lower and the range of immiscibility is wider.

Systems Consisting of Solid and Liquid Phases. The simplest type of binary system consisting of only solid and liquid phases is one in which the components are completely miscible in the liquid state and completely immiscible in the solid state, so that only the pure solid phases separate on cooling solutions. Such a phase diagram is illustrated in *Fig. 10-4.* Here again the diagram is for a constant pressure sufficiently high that there is no vapor phase. Such a diagram may be determined by studying the rate of cooling of solutions of various compositions.

When a *pure liquid* cools, the plot of temperature versus time is continuous. However, at the temperature at which the solid crystallizes out, the cooling curve becomes horizontal if the cooling is slow enough. The halt in the cooling curve results from the evolution of heat in the freezing process. Such horizontal sections are evident in the cooling curves for bismuth (labeled 0% Cd) and cadmium in Fig. 10-4 at 273° and 323°, respectively.

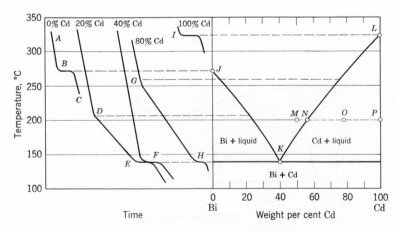

Fig. 10-4. Cooling curves and the temperature-concentration phase diagram for the system bismuth–cadmium.

When a *solution* is cooled, there is a change in slope of the cooling curve at the temperature at which one of the components begins to crystallize out. The change in slope is due to the evolution of heat by the progressive crystallization of the solid as the solution is cooled and to the change in heat capacity. Such changes in slope are evident in the cooling curves for 20 per cent cadmium and 80 per cent cadmium. These curves also show horizontal sections, both at 140°. At this temperature both solid cadmium and solid bismuth come out together. The temperature at which this occurs is called a *eutectic temperature*. A solution of cadmium and bismuth containing 40 per cent cadmium shows a single plateau F at 140°, and so this is the eutectic composition.

The temperatures at which new phases appear, as indicated by the cooling curves, are then transferred to the temperature-composition diagram as shown at the right in Fig. 10-4. In the area above JKL there is one liquid phase and $v = c - p + 1 = 2 - 1 + 1 = 2$. Along JK bismuth freezes out, and along LK cadmium freezes out. Thus along line JK and in the area under it and down to the eutectic temperature K there are two phases, solid bismuth and a solution having a composition which is determined by the temperature. Since $v = 2 - 2 + 1 = 1$, the system is univariant. When either the temperature or the composition of the liquid phase is specified, the other may be found from the diagram on the line JK. Also along the line KL and in the area under it there are two phases, solid cadmium and solution, and accordingly $v = 1$.

At the eutectic point K there are three phases—solid bismuth, solid cadmium, and liquid solution containing 40 per cent cadmium. Then $v = 2 - 3 + 1 = 0$, and so this is an invariant point. There is only one temperature and one composition of solution at which these three phases can exist together at equilibrium.

The area below the eutectic temperature K is a two-phase area in which solid bismuth and solid cadmium are present, and $v = 2 - 2 + 1 = 1$. Only the temperature need be specified to describe the system completely. The ratio of bismuth to cadmium may change, but there are only pure bismuth and pure cadmium, and there is no need to specify any concentration. The eutectic has a fine grain structure, but it is not a phase; it is simply a mixture of bismuth and cadmium as two separate phases.

Looking at the line $MNOP$, it is clear that M represents a 50–50 solution of bismuth and cadmium at 200°. As pure cadmium is added to this solution at 200°, it dissolves and increases the concentration of cadmium in the solution until the solution becomes saturated at N.

Further addition of pure cadmium will not make any further change in the composition of the liquid, but the ratio of solid cadmium to the solution of composition N continues to increase along the line NOP. When the gross composition is given by point O, there are equal weights of pure cadmium and solution of composition N because length NO is equal to length OP.

Curves JK and LK in Fig. 10-4 may be looked at as either freezing-point curves or solubility curves. For example, if cadmium is added to bismuth, the freezing point is lowered along the line JK. Alternatively this line gives the solubility of bismuth in liquid cadmium; at $200°$, for example, 78 weight per cent bismuth may be dissolved in liquid cadmium. Addition of more bismuth causes a solid bismuth phase to appear. If ideal solutions are formed, the solubility of one component in the other may be calculated by use of equation 20 in Chapter 8. The heat of fusion is used for the heat of solution. The differential enthalpy of solution, $\Delta \overline{H}_{sat}$, in a saturated solution at a particular temperature may be calculated using

$$\frac{\partial \ln X_1}{\partial T} = \frac{\Delta \overline{H}_{sat}}{RT^2} \tag{3}$$

Exercise II. Assuming that bismuth and cadmium form ideal solutions, plot lines JK and LK, using equation 23 in Chapter 8. The heat of fusion of cadmium is 1450 cal g-atom^{-1}, and the heat of fusion of bismuth is 2500 cal g-atom^{-1}. The heat of solution may depend significantly upon the temperature, but it is relatively constant over a narrow range of temperature.

The solubilities of a few crystalline substances in water at different temperatures are given in *Fig. 10-5*. They are expressed in grams of solute per 100 grams of solution, that is, in per cent by weight. Solubilities are also often expressed in terms of molality, molarity, or mole fractions.

Exercise III. The solubility data for $Ba(OH)_2 \cdot 8H_2O$ are as follows: $0°$, 0.0974 molal; $10°$, 0.1447 molal; $20°$, 0.227 molal. Calculate the differential heat of solution of a mole of $Ba(OH)_2 \cdot 8H_2O$ in a saturated aqueous solution, and predict the solubility at $30°$. The experimentally determined value at $30°$ is 0.326 molal.

The solubility of a solid in a liquid depends upon several factors. When a solid is placed in an evacuated vessel, volatilization goes on and the concentration of molecules in the gas phase increases until the sublimation pressure is reached and the vapor and solid are in equilibrium. However, when the solid is placed in contact with a liquid, the amount dissolved is generally much greater than the amount which would sublime into the same volume. This is a result of the interaction of the liquid with the molecules or ions of the solvent. In aqueous solu-

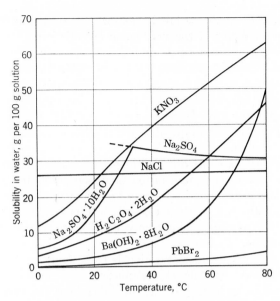

Fig. 10-5. Influence of temperature on the solubility of solids.

tions this interaction with the solvent is called *hydration*. The general term is *solvation*.

Sodium chloride will not dissolve, for example, in benzene or carbon tetrachloride because these liquids have no appreciable dipole moment (p. 501), and no attractive force exists between them and the sodium or chloride ions. However, sodium chloride is very soluble in water because the ions become hydrated by the molecules of water, which have a large dipole moment. If the heat evolved by hydration of the dissolved solute nearly offsets the heat absorbed in pulling molecules or ions out of the solid crystal, the over-all heat of solution is nearly zero. Sodium chloride is an example of a solute which neither evolves nor absorbs much heat when it dissolves in water. According to equation 3, the solubility of such a solute is not changed much by a change in temperature. Most salts have a higher solubility at higher temperatures, and by equation 3 an endothermic heat of solution. A few salts are known for which the process of solution is exothermic, that is, the energy released on hydration is greater than that absorbed in pulling apart the units of the crystal; and, in agreement with equation 3, the solubility then decreases as the temperature rises.

It is well recognized that the rate of solution of solute in a solvent is greatly accelerated by pulverizing the material so as to expose a larger area to the solvent. Quite apart from this effect, the actual equilibrium solubility of very small crystals is greater than that of large crystals. The greater solubility of the very small crystals is analogous to the higher vapor pressure of small droplets of liquid (p. 600). This increase in solubility with decreasing size is not a significant factor unless the crystals are extremely small. However, if a mixture of large crystals and very small ones is allowed to stand, the small ones disappear and the larger ones grow larger—a procedure which is followed in the digesting of precipitates in quantitative analysis to render them better suited for filtration.

Supersaturated solutions are solutions that contain more than the equilibrium-saturation concentration of dissolved solute. Supersaturated solutions of highly soluble solutes can sometimes be prepared by cooling the saturated solution carefully without agitation and with special precautions to eliminate any trace of solid particles of the crystalline solute.

The explanation of supersaturation is to be found in the fact that the submicroscopic crystals, crystal nuclei, which would normally be the first to deposit have a higher solubility, and the crystallization process cannot start easily. When a larger crystal of the solute is introduced, however, the extra dissolved material crystallizes out immediately.

Extremely small crystalline particles, occurring, for example, as dust in a room, provide nuclei on which crystals can form. Supersaturation can sometimes be relieved also by vibrations due to friction on glass or metal surfaces immersed in the solution. Important advances are being made in the study of nucleation which have practical applications in control of crystallization.

Compound Formation. The components of a binary system may react to form a solid compound which exists in equilibrium with liquid over a range of composition. This is illustrated by *Fig. 10-6* for the zinc-magnesium system. The composition which corresponds to the maximum temperature is the composition of the compound. On the mole per cent scale such maxima come at 50 per cent, 33 per cent, 25 per cent, etc., corresponding to integer ratios of the components of 1 to 1, 1 to 2, 1 to 3, etc. The phase diagram may be considered to consist simply of two phase diagrams of the type we have discussed placed side by side. In this case the one on the left is that formed by Zn and $MgZn_2$, and the one on the right is that formed by $MgZn_2$ and Mg.

In Fig. 10-6 the maximum falls at a composition corresponding to $MgZn_2$, which has a melting point of 590°. When Zn is added to melted $MgZn_2$, the freezing point is lowered along the curve CB; when

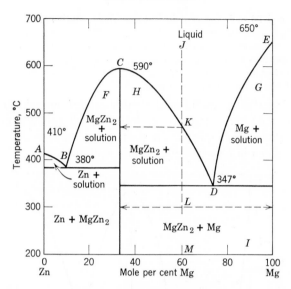

Fig. 10-6. Temperature-composition diagram, showing a maximum for the system zinc-magnesium.

Mg is added, the freezing point is lowered along CD. The compound $MgZn_2$ freezes out in both cases.

A broad, flat maximum in a temperature-composition diagram shows that the compound dissociates readily, whereas a sharp maximum coming to a narrow peak indicates that the dissociation in solution is slight.

Example 1. State the phases present and the variance at B, F, G, H, J, and L in Fig. 10-6.

	Phases	Variance			Phases	Variance
B	Solution, Zn, $MgZn_2$	0		H	Solution, $MgZn_2$	1
F	Solution, $MgZn_2$	1		J	Solution	2
G	Solution, Mg	1		L	$MgZn_2$, Mg	1

In the region H, it is sufficient to specify either temperature or concentration of the liquid phase. The ratio of amount of $MgZn_2$ to amount of liquid is not counted as a variable, because the phase rule does not deal with the relative amounts of various phases.

Example 2. Six-tenths mole of Mg and 0.40 mole of Zn are heated to 650°, represented by point J in Fig. 10-6. Describe what happens when this solution is cooled down to 200°, as indicated by the vertical line. (The experiment would have to be done in an inert atmosphere to prevent oxidation by air.) At 470° point K is reached and solid $MgZn_2$ is thrown out of solution. The freezing point is gradually lowered as the solution becomes richer in Mg. At 400° a considerable amount of $MgZn_2$ has come out of solution, leaving a solution of 0.68 mole fraction Mg and 0.32 mole fraction Zn. Finally, at 347°, when the liquid is 74 mole per cent in Mg and 26 mole per cent in Zn, the whole solution freezes, solid $MgZn_2$ and solid Mg coming out together.

From this temperature down to 200° there is no further change in the phases. At all temperatures below 347° there are pure solids Mg and $MgZn_2$. Since all the Zn present is in the form of $MgZn_2$, there is 0.20 mole of this compound and 0.40 mole of Mg in the eutectic mixture.

Phase diagrams are useful in the study of aqueous solutions as well as metallic solutions. Definite hydrates which produce maxima in phase diagrams are frequently encountered in aqueous solutions. An example is given in *Fig. 10-7* for sulfuric acid and water.

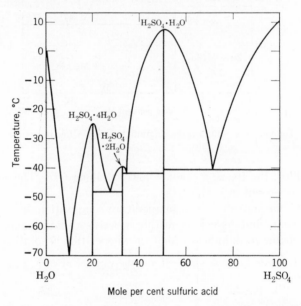

Fig. 10-7. Temperature-composition diagram for the system water–sulfuric acid.

When sulfuric acid is added to water, the freezing point is lowered, as shown by the line along which there is an equilibrium between solid ice and the liquid solution of sulfuric acid in water. This lowering continues until at about 10 mole per cent of sulfuric acid there is a eutectic temperature of about $-70°$. Further addition of sulfuric acid to the solution at temperatures below $-25°$ leads to the precipitation of a new solid phase $H_2SO_4 \cdot 4H_2O$. At the first eutectic there are two solid phases, ice and $H_2SO_4 \cdot 4H_2O$, and one liquid phase (10 mole per cent sulfuric acid), so that $v = 0$. In aqueous solutions a eutectic point is called a *cryohydric* point, and the eutectic mixture is called a *cryohydrate*.

When there are exactly 4 moles of water to 1 of sulfuric acid, the solution freezes sharply at the freezing point of this pure compound.

Addition of more sulfuric acid to the solution lowers the freezing point along the line leading to a second cryohydric point.

It is found that there are three compounds of sulfuric acid and water and four cryohydrates or eutectic mixtures. The chemical compound $H_2SO_4 \cdot H_2O$ melts 8.0° above the freezing point of water.

It is interesting to consider what happens when water is removed (by evaporation) from dilute sulfuric acid, isothermally at 0°. The remaining solution becomes more concentrated in sulfuric acid through loss of water, and the concentration moves along a horizontal line to the right until the solubility curve for $H_2SO_4 \cdot H_2O$ is intersected and crystals are formed. The solution gradually solidifies, but on further removal of water another solubility curve is intersected, and the crystals disappear. This alternate crystallization and melting by removal of water vapor would be difficult to understand without the phase diagram. Diagrams of this type are of great practical importance for obtaining specified products or properties through the control of concentration and temperature.

Incongruent Melting Point. Instead of melting, a compound may decompose into another compound and a solution, when heated to a definite temperature. Such a melting point is called an incongruent melting point and is illustrated in *Fig. 10-8*, which shows part of the phase diagram for the sodium sulfate-water system.

When pure $Na_2SO_4 \cdot 10H_2O$ is heated, it undergoes a transition at 32.38° to give anhydrous Na_2SO_4 and solution of composition C. The

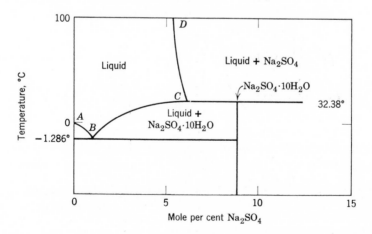

Fig. 10-8. Part of the phase diagram for $Na_2SO_4 \cdot H_2O$ showing incongruent melting of $Na_2SO_4 \cdot 10H_2O$ to rhombic anhydrous Na_2SO_4.

line BC gives the solubility of $Na_2SO_4 \cdot 10H_2O$ in water, and the line CD gives the solubility of Na_2SO_4 in water. These curves represent the same data as the solubility curves for Na_2SO_4 in Fig. 10-5. Below the transition temperature of $32.38°$ the solid phase in equilibrium with the solution is $Na_2SO_4 \cdot 10H_2O$, and above this temperature the solid phase is Na_2SO_4.

When the three phases Na_2SO_4, $Na_2SO_4 \cdot 10H_2O$, and saturated solution are in equilibrium with each other at constant temperature and pressure, the system is invariant.

Sodium sulfate crystals have been used for the storage of heat in solar-heated houses. When the temperature is above $32.38°$, the $Na_2SO_4 \cdot 10H_2O$ is dissociated and heat is absorbed. When it is below $32.38°$, the Na_2SO_4 becomes hydrated and evolves heat.

Systems Forming Solid Solutions. Often pure solid freezes out of a solution, but in other cases the solute crystallizes out with the solvent, forming a solid solution. Solid solutions are formed by iodine dissolved in benzene. When the temperature is lowered to about $5°$, the crystals of benzene which freeze out are colored with iodine, and the amount of iodine dissolved in the solid is proportional to the concentration of iodine in the liquid solution. There is a distribution of iodine between the liquid and solid phases, just as there is distribution between two immiscible solvents. A continuous series of solid solutions may be formed, as illustrated in *Fig. 10-9* for platinum and gold. The two lines in this diagram give the compositions of the liquid solutions (upper line) and solid solutions (lower line) which are in equilibrium with each other

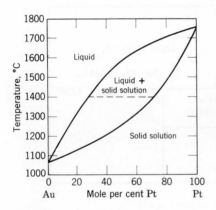

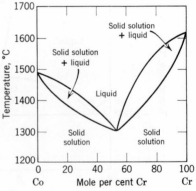

Fig. 10-9. Phase diagram for gold-platinum showing solid solutions.

Fig. 10-10. Phase diagram for cobalt-chromium showing two series of solid solutions.

analogous to the phase diagram for two miscible liquids, as shown in Fig. 7-1. In studying these solid solutions, it is convenient to remember that the liquid phase is richer in that component or mixture which has the lower melting point.

Above the upper line of Fig. 10-9 the two metals exist in liquid solutions; below the lower line the two metals exist in solid solutions. The upper curve is the freezing-point curve for the liquid, and the lower one is the melting-point curve for the solid. The space between the two curves represents mixtures of the two—one liquid solution and one solid solution in equilibrium. For example, a mixture containing 50 mole per cent gold and 50 mole per cent platinum, when brought to equilibrium at 1400°, will consist of two phases, a solid solution containing 70 mole per cent platinum and a liquid solution containing 28 mole per cent platinum. If the original mixture contained 60 mole per cent platinum, there would still be the same two liquid and solid solutions at 1400° of the same compositions, 70 and 28 mole per cent, but there would be a relatively greater amount of the solid solution which contains 70 mole per cent platinum.

It is possible to separate substances which form an unbroken series of solid solutions by fractional crystallization just as it was shown to be possible, in Fig. 7-9, to separate two completely miscible compounds by fractional distillation. For example, if it is desired to separate pure gold from an alloy containing 70 per cent platinum, the alloy is melted and cooled suddenly to 1400° to give a liquid richer in gold, which is removed and frozen completely. It is then melted and cooled to give liquid still richer in gold, and so on until nearly pure gold is obtained.

The fractional crystallization of solid solutions is seriously complicated by the fact that the attainment of equilibrium is much slower in solid solutions than in liquid solutions. It takes a considerable length of time, particularly at low temperatures, for a change in concentration at the surface to affect the concentration at a point in the interior of the solid solution. Slow diffusion does take place, however.

In view of the use of the freezing point as a criterion of purity it is important to note that when solid solutions are formed the freezing point may be *raised* by the presence of the other component.

Solid solutions may have minima in the freezing-point curves analogous to the minimum shown in the boiling-point curve in Fig. 7-10. An example is given by cobalt and chromium, for which the phase diagram is given in *Fig. 10-10*. Again, the substance or mixture with the lowest melting point is in excess in the liquid phase. In this case it is the mixture of 56 per cent chromium, melting at 1300°, which has the lowest melting point. There are two sets of solid solutions, those with less than 56 per cent chromium and those with more than 56 per cent chromium. It is theoretically possible to separate pure chromium from solutions having more than 56 per cent chromium and pure cobalt from solutions having less than 56 per cent chromium, but it is not possible to separate pure chromium starting with a solution containing less than 56 per cent chromium.

Many properties of alloys, ceramics, and structural materials depend on the presence of solid solutions. The hardening and tempering of steel involve the existence of solid solutions of carbon in different iron-carbon compounds. The solid solution stable at the high temperatures is hard; in order to retain this hardness, the proper compositions and temperatures are obtained, as indicated by the phase diagrams, and then the steel is quenched quickly in oil or water, so that it does not have time to form the solid solution which is stable at lower temperatures. By heating the steel again to a somewhat lower temperature, opportunity is given for partial conversion to the softer solid solution which is stable at the lower temperature. In this way the steel may be given different degrees of hardening.

Partial Miscibility of Solid Solutions. Sometimes partial miscibility is encountered in the solid state just as it is in the liquid state. When this occurs the diagram becomes analogous to that for a partially miscible liquid system, such as that shown in Fig. 10-3. The silver-copper system is an example of partial miscibility of solids. As shown by *Fig. 10-11*, at 800° copper dissolves in solid silver to the extent of 6 per cent by weight and silver dissolves in copper to the extent of 2 per cent by weight. At the eutectic point pure copper and silver do not crystallize out, but saturated solid solutions do. The regions α and

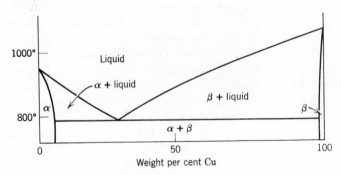

Fig. 10-11. Phase diagram for silver-copper showing partial miscibility of solid solutions.

β represent continuously variable solid solutions, and the variance v is 2 in these regions because there is a single phase.

Solid-Gas Equilibria. For the preceding phase diagrams for binary systems the pressure has been held constant and high enough so that there is no vapor phase. In order to represent the effect of pressure an additional coordinate is required. Concentration may be plotted along one axis and temperature and pressure along two other axes, giving a space model as shown in *Fig. 10-12* for the system copper sulfate and water.

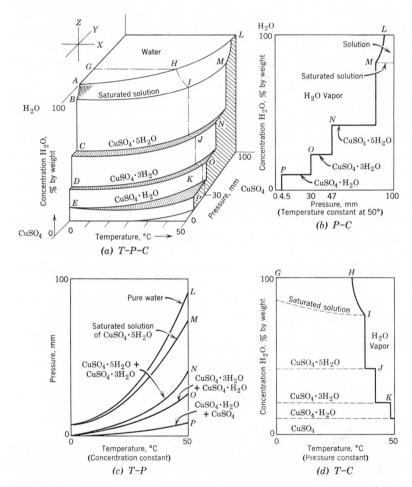

Fig. 10-12. Space model showing concentrations, temperature, and pressure for the system cupric sulfate–water.

Temperature is plotted horizontally along the X axis, concentration of water is plotted vertically along the Z axis, and pressure is plotted along the Y axis in the horizontal plane. The concentrations of water corresponding to the copper sulfate crystals with increasing amounts of water of crystallization are plotted vertically, leading at the higher concentrations of water to a saturated solution, then to unsaturated solutions, and finally to, pure water.

This space model is complete but is awkward to handle, and so it is convenient to project lines onto planes which are perpendicular to the three axes. First we consider (b), a cross section through the diagram at a temperature of $50°$. This constant-temperature plane intersects the surface of the figure along $LMNOP$. If a dilute solution of $CuSO_4$ is placed in an evacuated desiccator at $50°$ and water vapor removed so slowly that equilibrium is essentially maintained, the water-vapor pressure will change along the line in this figure.

As water is removed from the solution, the concentration of $CuSO_4$ increases, and the vapor pressure of the solution decreases along the line LM. When the solution becomes saturated, the pressure remains constant, as shown by the vertical line at M, while the water is removed from the saturated solution. The gross composition of the system changes as water is removed, and the relative amounts of saturated solution and $CuSO_4 \cdot 5H_2O$ change. However, the compositions of the two phases do not change; hence, the vapor pressure remains constant. Finally, when all the solution has disappeared, the pressure drops abruptly to 47 mm at N. The pressure over a mixture of $CuSO_4 \cdot 5H_2O$ and $CuSO_4 \cdot 3H_2O$ remains constant at 47 mm. When all the $CuSO_4 \cdot 5H_2O$ has been dehydrated to $CuSO_4 \cdot 3H_2O$, the partial pressure of water drops abruptly to 30 mm at O and remains constant until 2 more moles of water have been lost per mole of $CuSO_4$ at P. Then the water-vapor pressure drops to 4.5 mm and remains constant until dehydration is complete. In practice, the lines are less steep because of the slow diffusion of the water vapor.

The several equilibria may be represented as follows:

$$CuSO_4 \text{ (sat soln)} = CuSO_4 \cdot 5H_2O(s) + xH_2O(g)$$

$$CuSO_4 \cdot 5H_2O(s) = CuSO_4 \cdot 3H_2O(s) + 2H_2O(g)$$

$$CuSO_4 \cdot 3H_2O(s) = CuSO_4 \cdot H_2O(s) + 2H_2O(g)$$

$$CuSO_4 \cdot H_2O(s) = CuSO_4(s) + H_2O(g)$$

Since the activities of the solids are constant at constant temperature, an equilibrium constant for the second equilibrium, for example, can be written

$$K_p = p_{H_2O}{}^2$$

Similar equilibrium constants can be written for the other reactions. The vapor pressure is constant only when an equilibrium exists, and an equilibrium can exist only when two hydrated salts and water vapor (or a saturated solution and the highest hydrate) are present together.

The water partial pressures for these various equilibria are plotted in Fig. 10-12c as a function of temperature. The enthalpy changes for the above reactions could be calculated from plots of log K versus $1/T$.

The T-C diagram is shown in Fig. 10-12d, which indicates a section of the space model cut at a constant pressure of 30 mm along $GHIJK$.

Exercise IV. Apply the phase rule to the three-dimensional model, Fig. 10-12a, and calculate the variance v at typical points, lines, areas, and volumes.

Mixtures of two hydrates of a given crystalline salt are useful in establishing definite partial pressures of water. There are many different hydrated salts to choose from, so that it is possible to obtain a wide variety of pressures. If the humidity of the air is greater than that corresponding to the fixed partial pressure of water, the excess water will be removed by the lower hydrate. If the humidity of the air is less, water will be supplied by the higher hydrate and thus the water content of the air will be maintained constant.

TERNARY SYSTEMS

For a ternary system the phase rule yields $v = 5 - p$. If there is a single phase $v = 4$, and so a complete geometrical representation would require the use of four-dimensional space. If the pressure is constant a three-dimensional representation may be used, and one is shown later (Fig. 10-15). If both the temperature and pressure are constant $v = 3 - p$. The system, therefore, is bivariant when one phase is present, univariant when two phases are present, and invariant when three phases are present.

Graphical Representation. The equilibrium diagram for a ternary system at constant T and P may be plotted in rectangular coordinates by plotting the weight fraction of one component horizontally and the weight fraction of another vertically. The weight fraction of the third may be calculated from the fact that the sum of the three weight fractions is unity. However, to obtain a symmetrical representation for three components in a plane, it is necessary to use an equilateral triangle.

In an equilateral triangle, the sum of the distances from any given point to the three sides, along the perpendiculars to the sides, is equal to the height of the triangle. The distance from each apex to the center of the opposite side of the equilateral triangle is divided into 100 parts, corresponding to percentage composition, and the composition corresponding to a given point is readily obtained by measuring the perpendicular distance to the three sides. For example, in *Fig. 10-13* point F

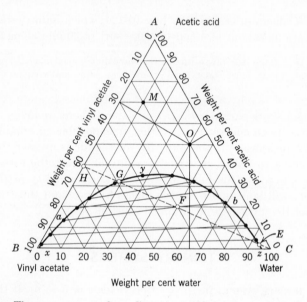

Fig. 10-13. Three-component phase diagram at 25° showing regions of miscibility and immiscibility.

represents a mixture with a gross composition of 20 per cent by weight acetic acid, 30 per cent by weight vinyl acetate, and 50 per cent by weight water.

A useful property of such a diagram is that a line from one apex of the diagram to a point on the opposite side, such as CH in Fig. 10-13, represents the compositions of all possible mixtures which have the same relative amounts of the other two components.

Of the many possible kinds of ternary systems we will consider only certain types formed by three liquids and by a liquid and two solids.

Systems Formed by Three Liquids. If two pairs of the liquids are completely miscible and one pair is partially miscible, a diagram of the type illustrated in Fig. 10-13 is obtained. This figure represents the system water–acetic acid–vinyl acetate at 25° and atmospheric pressure.*

When water is added to vinyl acetate along the line BC the water dissolves at first, forming a homogeneous solution. However, as more water is added, saturation is reached at composition x, and there are two liquid phases, vinyl acetate saturated with water and a little water saturated with vinyl acetate, having the composition z. As more water is added, the amount of the z phase increases and that of the x phase decreases, but the composition of each phase remains always the same. Finally, when the per cent of water exceeds that given by z, there is only one liquid phase, an unsaturated solution of vinyl acetate in water. At all compositions between x and z there are two liquid phases with compositions x and z.

If acetic acid, which is miscible with vinyl acetate and water in all proportions, is added, it is distributed between the two layers, forming two ternary solutions of vinyl acetate, water, and acetic acid which are in equilibrium with each other, provided that the gross composition of the mixture falls in the region below the xyz curve. For example, if the gross composition is represented by F, the two phases which are in equilibrium are represented by points a and b, as given by the tie line aFb.

Other tie lines are shown for other gross compositions; usually tie lines are not parallel to each other or to a side of the triangle. The compositions of the two phases which are in equilibrium with each other, corresponding to the intersection of the tie line with the curves xy and zy, have to be determined experimentally. As more acid is added, the two phases become more alike, and the tie lines become shorter. Ultimately, when the compositions of the two solutions become identical, the tie line shrinks to the single point y. Point y is a *critical point*, since further addition of acetic acid will result in the formation of a single homogeneous phase. Any point under the curve represents a ternary mixture which will separate into two liquid phases; any point above the curve represents a single homogeneous liquid phase.

Consider an experiment in which water is added to a solution of vinyl acetate and acetic acid having composition H. As water is added, the gross composition of the system moves along the dashed line HC. Along the line HG, the addition of water gives a single homogeneous liquid phase, in which the ratio of vinyl acetate to acetic acid is always equal to HA/HB. The percentages of vinyl acetate and acetic acid in the total system decrease as water is added, but the ratio of their

* J. C. Smith, *J. Phys. Chem.*, *45*, 1301 (1941).

percentages remains constant at 60/40. When point G is reached, the addition of more water produces two liquid phases. The compositions of these phases change as more water is added along the line GE. Between G and E the quantity of the phase which is richer in water increases, and the phase which has the smaller percentage of water decreases in quantity. Not only do the relative amounts of the two different liquid phases change, but also the composition of each phase changes as indicated by the intersections of the tie lines with the curve xyz. The over-all ratio of vinyl acetate to acetic acid in the two solutions, added together, is still, however, equal to HA/HB. From E to C there is a single homogeneous phase.

The mutual solubilities of vinyl acetate and water increase at higher temperatures, and the region where there are two phases becomes smaller. Thus the line xyz falls below its present position at higher temperatures. At sufficiently high temperatures only one liquid phase is obtained, no matter what the relative amounts of the three components.

In applying the phase rule to these triangular diagrams, it must be remembered that the temperature and pressure are fixed. Then $v = c - p + 0 = 3 - p$.

If there is a single liquid phase, the variance is 2, and the percentages of two of the three components have to be specified. The percentage of the third component can be obtained by subtracting the sum of the other two from 100 per cent.

If there are two liquid phases, as in the area below the line xyz, the variance is 1 so that it is necessary to specify the percentage of one component in only one phase in order to describe the system completely. The percentages of the other components in this phase can be obtained from the intersection of this percentage with the line xyz, and the composition of the other phase can be obtained from the intersection of the other end of the tie line with the line xyz. For example, if one phase in the two-phase system in Fig. 10-13 contains 5 per cent water, the composition of this phase is given by point a and the composition of the other phase by point b.

Distribution of a Solute between Two Phases. When a substance is added to a two-phase liquid mixture, it is in general distributed with different equilibrium concentrations in the two phases. The distribution of acetic acid between the water-rich and vinyl acetate-rich phases may be calculated from the data of Fig. 10-13. It is apparent from this figure that the ratio of the concentrations of acetic acid in the two phases, as given by the ends of the tie lines, changes with the amount of acetic acid added. However, if the amount of solute added is sufficiently small, it is often found that the distribution coefficient, which is defined as the ratio of the concentrations of the solute in the two phases, is relatively independent of concentration. This is illustrated by the data in Table I for the distribution of bromine between

Table I. Distribution of Bromine between Water and Bromoform

Moles per liter in water	0.0075	0.015	0.022	0.029	0.036
Moles per liter in bromoform	0.5	1.0	1.5	2.0	2.5
$K_c = c_{CHBr_3}/c_{H_2O}$	66.7	66.7	68.2	69.0	69.5

water saturated with bromoform and bromoform saturated with water.

The distribution law may be derived from the fact that at equilibrium the chemical potential of a substance present in phases α and β must be the same in the two phases.

$$\mu_{i\alpha} = \mu_{i\beta} \tag{4}$$

Assuming that the substance i forms ideal solutions in both phases,

$$\mu^{\circ}_{i\alpha} + RT \ln X_{i\alpha} = \mu^{\circ}_{i\beta} + RT \ln X_{i\beta} \tag{5}$$

Then

$$\ln \frac{X_{i\beta}}{X_{i\alpha}} = \frac{\mu^{\circ}_{i\alpha} - \mu^{\circ}_{i\beta}}{RT}$$

$$\frac{X_{i\beta}}{X_{i\alpha}} = K \tag{6}$$

and the distribution coefficient K is given by

$$K = e^{(\mu^{\circ}_{i\alpha} - \mu^{\circ}_{i\beta})/RT} \tag{7}$$

For nonideal solutions it is necessary to introduce activity coefficients. In some cases the distribution coefficient depends markedly on concentration because the solute exists in dissociated or associated forms in one of the phases. For example, hydrochloric acid dissolves in water to give H^+ and Cl^- ions, but in benzene it is not dissociated into ions. Other solutes, as, for example, benzoic acid, associate in a nonpolar solvent like benzene to give double molecules, as determined by boiling-point or freezing-point measurements, but they do not associate in a polar solvent like water or ether. The association is due to the formation of hydrogen bonds.

Exercise V. If a substance is associated to form double molecules in phase α but has its normal molecular weight in phase β, the equilibrium may be written

$$A_2, \alpha = 2A, \beta$$

Starting with

$$\mu_{A_2,\alpha} = 2\mu_{A,\beta}$$

show that if the solutions are ideal the distribution coefficient

$$K = X^2_{A,\beta}/X_{A_2,\alpha}$$

is independent of concentration.

Liquid-Liquid Extraction. Extraction with immiscible solvents finds many practical applications. Organic compounds are frequently more soluble in hydrocarbons than in water and can be extracted from water into a hydrocarbon phase. The presence of other solutes may profoundly affect the distribution ratio either by forming some complex compound with the solute or by changing the character of the solvent. A common example of the latter is the "salting-out" procedure in solvent extraction. The extraction of organic substances from water can frequently be improved by saturating the water with sodium chloride or other salt which does not dissolve in the organic solvent. Some inorganic salts, like ferric chloride and uranyl nitrate, are soluble in organic solvents. A separation can then be effected from salts of metals such as potassium which are not soluble. Choice of solvent, addition of salting-out solutes, change of valence, and use of "complexing" agents are some of the variables that can be used to increase the efficiency of the separations.

Substances having slightly different distribution coefficients between two immiscible solvents may be separated by means of successive extractions. Craig * and others have designed apparatus for carrying out multiple extractions systematically and automatically. Many substances, particularly biological products, which are difficult to separate by other procedures have been separated by these methods. This solvent extraction is used in the separation of some of the products obtained in nuclear fission and in the separation of plutonium from uranium.

Exercise VI. Show that in a solvent extraction a given volume of the insoluble solvent will extract more solute from a given volume of aqueous solution if the solvent is divided into several small parts and used in a series of successive extractions. For a given concentration and distribution ratio calculate the amount of solute extracted from 100 ml of aqueous solution by 100 ml of solvent. Repeat the calculation, using two extractions with 50 ml each and then n extractions with $100/n$ ml of solvent in each extraction.

The greater the surface area exposed between the two liquids, the more rapidly will equilibrium be achieved. Accordingly, it is common

---

* L. C. Craig and N. L. Craig in, *Technique of Organic Chemistry*, Vol. III, ed. by A. Weissberger, Interscience Publishers, New York, 1950.

practice to shake the two solutions together. For large-scale separations two different immiscible solvents of different densities are made to flow in opposite directions through tall towers filled with special packing which gives a large surface, like the fractionation towers used for separating liquids by vaporization and condensation. These packed towers are equivalent to a large number of batch extractions; like any continuous process, they are preferred for industrial or large-scale operations. The number of theoretical plates equivalent to the number of batch operations replaced can be calculated for a solvent-extraction tower in much the same manner that the number of theoretical plates is calculated for a distillation column.

Substances having slightly different distribution coefficients may also be separated by a column operation in which one liquid phase is held by a finely divided solid with a large surface area and the other liquid phase flows through the column. This process is referred to as *partition chromatography* and is closely related to chromatography experiments depending upon adsorption (p. 613). In column operation the equivalent of many theoretical plates (p. 166), each equivalent to a batch extraction, is obtained. The components of a mixture emerge at the bottom of the column one by one at different times if their distribution coefficients are sufficiently different. The volume of solvent which must be passed through the column before a component appears varies with the nature of the solvent.

Systems Involving Two Solids and a Liquid. This type of system is of considerable practical importance. *Figure 10-14* shows an example

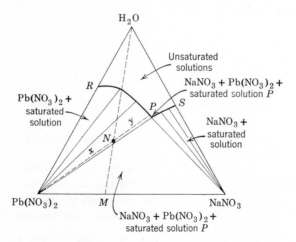

Fig. 10-14. Phase diagram for the system lead nitrate-sodium nitrate-water at 25°.

of such a system at 25° and atmospheric pressure in which no compounds are formed.* Solutions along RP are saturated with $Pb(NO_3)_2$, and solutions along PS are saturated with $NaNO_3$. At the intersection of these two solubility curves (point P) the solution is saturated with respect to both $Pb(NO_3)_2$ and $NaNO_3$; there are three phases in equilibrium, and so this point is invariant if the temperature and pressure are constant. A few typical tie lines are shown in the two-phase regions.

A diagram such as Fig. 10-14 is useful in deciding how to obtain the maximum amount of pure substance from a mixture. For example, if water is added to mixture M, the gross composition moves along the dashed line toward the H_2O apex. If only a small amount of water is added, the phases $Pb(NO_3)_2$, $NaNO_3$, and solution of composition P will be present. If sufficient water is added to reach point N, the only solid phase at equilibrium will be $Pb(NO_3)_2$. If the solution is heated to get all the $NaNO_3$ into solution and then cooled to 25°, the solid phase will be pure $Pb(NO_3)_2$. The composition of the mother liquor would be only slightly different from P. The relative amounts of $Pb(NO_3)_2$ and mother liquor are given by y/x. Thus it is seen that if more water is added the recovery of $Pb(NO_3)_2$ will be reduced. If the mixture is richer in $NaNO_3$, so that the line to the H_2O apex passes through PS, only $NaNO_3$ may be crystallized out by cooling after hot water is added.

Compounds may be formed between components of a ternary system as illustrated by *Fig. 10-15*. The area at the left of the curve $ONML$ represents unsaturated solution. The solubility in water of pure $(NH_4)_2SO_4$ in per cent by weight at 30° is given by L, and the solubility of pure Li_2SO_4 by O. The line LM shows how the solubility of $(NH_4)_2SO_4$ is decreased by the addition of Li_2SO_4, and the line ON shows how the solubility of Li_2SO_4 is increased by the addition of $(NH_4)_2SO_4$. Along the line MN, a double salt $Li_2SO_4 \cdot (NH_4)_2SO_4$ precipitates out when water is removed from the saturated solution. Along the line ON a hydrate crystallizes out as water is removed from the saturated solution. The tie lines give the composition of the solution that is in equilibrium with the solids for any total composition specified within these areas.

It is possible to represent temperature as a variable in a three-component system, using a triangular prism in which the temperature is plotted perpendicular to the base of the prism. Such space models are useful in determining the composition of a three-metal alloy which

---

* The determination of this particular phase diagram has been described in detail by E. L. Heric, *J. Chem. Educ.*, *35*, 510 (1958).

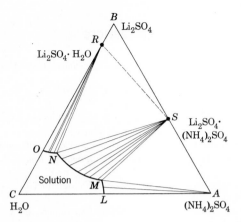

Fig. 10-15. Phase diagram showing regions of solubility and double salt formation for two salts in water.

will give the lowest possible melting point. Low-melting alloys are used, for example, in automatic water sprinklers for fire protection. *Figure 10-16* represents the influence of temperature on the simplest type of ternary system, that is, one in which no compounds or solid solutions are formed. The front plane gives the freezing-point curves of bismuth and tin with a eutectic at 135°; the plane at the left of the back gives the freezing-point curves for bismuth and lead with a eutectic at 125°; and the remaining plane for lead and tin gives a eutectic at 181°. When these three binary freezing-point curves are placed vertically and joined along the edges, a triangular prism is formed. The investigation of ternary mixtures shows that the ternary eutectic point is at 96°. This is the lowest possible melting temperature that can be obtained from any mixture of these three metals, and the exact composition of this ternary alloy is found by projecting a vertical line down from this point until it hits the triangular base. Without the help of such curves and space models a great many more cut-and-try experiments would be required to find the composition of the alloy with the lowest melting point.

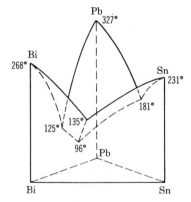

Fig. 10-16. Triangular prism showing solid and liquid phases for a three-component system at different temperatures.

REFERENCES

S. T. Bowden, *The Phase Rule and Phase Reactions*, The Macmillan Co., New York, 1938.

A. Findlay, A. N. Campbell, and N. O. Smith, *The Phase Rule and Its Applications*, Dover Publications, New York, 1951.

R. M. Garrels, *Mineral Equilibria*, Harper & Brothers, New York, 1959.

F. P. Hall and H. Insley, *A Compilation of Phase-Rule Diagrams of Interest to the Ceramicist and Silicate Technologist*, American Ceramic Society, 1933.

F. F. Purdon and V. W. Slater, *Aqueous Solutions and Phase Diagrams*, Edward Arnold & Co., London, 1946.

J. E. Ricci, *The Phase Rule and Heterogeneous Equilibrium*, D. Van Nostrand Co., Princeton, N. J., 1951.

A. Seidell, *Solubility of Organic and Inorganic Compounds*, D. Van Nostrand Co., Princeton, N. J., 1954.

H. N. V. Temperley, *Changes in State: A Mathematical-Physical Assessment*, Interscience Publishers, New York, 1956.

J. Zernike, *Chemical Phase Theory*, N. V. Uitgevers-Maatschappij Æ. E. Kluwer, Deventer, 1955.

PROBLEMS

1. The phase diagram for magnesium-copper at constant pressure shows that two compounds are formed: $MgCu_2$, which melts at 800°, and Mg_2Cu, which melts at 580°. Copper melts at 1085°, and Mg at 648°. The three eutectics are at 9.4 per cent Mg (680°), 34 per cent Mg (560°), and 65 per cent Mg (380°). Construct the phase diagram. State the variance for each area and eutectic point.

Ans. In the liquid region $v = 2$, in the two-phase regions $v = 1$, and at the eutectic points $v = 0$.

2. Sketch the phase diagram for thallium and mercury with freezing points plotted against per cent by weight. Use the following facts: Hg melts at −39°; the compound Tl_2Hg_5 melts at 15°; Tl melts at 303°; Tl lowers the freezing point of Hg down to a minimum of −60° at a composition of 8 per cent by weight Tl; the eutectic point for Tl and Tl_2Hg_5 is 0.4° at a composition corresponding to 41 per cent by weight Tl. Label the phases present and state the variance at each area and eutectic point.

Ans. In the liquid region $v = 2$, in the two-phase regions $v = 1$, and at the eutectic points $v = 0$.

3. The data for the solubility of urea in water are given below. Calculate the differential heat of solution of urea in its saturated solution in water at 100°.

X_{urea}	1.000	0.9004	0.8190	0.7217	0.5680	0.4741
t, °C	132.6	123.2	115.3	104.4	84.4	68.5

Ans. 3.2 kcal mole^{-1}.

4. (*a*) Under what conditions of temperature and composition is it possible to produce crystals of $H_2SO_4 \cdot H_2O$? (*b*) How would you prepare the compound MoCo?

Ans. (*a*) 50 mole % H_2SO_4 below 8°.

(*b*) 50 mole % Mo below 1480°.

5. For the ternary system benzene-isobutanol-water at $25°$ and 1 atm the following compositions have been obtained for the two phases in equilibrium:

Water-Rich Phase		Benzene-Rich Phase	
Isobutanol, wt. %	Water, wt. %	Isobutanol, wt. %	Benzene, wt. %
2.33	97.39	3.61	96.20
4.30	95.44	19.87	79.07
5.23	94.59	39.57	57.09
6.04	93.83	59.48	33.98
7.32	92.64	76.51	11.39

Plot these data on a triangular graph, indicating the tie lines. (a) Estimate the compositions of the phases which will be produced from a mixture of 20 per cent isobutanol, 55 per cent water, and 25 per cent benzene. (b) What will be the composition of the first drop of the second phase which separates when water is added to a solution of 80 per cent isobutyl alcohol in benzene?

$Ans.$ (a) H_2O layer: 5.23% isobutanol, 94.5% H_2O.

Benzene layer: 39.57% isobutanol, 57.09% benzene.

(b) 10% H_2O; 72% isobutanol; 18% benzene.

6. Picric acid is distributed between benzene and water as indicated by the following equilibrium concentrations in moles per liter:

Aqueous phase, $c \times 10^3$	2.08	3.27	7.01	10.1
Benzene phase, $c \times 10^3$	0.932	2.25	10.1	19.9

Picric acid exists as nondissociated and nonassociated $C_6H_2(NO_2)_3OH$ in benzene. What conclusions can you draw regarding dissociation or association in the water phase? $Ans.$ Picric acid dissolved in water dissociates into two ions.

7. The following data are available for the system nickel sulfate-sulfuric acid-water at $25°$. Sketch the phase diagram on triangular coordinate paper, and draw appropriate tie lines.

Liquid Phase		Solid Phase
$NiSO_4$, wt. %	H_2SO_4, wt. %	
28.13	0	$NiSO_4 \cdot 7H_2O$
27.34	1.79	"
27.16	3.86	"
26.15	4.92	$NiSO_4 \cdot 6H_2O$
15.64	19.34	"
10.56	44.68	"
9.65	48.46	$NiSO_4 \cdot H_2O$
2.67	63.73	"
0.12	91.38	"
0.11	93.74	$NiSO_4$
0.08	96.80	"

8. The following cooling curves have been found for the system antimony-cadmium:

Cd, % by weight	0	20	37.5	47.5	50	58	70	93	100
First break in curve, °C	...	550	461	...	419	...	400	...	...
Continuing constant temp., °C	630	410	410	410	410	439	295	295	321

Construct a phase diagram, assuming that no breaks other than these actually occur in any cooling curve. Label the diagram completely, and give the formula of any compound formed. State the variance in each area and at each eutectic point.

9. Calculate the solubility of monoclinic sulfur in carbon tetrachloride at 25°. That of rhombic sulfur is 0.84 gram per 100 grams of CCl_4. Sulfur exists in both solutions as S_8. The Gibbs free energy of formation of monoclinic sulfur is 23 cal g atom^{-1} greater than that of rhombic sulfur at 25°.

10. The solubility of alanine ($M = 89.1$) in water is 21.7 grams per 100 grams of H_2O at 17° and 32 grams per 100 grams of H_2O at 75°. Estimate the differential heat of solution of alanine in its saturated solution in H_2O.

11. Interpret the phase diagram for calcium oxide and zirconium oxide, *Fig. 10-17*, stating the phases and the variance for each area and eutectic point.

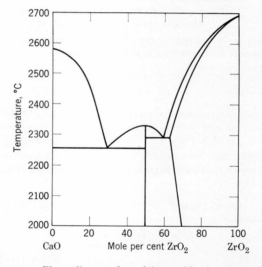

Fig. 10-17. Phase diagram for calcium oxide-zirconium oxide.

12. The melting points of magnesium and nickel are 651° and 1450°, respectively. As Ni is added to Mg, the freezing point is lowered until a eutectic point is reached at 510° and 28 per cent by weight Ni. The other phase which separates contains 54.7 per cent by weight Ni. As the weight per cent Ni is increased past 28 per cent, the temperature of first-phase separation rises to a maximum of 1180°. Above 770° and 38 per cent Ni, the solid phase which separates out contains 83 per cent Ni. The phase containing 83 per cent Ni melts sharply at 1180°. There is a eutectic point at 88 per cent Ni and 1080°. Draw the phase diagram and indicate the phases present in each region.

13. The following are the compositions of the phases in equilibrium with each other in the system methylcyclohexane–aniline–n-heptane at 1 atm and 25°. Draw a triangular diagram for the system, including tie lines, and compute the exact composition of the first drop of the new liquid phase to form when a sufficient quantity of pure aniline is added to a 40 per cent solution of methylcyclohexane in n-heptane to give separation into two phases.

Hydrocarbon Layer		Aniline Layer	
Methylcyclo-hexane, wt. %	n-Heptane, wt. %	Methylcyclo-hexane, wt. %	n-Heptane, wt. %
0.0	92.0	0.0	6.2
9.2	83.0	0.8	6.0
18.6	73.4	2.7	5.3
33.8	57.6	4.6	4.5
46.0	45.0	7.4	3.6
59.7	30.7	9.2	2.8
73.6	16.0	13.1	1.4
83.3	5.4	15.6	0.6
88.1	0.0	16.9	0.0

14. The distribution coefficient at 25° of lactic acid between water and chloroform, c_{CHCl_3}/c_{H_2O}, is 0.0203 when concentrations are expressed in moles per liter. (a) How much lactic acid will be extracted from 100 ml of a 0.8 molar solution of lactic acid in $CHCl_3$ by shaking with 100 ml of H_2O? (b) How much will be extracted if the 100 ml of $CHCl_3$ is shaken first with 50 ml of H_2O and later with another 50 ml of water?

15. The following data are available for the system Na_2SO_4-$Al_2(SO_4)_3$-H_2O at 42°. Draw the phase diagram on triangular coordinate paper, and draw appropriate tie lines.

Liquid Phase		Solid Phase
Na_2SO_4, wt. %	$Al_2(SO_4)_3$, wt. %	
33.20	0	Na_2SO_4
32.00	1.52	"
31.79	1.87	"
28.75	1.71	$Na_2SO_4 \cdot Al_2(SO_4)_3 \cdot 14H_2O$
24.47	2.84	"
16.81	5.63	"
10.93	10.49	"
4.72	17.11	"
1.75	18.59	$Al_2(SO_4)_3$
0	16.45	"

16. From the phase diagram for $Pb(NO_3)_2$-$NaNO_3$-H_2O in Fig. 10-14, what solid phase will crystallize out when water is evaporated (a) from a solution containing 10% $NaNO_3$ and 30% $Pb(NO_3)_2$, (b) from a solution containing 20% $NaNO_3$ and 5% $Pb(NO_3)_2$?

17. Construct and interpret the phase diagram based on the following data, where X_{PbI_2} is the mole fraction of lead iodide and t is the freezing point of the solution for the system potassium iodide-lead iodide:

X_{PbI_2}	1.00	0.90	0.80	0.70	0.60	0.50	0.40	0.30	0.20	0.10	0.0
t, °C	412	395	367	324	337	349	422	504	585	641	686

For all compositions below $X_{PbI_2} = 0.5$ the final solidification temperature is 346°.

18. The following data are obtained by cooling solutions of magnesium and nickel:

	0	10	28	38	60	83	88	100
Ni, wt. %								
Inflection in cooling curve, °C	...	608	...	770	1050	...	...	...
Plateau in cooling curve, °C	651	510	510	510	770	1180	1080	1450

It is found that in addition cooling solutions containing between 28 and 38% Ni deposit Mg_2Ni, whereas solutions containing between 38 and 82% Ni deposit $MgNi_2$. Plot the phase diagram.

19. The solubility of succinamide ($M = 116.1$) in water is 0.5 gram per 100 grams of H_2O at 15° and 11 grams per 100 grams of H_2O at 100°. Estimate the differential heat of solution of succinamide in its saturated solution in water.

20. (a) Referring to Fig. 10-9, choose two areas, two lines, and two points, and state what components and what phases are present. (b) State the variance for each area and eutectic point. (c) Name the solid and liquid phases which appear in succession as water vapor is pumped away from a dilute solution of sulfuric acid which is maintained at $-30°$.

21. At 25° the solubility of KNO_3 in pure H_2O is 46.2 per cent by weight, the solubility of $NaNO_3$ in pure H_2O is 52.2 per cent by weight, and $NaNO_3$, KNO_3, and saturated solution are in equilibrium when the composition of the solution is H_2O 31.3 per cent, KNO_3 28.9 per cent, and $NaNO_3$ 39.8 per cent. No crystalline hydrates or double salts are formed. Sketch this system on a triangular diagram, labeling the areas in which you would expect to find (a) only solution; (b) a mixture of solution and solid KNO_3; (c) a mixture of solution and solid $NaNO_3$; (d) a mixture of solid KNO_3, solid $NaNO_3$, and solution.

KINETIC THEORY

11

Thermodynamics yields relations between various thermodynamic measurements but does not provide the basis for predicting the magnitudes of thermodynamic quantities from information on molecular structure. In calculating thermodynamic quantities from molecular models, a deeper understanding of the thermodynamic quantities is obtained but mathematical difficulties become very great, especially in the case of unsymmetrical molecules with many atoms and in the theory of liquids.

The general treatment of matter from a molecular point of view is called *statistical mechanics*, and both equilibrium and nonequilibrium processes may be considered. The nonequilibrium treatment of ideal gases is referred to as *kinetic theory*. It is possible to devise a simple model system which gives very good predictions for ideal gases.

Assumptions of the Kinetic Theory of Ideal Gases. In order to make simple calculations possible a simple model of an ideal gas is adopted. The following assumptions are made. (1) The volume of gas considered contains a very large number of molecules. This is reasonable for ordinary volumes and pressures because of the size of Avogadro's number. (2) The molecules are small compared with the distances between them and are in a state of continuous motion in straight lines between collisions. (3) The molecules are spherical and do not interact with each other except by colliding. The molecules undergo perfectly elastic collisions when they collide with each other or with a wall of the container. A perfectly elastic collision is one in which no energy is used up inside the molecules by rearrangement of their parts.

Distribution of Molecular Velocities. The velocity of a molecule is changed by each collision with another gas molecule, and there is a distribution of velocities at any given instant. At equilibrium the distribution of instantaneous velocities is independent of time. The distribution of velocity components in the x direction, v_x, at any instant may be described by dividing the span of velocities into equal-sized intervals Δv_x and determining the number of molecules whose v_x values fall in the different intervals. It is convenient to plot as the ordinate, not the fraction of molecules in a given velocity interval, but the fraction divided by the width of the interval, as shown in *Fig. 11-1a*. When this is done the *area* of each rectangle in the bar graph gives the *fraction* of the molecules in the specified interval.

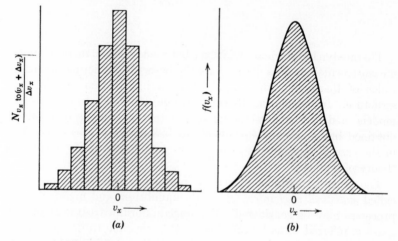

Fig. 11-1. (*a*) Block graph and (*b*) continuous distribution curve for the distribution of velocities in the x direction.

A more accurate representation can be obtained by considering a very large number of molecules and reducing the interval Δv_x considered. When this is done the top of the bar graph approaches a smooth curve. In the limit of smaller and smaller intervals the fraction of molecules per unit velocity interval is represented by $f(v_x)$, the *probability density* function for molecular velocities. The *fraction* of molecules having velocities in the interval v_x to $v_x + dv_x$ is then $f(v_x)\, dv_x$. The dv_x appears here because the fraction of molecules in the velocity range of width dv_x depends directly upon the magnitude of dv_x. A plot of $f(v_x)$ versus v_x such as that shown in *Fig. 11-1b* completely describes the distribution of molecular velocities.

Boltzmann Equation. The equation which makes it possible to calculate the fraction of the gas molecules having velocities in a given range is the Boltzmann equation. If molecules can exist in states with energies ϵ_1, ϵ_2, etc., the numbers of molecules N_1, N_2, etc., in these states at equilibrium depend upon the absolute temperature T according to

$$N_i = Ke^{-\epsilon_i/kT} \tag{1}$$

where N_i is the number of molecules with energy ϵ_i. The value of constant K is fixed by the condition that $\Sigma N_i = N$, where N is the total number of molecules in the system.*

In the Boltzmann factor $e^{-\epsilon_i/kT}$ the exponent involves the ratio of the energy of the molecule to the thermal energy kT. The Boltzmann constant, or molecular gas constant k, is equal to the ideal gas constant divided by Avogadro's number N_0.

$$k = \frac{8.314 \times 10^7 \text{ ergs deg}^{-1} \text{ mole}^{-1}}{6.023 \times 10^{23} \text{ mole}^{-1}}$$

$$= 1.380 \times 10^{-16} \text{ erg deg}^{-1} \tag{2}$$

Probability of Molecular Velocities. Consider first the probability of various velocities in the x direction. The component of the kinetic energy in the x direction is $mv_x^2/2$, and so, according to equation 1, the fraction of the molecules with x velocities between v_x and $v_x + dv_x$, which is represented by $f(v_x)\, dv_x$, is given by

$$f(v_x)\, dv_x = Ke^{-mv_x^2/2kT}\, dv_x \tag{3}$$

This fraction is also the probability that a molecule will have a velocity in the x direction between v_x and $v_x + dv_x$. The value of K may be calculated from the fact that the sum of the fractions of the molecules in all the velocity intervals must equal unity. This calculation, which is given in the Appendix (p. 719), leads to

$$f(v_x)\, dv_x = \left(\frac{m}{2\pi kT}\right)^{1/2} e^{-mv_x^2/2kT}\, dv_x \tag{4}$$

A plot of $f(v_x)$ versus v_x calculated with this equation is shown in Fig. 11-1b for hydrogen gas at $0°$. This graph gives the probability that an arbitrarily chosen molecule will have the instantaneous velocity v_x given on the abscissa. The most probable velocity in the x direction is zero. The probabilities of velocities in the positive and negative directions are of course equal, the gas as a whole being sta-

---

* The constant K is closely related to the partition function, to be introduced in Chapter 19. A very simple example of the Boltzmann equation is the expression for the pressure in an isothermal atmosphere, $P = P_0 e^{-mgh/kT}$, where P_0 is the pressure at height $h = 0$, m is the mass of the molecules, and g is the acceleration of gravity.

tionary. The probabilities of very high velocities in either the positive or the negative x direction are very small. The velocity distributions in the y and z directions are identical with that in the x direction.

The distribution of actual molecular velocities is of greater interest than the distribution of the component velocities v_x, v_y, and v_z in the x, y, and z directions. In order to discuss the distribution of molecular velocities it is convenient to represent the velocity and direction of motion of each molecule in a gas at a given instant by a vector pointed in the direction of motion and having a length proportional to the velocity. We then imagine that these vectors are moved so that they all originate at a center of a Cartesian coordinate system. The magnitude v of each vector is related to the magnitudes of the components in the three mutually perpendicular directions by

$$v^2 = v_x{}^2 + v_y{}^2 + v_z{}^2 \tag{5}$$

If we imagine a point at the end of each vector, the number of points in a slice perpendicular to the v_x axis with thickness dv_x is proportional to the probability $f(v_x)\, dv_x$ that the x component of the velocity of an arbitrarily selected molecule is in the range v_x to $v_x + dv_x$.

The number of points in any small volume element $dv_x\, dv_y\, dv_z$ whose coordinates are v_x, v_y, and v_z gives the number of molecules having velocities with components between v_x and $v_x + dv_x$, v_y and $v_y + dv_y$, and v_z and $v_z + dv_z$. The fraction of the molecules having velocities in this range is simply equal to the *product* of the three individual probabilities and is represented by $f(v_x, v_y, v_z)\, dv_x\, dv_y\, dv_z$. Since $e^a e^b e^c = e^{a+b+c}$,

$$f(v_x, v_y, v_z)\, dv_x\, dv_y\, dv_z = \left(\frac{m}{2\pi kT}\right)^{3/2} e^{-m(v_x{}^2+v_y{}^2+v_z{}^2)/2kT}\, dv_x\, dv_y\, dv_z \tag{6}$$

It is desirable to write this equation in terms of the magnitude of the molecular velocity v rather than in terms of the x, y, and z components. The infinitesimal element of volume $dv_x\, dv_y\, dv_z$ may be written $v^2\, dv\, d\omega$, where $d\omega$ is the infinitesimal solid angle. Since no direction in space is favored, the density of points is uniform in a thin spherical shell of radius v. The velocity distribution $f(v)\, dv$ is obtained by integrating equation 6 over the full solid angle of 4π to obtain the probability $f(v)\, dv$ that an arbitrarily selected molecule will have a velocity between v and $v + dv$.

$$f(v)\, dv = \int \left(\frac{m}{2\pi kT}\right)^{3/2} e^{-mv^2/2kT} v^2\, dv\, d\omega$$

$$f(v)\, dv = \left(\frac{m}{2\pi kT}\right)^{3/2} e^{-mv^2/2kT} 4\pi v^2\, dv \tag{7}$$

This equation was first derived by Maxwell in 1860. It is of fundamental importance to the kinetic theory of gases.

A plot of $f(v)$ versus the magnitude of the molecular velocity v is shown in *Fig. 11-2* for hydrogen gas at 0° and 100°. In contrast with Fig. 11-1*b* for the velocity components in a given direction it can be seen that the probability of a zero velocity is zero. Figure 11-1*b* is based on equation 4, which does not have the term v^2 contained in equation 7. Small velocities are favored by the exponential factor in equation 7, and the density of points in the plot of the velocity vectors is greatest at the origin. However, the volume of the spherical shell containing all the ends of vectors for molecules with velocities between v and $v + dv$ increases with increasing v^2. Therefore, the plot of $f(v)$ versus v is approximately parabolic near the origin. At higher velocities the probability decreases toward zero because the exponential term decreases much more rapidly than v^2 increases. Thus very few molecules have very high or very low velocities. The fraction of the molecules having speeds greater than 10 times the most probable speed is 4.22×10^{-43} at 25°. This number is so small that it is almost physically meaningless in comparison with Avogadro's number of 6.02×10^{23}. As the temperature is increased, the most probable velocity (which is given by the maximum in the plot) moves to higher velocities and the distribution of velocities also becomes broader. Since there is a distribution of velocities, various types of averages may be considered. The most probable velocity v_p is obtained by setting $df(v)/dv$ equal to zero. As shown in the Appendix (p. 720), this yields

$$v_p = \left(\frac{2kT}{m} \right)^{\frac{1}{2}} = \left(\frac{2RT}{M} \right)^{\frac{1}{2}} \tag{8}$$

Types of Average Velocities. The arithmetic mean velocity $\bar{v}$ is obtained by summing all the velocities and dividing by the total number of molecules n.

$$\bar{v} = \frac{1}{n} \sum_{i=1}^{n} v_i \tag{9}$$

The symbol Σv_i indicates the sum of the velocities $v_1, v_2, v_3, \cdots, v_n$ of all the n individual molecules. Since the velocity distribution is continuous (a very large number of molecules having been considered), the arithmetic mean velocity is obtained by multiplying each velocity by the probability of that velocity and integrating over all velocities as shown in the Appendix (p. 720).

$$\bar{v} = \int_0^\infty v f(v) \, dv = \left(\frac{8kT}{\pi m} \right)^{\frac{1}{2}} = \left(\frac{8RT}{\pi M} \right)^{\frac{1}{2}} \tag{10}$$

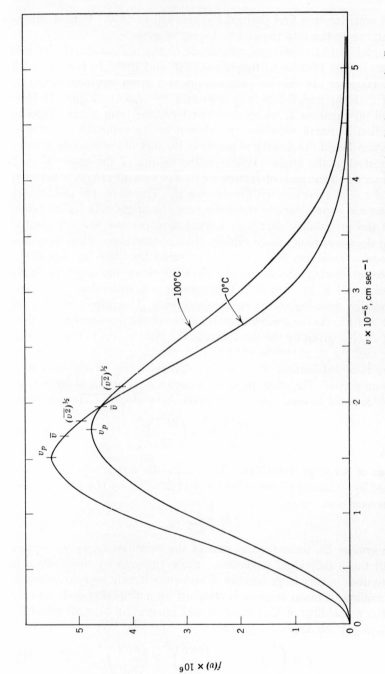

Fig. 11-2. Probability density of various molecular velocities v for hydrogen at $0°$ and $100°$, calculated using equation 7.

The root-mean-square velocity $(\bar{v}^2)^{1/2}$ is defined by

$$(\bar{v}^2)^{1/2} = \left(\frac{1}{n}\sum_{i=1}^{n} v_i^2\right)^{1/2} \tag{11}$$

The symbol Σv_i^2 indicates the sum of the squares of the velocities, v_1, v_2, v_3, $\cdots$, v_n of all of the n individual molecules. Since the velocity distribution is continuous, the root-mean-square velocity is obtained by multiplying each velocity squared by the probability of that velocity, integrating over all velocities, and taking the square root:

$$(\bar{v}^2)^{1/2} = \left[\int_0^\infty v^2 f(v)\, dv\right]^{1/2} = \left(\frac{3kT}{m}\right)^{1/2} = \left(\frac{3RT}{M}\right)^{1/2} \tag{12}$$

The details of this calculation are given in the Appendix (p. 720).

Example 1. Calculate the most probable velocity, the arithmetic mean velocity, and the root-mean-square velocity for hydrogen molecules at $0°$.

$$v_p = (2RT/M)^{1/2} = [(2)(8.314 \times 10^7)(273)/2.016]^{1/2}$$
$$= 1.50 \times 10^5 \text{ cm sec}^{-1}$$

$$\bar{v} = (8RT/\pi M)^{1/2}$$
$$= [(8)(8.314 \times 10^7 \text{ ergs})(273 \text{ deg}^{-1}\text{ mole}^{-1})/(3.14)(2.016 \text{ g mole}^{-1})]^{1/2}$$
$$= 1.69 \times 10^5 \text{ cm sec}^{-1}$$

$$(\bar{v}^2)^{1/2} = (3RT/M)^{1/2}$$
$$= [(3)(8.314 \times 10^7 \text{ ergs deg}^{-1}\text{ mole}^{-1})(273.1 \text{ deg})/2.016 \text{ g mole}^{-1}]^{1/2}$$
$$= 1.84 \times 10^5 \text{ cm sec}^{-1}$$

Alternatively, since $m = 2.016/6.02 \times 10^{23} = 3.34 \times 10^{-24}$ g molecule^{-1},

$$(\bar{v}^2)^{1/2} = (3kT/m)^{1/2} = [(3)(1.38 \times 10^{-16} \text{ erg deg}^{-1}\text{ molecule}^{-1})(273.1 \text{ deg})/$$
$$(3.34 \times 10^{-24} \text{ g molecule}^{-1})]^{1/2}$$
$$= 1.84 \times 10^5 \text{ cm sec}^{-1}$$

It is seen that the root-mean-square velocity of a hydrogen molecule at $0°$ is 4120 miles per hour, but at ordinary pressures it travels only an exceedingly short distance before colliding with another molecule and changing direction. Heavier molecules move more slowly, the various average velocities being inversely proportional to the square root of the molecular weight.

While kinetic molecular theory is in agreement with the ideal gas law and Avogadro's law (p. 11), more direct confirmation has been obtained by use of molecular-beam experiments. Beams of molecules moving in a vacuum may be collimated by slits, and the velocity distribution measured by use of rotating slotted disks.

Collisions with a Wall or Opening. A rough approximation of the number of collisions with a wall may be obtained by assuming that the molecules move only in the three mutually perpendicular directions perpendicular to the faces of a cube rather than at random. Thus one-sixth are traveling in the $+x$ direction, one-sixth in the $-x$ direction, one-sixth in the $+y$ direction, etc. It is further assumed that the molecules are all moving with the same velocity rather than with a Maxwellian distribution. This velocity is taken to be the mean velocity $\bar{v}$. According to this simplified way of looking at the problem, the number of collisions ν per square centimeter of wall per second is equal to one-sixth of the number of molecules within $\bar{v}$ cm of the wall, since this number of molecules will reach the wall in a second. If the number of molecules per cubic centimeter is represented by n', $\nu = n'\bar{v}/6$. A detailed calculation * allowing for all angles of approach of molecules to the surface and providing for the distribution of molecular velocities shows that with $\bar{v}$, the mean velocity, the correct equation is

$$\nu = \frac{n'\bar{v}}{4} \tag{13}$$

This is also the number of molecules per square centimeter per second that would escape through a small hole in the vessel containing the gas, provided that the leakage is small enough so that the equilibrium pressure in the gas is not appreciably affected and the pressure is zero outside so that no molecules return. Substituting equation 10 into equation 13 gives

$$\nu = n'\left(\frac{RT}{2\pi M}\right)^{\frac{1}{2}} \tag{14}$$

The rates of flow of two gases through a small aperture are inversely proportional to the square root of the molecular weight. The proportionality is exact if the cross section of the aperture is small compared with the average distance through which a molecule travels before colliding with another molecule.

Equation 14 is the basis for the Knudsen method (p. 128) for measuring the vapor pressures of solids. The mass w of molecules striking an opening per square centimeter per second is

$$w = \frac{\nu M}{N_0} \tag{15}$$

---

* F. W. Sears, *An Introduction to Thermodynamics, the Kinetic Theory of Gases, and Statistical Mechanics*, Addison-Wesley Publishing Co., Cambridge, Mass., 1953, p. 204.

Introducing the ideal gas law in the form $P = n'RT/N_0$, where n' is the number of gas molecules per cubic centimeter, and substituting equation 14 into equation 15, we obtain

$$P = w \left(\frac{2\pi RT}{M} \right)^{1/2} \tag{16}$$

where P is pressure in dynes per square centimeter, and w is the rate of effusion through the hole in grams per square centimeter per second. A sufficiently large surface area of the solid must be exposed to maintain the saturation vapor pressure.

Example 2. The vapor pressure of solid beryllium was measured by R. B. Holden, R. Speiser, and H. L. Johnston [*J. Am. Chem. Soc.*, *70*, 3897 (1948)] using a Knudsen cell. The effusion hole was 0.318 cm in diameter, and they found a weight loss of 9.54 mg in 60.1 min at a temperature of 1457°K. Calculate the vapor pressure.

$$P = w \sqrt{\frac{2\pi RT}{M}}$$

$$= \frac{(0.00954)}{\pi(0.159)^2(60.1)(60)} \sqrt{\frac{2\pi(8.31 \times 10^7)(1457)}{9.013}}$$

$$= 9.65 \text{ dynes cm}^{-2}$$

$$= \frac{9.65 \text{ dynes cm}^{-2}}{(76 \text{ cm atm}^{-1})(13.6 \text{ g cm}^{-3})(980 \text{ cm sec}^{-2})} = 9.52 \times 10^{-6} \text{ atm}$$

where 13.6 g cm^{-3} is the density of mercury.

Derivation of the Equation of State of an Ideal Gas. The pressure of a gas on the walls of a container is due to the impact of the molecules colliding with the wall. The force per unit area, that is the pressure on the wall, can be calculated from the fact that the force is equal to the rate of change of momentum of the molecules striking the wall. It can readily be seen that $d(mv)/dt$ is equal to mass times acceleration $(m\, dv/dt)$, which is force.

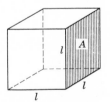

Fig. 11-3. Imaginary cube used in the derivation of the equation, $PV = \frac{1}{3}nmu^2$.

The equation of state for an ideal gas may be derived by considering the cube of gas in *Fig. 11-3*, which contains n molecules. The edges of the cube are l cm in length, so that the volume of the cube is $l^3 \text{ cm}^3$.

The approximation will be made that one-third of the molecules are traveling in the x direction, one-third in the y direction, one-third in the z direction. A detailed calculation * shows that the result has the simplest form when the root-mean-square velocity is used in the derivation. To simplify the following equations u will represent the root-mean-square velocity rather than $(\overline{v^2})^{1/2}$.

Considering the collisions of molecules with the perfectly smooth wall A, one molecule moving back and forth across the box will strike A every $2l$ cm of path. If its velocity is u cm sec^{-1}, it will collide $u/2l$ times per sec with A. Since the collisions are perfectly elastic, an individual molecule will rebound with velocity $-u$, having suffered no loss in kinetic energy. The mass of one molecule is represented by m. Since momentum is equal to the product of mass and velocity, the momentum before collision with the wall is mu and after collision with the wall is $-mu$, so that the change in momentum per collision per molecule is $2mu$. Since there are $u/2l$ collisions per sec with wall A, the change in momentum per molecule per second is then

$$2mu \frac{u}{2l} = \frac{mu^2}{l} \tag{17}$$

The total change in momentum per second of the $n/3$ molecules hitting wall A is the force exerted on the wall by the enclosed gas. The pressure P, which is equal to force per unit area, is given by the expression

$$P = \frac{n}{3} \frac{mu^2}{l} \frac{1}{l^2} \tag{18}$$

Since the volume V of the cubical box is l^3, equation 18 may be written

$$PV = \tfrac{1}{3}nmu^2 \tag{19}$$

Since the kinetic energy of a molecule is given by $\tfrac{1}{2}mu^2$, equation 19 may be written $PV = (\tfrac{2}{3}n)(\tfrac{1}{2}mu^2) = \tfrac{2}{3}n$(kinetic energy). Although this equation has been obtained in a highly idealized way, the same result is obtained by more exact methods, provided that there is no attraction or repulsion between the molecules.

If we consider a volume $\overline{V}$ containing a mole, equation 19 may be written in the form

$$P\overline{V} = (\tfrac{2}{3})(\tfrac{1}{2}N_0mu^2) = (\tfrac{2}{3})(\tfrac{1}{2}Mu^2) = \tfrac{2}{3}\overline{E} \tag{20}$$

where M is the molecular weight, obtained by multiplying the weight of one molecule by the Avogadro number N_0, and $\overline{E} = N_0mu^2/2 = Mu^2/2$

---

* F. W. Sears, *An Introduction to Thermodynamics, the Kinetic Theory of Gases, and Statistical Mechanics*, Addison-Wesley Publishing Co., Cambridge, Mass., 1953, p. 209.

is the total kinetic energy of a mole of molecules. In order to make this equation agree with the ideal gas law $P\overline{V} = RT$, it is necessary to take the kinetic energy $\overline{E}$ directly proportional to the absolute temperature for an ideal gas. Solving equation 20 for $\overline{E}$ and introducing the ideal gas law, we obtain

$$\overline{E} = \tfrac{3}{2}P\overline{V} = \tfrac{3}{2}RT \tag{21}$$

At room temperature the kinetic energy amounts to $(\tfrac{3}{2})(1.987)$ $(300) \cong 900$ cal mole^{-1}. At $1000°$ it amounts to 3800 cal mole^{-1}. It is important to notice that for an ideal gas the kinetic energy is independent of the volume or pressure and the molecular weight or type of molecule and depends only upon the temperature. Thus a helium atom has the same kinetic energy as a heavy hydrocarbon molecule. In general for two gases at the same temperature we can write

$$\tfrac{1}{2}m_1 u_1{}^2 = \tfrac{1}{2}m_2 u_2{}^2 \quad \text{or} \quad M_1 u_1{}^2 = M_2 u_2{}^2 \tag{22}$$

The ratio of the root-mean-square velocities is given by

$$\frac{u_1}{u_2} = \left(\frac{M_2}{M_1}\right)^{1/2} \tag{23}$$

Exercise I. Show that equation 19 applied to ideal gases leads to Avogadro's law if two different kinds of molecules have the same kinetic energy at the same temperature.

Fractional diffusion of gases may be used in separating isotopes. Although this method is more efficient for isotopes of low mass, nevertheless it is used in separating U^{238} and U^{235} on a very large scale.

Example 3. Calculate the ratio of the rates with which $U^{238}F_6$ and $U^{235}F_6$ diffuse through a porous barrier.

$$\frac{u_{235}}{u_{238}} = \left[\frac{238 + 6(19)}{235 + 6(19)}\right]^{1/2} = 1.0043$$

Because of this small separation factor many, many stages are required to obtain nearly pure U^{235}.

Heat Capacities of Gases. Differentiating equation 21 with respect to temperature at constant volume,

$$\overline{C}_V = \left(\frac{\partial \overline{E}}{\partial T}\right)_V = \tfrac{3}{2}R = 2.98 \text{ cal deg}^{-1} \text{ mole}^{-1}$$

This is in excellent agreement with the values of $\overline{C}_V$ for monatomic gases given on p. 51.

Since for an ideal gas $\overline{C}_P = \overline{C}_V + R$, we would expect for an ideal monatomic gas $\overline{C}_P = \frac{3}{2}R + R = \frac{5}{2}R = 4.97$ cal deg^{-1} mole^{-1} and

$$\gamma = \frac{\overline{C}_P}{\overline{C}_V} = \frac{4.97}{2.98} = 1.67$$

This is borne out by the experimental data, as shown on p. 51.

The fact that $\overline{C}_V = \frac{3}{2}R$ may be interpreted by saying that a molecule of a monatomic gas has three degrees of translational freedom, along three axes in space, each of which contributes $R/2$ to $\overline{C}_V$. Polyatomic molecules may have also rotational and vibrational degrees of freedom.

Degrees of freedom are the independent coordinates required to locate a molecule and specify the position of each atom. The position of a molecule as a whole in space may be described by giving the three Cartesian coordinates of its center of mass. Thus, a molecule has three degrees of translational freedom; these are the only degrees of freedom for a monatomic molecule. For a molecule containing N atoms, $3N$ coordinates are required to specify the position of each atom. Thus, $3N - 3$ coordinates, or degrees of freedom, remain to describe the internal motions of the molecule. For a diatomic molecule, $3 \times 2 - 3 = 3$ coordinates (or degrees of freedom) remain. Two coordinates are required to fix the orientation of the diatomic molecule in space (in this case two angles like the latitude and longitude of a line passing through the center of the earth), and this leaves one coordinate to specify the internuclear distance. Thus there are two degrees of rotational freedom and one degree of vibrational freedom.

Since $\frac{3}{2}R$ is associated with the three degrees of translational freedom, $R/2$ is associated with any one degree of freedom.

The approximation that energy is divided equally between various motions is called the principle of equipartition. This classical principle is useful but it is not exact, as we shall soon see. If $R/2$ cal deg^{-1} mole^{-1} are contributed by each rotational degree of freedom to $\overline{C}_V$, we would expect that for a rigid diatomic molecule which has two degrees of rotational freedom $\overline{C}_V = \frac{3}{2}R + 2(R/2) = 4.97$ cal deg^{-1} mole^{-1}. This is in good agreement with the values for H_2, O_2, N_2, CO, and HCl at 25° as shown in Table II in Chapter 3. This agreement shows that any additional contribution to the heat capacity caused by vibration of the atoms is negligible in the range of room temperature. The value of $\overline{C}_V$ for Cl_2 (6.14 cal deg^{-1} mole^{-1}) indicates that vibrational motions are important in this molecule at room temperature.

Two kinds of energy are associated with a vibration—kinetic energy and potential energy. According to the principle of equipartition, each contributes $R/2$ to $\bar{C}_V$ so that $\bar{C}_V$ for a diatomic molecule which vibrates would have an extra term, $2(R/2)$, and $\bar{C}_V = 4.97 + 2(R/2)$ = 6.96 cal deg^{-1} mole^{-1}. The fact that different diatomic gases have $\bar{C}_V$ values between 4.97 and 6.96 cal deg^{-1} mole^{-1} cannot be explained by classical mechanics. It can be explained by quantum mechanics, and the reason will be given later (p. 566). For diatomic molecules $\bar{C}_V$ does approach 6.96 cal deg^{-1} mole^{-1} at very high temperatures, but this limit is seldom reached because the molecules become dissociated before reaching these temperatures.

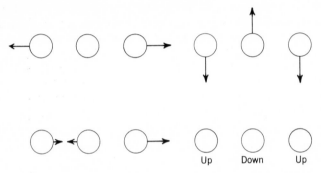

Up   Down   Up

Fig. 11-4. Normal modes of vibration of a symmetrical linear triatomic molecule like CO$_2$.

For a triatomic molecule, $3N - 3 = 6$ and so there are six internal degrees of freedom. For a linear triatomic molecule like CO$_2$ there are only two degrees of rotational freedom (as there are for a diatomic molecule), leaving four degrees of vibrational freedom. The vibratory motion of a linear triatomic molecule may be very complicated, but all the possible motions may be described in terms of four simple motions, called the *normal modes of vibration.* The natures of these motions are shown in *Fig. 11-4.* The two on the left are symmetrical and asymmetrical stretching vibrations. The two on the right are bending motions which differ only in that they are in mutually perpendicular planes. Such vibrations which have the same energy are called degenerate vibrations.*

For a linear triatomic molecule there are three more vibrational degrees of freedom than for a diatomic molecule, and so we would expect the heat capacities at sufficiently high temperatures to be $3R = 6$ cal deg^{-1} mole^{-1} greater than for a diatomic molecule; that is, $\bar{C}_V =$

---

* These and other types of molecular vibrations are very well described in a motion picture, "Molecular Vibrations," which is available through Sutherland Productions, 201 N. Occidental Ave., Los Angeles 26, Calif.

13 cal deg^{-1} $mole^{-1}$ and $\overline{C}_P = 15$ cal deg^{-1} $mole^{-1}$ would be approached, but not reached, as the temperature is raised. For H_2O, which is a bent molecule, there are three rotational degrees of freedom and three vibrational degrees of freedom. The number of normal modes of vibration is $3N - 6$ for a nonlinear molecule and $3N - 5$ for a linear molecule. Thus CH_4 would have $3 \times 5 - 6 = 9$ normal modes; because this molecule is symmetrical there is a lot of degeneracy in its normal modes of vibration. The more complex the molecule, the greater the number of vibrational modes. Even if each normal mode of vibration makes only a small contribution to $\overline{C}_V$ and $\overline{C}_P$ in the neighborhood of room temperature, the net result is a greater molar heat capacity, a greater change of heat capacity with temperature, and a value of γ closer to unity.

Molecular Collisions in a Gas.* The preceding results have been obtained without any consideration of the size or shape of gas molecules. In order to discuss the frequency of collisions in a gas, the mean free path, or the transport properties (diffusion, heat conductivity, and viscosity) it is necessary to introduce the size of the molecules. Molecules of a real gas repel each other at very short distances and attract each other at greater distances, so that when they approach they interact in a very complex fashion. However, for certain purposes useful results may be obtained by assuming that the molecules are rigid, noninteracting spheres with diameter σ. In deriving an approximate equation for the number of collisions per second it is convenient to assume that the molecules all travel with the same speed, the arithmetic mean velocity $\bar{v}$.

If the molecular diameter is σ, two identical molecules will just touch when the distance separating their centers is σ. Thus a moving molecule will collide with other molecules whose centers come within a distance of σ. The quantity $\pi\sigma^2$ is called the *collision cross section* for the rigid spherical molecule because it is the cross-sectional area of an imaginary sphere surrounding the molecule into which the center of another molecule cannot penetrate. A molecule moving with a constant velocity of $\bar{v}$ will sweep out $\pi\sigma^2\bar{v}$ cm^3 sec^{-1} and strike $\pi\sigma^2\bar{v}n'$ molecules, where n' is the number of molecules per cubic centimeter. A complete treatment allowing for the distribution of molecular velocities yields a number of collisions per second per molecule, z, larger than this by a factor of $\sqrt{2}$.

$$z = \sqrt{2}\,\pi\sigma^2\bar{v}n' \qquad (24)$$

* J. O. Hirschfelder, C. F. Curtiss, and R. B. Bird, *The Molecular Theory of Gases and Liquids*, John Wiley & Sons, New York, 1954.

Since there are n' molecules per cubic centimeter, there will be $\sqrt{2}\pi\sigma^2(n')^2\bar{v}$ molecules undergoing collision per second. The number Z of collisions per unit time per unit volume is given by

$$Z = \frac{\sqrt{2}}{2}\pi\sigma^2\bar{v}(n')^2 \qquad (25)$$

since the number of collisions is one-half the number of identical molecules colliding.

Example 4. For oxygen at 25° calculate the number z of collisions per second per molecule, the number Z of collisions per cubic centimeter per second, and the number of moles of collisions per liter per second at (a) a pressure of 1 atm and (b) a pressure of 0.001 mm of mercury. The molecular diameter of oxygen is 3.61 A, as determined in a manner to be described shortly.

(a) $\quad n = \dfrac{PV}{RT}$, where n is the number of moles

$$n' = \frac{PVN_0}{RT} = \frac{(1)(10^{-3})(6.02 \times 10^{23})}{(0.082)(298)}$$

$$= 2.46 \times 10^{19} \text{ molecules cm}^{-3}$$

$$\bar{v} = (8RT/\pi M)^{\frac{1}{2}} = [(8)(8.314 \times 10^7)(298)/(3.14)(32)]^{\frac{1}{2}}$$

$$= 4.44 \times 10^4 \text{ cm sec}^{-1}$$

$$z = \sqrt{2}\,\pi\sigma^2\bar{v}n' = (1.414)(3.14)(3.61 \times 10^{-8})^2(4.44 \times 10^4)(2.46 \times 10^{19})$$

$$= 6.31 \times 10^9 \text{ collisions molecule}^{-1}\text{ sec}^{-1}$$

$$Z = \frac{\sqrt{2}}{2}\pi\sigma^2\bar{v}(n')^2$$

$$= (0.707)(3.14)(3.61 \times 10^{-8})^2(4.44 \times 10^4)(2.46 \times 10^{19})^2$$

$$= 7.81 \times 10^{28} \text{ collisions cm}^{-3}\text{ sec}^{-1}$$

$$= (7.81 \times 10^{28})(10^3)/6.02 \times 10^{23}$$

$$= 1.29 \times 10^8 \text{ moles of collisions liter}^{-1}\text{ sec}^{-1}$$

(b) $\quad n' = \dfrac{PVN_0}{RT} = \dfrac{(10^{-4}/76)(10^{-3})(6.02 \times 10^{23})}{(0.082)(298)}$

$$= 3.24 \times 10^{13} \text{ molecules cm}^{-3}$$

$$z = 8.30 \times 10^3 \text{ collisions molecule}^{-1}\text{ sec}^{-1}$$

$$Z = 13.6 \times 10^{16} \text{ collisions cm}^{-3}\text{ sec}^{-1}$$

$$= (13.6 \times 10^{16})(10^3)/(6.02 \times 10^{23})$$

$$= 2.24 \times 10^{-4} \text{ mole of collisions liter}^{-1}\text{ sec}^{-1}$$

Thus it can be seen that when gaseous molecules react on the first collision very fast reaction rates are obtained.

The Mean Free Path. The mean free path is the average distance traversed by a molecule between collisions. In a second a molecule will on the average traverse $\bar{v}$ cm and suffer z collisions. Thus from equation 24 the mean free path is

$$l = \frac{\bar{v}}{z} = \frac{1}{\sqrt{2}\,\pi\sigma^2 n'} = \frac{kT}{\sqrt{2}\,\pi\sigma^2 P} \tag{26}$$

where the last form of this equation is obtained by substituting the ideal gas law in the form $n' = P/kT$. It is seen that at constant density the mean free path is independent of temperature (assuming σ to be independent of temperature) and at constant pressure the mean free path is directly proportional to the absolute temperature.

At pressures so low that the mean free path becomes comparable with the dimensions of the containing vessel, the flow properties of the gas become markedly different.

Example 5. For oxygen at 25° calculate the mean free path at (a) 1 atm pressure and (b) a pressure of 0.001 mm of mercury.

(a) From example 4, $n' = 2.46 \times 10^{19}$ molecules cm^{-3}

$$l = [(1.414)(3.14)(3.61 \times 10^{-8})^2(2.46 \times 10^{19})]^{-1}$$
$$= 144 \times 10^{-8}\,\text{cm}$$

(b) From example 4, $n' = 3.24 \times 10^{13}$ molecules cm^{-3}

$$l = [(1.414)(3.14)(3.61 \times 10^{-8})^2(3.24 \times 10^{13})]^{-1} = 5.3\,\text{cm}$$

Transport of Mass, Energy, and Momentum. The transfer of mass, energy, and momentum are irreversible processes which lead to the increase of entropy. Quantitative treatments can be made of these processes in gases under certain conditions. The transport of molecules in the absence of bulk flow is referred to as *diffusion*. The flux of matter due to diffusion is proportional to the concentration gradient. Thus the flux J_{iz} of component i in the z direction in terms of moles cm^{-2} sec^{-1} due to its concentration gradient in that direction, dn_i/dz, where n_i is the concentration of molecules i, is given by

$$J_{iz} = -D\frac{dn_i}{dz} \tag{27}$$

where the proportionality constant is the diffusion coefficient D. Since dn_i/dz has the units of moles cm^{-4}, D has the units of cm^2 sec^{-1}. The negative sign comes from the fact that if n_i increases in the positive z direction, dn_i/dz is positive, but the flux is in the negative z direction because the flow is in the direction of lower concentration.

The diffusion coefficient of a gas may be obtained through the use of isotopic molecules. The experimental arrangement is shown schematically in *Fig. 11-5a*. A sample of the gas which is enriched in the heavier isotope is placed in chamber A, and an unenriched sample is placed in

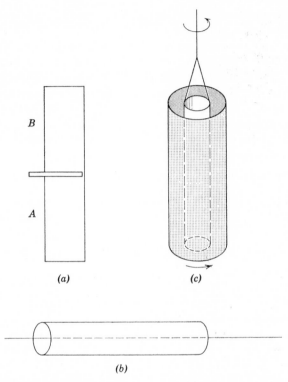

(a) (c)

(b)

Fig. 11-5. Schematic diagrams of apparatus for the measurement of (a) the diffusion coefficient D, (b) the coefficient of thermal conductivity λ, and (c) the coefficient of viscosity η of gases.

B at the same pressure. The partition is withdrawn for a definite interval of time. From the isotopic compositions of the two volumes of gas at the end of the experiment D may be calculated.

The transport of energy is referred to as thermal conductivity and is due to a gradient in temperature. Thus the flux of energy q_z in the z direction due to the temperature gradient in that direction is given by

$$q_z = -\lambda \frac{dT}{dz} \tag{28}$$

where the proportionality constant λ is the coefficient of thermal conductivity. Since q_z has the units of cal cm^{-2} sec^{-1} and dT/dz has the units of deg cm^{-1}, λ has the units of cal cm^{-1} sec^{-1} deg^{-1}. The negative sign in equation 28 indicates that if dT/dz is positive the flow of heat is in the negative z direction, which is the direction of lower temperature.

The determination of the coefficient of thermal conductivity by the hot-wire method is illustrated schematically in *Fig. 11-5b*. The outer cylinder is kept at a constant temperature by use of a thermostatically controlled bath. The tube is filled with the gas under investigation, and the fine wire at the axis of the tube is heated electrically. When a steady state is achieved, the temperature of the wire is measured by determining its electrical resistance. The coefficient of thermal conductivity is calculated from the temperature of wire and wall, the heat dissipation, and the dimensions of the apparatus.

The viscosity is a measure of the resistance that a fluid offers to an applied shearing force, this frictional resistance being due to a transfer of momentum from one layer of the moving fluid to the next. In order to understand the definition of the coefficient of viscosity consider two infinite plane surfaces which are parallel to each other in a fluid. One of these planes is moved relative to the other by application of a force under conditions such that the distance between the planes is maintained constant. The layer of fluid immediately adjacent to the moving plane moves with the velocity of that plane, but successive layers move with successively lower velocities, and the layer immediately adjacent to the stationary plane remains stationary. If one plane moves in the y direction and the distance between the planes is represented by z, we say there is a gradient dv_y/dz in the y velocity of the fluid between the planes. It is found that for most fluids the force f per unit area required to push one plane relative to the other is directly proportional to the velocity gradient.

$$f = -\eta \frac{dv_y}{dz} \tag{29}$$

The proportionality constant η is the coefficient of viscosity. The negative sign comes from the fact that, if f is in the $+y$ direction, the velocity v_y decreases in successive layers away from the moving plane and dv_y/dz is negative. Since f has the units of g cm sec^{-2}/cm^2 and dv_y/dz has the units of cm sec^{-1}/cm, η has the units of g sec^{-1} cm^{-1}. This unit is referred to as the *poise* after Poiseuille, who pioneered in the study of viscosity.

Although the coefficient of viscosity is conveniently defined in terms of this hypothetical experiment, it is easier to measure it by determining the rate of flow through a tube, the twisting force on a disk which is rotated in the fluid, or other experimental arrangement. An experimental arrangement is illustrated in *Fig. 11-5c*. The outer cylinder is rotated at a constant velocity by an electric motor. The inner coaxial cylinder is suspended on a torsion wire. A torque is transmitted to the inner cylinder by the gas, and this torque is calculated from the angular twist of the torsion wire.

The kinetic theory of gases provides the means for calculating the coefficients of diffusion, thermal conductivity, and viscosity for ideal gases. The treatments are too complicated to give here, but the theoretical results for gases of rigid spherical molecules are given because of their use for the determination of collision diameters of gas molecules. The rigorous theory for rigid spherical molecules yields the following result for the coefficient of viscosity of a dilute gas:

$$\eta = \frac{5}{16} \frac{(\pi m k T)^{1/2}}{\pi \sigma^2} \tag{30}$$

where m is the mass of a single molecule. Some collision diameters calculated from gas viscosities by use of this equation are summarized in Table I. It is interesting that equation 30 does not involve the pressure or the concentration of molecules. The lack of dependence of the coefficient of viscosity on pressure is confirmed with real gases at low pressures.

Equation 30 indicates that the coefficient of viscosity should be proportional to $T^{1/2}$, but a somewhat larger exponent is obtained for real gases, partly because the cross-sectional diameter becomes smaller

Table I.[1] Rigid-Sphere Molecular Diameters

(Calculated from gas viscosity measurements at 0° and 1 atm)

Gas	$\eta \times 10^7,$ g cm^{-1} sec^{-1}	$\sigma \times 10^8,$ cm
A	2099	3.64
Ne	2967	2.58
N$_2$	1663	3.75
O$_2$	1918	3.61
CH$_4$	1030	4.14
CO$_2$	1366	4.63

[1] J. O. Hirschfelder, C. F. Curtiss, and R. B. Bird, *The Molecular Theory of Gases and Liquids*, John Wiley & Sons, New York, 1954.

at high temperatures. In contrast with the viscosity of ideal gases, the viscosity of liquids decreases with increasing temperature, as described on p. 353.

Exercise II. Show that equation 30 may be written

$$\eta = 2.67 \times 10^{-5}(MT)^{1/2}/\sigma^2$$

where the molecular diameter is expressed in angstrom units (10^{-8} cm), and calculate the coefficient of viscosity of nitrogen at 0°. The molecular diameter of nitrogen is 3.75 A.

$$\eta = (2.67 \times 10^{-5})(28 \times 273)^{1/2}/(3.75)^2 = 1660 \times 10^{-7}\,g\,cm^{-1}\,sec^{-1}$$

The kinetic-theory expressions for the diffusion coefficient D and coefficient of thermal conductivity λ of gases of rigid spherical molecules are *

$$D = \frac{3}{8}\frac{(\pi m k T)^{1/2}}{\pi\sigma^2\rho} = \frac{12\lambda m}{25\rho c_v} = \frac{6}{5}\cdot\frac{\eta}{\rho} \tag{31}$$

$$\lambda = \frac{25}{32}\frac{(\pi m k T)^{1/2}c_v}{\pi\sigma^2 m} = \frac{5}{2}\cdot\frac{c_v\eta}{m} \tag{32}$$

where m is the mass of a single molecule, $\rho = n'm = Pm/kT$ is the density of the gas, and c_v is the heat capacity per molecule ($\overline{C}_V/N_0$). It is interesting to note that the coefficient of thermal conductivity is also independent of pressure, according to this theory. Real gases show deviations from these relations because they are not made up of rigid spheres. More accurate relations may be derived by taking more realistic molecular interactions into account.

REFERENCES

R. B. Bird, W. E. Stewart, and E. N. Lightfoot, *Transport Phenomena*, John Wiley & Sons, New York, 1960.

E. A. Guggenheim, *Boltzmann's Distribution Law*, North-Holland Publishing Co., Amsterdam, 1955.

K. F. Herzfeld and H. M. Smallwood, "Kinetic Theory of Ideal Gases" in *Treatise on Physical Chemistry*, Vol. II, ed. by H. S. Taylor and S. Glasstone, D. Van Nostrand Co., Princeton, N. J., 1951.

J. O. Hirschfelder, C. F. Curtiss, and R. B. Bird, *The Molecular Theory of Gases and Liquids*, John Wiley & Sons, New York, 1954.

J. H. Jeans, *Introduction to the Kinetic Theory of Gases*, Cambridge University Press, Cambridge, 1940.

M. H. C. Knudsen, *The Kinetic Theory of Gases*, Methuen & Co., London, 1950.

* J. O. Hirschfelder, C. F. Curtiss, and R. B. Bird, *The Molecular Theory of Gases and Liquids*, John Wiley & Sons, New York, 1954.

R. D. Present, *Kinetic Theory of Gases*, McGraw-Hill Book Co., New York, 1958.
F. W. Sears, *An Introduction to Thermodynamics, the Kinetic Theory of Gases, and Statistical Mechanics*, Addison-Wesley Publishing Co., Cambridge, Mass., 1953.

PROBLEMS

1. (a) What is the volume per molecule for an ideal gas at 1 atm and $0°$? (b) If the diameter of a molecule is 4 A and each is imagined to be in a separate cube, what is the length of the side of the cube in molecular diameters?
 Ans. (a) 3.72×10^{-20} cm^3 molecule^{-1}. (b) 8.4 molecular diameters.

2. Assuming that the atmosphere is isothermal at $0°$ and that the average molecular weight of air is 29, calculate the atmospheric pressure at 20,000 ft above sea level, using the Boltzmann equation. The potential energy of a mole of gas at height h is Mgh, where the acceleration of gravity g is assumed constant.
 Ans. 0.465 atm.

3. Plot the probability density $f(v)$ of various molecular velocities versus velocity for oxygen at $25°$.

4. Calculate the ratio of the root-mean-square velocity to the arithmetic mean velocity to the most probable velocity. Ans. $1.224:1.128:1.000$.

5. (a) What is the root-mean-square velocity of methane molecules at $27°$? (b) At what temperature do ethane molecules have the same velocity as methane molecules at $27°$? Ans. (a) 6.84×10^4 cm sec^{-1}. (b) $289°$.

6. (a) Calculate the number of collisions per square centimeter per second of oxygen molecules with a wall at a pressure of 1 atm and $25°$. (b) What is the number in moles per square centimeter per second? Ans. (a) 2.74×10^{23}. (b) 0.455.

7. A Knudsen cell containing crystalline benzoic acid ($M = 122$) is carefully weighed and placed in an evacuated chamber thermostated at $70°$ for 1 hr. The circular hole through which effusion occurs is 0.60 mm in diameter. Calculate the sublimation pressure of benzoic acid at $70°$ in millimeters of mercury from the fact that the weight loss is 56.7 mg. Ans. 0.16 mm.

8. A 6-to-1 mixture by volume of neon and argon is allowed to diffuse through a small orifice into an evacuated space. What is the composition of the mixture that first passes through? Ans. 89.4% Ne, 10.6% A.

9. List the numbers of translational, rotational, and vibrational degrees of freedom for (a) Ne, (b) N$_2$, (c) CO$_2$ (a linear molecule), (d) SO$_2$ (a bent molecule), and (e) NH$_3$. Ans. (a) 3, 0, 0; (b) 3, 2, 1; (c) 3, 2, 4; (d) 3, 3, 3; (e) 3, 3, 6.

10. Oxygen is contained in a vessel at 2 mm pressure and $25°$. Calculate (a) the number of collisions between molecules per second per cubic centimeter, (b) the mean free path. Ans. (a) 5.42×10^{23} sec^{-1} cm^{-3}. (b) 2.67×10^{-3} cm.

11. Calculate the mean free path of nitrogen in angstrom units at 1 atm and $25°$.
 Ans. 650 A

12. The coefficient of viscosity of helium at $500°$K is 2.79×10^{-4} g cm^{-1} sec^{-1}. (a) Calculate the collision diameter in angstrom units. Estimate (b) the coefficient of diffusion and (c) the coefficient of thermal conductivity at 1 atm.
 Ans. (a) 2.07 A. (b) 3.43 cm^2 sec^{-1}. (c) 5.22×10^{-4} cal cm^{-1} sec^{-1} deg^{-1}.

13. Calculate the kinetic energy of a mole of an ideal gas at 500° in (a) ergs and (b) calories.

14. Assuming that the atmosphere is isothermal, the Boltzmann equation shows that the pressure may be represented by $P = P_0 e^{-Mgh/RT}$, where P_0 is the pressure at $h = 0$. At sea level and 25° what is the change in barometric pressure in (a) centimeters of mercury and (b) inches of mercury per 1000-ft change in altitude?

15. Plot the probability density $f(v)$ of various molecular velocities versus velocity for oxygen at 1000°.

16. Calculate the root-mean-square, arithmetic mean, and most probable velocities for oxygen molecules at 25°.

17. Suppose that a gas contains 10 molecules having an instantaneous velocity of 2×10^4 cm sec^{-1}, 30 molecules with a velocity of 4×10^4 cm sec^{-1}, and 15 molecules with a velocity of 6×10^4 cm sec^{-1}. Calculate $\bar{v}$, v_p, and $(v^2)^{1/2}$.

18. Calculate the root-mean-square velocity of smoke particles of mass 10^{-13} gram in their Brownian motion in air at 25°.

19. The vapor pressure of naphthalene ($M = 128.16$) is 0.133 mm at 30°. Calculate the weight loss of a Knudsen cell filled with naphthalene and having a round hole 0.50 mm in diameter in a period of 2 hr.

20. Calculate the root-mean-square velocity of (a) carbon tetrachloride molecules at 100°; (b) ammonia molecules at 100°. (c) How many times longer will it take for a millimole of CCl_4 vapor to diffuse out of a small opening than a millimole of NH_3? (d) How many times longer will it take for a milligram of NH_3 to diffuse out of a small opening than a milligram of CCl_4 vapor?

21. Estimate $\bar{C}_V$ and $\bar{C}_P$ for I_2 and SO_2 (a bent molecule) at room temperature.

22. (a) Calculate the number of collisions per second undergone by a single nitrogen molecule in nitrogen at 1 atm pressure and 25°. (b) What is the number of collisions per cubic centimeter per second? What is the effect on the number of collisions (c) of doubling the absolute temperature at constant pressure and (d) of doubling the pressure at constant temperature?

23. (a) At a pressure of 10^{-10} mm of mercury, how many molecules are there per cubic centimeter at 0°? (b) What is the mean free path for oxygen molecules at this pressure?

24. Calculate the coefficient of viscosity of nitrogen gas at 227° and 1 atm and the coefficients of diffusion and thermal conductivity.

---

25. Calculate the root-mean-square velocity of oxygen molecules having a kinetic energy of 2 kcal mole^{-1}. At what temperature would this be the root-mean-square velocity?

26. Calculate the ratio of the probability that a gas molecule will have a velocity twice as large as the most probable velocity to the probability of the most probable velocity.

27. Calculate the root-mean-square, arithmetic mean, and most probable velocities for butane molecules at 100°.

28. R. B. Holden, R. Speiser, and H. L. Johnston [*J. Am. Chem. Soc.*, *70*, 3897 (1948)] found the rate of loss of weight of a Knudsen effusion cell containing finely divided beryllium to be 19.8×10^{-7} g cm^{-2} sec^{-1} at 1320°K and 1210×10^{-7} g cm^{-2} sec^{-1} at 1537°K. Calculate ΔH_{sub} for this temperature range.

29. It takes 30 min for the pressure of a certain evacuated vessel of 1-liter volume to rise from 0.001 to 0.003 mm by leakage of air through a pinhole in the glass. How long will it take for chlorine at the same temperature and external pressure to leak in and raise the pressure from 0.001 to 0.003 mm? The average molecular weight of air is 28.8.

30. List the numbers of translational, rotational, and vibrational degrees of freedom of (a) Cl_2, (b) H_2O (a bent molecule), and (c) CH_4.

31. Calculate the number of acetaldehyde (CH_3CHO) molecules colliding per milliliter per second at $800°K$ and 760 mm pressure. The molecular diameter may be taken as 5 A.

32. (a) Calculate the mean free path for hydrogen gas ($\sigma = 2.47$ A) at 1 atm and 1 micron of mercury pressure at $25°$. (b) Repeat the calculation for chlorine gas ($\sigma = 4.96$ A).

33. The collision diameter for helium is 2.18 A and for methane is 2.58 A. (a) How does the mean free path for He compare with that for CH_4 under the same conditions? (b) How does the coefficient of viscosity of He compare with that of CH_4?

34. The velocity v of sound in a gas is given by

$$v = \sqrt{\frac{\gamma R T}{M}}$$

Calculate the velocity of sound in (a) He and (b) N_2 at $25°$.

CHEMICAL KINETICS

12

Chemical equilibria and thermodynamics involve only the initial and final states; they are not concerned with the mechanism of the process or with the rate of approach to equilibrium. In chemical kinetics, however, we are interested in the intermediate steps which lead to the final products, the rates of these steps, and the factors, such as concentration, temperature, solvent, and catalyst, which determine the rate. In seeking this objective the stoichiometric equation for the over-all reaction does not tell us the mechanism of the reaction. Most reactions consist of a number of simpler elementary steps. In order to understand the rates of chemical reactions it is important to determine the elementary steps and thus the reaction mechanism. Methods for determining reaction mechanisms are given in this chapter. The deduction of reaction mechanisms from various types of kinetic data cannot be completely certain because it is impossible to rule out the possibility that there is another mechanism which could also account for the experimental data.

If two substances are mixed together, there may be many different products which are all possible according to thermodynamics, and the relative rates of competing reactions and the nature of the catalysts present are often more important considerations than equilibria in determining the final products. By altering the concentrations and the temperature and by using specific catalysts, it is possible to change the relative amounts of the various products. Only if one of the reactions goes much faster than all the others can a high yield of a single product be obtained. Science has not progressed very far in the prediction of reaction rates, but the mere fact that the study of kinetics is a pioneer field adds interest to the subject.

Experimental Measurements of Reaction Rates. Usually, reaction rates are measured under conditions of constant temperature, preferably at two or more temperatures. The rate of a chemical reaction may be followed in many different ways. Samples may be removed from the thermostated reaction vessel at intervals, chilled rapidly or quenched chemically, and analyzed. Again, several bulbs of reacting material may be started together, and each may be chilled quickly at a different time and analyzed. The chilling must be so rapid that the concentration does not change appreciably during the sampling operation.

Physical means of analysis are convenient because they do not disturb the reaction. For example, the concentration of one of the reactants or products may be determined by measuring the absorption of light at a given wavelength and applying Beer's law. The use of ultraviolet and infrared light makes possible wider applications of this method. If one of the reactants or products rotates the plane of polarized light, its concentration may be determined during the course of the reaction with the help of a polarimeter.

A change in volume of a solution during the course of the reaction may be followed with a dilatometer, which consists of a large bulb and capillary neck with a scale, like a thermometer. Again, the volume of gas evolved by certain reactions in a liquid solution may be taken as a measure of the extent of the reaction. The volume V_0 is measured at the beginning and the volume V_∞ when the reaction has been completed. Measurements of volume V_t are taken at various times t during the reaction. Then $V_\infty - V_0$ is a measure of the total amount of material that can react, and $V_\infty - V_t$ is the measure of the amount of material that still remains unreacted at time t. The fraction of material remaining unreacted at time t is given by the expression $(V_\infty - V_t)/(V_\infty - V_0)$.

Example 1. When nitrogen pentoxide decomposes in carbon tetrachloride solution, oxygen gas is evolved. In one experiment 23.95 ml of gas was evolved during 1 hour's time. After standing until no more gas was given off, the total volume of the gas was 34.75 ml. What fraction of nitrogen pentoxide remained unreacted after 1 hour?

$$\text{Fraction unreacted} = (34.75 - 23.95)/34.75 = 0.311$$

Electrical conductivity of a solution and total pressure of a gas are other physical properties that may be used in a similar manner to follow the rate of a chemical reaction. In complicated reactions, however, it is unwise to employ total pressure as a measure of the extent of decomposition unless the measurements are accompanied by chemical or physical analyses which are specific for one or more of the reacting substances.

Example 2. In the reaction $C_2H_5Br(g) = C_2H_4(g) + HBr(g)$, the pressure increased from 200 mm at the beginning to 390 mm at the end. After 500 sec the pressure was 300 mm. What fraction remained undecomposed? If the reaction goes to completion, the pressure should double to 400 mm at the end, as indicated by the chemical equation. After 500 sec half the material would be left, that is, $(400 - 300)/(400 - 200) = 0.50$. However, the fact that the final pressure was 10 mm less than 400 mm indicates that some complication is involved, and the calculation is not entirely safe. Obviously, some other reaction in addition to the one written above is involved. In this example the polymerization of ethylene on the walls accounts for part of the pressure change.

The flow method, as distinguished from a closed-vessel or static method, is often useful, especially for gas reactions. The volume of the vessel divided by the volume of the gases passing through the vessel in 1 sec gives a measure of the time in seconds during which the gases are in the vessel. The reaction vessel or tube may be filled with a solid catalyst, or the temperature may be raised so as to accelerate the reaction. The inlet and outlet tubes are small so that the gases will enter and leave the reaction zone quickly and thus be exposed to regions of intermediate temperature for only negligible periods of time. The exact time of residence in the reaction tube is difficult to determine, particularly if there is a change in the number of gaseous molecules during the reaction. Nevertheless the flow method has the advantages * that it makes possible the use of large quantities of materials for analysis and that it simulates the flow processes of industrial chemistry.

Example 3. A volume of 1200 ml of gas is passed through a 100-ml heated tube in 300 sec. The volume of gas is the calculated volume at the temperature of the furnace. How long is each molecule at this higher temperature, assuming no change in the number of molecules due to chemical reaction?
The flow of gas is 1200/300, or 4 ml sec^{-1}. The time t of residence of the gas in the tube is given by the calculation:

$$t = (100 \text{ ml})/(4 \text{ ml sec}^{-1}) = 25 \text{ sec}$$

The rate of a reaction may be expressed as a rate of change of concentration, dc/dt, or any property directly proportional to concentration, such as a rate of change of partial pressure, dp/dt, for a gas reaction. The concentration of one reactant is often determined by the stoichiometry of the reaction from the concentration of one of the other reactants or products, which can be determined experimentally

* O. A. Hougen, K. M. Watson, and R. A. Ragatz, *Chemical Process Principles,* Part III: *Kinetics and Catalysis,* John Wiley & Sons, New York, 1947, p. 832.

more easily. Thus in the reaction $A + 2B = AB_2$

$$\frac{-d(A)}{dt} = \frac{-d(B)}{2dt} = \frac{d(AB_2)}{dt} \tag{1}$$

Parentheses around symbols which represent chemical compounds will be used to indicate concentrations in moles per liter.

Reaction Order. In general, the rate of a chemical reaction depends upon the concentrations of the reactants. However, the rate may also depend upon the concentrations of other substances not involved in the stoichiometric equation. The equation expressing the rate as a function of the concentration of each of the substances which affect the rate is called the *rate law* for the reaction. When the rate equation involves powers of concentrations, the *order* of the reaction with respect to a reactant is equal to its exponent in the rate law. For a reaction with reactants A, B, and C the rate law might have one of the following forms:

First order in A: $\quad -d(A)/dt = k(A) \quad$ or $\quad k(A)(B)$

Second order in A: $\quad -d(A)/dt = k(A)^2(B) \quad$ or $\quad k(A)^2$

Third order in A: $\quad -d(A)/dt = k(A)^3 \quad$ or $\quad k(A)^3(B)^2$

Zero order in A: $\quad -d(A)/dt = k(A)^0 = k$

If the reaction is first order in A and first order in B, it is said to be second order over-all.

However, not all rate equations have these simple forms, and more complicated functions of the concentrations are often encountered, as illustrated by equation 59 and equation 75. Rate equations involving fractional orders may be obtained, as illustrated in equation 62 on p. 329.

The rate law for a reaction can be determined only by experimental kinetic studies and cannot be deduced from the balanced chemical equation.

First-Order Reactions. The rate of a first-order reaction is expressed by

$$\frac{dc}{dt} = -kc \tag{2}$$

where c is the concentration of reacting substance, t is the time, dc/dt is the rate of change of concentration of reactant, and k is the *rate constant*. The first-order rate constant has the dimensions of t^{-1} and may be expressed in reciprocal seconds (or other units of time).

Integrating, we have

$$\int \frac{dc}{c} = -k \int dt \tag{3}$$

$$\ln c = -kt + \text{constant} \tag{4}$$

$$\log c = -\frac{k}{2.303} t + \text{constant} \tag{5}$$

Thus for a first-order reaction a straight line is produced when log c for the reactant is plotted against time. The rate constant k can be evaluated by multiplying the slope of the line by -2.303.

Integrating equation 5 between the limits, concentration c_1 at time t_1 and c_2 at a later time t_2, we have

$$-\int_{c_1}^{c_2} \frac{dc}{c} = k \int_{t_1}^{t_2} dt \tag{6}$$

$$-\ln c_2 - (-\ln c_1) = k(t_2 - t_1) \tag{7}$$

$$k = \frac{2.303}{t_2 - t_1} \log \frac{c_1}{c_2} \tag{8}$$

This equation may be modified to give the following equation:

$$k = \frac{2.303}{t} \log \frac{c_0}{c} \tag{9}$$

where c_0 is the concentration at the beginning of the reaction when the time is zero, and c is the concentration after time t has elapsed.

Still another modification is used, in which a is the initial quantity of reacting material in a given volume, x is the amount reacting in time t, and $a - x$ is the amount remaining at time t.

$$k = \frac{2.303}{t} \log \frac{a}{a - x} \tag{10}$$

It is evident from the last three equations that in order to determine a first-order rate constant it is only necessary to determine the *ratio* of the concentrations at two times. Quantities proportional to concentration may be substituted for c in these equations, since the proportionality constants would cancel. For example, suppose that an ester is hydrolyzed by an acid and the reaction is followed by titrating the total acid with sodium hydroxide solution at various times. The difference $V_\infty - V$, where V is the volume of sodium hydroxide required at any time and V_∞ is the volume required when the reaction has gone to completion, is proportional to the concentration of ester *remaining unhydrolyzed* at any time. Thus the first-order rate constant could be calculated from

$$k = \frac{2.303}{t_2 - t_1} \log \frac{V_\infty - V_1}{V_\infty - V_2}$$

Equation 9 may be written in exponential form:

$$c = c_0 e^{-kt} \tag{11}$$

The concentration of product is then given by $c_0(1 - e^{-kt})$. If the analytical method yields the concentration of product, the concentration of reactant is generally calculated so that the rate constant can be determined using equation 5 or 8–10.

Reaction rates may be described by giving the numerical value of k, or sometimes by giving the *half-life*, $t_{1/2}$, that is, the time necessary for half the substance initially present to react. For a first-order reaction half the substance disappears in each half-life, so that 25 per cent remains after two half-lives and 12.5 per cent after three. The relation between the half-life and the rate constant is obtained from equation 9.

$$k = \frac{2.303}{t_{1/2}} \log \frac{1}{\frac{1}{2}} = \frac{0.693}{t_{1/2}} \tag{12}$$

The half-life for a first-order reaction then is

$$t_{1/2} = \frac{0.693}{k} \tag{13}$$

The calculation of first-order rate constants may be illustrated for the decomposition of nitrogen pentoxide.* Nitrogen pentoxide decomposes completely in the gas phase, or when dissolved in inert solvents, at a rate which is conveniently measured at room temperature. The reaction is strictly first order (except at very low pressures), and the end products are oxygen and a mixture of nitrogen tetroxide and nitrogen dioxide. The following equation represents the over-all reaction:

$$N_2O_5 \rightarrow N_2O_4 + \tfrac{1}{2}O_2$$

$$\updownarrow$$

$$2NO_2$$

---

* F. Daniels and E. H. Johnston, *J. Am. Chem. Soc.*, *43*, 53 (1921); H. Eyring and F. Daniels, *J. Am. Chem. Soc.*, *52*, 1472 (1930).

For every molecule of oxygen produced, two molecules of nitrogen pentoxide have decomposed. It will be shown later (p. 327), however, that this reaction is much more complicated, having several intermediate steps. It may be suggested that in chemical kinetics the only simple reactions are the ones that have not been studied very thoroughly.

When a solution of nitrogen pentoxide in carbon tetrachloride decomposes, the nitrogen tetroxide and nitrogen dioxide remain in solution while the oxygen escapes and may be measured in a gas buret. The reaction vessel is carefully thermostated, and it is agitated to prevent supersaturation of the oxygen.

Experimental data for the decomposition of nitrogen pentoxide dissolved in carbon tetrachloride at 45° were interpreted as illustrated in Example 1. They are given in Table I and plotted in the accompanying figures.

In *Fig. 12-1a* the concentration of nitrogen pentoxide calculated from the volume of oxygen evolved is plotted against time, and it is seen that the concentration decreases with time, rapidly at first, then more slowly, and finally approaches zero asymptotically.

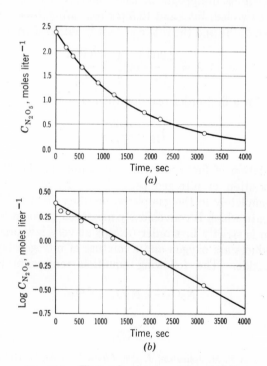

Fig. 12-1. First-order decomposition of N_2O_5.

In *Fig. 12-1b* the straight line produced by plotting the logarithm of the concentration against time shows that the reaction is first order and follows strictly the relation given by equation 5.

The value of the first-order rate constant, as given in the last column of Table I, ranges around 6.2×10^{-4} sec^{-1}. The best value is 6.22×10^{-4} sec^{-1}, obtained by multiplying the slope of the line in Fig. 12-1b by -2.303 as required by equation 5.

Table I. Decomposition of Nitrogen Pentoxide (N_2O_5) in Carbon Tetrachloride Solution at 45°

t, sec	c, moles liter^{-1}	$\log c$	$k \times 10^4$, sec^{-1} (equation 9)
0	2.33	0.367	...
184	2.08	0.318	6.14
319	1.91	0.281	6.23
526	1.67	0.223	6.32
867	1.36	0.133	6.23
1198	1.11	0.045	6.20
1877	0.72	−0.143	6.27
2315	0.55	−0.250	6.25
3144	0.34	−0.469	6.14

If the reaction is first order, it will take twice as long for three-fourths of the material to react as it takes for half to react. This single criterion is sometimes useful in determining whether or not a given reaction is first order.

After proving with a sufficient number of properly spaced measurements that the reaction is strictly first order, the best value of the constant k can be determined from the slope of the straight line, as in Fig. 12-1b, or by substituting two widely separated readings into equation 8.

Exercise I. Show that it is not satisfactory to average all the constants obtained in successive time intervals using equation 8. If the time intervals are all the same, an average of the k's would exclude all the intermediate measurements and base the value only on the first and last, which might well be the least accurate.* Thus,

* Mathematical methods for calculating rate constants are discussed critically by W. E. Roseveare, *J. Am. Chem. Soc.*, *53*, 1651 (1931); and by L. J. Reed and E. J. Theriault, *J. Phys. Chem.*, *35*, 673 (1931).

$$k = \frac{2.303}{t_2 - t_1} \log \frac{c_1}{c_2} \quad k = \frac{2.303}{t_3 - t_2} \log \frac{c_2}{c_3} \quad \text{and} \quad k = \frac{2.303}{t_4 - t_3} \log \frac{c_3}{c_4}$$

$$k_{\text{avg}} = \frac{2.303}{3(t' - t)} [\log c_1 - \log c_2 + \log c_2 - \log c_3 + \log c_3 - \log c_4]$$

$$= \frac{2.303}{3(t' - t)} \log \frac{c_1}{c_4}$$

Second-Order Reactions. When the rate of a reaction is proportional to the concentration of each of two reactants or to the square of the concentration of one reactant, the reaction is of the second order. For example, if the stoichiometry is given by $A + B = C$ and if a and b represent the initial molar concentrations of the two reacting substances A and B, and x denotes the number of moles per liter which react in time t, then the velocity of the reaction is expressed by the equation

$$\frac{dx}{dt} = k(a - x)(b - x) \tag{14}$$

In the simplest case the two substances $(A$ and $B)$ are present at equal concentrations, and $a = b$. Under these conditions, the rate equation becomes

$$\frac{dx}{dt} = k(a - x)^2$$

Integrating,

$$\frac{1}{(a - x)} = kt + C \tag{15}$$

Evaluating the integration constant C by setting $x = 0$ when $t = 0$, we obtain

$$k = \frac{1}{t} \cdot \frac{x}{a(a - x)} \tag{16}$$

If the reacting substances are not present at equal concentrations, then equation 14 must be employed. On integrating by partial fractions and evaluating the integration constant, equation 14 becomes

$$kt = \frac{1}{(a - b)} \ln \frac{b(a - x)}{a(b - x)}$$

or

$$k = \frac{2.303}{t(a - b)} \log \frac{b(a - x)}{a(b - x)} \tag{17}$$

The graphical method for obtaining the best value of k is convenient. When log $[b(a - x)/a(b - x)]$ * is plotted as ordinate against t, a straight line is obtained if the reaction is second order. Its slope is $k(a - b)/2.303$, and k is then obtained by multiplying the slope of the line by $2.303/(a - b)$.

The value of k for a second-order reaction depends on the units in which the concentration is expressed, since the magnitude of the term $(a - b)$ depends on the units used. For the sake of uniformity it is customary to express concentrations in moles per liter and time in seconds. Then the second-order rate constant k has the units liters per mole per second. In a first-order reaction the form of the rate equation is such that the units of concentration cancel out.

The saponification of an ester in alkaline solution is an illustration of a second-order reaction.

$$CH_3COOC_2H_5 + OH^- = CH_3COO^- + C_2H_5OH$$

Solutions of ester and alkali are placed in separate flasks in a thermostat and then mixed. At frequent intervals, a portion of the reaction mixture is removed, discharged into a measured volume of standard acid, and back-titrated with standard alkali. The decrease in concentration of OH^- ions is a measure of the extent of the reaction. A final titration, after the reaction is completed, is necessary in order to determine the number of equivalents of hydroxide ion left after the reaction is complete and thus by difference to obtain the number of moles per liter of ethyl acetate which were present at the beginning of the experiment. The reaction may be followed also by measuring the change in the electrical conductivity of the system or by measuring the slight increase in volume of the solution as the reaction proceeds.

Experimental data obtained by titration are recorded in the first two columns of Table II, and the second-order rate constant k is given in the last column, as calculated by use of equation 17.

The second-order rate constant k can also be determined by a graphical method.

Example 4. Calculate k from the data of Table II as shown in *Fig. 12-2*. The slope of the line is $0.550/2400 = 2.29 \times 10^{-4}$ sec^{-1}. The second-order rate constant may be calculated from

$$k = \frac{(2.303)(\text{slope})}{(a - b)} = \frac{(2.303)(2.29 \times 10^{-4})}{(0.00494)}$$

$$= 0.107 \text{ liter mole}^{-1} \text{ sec}^{-1}$$

---

* This may be replaced for purposes of graphing by log $[(a - x)/(b - x)]$, which will give a plot of the same slope.

Table II. Hydrolysis of Ethyl Acetate at 25°

a = initial concentration of NaOH = 0.00980 mole l^{-1}.
b = initial concentration of $CH_3COOC_2H_5$ = 0.00486 mole l^{-1}.

Time, sec	$x,$ mole l^{-1}	$a - x,$ mole l^{-1}	$b - x,$ mole l^{-1}	$\log\dfrac{b\,(a-x)}{a\,(b-x)}$	$k = \dfrac{2.303}{t(a-b)}\log\dfrac{b\,(a-x)}{a\,(b-x)}$
0	0.00000	0.00980	0.00486	. . .	. . .
178	0.00088	0.00892	0.00398	0.0412	0.108
273	0.00116	0.00864	0.00370	0.0640	0.109
531	0.00188	0.00792	0.00297	0.1208	0.106
866	0.00256	0.00724	0.00230	0.1936	0.104
1510	0.00335	0.00645	0.00151	0.3266	0.101
1918	0.00377	0.00603	0.00109	0.4390	0.106
2401	0.00406	0.00574	0.00080	0.5518	0.107

Third-Order Reaction. For a third-order reaction which is first order in each of the reactants A, B, and C reacting with the stoichiometry $A + B + C$ = products, the rate equation may be written

$$\frac{dx}{dt} = k(a - x)(b - x)(c - x) \tag{18}$$

and, in the special case that $a = b = c$,

$$\frac{dx}{dt} = k(a - x)^3 \tag{19}$$

Integrating,

$$\frac{1}{2(a - x)^2} = kt + \text{const}$$

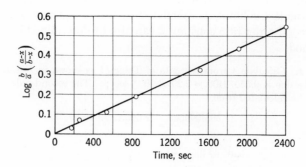

Fig. 12-2. A linear plot for a second-order reaction, the hydrolysis of ethyl acetate at 25°.

The constant may be evaluated by setting $x = 0$ when $t = 0$, and thus

$$\frac{1}{2(a - x)^2} = kt + \frac{1}{2a^2}, \quad \text{or} \quad k = \frac{1}{2t}\left[\frac{1}{(a - x)^2} - \frac{1}{a^2}\right] \quad (20)$$

Other integrated forms are obtained if $a \neq b \neq c$ or if the stoichiometry is given by $2A + B =$ products or $A + B =$ products.*

The oxidation of nitric oxide to nitrogen dioxide

$$2NO + O_2 = 2NO_2$$

is a third-order reaction † because the rate equation is found to be

$$\frac{dc_{NO_2}}{dt} = kc_{NO}^2 c_{O_2}$$

Zero-Order Reactions. There are reactions in which the rate is unaffected by changes in the concentrations of one or more reactants because it is determined by some limiting factor other than concentration, such as the amount of light absorbed in a photochemical reaction or the amount of catalyst in a catalytic reaction. Then

$$\frac{dc}{dt} = -k \quad (21)$$

A catalytic reaction might be first order in catalyst and zero order in reactant.

Again, the concentration of reactant may be kept constant automatically as in a saturated solution in contact with an excess of undissolved solute. Then, the concentration of the reactant is a constant, but the concentration of product x increases according to the expression

$$\frac{dx}{dt} = k \quad (22)$$

$$x = kt + \text{constant} \quad (23)$$

The value of k calculated in this way may include constants corresponding to the intensity of light or the amount of catalyst.

Example 5. Three substances, A, B, and C, are dissolved to form a liter of solution so that $c_A = c_B = c_C$. At the end of 1000 sec half of A is still left. What will be the concentration of A after 2000 sec?

* A. A. Frost and R. G. Pearson, *Kinetics and Mechanism*, John Wiley & Sons, New York, 1961.

† R. L. Hasche and W. A. Patrick, *J. Am. Chem. Soc.*, *47*, 1207 (1925); J. C. Treacy and F. Daniels, *J. Am. Chem. Soc.*, *77*, 2033 (1955).

If the reaction is first order with respect to A and unaffected by the concentrations of B and C, one-half will remain after 1000 sec and one-half of the remaining half, or 25 per cent, will remain after the second 1000-sec period. If the reaction is first order with respect to A and first order with respect to B but independent of the concentration of C, equation 16 shows that 33 per cent of A (and B) will be left after 2000 sec. If the reaction is first order with respect to A, B, and C, that is, third order for the over-all reaction, 38 per cent of A (and B and C) will be left after 2000 sec according to equation 20. If the reaction $A + B + C$ is zero order with respect to all three reactants, all three will have completely reacted at the end of 2000 sec.

Determination of the Order of a Reaction. There are several different ways in which the order of a reaction may be determined.

Substitution into formulas. If a reaction is of first, second, third, or zero order, a constant value of k will be obtained throughout the course of the reaction when the data are substituted into the corresponding equation. If the data do not fit any of these equations, the rate law is more complicated.

Graphing. The order may sometimes be determined by plotting different functions of the concentration against the time. If a straight line is obtained when $\log c$ is plotted against time, the reaction is first order, as shown in equation 5. Data for a first-order reaction and a second-order reaction are not very different in the first 50 per cent of reaction.

In the special case where all the reactants have the same initial concentration, the reaction is second order if a straight line is obtained when $1/c$ is plotted against time, as shown in equation 15, and third order if a straight line is obtained when $1/c^2$ is plotted against time, as shown in equation 20.

In a zero-order reaction a straight line is obtained when the concentration of product x is plotted against time, as is evident from equation 23.

Half-life periods. In a first-order reaction the half-life (or in fact the time required for any given fraction of the reacting substance to react) is independent of the initial concentration, as shown in equation 13.

In a second-order reaction in which $a = b$, the time required for half the reacting substances to react is inversely proportional to the initial concentration, and $t_{1/2} = 1/ka$, as can be derived from equation 16.

Determination of initial velocities. Much information can be gained about a complex rate law by increasing the concentrations of the reactants one at a time while holding the other concentrations constant, and observing the initial reaction rate (for example, over a period in which there is only 10 per cent reaction). The initial rate may be expressed in terms of the initial concentrations of the reactants.

Example 6. The chemical equation for the reaction between oxalate ion and mercuric chloride is

$$2HgCl_2 + C_2O_4^{2-} = 2Cl^- + 2CO_2 + Hg_2Cl_2$$

The rate may be determined by measuring the amount of Hg_2Cl_2 precipitated. At 100° the initial rates, as moles per liter of Hg_2Cl_2 per minute, are as follows:

	$HgCl_2$, M	$K_2C_2O_4$, M	$dx/dt \times 10^4$
(1)	0.0836	0.202	0.26
(2)	0.0836	0.404	1.04
(3)	0.0418	0.404	0.53

In going from the first experiment to the second, the concentration of oxalate ion is doubled but the initial rate is increased by a factor of 4. Thus the rate is proportional to $(C_2O_4^{2-})^2$. In going from the second experiment to the third, the concentration of $HgCl_2$ is reduced to half and the initial rate is similarly reduced to half. Thus the experimental rate equation is

$$dx/dt = k(HgCl_2)(C_2O_4^{2-})^2$$

It should be noted that the exponents are quite different from what they would be if the balanced chemical equation actually gave the mechanism.

An important technique for determining the form of the rate law involves adding a large excess of one or more of the reactants so that its concentration does not change appreciably during the reaction. If all but one of the reacting substances are present in large excess, the order with respect to this remaining reactant may be determined directly from the relation between the rate of reaction and the concentration of this reactant.

Complex Reactions. Many reactions are not zero, first, second, or third order because they proceed by a mechanism which involves more than one step. However, multistep reactions may behave as zero-, first-, second-, or third-order reactions. Important among the complications which are encountered with complex reactions are *parallel steps, consecutive steps,* and *reversible steps.* The following simple examples will be discussed in some detail:

Parallel first-order reactions: $A \xrightarrow{k_1} B$

                                          $A \xrightarrow{k_2} C$

Consecutive first-order reactions: $A \xrightarrow{k_1} B \xrightarrow{k_2} C$

Reversible first-order reactions: $A \underset{k_2}{\overset{k_1}{\rightleftharpoons}} B$

Complex reactions are made up of various combinations of these and other types of steps. Under particular conditions complex reactions often appear to be simply zero, first, second, or third order because the rate-limiting step is zero, first, second, or third order and the other steps are very fast.

Parallel First-Order Reactions. Parallel first-order reactions which compete for the reactant are often encountered because many products may be possible according to the laws of thermodynamics. For example, in the nitration of bromobenzene, o-, m-, and p-nitrobromobenzene are obtained. Under certain conditions the yields are indicated by

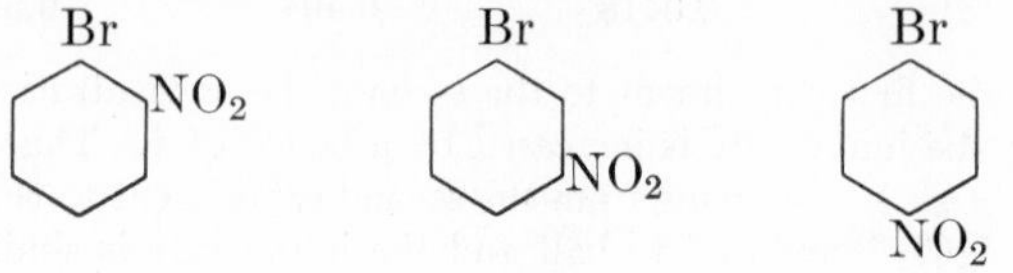

| *ortho* | *meta* | *para* |
| 13.5 per cent | 0.3 per cent | 86.2 per cent |

Often such yields do not indicate the equilibrium concentrations of the products but indicate the different rates with which the various products are formed. Thus, if conditions can be arranged so that one product is formed much faster than the others, a high yield of this product will be obtained.

For the reactions

$$A \xrightarrow{k_1} B$$
$$A \xrightarrow{k_2} C$$

the rate equation for A is

$$-\frac{d(A)}{dt} = k_1(A) + k_2(A) = (k_1 + k_2)(A) \tag{24}$$

Thus the disappearance of A will be first order, and on the basis of the earlier discussion of first-order reactions we can write

$$(A) = (A)_0 e^{-(k_1+k_2)t} \tag{25}$$

The rate equation for B is

$$\frac{d(B)}{dt} = k_1(A) = k_1(A)_0 e^{-(k_1+k_2)t}$$

Integration yields

$$(B) = \frac{-k_1(A)_0}{(k_1 + k_2)} e^{-(k_1+k_2)t} + \text{constant}$$

If $(B) = 0$ at $t = 0$, const $= k_1(A)_0/(k_1 + k_2)$ and

$$(B) = \frac{k_1(A)_0}{(k_1 + k_2)} [1 - e^{-(k_1+k_2)t}] \tag{26}$$

Thus the fraction of A that is converted to B at infinite time is $k_1/(k_1 + k_2)$. At any time the sum of (A), (B), and (C) must be equal to the total concentration of A at the beginning, $(A)_0$. Consequently

$$(C) = \frac{k_2(A)_0}{(k_1 + k_2)} [1 - e^{-(k_1+k_2)t}] \tag{27}$$

Thus B and C appear with the *same half-life*, although they are formed in first-order reactions with different rate constants.

Consecutive First-Order Reactions. Consecutive reactions occur when the product of a reaction undergoes further reaction. Many excellent examples of consecutive first-order reactions are found among the nuclear reactions of the radioactive elements (p. 691). These radioactive reactions can be expressed with exactness by simple first-order equations.

Two consecutive first-order reactions may be represented by

$$A \xrightarrow{k_1} B \xrightarrow{k_2} C$$

In order to determine the way in which the concentrations of the compounds in such a mechanism depend upon time, the rate equations are first written down for each substance. It is then necessary to obtain the solution of these simultaneous differential equations. For the above reactions the rate equations are as follows:

$$\frac{d(A)}{dt} = -k_1(A) \tag{28}$$

$$\frac{d(B)}{dt} = k_1(A) - k_2(B) \tag{29}$$

$$\frac{d(C)}{dt} = k_2(B) \tag{30}$$

It will be assumed that, at $t = 0$, $(A) = (A)_0$, $(B) = 0$, and $(C) = 0$. The rate equation for A is readily integrated to obtain

$$(A) = (A)_0 e^{-k_1 t} \tag{31}$$

Substitution of this expression into equation 29 yields

$$\frac{d(B)}{dt} = k_1(A)_0 e^{-k_1 t} - k_2(B) \tag{32}$$

which may be integrated * to obtain

$$(B) = \frac{k_1(A)_0}{(k_2 - k_1)}[e^{-k_1 t} - e^{-k_2 t}] \tag{33}$$

Because of conservation of material $(A)_0 = (A) + (B) + (C)$ at any time, and so the concentration of C is given by

$$(C) = (A)_0 - (A) - (B) = (A)_0 \left[1 + \frac{1}{k_1 - k_2}(k_2 e^{-k_1 t} - k_1 e^{-k_2 t}) \right] \tag{34}$$

The concentrations of A, B, and C are shown in *Fig. 12-3* for the case that $(A)_0 = 1$ mole liter^{-1}, $k_1 = 0.1$ hr^{-1}, and $k_2 = 0.05$ hr^{-1}.

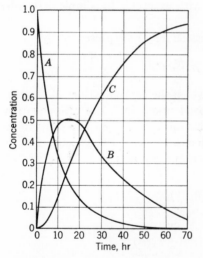

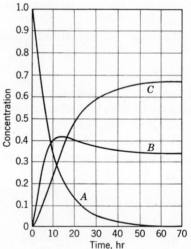

Fig. 12-3. Consecutive first-order reactions: $A \xrightarrow{k_1} B \xrightarrow{k_2} C$; $k_1 = 0.10$ hr^{-1}, $k_2 = 0.05$ hr^{-1}.

Fig. 12-4. Consecutive first-order reactions with a reversible step: $A \xrightarrow{k_1} B \underset{k_3}{\overset{k_2}{\rightleftharpoons}} C$; $k_1 = 0.10$, $k_2 = 0.10$, $k_3 = 0.05$ hr^{-1}.

Exercise II. Calculate the concentrations of A, B, and C at 35 hr.

* G. B. Thomas, Jr., *Calculus and Analytic Geometry*, Addison-Wesley Publishing Co., Cambridge, Mass., 1953, p. 653.

If the course of the reaction were followed by analyzing for A, curve A would be obtained; if it were followed by measuring the concentration of the end product C, curve C would result; and, finally, if only the intermediate product B were determined, it would be found that its concentration would rise to a maximum and then fall off, as shown by curve B. The actual rate of production of C is seen to be quite complicated, and the existence of an induction period or time lag at the beginning of the reaction is evident.

If either one or both of the steps in the reaction $A \to B \to C$ are reversible, more complicated expressions are obtained.* If, for example, the second step is reversible, both B and C will be present at equilibrium. This is illustrated by the plot in *Fig. 12-4* for the case that

$$A \xrightarrow{0.10 \text{ hr}^{-1}} B \underset{0.05 \text{ hr}^{-1}}{\overset{0.10 \text{ hr}^{-1}}{\rightleftharpoons}} C$$

Reversible First-Order Reaction. The integrated rate equation for a reversible first-order reaction

$$A \underset{k_2}{\overset{k_1}{\rightleftharpoons}} B$$

may readily be derived. The rate equation is

$$\frac{d(A)}{dt} = -k_1(A) + k_2(B) \tag{35}$$

At equilibrium $d(A)/dt = 0$, and the concentrations of A and B are represented by $(A)_{eq}$ and $(B)_{eq}$, so that

$$\frac{(B)_{eq}}{(A)_{eq}} = \frac{(A)_0 - (A)_{eq}}{(A)_{eq}} = \frac{k_1}{k_2} = K \tag{36}$$

where K is the equilibrium constant. This relationship between the rate constants for the forward and reverse reactions and the equilibrium constant may also be derived by stating that at equilibrium the rates of the forward and reverse reactions are equal. The rate of the forward reaction is $k_1(A)_{eq}$, and the rate of the reverse reaction is $k_2(B)_{eq}$; thus $k_1(A)_{eq} = k_2(B)_{eq}$ and rearrangement yields equation 36.

There is always a relation between the rate laws for the forward and reverse reactions and the equilibrium constant. The nature of this re-

---

* For these equations and also discussion of other special cases of the mechanism $A \rightleftharpoons B$, see R. A. Alberty and W. G. Miller, *J. Chem. Phys.*, *26*, 1231 (1957).

lationship for more complicated reactions and mechanisms is discussed in the Appendix (p. 721).

Equation 36 may be integrated after introducing the conservation equation $(A)_0 = (A) + (B)$. The concentration of A is $(A)_0$ at $t = 0$ and (A) at time t.

$$\int_{(A)_0}^{(A)} \frac{d(A)}{k_2(A)_0 - (k_1 + k_2)(A)} = \int_0^t dt$$

$$- (k_1 + k_2)t = \ln\left[\frac{(k_1 + k_2)(A) - k_2(A)_0}{k_1(A)_0}\right] \tag{37}$$

It is convenient to rearrange this integrated equation by introducing the equilibrium concentration of A, namely, $(A)_{eq}$.

Equation 36 may be solved for the equilibrium concentration of A to obtain

$$(A)_{eq} = \frac{k_2(A)_0}{k_1 + k_2} \tag{38}$$

Thus

$$(A)_0 - (A)_{eq} = \frac{k_1(A)_0}{k_1 + k_2} \tag{39}$$

Equation 37 may be written

$$- (k_1 + k_2)t = \ln\left[\frac{(A) - \dfrac{k_2(A)_0}{k_1 + k_2}}{\dfrac{k_1(A)_0}{k_1 + k_2}}\right] \tag{40}$$

Substituting equations 38 and 39, we obtain

$$(k_1 + k_2)t = \ln\left[\frac{(A)_0 - (A)_{eq}}{(A) - (A)_{eq}}\right] \tag{41}$$

Thus a plot of $-\log[(A) - (A)_{eq}]$ versus time is linear, and $(k_1 + k_2)$ may be calculated from the slope. It should be especially noted that such a plot yields the sum of the rate constants of the forward and reverse reactions, not the rate constant for the forward reaction. Since the ratio k_1/k_2 may be calculated from the equilibrium concentrations by use of equation 36, the values of k_1 and k_2 may be obtained.

Theoretically all reactions are reversible to at least a slight extent, but many reactions go to completion as far as ordinary experimental measurements are concerned. Equations have also been derived for opposing first- and second-order reactions, opposing second-order reactions, and opposing second- and third-order reactions.*

The rate equations may be integrated for a number of mechanisms involving parallel, consecutive, and reversible steps of first and second orders. However, for more complicated mechanisms the differential equations cannot be solved explicitly, and it is necessary to use digital or analog computers to obtain numerical solutions or to introduce experimentally suitable approximations to simplify the mathematics. Valuable information can be obtained by writing down the rate equations for a complex reaction even if the equations cannot be solved explicitly. Through them it is often possible to understand why there are sometimes induction periods in which the reaction proceeds very slowly at first, why complex reactions may approach a first order or a second order or a fractional order, and how these apparent orders can change during the course of the reaction.

The Principle of Detailed Balancing. Whenever there are more than two paths for a given reaction, there is another principle which must be applied in order to obtain correct results.

Suppose the transformation of A to B occurs by the following two parallel paths:

$$A \underset{k_2}{\overset{k_1}{\rightleftharpoons}} B$$

$$A + H^+ \underset{k_4}{\overset{k_3}{\rightleftharpoons}} B + H^+$$

The rate equation for the formation of B is

$$\frac{d(B)}{dt} = k_1(A) - k_2(B) + k_3(A)(H^+) - k_4(B)(H^+) \tag{42}$$

Since at equilibrium $d(B)/dt = 0$, equation 42 leads to

$$K = \frac{(B)_{eq}}{(A)_{eq}} = \frac{k_1 + k_3(H^+)}{k_2 + k_4(H^+)} \tag{43}$$

But this is a paradoxical result, since the equilibrium constant would not be expected to depend upon the hydrogen-ion concentration according to the above reactions taken individually. This paradox is eliminated, and the dependence of K on the concentration of hydrogen ions is removed, by bringing in the principle of detailed balancing, which

* E. A. Moelwyn-Hughes, *Physical Chemistry*, Pergamon Press, New York, 1957.

is not derivable from thermodynamics. According to this principle, *the forward and reverse rates for each path in the over-all reaction must be equal at equilibrium.* Thus at equilibrium

$$k_1(A)_{eq} = k_2(B)_{eq} \tag{44}$$

and

$$k_3(A)_{eq}(H^+) = k_4(B)_{eq}(H^+) \tag{45}$$

Substituting equations 44 and 45 into equation 43, it is found that the terms in hydrogen-ion concentration disappear as they should. From equations 44 and 45 it can be seen that

$$K = \frac{(B)_{eq}}{(A)_{eq}} = \frac{k_1}{k_2} = \frac{k_3}{k_4} \tag{46}$$

Thus the ratio k_3/k_4 is necessarily equal to the ratio k_1/k_2. The principle of detailed balancing has other applications and is an important supplement to the laws of thermodynamics and kinetics in the study of the mechanisms of reaction.

Determination of Reaction Mechanism. The mechanisms of reactions are generally more complicated than would be indicated by the balanced chemical equations. The series of steps which add up to give the over-all reaction is often revealed by the rate equation for the reaction. Several examples of mechanisms and the corresponding rate laws will be discussed later in the chapter. In discussing mechanisms the various steps are referred to as *unimolecular, bimolecular,* or *termolecular,* depending on the number of molecules involved in the step.

A *unimolecular* step is one in which one molecule rearranges or breaks into smaller parts, as in

$$\begin{array}{c} H_2C-CH_2 \\ | \quad | \\ H_2C-CH_2 \end{array} \rightarrow 2CH_2 = CH_2$$

A *bimolecular* step is one in which two molecules must come together before a reaction can take place, as in

$$H_2 + I_2 \rightarrow 2HI$$

A *termolecular* step is one in which three molecules must collide simultaneously in order to make possible a reaction.

$$2NO + O_2 \rightarrow 2NO_2$$

In order to obtain the rate law for a mechanism the rate equations for each reactant and intermediate are written down, and these equations are solved simultaneously. The term in a rate equation for a unimolecular step is, of course, first order and for a bimolecular step, second order; but the final rate equation for the product may be more complicated or even show a lower order than some step. Although the decomposition of nitrogen pentoxide is a beautiful first-order reaction, the primary unimolecular decomposition, $N_2O_5 \rightarrow NO_2 + NO_3$, is not the rate-determining step, and the over-all reaction involves several steps (p. 327) which happen to give a first-order reaction rate.

In other cases the concentration of a reactant may be essentially constant because it is in excess. For example, in the inversion of sucrose

$$C_{12}H_{22}O_{11} + H_2O = C_6H_{12}O_6 + C_6H_{12}O_6$$

Sucrose   Fructose   Glucose

which may be followed by measurements of optical rotation, the concentration of water does not change appreciably since it is in large excess. Thus the order of the reaction with respect to water cannot be determined in dilute aqueous solutions.

The problem encountered in the laboratory is that once the rate law has been determined the mechanism has to be deduced. This is a process which requires imagination and cannot be summarized by a few simple rules. When a mechanism has been devised which gives the correct rate law, this does not mean that it is the only mechanism which is in accord with the experimental facts.

Influence of Temperature on Reaction Rate. It has long been known as an empirical fact that many, but certainly not all, reactions approximately double or triple their velocity for a 10° rise in temperature in the neighborhood of room temperature.

Kinetic data over a range of temperature can usually be represented by use of an empirical equation proposed by Arrhenius.

$$k = se^{-E_a/RT} \tag{47}$$

where s is a constant referred to as the frequency factor,* and E_a is the Arrhenius activation energy. Set in logarithmic form,

$$\log k = \frac{-E_a}{2.303R} \frac{1}{T} + \log s \tag{48}$$

According to this equation, a straight line should be obtained when the logarithm of the rate constant is plotted against the reciprocal of the.

---

* The constant s has the units of frequency only for first-order reactions, and it is sometimes called the pre-exponential factor. Benson has suggested that s be called the Arrhenius factor.

absolute temperature. Differentiating equation 48 with respect to temperature,

$$\frac{d \ln k}{dT} = \frac{E_a}{RT^2} \tag{49}$$

and integrating between limits,

$$\log \frac{k_2}{k_1} = \frac{E_a}{2.303R} \left(\frac{T_2 - T_1}{T_1 T_2} \right) \tag{50}$$

It may be noted that these equations are similar to those for equilibrium constants studied on p. 215.

The rate constants for the decomposition of gaseous nitrogen pentoxide * at different temperatures are given in the third column of Table III in seconds^{-1}. The values of log k are plotted against $1/T$ in *Fig. 12-5*.

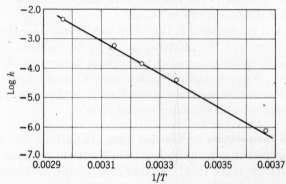

Fig. 12-5. Graph of log k versus $1/T$ for the decomposition of N_2O_5, from which the Arrhenius activation energy may be calculated.

The slope of the line in Fig. 12-5 is -5400, and E_a has the value of $-2.3R$ (slope) $= 24,700$ cal mole^{-1}. Equation 48 becomes

$$\log k = -\frac{24,700}{2.303 \times 1.987} \frac{1}{T} + 13.638$$

and equation 47

$$k = 4.3 \times 10^{13} e^{-24,700/1.987T}$$

The values of the rate constants k in reciprocal seconds, as calculated using this equation, are given in the fifth column of Table III, and the half-lives are given in the last column.

* F. Daniels and E. H. Johnston, *J. Am. Chem. Soc.*, *43*, 53 (1921).

Table III.   Rate Constants for the Decomposition of Nitrogen Pentoxide at Different Temperatures

t, °C	$1/T$	$k_{obs} \times 10^5$	$\log k$	$k_{calc} \times 10^5$	Half-Life [1]
65	0.002959	487 sec^{-1}	-2.313	477 sec^{-1}	2.38 m
55	0.003048	150	-2.824	155	7.72 m
45	0.003145	49.8	-3.303	47.2	21.8 m
35	0.003247	13.5	-3.871	13.2	85.9 m
25	0.003357	3.46	-4.461	3.46	5.71 h
0	0.003663	0.0787	-6.104	0.0733	10.2 d

[1] h, hour; d, day; m, minute.

Exercise III. Show that, if the activation energy for the decomposition of nitrogen pentoxide is independent of temperature, the half-life will be 3 years at $-25°$ and 0.56 sec at 125°.

The temperature dependences for several reactions are given in Table IV.

Table IV.   Gas-Phase Reactions

First-Order

$N_2O_5 \rightarrow NO_3 + NO_2$	$k = 6 \times 10^{12} e^{-18,500/RT}$ sec^{-1}
$N_2O_5 \rightarrow (N_2O_4 \rightleftharpoons 2NO_2) + \frac{1}{2}O_2$	$k = 4.3 \times 10^{13} e^{-24,700/RT}$ sec^{-1}
Cyclobutene $\rightarrow$ 1,3-butadiene	$k = 1.2 \times 10^{13} e^{-32,500/RT}$ sec^{-1}
$C_2H_5Br \rightarrow C_2H_4 + HBr$	$k = 2.6 \times 10^{13} e^{-53,900/RT}$ sec^{-1}
Cyclobutene $\rightarrow$ propylene	$k = 1.5 \times 10^{15} e^{-65,000/RT}$ sec^{-1}

Second-Order [1]

$NO + NO_3 \rightarrow NO_2 + O_2$	$k = 6.3 \times 10^7 T^{-\frac{1}{2}} e^{-2,300/RT}$ liter mole^{-1} sec^{-1}
$H + D_2 \rightarrow HD + H$	$k = 10^9 T^{-\frac{1}{2}} e^{-6,500/RT}$ liter mole^{-1} sec^{-1}
$CH_3 + H_2 \rightarrow CH_4 + H$	$k = 1.8 \times 10^7 T^{-\frac{1}{2}} e^{-10,000/RT}$ liter mole^{-1} sec^{-1}
$NO_2 + NO_2 \rightarrow 2NO + O_2$	$k = 2.6 \times 10^8 T^{-\frac{1}{2}} e^{-26,600/RT}$ liter mole^{-1} sec^{-1}
$H_2 + I_2 \rightarrow 2HI$	$k = 3.3 \times 10^9 T^{-\frac{1}{2}} e^{-38,900/RT}$ liter mole^{-1} sec^{-1}
$HI + HI \rightarrow H_2 + I_2$	$k = 2.0 \times 10^9 T^{-\frac{1}{2}} e^{-42,500/RT}$ liter mole^{-1} sec^{-1}

[1] The empirical equation for the second-order rate constant is written with a $T^{-\frac{1}{2}}$ factor because the collision theory leads to such a factor (cf. equation 54).

Very few reactions which have been studied have activation energies greater than 100 kcal mole^{-1}, and the ones with less than 5 kcal mole^{-1} are usually extremely fast. A very large number of activation energies range from 15 to 60 kcal mole^{-1}, which is in the range of chemical-bond energies.

Exercise IV. (a) Calculate the activation energy for a reaction which doubles in rate between 300 and 310°K.

$$\log 2 = \frac{E_a(310 - 300)}{(2.303)(1.987)(310)(300)}$$

$$E_a = 12.8 \text{ kcal mole}^{-1}$$

(b) Calculate the activation energy for a reaction which doubles in rate between 1000 and 1010°K.

$$\log 2 = \frac{E_a(1010 - 1000)}{(2.303)(1.987)(1010)(1000)}$$

$$E_a = 139 \text{ kcal mole}^{-1}$$

Activation Energy. The form of the Arrhenius equation is reminiscent of the Boltzmann equation (p. 273) and suggests that molecules must have a certain amount of energy E_a in order to react. If molecules were always in a reactive state, it would be difficult to account for the existence of slow reactions, since collision frequencies are exceedingly high. Neutralizations of acids and bases and certain other reactions, such as the quenching of fluorescence, are limited only by the rate with which the reactant molecules can diffuse together, but generally molecules have to be activated before they can react. The greater the activation energy the fewer are the collisions involving sufficient energy to cause reaction at a given temperature, and the slower is the reaction.

For the simple reaction $A \rightleftharpoons B$ the fleeting existence of an activated complex X^* can be represented by

$$A \rightleftharpoons X^* \rightleftharpoons B$$

The activated complex is not simply an intermediate compound such as the intermediates which occur in many chemical reactions. It is a molecule in which a bond is in the process of being broken or formed. In other words, it is a molecule with four rather than the usual three degrees of translational freedom. The nature of the activated complex will be discussed again later in connection with the absolute rate theory (p. 649).

In order for A to be converted to B it is necessary for it to be activated to X^*, and similarly B can be converted to A only through this activated complex. Both the forward and reverse reactions go through

Collision Theory of Gas Reactions. The modern theory of kinetics and and absolute rate theory of Eyring are discussed in Chapter 23 after some of the basic ideas of quantum mechanics, upon which they are based, have been presented. However, at this point we may discuss the application of some of the ideas of Chapter 11 to chemical kinetics. In discussing the kinetic theory of gases the following equation was derived (p. 285) for the number of collisions of like molecules per cubic centimeter per second:

$$Z = \frac{\sqrt{2}}{2} \pi\sigma^2 (n')^2 \bar{v} = 2\left(\frac{\pi kT}{m}\right)^{\frac{1}{2}} \sigma^2 (n')^2 \tag{52}$$

where σ is the collision diameter for the spherical molecules, $\bar{v}$ is the arithmetic mean velocity $(8kT/\pi m)^{\frac{1}{2}}$ (p. 275), and n' is molecules per cubic centimeter. Thus the number of collisions is proportional to the square of the concentration of the molecules. According to this simple theory, if gas-decomposition reactions were the immediate result of molecular collisions, they would be second order, but this is not the case (p. 317).

The second-order rate constant for a gas-decomposition reaction involving no activation energy may be calculated from equation 52. Second-order rate constants are ordinarily expressed in liters mole^{-1} sec^{-1}, since concentrations are expressed in moles liter^{-1}. The concentration c in moles liter^{-1} is related to the concentration n' in molecules cm^{-3} by $c = 10^3 n'/N_0$. The rate of reaction dc/dt in moles liter^{-1} sec^{-1} is therefore related to the rate of collisions Z in molecules cm^{-3} sec^{-1} by $10^3/N_0$. The second-order rate constant is defined by

$$k = \frac{dc/dt}{c^2} = \frac{10^3 Z/N_0}{(10^3/N_0)^2 (n')^2} = \frac{N_0 Z}{10^3 (n')^2} \tag{53}$$

The second-order rate constants calculated by substituting equation 52 in this equation are of the order of 10^{10}–10^{12} liter mole^{-1} sec^{-1} for gas molecules of average size and cross section. The fact that the second-order rate constants for most gas reactions are much slower than this indicates that reaction does not occur in each collision. A collision may be ineffective in producing chemical change for two reasons: (1) the collision is not sufficiently energetic to supply the activation energy, and (2) the colliding molecules are not oriented in such a way that they can react with each other.

The fact that a molecule has a high translational energy does not make it unstable, but if this energy is converted into internal energies of the parts of a molecule in a collision, the molecule may be activated in the collision. The energy which is effective in promoting reaction is not the total kinetic energy of the two colliding molecules. A full theory would have to involve details about the reaction which are unknown. It is generally assumed that the effective energy of the collision is the component of the kinetic energies of the two molecules along the line of their centers at the moment of collision. This is the energy with which the two molecules are pressed together. Assuming that the kinetic energy of this component of the relative velocity must be greater than some minimum value E, the activation energy, it may be shown * from kinetic theory that the fraction of all collisions having the desired energy E is given by the very simple factor $e^{-E/RT}$.

The final result of gas-collision theory is that the second-order rate constant should be given by

$$k = \frac{N_0 Z p}{10^3 (n')^2} e^{-E/RT}$$
$$= 2 \times 10^{-3} N_0 p \left(\frac{\pi RT}{M} \right)^{1/2} \sigma^2 e^{-E/RT} \tag{54}$$

if the reacting molecules are the same. The expression for Z is given by equation 52. The factor p is introduced to allow for the fact that a certain orientation may be required in order for the reaction to occur. The geometrical factors involved in chemical reactions are not sufficiently well understood for p to be calculated theoretically. Generally p decreases with increasing complexity of the reactants.

Equation 54 is in satisfactory agreement with the fact that log k is a linear function of $1/T$, since the $T^{1/2}$ temperature dependence introduced by the Z factor is usually almost negligible.

Exercise V. Show that for a reaction with an activation energy of 25 kcal mole^{-1} the fraction of the collisions in which the component of the kinetic energies of the two molecules along the line of their centers at the moment of collision is greater than the activation energy is increased by a factor of 3.7 in going from 25 to 35°. The number of energy-rich collisions increases much more rapidly with increasing temperature than does the average translational energy of the gas molecules. In going from 298 to 308°, $\frac{3}{2}RT$ increases by only $(10/298)100 = 3.3$ per cent, while the number of collisions which would result in activation if the orientation were right is increased by 370 per cent.

Example 7. The decomposition of gaseous hydrogen iodide is second order, and the second-order rate constant at 393.7° is 2.6×10^{-4} liter mole^{-1} sec^{-1}. The Arrhenius activation energy is found to be 45.6 kcal mole^{-1}. Calculate the second-order rate constant for this reaction to be expected from the collision theory described above. The collision diameter may be taken as 3.5 A, and the orientation factor p as unity. The molecular weight of HI is 127.9 g mole^{-1}.

* A. A. Frost and R. G. Pearson, *Kinetics and Mechanism*, John Wiley & Sons, New York, 1961.

Using equation 54,

$$k = (2 \times 10^{-3})(6.02 \times 10^{23}) \left[\frac{\pi(8.31 \times 10^7)(666.8)}{127.9} \right]^{\frac{1}{2}} (3.5 \times 10^{-8})^2 e^{-45,600/(1.987)(666.8)}$$

$$= 0.6 \times 10^{-4} \text{ liter mole}^{-1} \text{ sec}^{-1}$$

The agreement with the experimental value of 2.6×10^{-4} is regarded as satisfactory because small errors in the activation energy make very large changes in k.

Mechanism of Gaseous-Decomposition Reactions. From the fact that the activation energy for the decomposition of a gas is supplied in bimolecular collisions, it might be expected that gaseous decomposition reactions would necessarily be second order. However, it is a fact that at atmospheric pressure such reactions are uniformly of first order. A further puzzling feature of such reactions is that their p values (equation 54) may considerably exceed unity, even reaching values of 10^3–10^5.

These experimental facts are explained by the following mechanism proposed by Lindemann in 1922:

$$A + A \underset{k_2}{\overset{k_1}{\rightleftarrows}} A' + A$$

$$A' \overset{k_3}{\to} B + C$$

The first step represents collisions between A molecules which result in one of them receiving into its internal motions energy equivalent to the activation energy for the decomposition. Lindemann assumed that there is a time lag between activation by collision and the actual decomposition. Therefore activated molecule A' (which is not to be confused with an activated complex A^*) will suffer one of two fates: (a) if it collides with another A molecule before it decomposes, it will in all probability lose its excess energy; (b) as a result of the complicated vibrations and internal rotations of A' the required energy for decomposition E_a may collect in a single vibrational degree of freedom so that the molecule decomposes. Possibility (a) is represented by the reverse of the first step of the mechanism and has a second-order rate constant k_2, and possibility (b) is represented by the second step, which is a true unimolecular reaction with a unimolecular rate constant k_3.

The following equations give the rate of formation of A' and B:

$$\frac{d(A')}{dt} = k_1(A)^2 - k_2(A')(A) - k_3(A') \tag{55}$$

$$\frac{d(B)}{dt} = k_3(A') \tag{56}$$

These differential equations cannot be solved explicitly, but a useful result may be obtained by introducing the *steady-state approximation*. Since A' is continually being formed and used up, we may expect that after the reaction has been going a short time there will be a steady state in which the concentration of A' is nearly constant, so that $d(A')/dt$ is negligible in comparison with other terms in equation 55; thus $d(A')/dt$ may be taken as zero. The steady-state approximation is an excellent one in this case, since the concentration of A' is never very large. When $d(A')/dt$ in equation 55 is taken as zero, this equation may be written

$$k_1(A)^2 = (A')[k_2(A) + k_3] \tag{57}$$

so that

$$(A') = \frac{k_1(A)^2}{k_3 + k_2(A)} \tag{58}$$

Substituting this equation into equation 56,

$$\frac{d(B)}{dt} = \frac{k_1 k_3 (A)^2}{k_3 + k_2(A)} \tag{59}$$

Since $(A') \ll (A)$ this equation may be considered to give the reaction rate in terms of the total concentration of A.

At sufficiently high pressures $k_2(A) \gg k_3$ and equation 59 reduces to

$$\frac{d(B)}{dt} = \left(\frac{k_1 k_3}{k_2}\right)(A) \tag{60}$$

Thus under these conditions the reaction is first order, in spite of the fact that the activation step is bimolecular.

At sufficiently low pressures $k_2(A) \ll k_3$ and equation 59 reduces to

$$\frac{d(B)}{dt} = k_1(A)^2 \tag{61}$$

Thus a reaction following mechanism 1 should show a transition to second-order behavior as the pressure is lowered. At very low pressures the rate of decomposition is equal to the rate of activation, since essentially all the activated molecules decompose to products. The time between collisions is so long that the internal motions in molecule A' go through many changes, and there is a high probability of the energy becoming localized in a susceptible bond before the molecule is inactivated in a collision with another A molecule.

The frequency factors s for a number of simple bond-breaking unimolecular reactions lie between 10^{11} and 10^{15} sec^{-1}. Frequently

$s = 10^{13}$ sec^{-1} for this type of reaction, and so this would be a reasonable guess in the absence of other data. It should be realized that for any given frequency factor there is a fairly narrow range of activation energies which will give reaction rates in the readily measurable range, that is, with half-lives from seconds to months. For example, if $s = 10^{13}$ sec^{-1} and the temperature is 500°, reactions with activation energies less than about 25 kcal will be too fast to study with ordinary methods, and reactions with activation energies greater than about 45 kcal will be too slow.

Free-Radical Reactions. Free radicals are reactive molecules (or atoms) with unpaired electrons. This term is not applied to stable species like Fe^{3+} and O_2 in spite of the fact that their paramagnetic behavior demonstrates that they have unpaired electrons. At very high temperatures organic molecules may be partially dissociated into free radicals, and hexaphenyl ethane is partially dissociated into two triphenyl methyl radicals at room temperature, as proved by Gomberg in 1900. His measurements of the freezing-point depression of solvents showed dissociation into smaller units even though the solutions were not electrically conducting. Alkyl free radicals in the gas phase may be prepared by the thermal decomposition of metal alkyls. For example, methyl radicals $CH_3 \cdot$ may be obtained from

$$Pb(CH_3)_4 \rightarrow Pb + 4CH_3 \cdot$$

When this reaction is carried out by flowing gas down a heated glass tube, a lead mirror is produced on the inside of the tube. If a gas containing free radicals is passed over such a mirror, the mirror is removed. The removal of the lead mirror by methyl radicals is just the reverse of the above reaction. During flow down a tube the radicals disappear by colliding with the wall or by combining with each other. Free radicals may also be produced for research purposes by the absorption of light of sufficiently short wavelength (Chapter 23), or by passing a gas through an electrical discharge.

The existence of a free-radical mechanism may sometimes be deduced from the nature of the rate law for the reaction, the fact that sharp explosion limits are found, or the nature of the products of the reaction. The radicals produced in a reaction are sometimes trapped by adding iodine gas, which reacts readily as indicated by

$$CH_3 + I_2 \rightarrow CH_3I + I$$

Thus the methyl iodide in the products would indicate the presence of methyl radicals. The addition of substances like nitric oxide and propylene which combine with free radicals will greatly inhibit a reaction involving free radicals. Since considerable heat is evolved when free radicals or atoms recombine, they may be detected calorimetrically by their heat of recombination or heat of reaction with some substance.

Recombination of Atoms. The activation energy for the dissociation of a diatomic molecule must, of course, be at least as large as the bond energy (p. 73). As a matter of fact, it is often found that the activation energy for dissociation is very nearly equal to the bond energy, since the activation energy for the reverse reaction, the combination of two atoms, is nearly zero. It is interesting that the p value (p. 322) for the recombination of two atoms may be quite small in spite of the fact that orientation of the colliding atoms cannot be important. In a bimolecular reaction in which two or more product molecules are formed the excess energy may be carried off as kinetic energy of the product molecules. However, if a single product molecule is formed, the excess energy due to activation and the heat of reaction remains in the product molecule. Thus the product molecule has enough energy to dissociate and may do so before the excess energy is lost in the next collision or is distributed among the various internal degrees of freedom. In atom-recombination reactions there is only one internal degree of freedom, the vibration, and thus the molecule has a high probability of flying apart. For example, in the reaction

$$H + H \rightarrow H_2$$

the heat evolved is large (103 kcal mole^{-1}), and if all this energy remains in an isolated, newly formed molecule, there is no way of dissipating it except by the dissociation of the molecule. In other words, a stable molecule of H_2 can be formed only if there is some way of stabilizing the molecule by taking away energy, such as in the increase of kinetic or translational energy given to a colliding molecule. Thus recombination can occur only in a three-body collision

$$H + H + M \rightarrow H_2 + M$$

where M represents a colliding molecule or a wall surface.

If the rate of combination of two atoms or radicals is proportional to the concentration of some third molecule M, the rate of decomposition of the molecule into radicals must also be proportional to (M) according to the principle of detailed balancing.

Triple collisions are very rare, and so the reaction given above between H, H, and M is slow. This is the principle of the atomic hydrogen torch invented by Langmuir, in which pure hydrogen gas is passed through an electrical discharge. The issuing gas contains a considerable quantity of hydrogen atoms, which persist for a few seconds because of the infrequency of triple collisions and evolve 103 kcal mole^{-1} at a convenient rate for welding. The fact that no oxygen is involved makes this type of welding useful under special conditions where oxidation is a problem.

The recombination of iodine atoms and of bromine atoms has been studied following the flash photolysis (p. 662) of gaseous I_2 and Br_2.* The rate equation is

$$\frac{d(X_2)}{dt} = k(X)^2(M)$$

where X is a halogen atom and M is a third body which may be a halogen molecule or a molecule of an added gas. The effects of $M = Ar$, N_2, O_2, and I_2 were determined.

A rather surprising fact is that the rate constant k is smaller at higher temperatures; the apparent activation energy is -1.4 kcal mole^{-1} for the recombination of iodine atoms in argon. The negative temperature coefficient may result from the formation of a complex

$$I + M = IM$$

which must precede the reaction step

$$IM + I = I_2 + M$$

The explanation of the inverse temperature dependence of the iodine atom-recombination reaction is that ΔH is negative for the formation of IM, so that the concentration of IM decreases as the temperature is raised.

Decomposition of Nitrogen Pentoxide. The decomposition of nitrogen pentoxide was used earlier as an example of a reaction which is experimentally first order over a range of temperatures and pressures. The mechanism is not a simple unimolecular decomposition but is given by

$$N_2O_5 \underset{k_2}{\overset{k_1}{\rightleftharpoons}} NO_2 + NO_3$$

$$NO_2 + NO_3 \overset{k_3}{\rightarrow} NO + O_2 + NO_2$$

$$NO + NO_3 \overset{k_4}{\rightarrow} 2NO_2$$

* R. L. Strong, J. C. W. Chien, P. E. Graf, and J. E. Willard, *J. Chem. Phys.*, *26*, 1287 (1957).

where $k_2 > k_3$ and $k_4 > k_3$, so that the reaction with the rate constant k_3 is the slow one. The steady-state rate equations for the intermediates NO_3 and NO are

$$\frac{d(NO_3)}{dt} = 0 = k_1(N_2O_5) - (k_2 + k_3)(NO_2)(NO_3) - k_4(NO)(NO_3)$$

$$\frac{d(NO)}{dt} = 0 = k_3(NO_2)(NO_3) - k_4(NO)(NO_3)$$

These equations yield the following steady-state concentrations for NO and NO_3:

$$(NO) = \left(\frac{k_3}{k_4}\right)(NO_2)$$

$$(NO_3) = \frac{k_1(N_2O_5)}{(k_2 + 2k_3)(NO_2)}$$

Substitution of these equations into the rate equation for N_2O_5 yields

$$-\frac{d(N_2O_5)}{dt} = \frac{2k_1k_3}{k_2 + 2k_3}(N_2O_5)$$

so that the over-all reaction behaves in a first-order manner, as shown experimentally in Fig. 12-1b.

Shock-Tube Experiments. In order to study certain gas reactions at high temperatures it is necessary to heat the gas to the higher temperature very quickly because the reaction occurs rapidly. This may be accomplished by means of a shock tube * in which a shock wave is used to heat the gas suddenly. A tube is divided into two sections separated by a diaphragm which can be ruptured. The gas to be studied is placed on one side of the diaphragm, and a driver gas at a higher pressure on the other side. When the diaphragm is ruptured, a shock wave passes through the reacting gas, heating it suddenly to a higher temperature. The extent of reaction may be determined as a function of time after passage of the shock wave by measuring the absorption of a beam of light perpendicularly across the tube.

Chain Reactions. Since a radical has an unpaired electron, its reaction with a molecule having paired electrons will give rise to another radical. In this way the reactive center is maintained and can give rise to a chain of reactions. One may ask why such a reaction ever stops. Sometimes, as a matter of fact, the chain reaction does not stop until

* D. Britton, N. Davidson, and G. Schott, *Discussions Faraday Soc.*, *17*, 58 (1954).

all the material is consumed. At other times, however, the chain is broken when one of the activated molecules in it collides with the wall of the containing vessel or with another radical to form a neutral molecule. The length of the chain, that is, the number of molecules reacting per molecule activated, is determined by the relative rates of the chain-propagating and the chain-breaking reactions.

Many thermal decomposition reactions of hydrocarbons, ethers, aldehydes, and ketones appear to go by free-radical chain reactions. In 1935 F. O. Rice and K. F. Herzfeld * showed how free-radical chain mechanisms could be devised for these reactions which would lead to simple over-all kinetics. The free radicals involved in these reactions include CH_3, C_2H_5, and H. The presence of free radicals in a number of such reactions has been shown by the removal of metallic mirrors, by catalyzing a reaction, such as the polymerization of an olefin, which is known to go by a chain mechanism, or by inhibition by a compound such as nitric oxide or propylene. If each molecule of the inhibitor stops a chain and each chain produces a great many molecules of product, it is obvious that mere traces of inhibitors may have a pronounced effect. For example, the oxidation of sulfite ion in solution by atmospheric oxygen is inhibited markedly by the addition of traces of alcohols.

The Hydrogen-Bromine Reaction. The formation of HI from H_2 and I_2 vapor follows the simple second-order rate law, but the rate laws for the formation of HBr and HCl from their elements are much more complicated. In the temperature range 200–300° the rate data for the reaction

$$H_2 + Br_2 = 2HBr$$

may be represented by a rather complicated rate law given by

$$\frac{d(\text{HBr})}{dt} = \frac{k(\text{H}_2)(\text{Br}_2)^{1/2}}{1 + k'(\text{HBr})/(\text{Br}_2)} \tag{62}$$

It will now be shown that this rate law can be explained by the following mechanism:

Chain initiation	1. $Br_2 \rightarrow 2Br$
Chain propagation	2. $Br + H_2 \rightarrow HBr + H$
	3. $H + Br_2 \rightarrow HBr + Br$
Chain inhibition	4. $H + HBr \rightarrow H_2 + Br$
Chain breaking	5. $2Br \rightarrow Br_2$

* *J. Am. Chem. Soc.*, *56*, 284 (1934).

The fourth step is the reverse of the second step and leads to an inhibition of the reaction. The fifth step is the reverse of the first step. Since HBr is formed by reactions 2 and 3 and is decomposed by reaction 4, the rate of the over-all reaction is expressed by the following equation:

$$\frac{d(\text{HBr})}{dt} = k_2(\text{Br})(\text{H}_2) + k_3(\text{H})(\text{Br}_2) - k_4(\text{H})(\text{HBr}) \tag{63}$$

where the subscripts on the rate constants refer to the steps in the reaction.

In order to write the rate of the over-all reaction in terms of the concentrations of H_2, Br_2, and HBr it is necessary to eliminate the concentrations of the atoms H and Br from equation 63. Since these atoms are both formed and used up in the reaction, their concentrations reach a steady state. In the steady state the following equations apply:

$$\frac{d(\text{Br})}{dt} = 0 = 2k_1(\text{Br}_2) - k_2(\text{H}_2)(\text{Br})$$
$$+ k_3(\text{H})(\text{Br}_2) + k_4(\text{HBr})(\text{H}) - 2k_5(\text{Br})^2 \tag{64}$$

$$\frac{d(\text{H})}{dt} = 0 = k_2(\text{H}_2)(\text{Br}) - k_3(\text{H})(\text{Br}_2) - k_4(\text{H})(\text{HBr}) \tag{65}$$

When the equations are added it is found that

$$(\text{Br}) = \left[\frac{k_1}{k_5}(\text{Br}_2)\right]^{1/2} \tag{66}$$

It should be noted that this is simply the equilibrium expression for the dissociation of Br_2, so that Br_2 and Br are in equilibrium during the reaction. Solving equation 65 for the concentration of H atoms, we find that

$$(\text{H}) = \frac{k_2(\text{Br})(\text{H}_2)}{k_3(\text{Br}_2) + k_4(\text{HBr})} \tag{67}$$

Substituting equations 66 and 67 into equation 63 to eliminate the atom concentrations, the following rate law is obtained for the over-all reaction:

$$\frac{d(\text{HBr})}{dt} = \frac{k_2 k_3 k_4^{-1} k_1^{1/2} k_5^{-1/2}(\text{H}_2)(\text{Br}_2)^{1/2}}{k_3 k_4^{-1} + (\text{HBr})/(\text{Br}_2)} \tag{68}$$

The form of this rate equation is in agreement with the experimental observations. If no HBr is initially present, the initial velocity $d(\text{HBr})/dt$ is directly proportional to $(\text{H}_2)(\text{Br}_2)^{1/2}$. If sufficient HBr is added initially so that $(HBr)/(Br_2) \gg k_3/k_4$, then the initial velocity is directly proportional to $(H_2)(Br_2)^{3/2}/(HBr)$, and it is seen that doubling the initial HBr concentration will cut the initial velocity in half.

Branching-Chain Reactions. Certain reactions which are evidently propagated by a chain reaction show characteristics which cannot be explained in terms of a simple chain reaction. For example, at about 550° stoichiometric hydrogen-oxygen mixtures react very slowly at pressures below 1 mm. As the pressure is increased the reaction rate increases slowly, but at a pressure of about 1 mm, depending upon the volume of the vessel, there is a sudden explosion. On the other hand, if the gases are at a considerably higher pressure the rate is again quite slow. For example, Hinselwood found that, if hydrogen at 200 mm pressure and oxygen at 100 mm pressure are placed in a 300-cm^3 quartz vessel at 550°, the rate of reaction is quite slow and becomes slower if the pressure is further reduced to 100 mm. However, if the pressure is reduced to 98 mm, an explosion occurs. Finally, as the total pressure is increased above the explosion zone, the reaction rate increases until it becomes so fast that the reaction mixture may be said to explode. These data are represented by *Fig. 12-7*, which shows the pressure-temperature conditions for the explosion limits for a stoichiometric hydrogen-oxygen mixture.

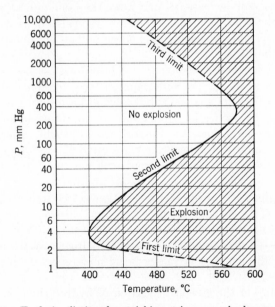

Fig. 12-7. Explosion limits of a stoichiometric oxygen-hydrogen mixture.

In order to explain such complicated behavior it is necessary to introduce the idea of branching chains, that is, chains in which one radical gives rise to more than one radical so that the number of radicals increases in a geometric progression. The steps which are involved in the hydrogen-oxygen reaction are as follows:

$$1. \quad H_2 = 2H$$

$$2. \quad H + O_2 = OH + O$$

$$3. \quad OH + H_2 = H_2O + H$$

$$4. \quad O + H_2 = OH + H$$

The OH radical produced in reaction 4 undergoes reaction 3. Therefore, for every H atom produced in reaction 1, *three* others are produced as a result of reactions 2, 3, and 4. The H atoms and OH radicals which permit the propagation of a chain may be destroyed by collision with the wall. If more than two of the three radicals formed per H from H_2 are destroyed at the wall, there will not be a geometric increase in the number of radicals and an explosion, but simply a steady state in which the concentrations of the various radicals remain constant. This is the situation below the first explosion limit. As the pressure is increased, the fraction of radicals removed by diffusion to the wall decreases so that more than one radical is produced per H atom formed, and the number of radicals builds up in a geometric progression, producing an explosion. This explanation is in accord with the fact that the explosion occurs at a lower pressure in a larger reaction vessel, and that the addition of glass beads to the reaction vessel raises the pressure required for explosion. Adding inert gases lowers the explosion limit by slowing down diffusion of radicals to the wall. The transition from slow reaction to explosion is abrupt because, if one radical leads to the formation of slightly more than one radical, the number of radicals increases rapidly.

At pressures just above the second explosion limit the rate of reaction again becomes slow. The pressure and temperature at this limit are independent of the size of the reaction vessel, indicating that the quenching of the reaction chains occurs in collisions of radicals with gas molecules rather than with the wall. The second limit is displaced to lower partial pressures of oxygen and hydrogen by the addition of inert gases, the lighter inert gases being more effective in preventing explosions.

The kinetics of the gaseous oxidation of hydrocarbons is related to the oxidation of hydrogen in that branching-chain reactions are involved but is much more complicated.* In order to reduce the too rapid propagation of chains, which leads to "knock" in internal-combustion engines, tetraethyl lead, which reacts readily with atoms and radicals and breaks the chains, is added to gasoline.

Chain reactions and molecular reactions often occur together. The activation energy is generally lower for the molecular reaction, and therefore at low temperatures more molecules react this way than initiate chains. As the temperature is raised, the rate of the chain reaction increases more rapidly than the rate of the molecular reaction because of the greater activation energy, and eventually the chain reaction predominates.

Reaction in Solution. The mechanisms of reactions in solution often involve ions, especially in polar solvents. In such a case the solvent has a very important role in the reaction because the rate of the ionic reaction may be quite different from that of the molecular reaction. The factors involved in ionic reactions are discussed later in connection with the Brönsted theory. Although the total numbers of collisions per second between reactants in the gas and in the liquid phases appear not to be very different, there is a difference in their distribution in time. In solution, collisions between two molecules which have just collided are likely to be repeated because the solvent molecules tend to surround the reactant molecules, forming a "cage." Thus there is a greater opportunity for the products to recombine.

Some reactions, such as the quenching of fluorescence and the reaction of H^+ with OH^- or other base, occur on the first collision. In this case the reaction is said to be diffusion controlled. The rate of such a very fast reaction cannot be measured by mixing techniques because the reaction occurs faster than solutions can be mixed. Flow methods for mixing solutions permit two solutions to be mixed in about a millisecond (10^{-3} sec); this limits the range of these methods to half-lives greater than about a millisecond.

Faster reactions can be studied by perturbing a solution which is at equilibrium and then following the return to equilibrium.† The equilibrium may be disturbed by a sudden temperature or pressure change, or a periodic pressure change as in a sound wave. The equilibrium of a reaction involving ions may also be disturbed by the application of a powerful electric field which alters the equilibrium constant. The return to equilibrium for a simple system is first order, provided that the

* N. N. Semenoff, *Some Problems of Chemical Kinetics and Reactivity*, Vols. I and II, Pergamon Press, New York, 1958.
† M. Eigen, *Discussions Faraday Soc.*, 17, 194 (1954).

displacement from equilibrium is small. This method is called a *relaxation method*, and the time required for the concentration to return to $1/e$ of its equilibrium value is called the *relaxation time*. The relaxation time is just the reciprocal of the first-order rate constant. Eigen has measured the second-order rate constant $(1.4 \times 10^{11}$ liter mole^{-1} sec^{-1} at 25°) for the fastest reaction in aqueous solution, $H^+ + OH^- \rightarrow H_2O$.

Catalysis. A substance that increases the rate of a chemical reaction without being used up in the over-all reaction is called a *catalyst*. There are many different kinds of catalysts and many different mechanisms by which catalysts operate. The catalyst goes through a cycle in which it is used and regenerated so that it is used over and over again. In homogeneous catalysis the catalyst is a molecule or ion in homogeneous solution; in heterogeneous catalysis the reaction occurs on a surface.

The catalyst operates by providing another path for the reaction which has a higher rate than that available in the absence of the catalyst. The rate may be greater because of lower activation energies or higher frequency factors or both.

It should be remembered that the catalyst must speed up the reverse reaction as well as the forward reaction so that the equilibrium constant is unaffected, since the position of chemical equilibrium is independent of mechanism. Sometimes the catalyst may *appear* to change the equilibrium; however, in such cases large quantities of the catalyst are usually required, and the catalyst not only speeds up the reaction but also changes the activity coefficients of the reactants.

The catalytic action of nitrogen dioxide in the oxidation of sulfur dioxide offers an example of homogeneous catalysis. The reaction represented by the equation

$$2SO_2 + O_2 \rightarrow 2SO_3$$

is very slow. The accelerating action of nitric oxide on the reaction, which was used industrially in the chamber process for the manufacture of sulfuric acid, may be represented in the following simplified manner:

$$2NO + O_2 \rightarrow 2NO_2$$
$$2SO_2 + 2NO_2 \rightarrow 2SO_3 + 2NO$$

$$\overline{2SO_2 + O_2 \rightarrow 2SO_3}$$

Thus the catalyst is alternately oxidized by O_2 and reduced by SO_2.

Another example of catalysis through alternate oxidation and reduction of the catalyst is the bromide-ion catalysis of the hydrogen peroxide decomposition.* In acid solutions bromide ion is oxidized to hypobromous acid by hydrogen peroxide according to the equation

$$H_2O_2 + Br^- + H^+ \rightarrow HBrO + H_2O$$

and the hypobromous acid, in turn, is reduced by hydrogen peroxide according to the equation

$$H_2O_2 + HBrO \rightarrow H_2O + Br^- + H^+ + O_2$$

The bromide ion produced reacts with another hydrogen peroxide molecule, and so on. The sum of these reactions is the catalyzed reaction

$$2H_2O_2 \rightarrow 2H_2O + O_2$$

Exercise VI. Using a steady-state treatment, show that the above reaction is first order in hydrogen peroxide.

There are many examples in organic chemistry in which the catalyst accelerates the reaction by forming an intermediate compound which reacts faster than the original reactants. One of the earliest examples was discovered when ethyl sulfate was detected in the reaction of alcohol to give ether, using sulfuric acid as a catalyst. Another important example is the catalytic action of aluminum chloride in the well-known Friedel-Crafts synthesis of organic compounds, which involves the formation of an addition compound.

Sometimes one of the products of the reaction functions as a catalyst. Such a reaction is said to be autocatalytic.

Heterogeneous Catalysis. Reactions are often catalyzed on surfaces, and such reactions are carried out on a large scale in industry. The development of catalysts is especially important for reactions which evolve heat. Although the equilibrium constant may be favorable at room temperature, the rate may be so low that the reaction cannot be used practically. When the temperature is raised the rate is increased, but at high temperatures the equilibrium constant may be unfavorable, as is readily surmised from Le Châtelier's principle. A reaction of this type is $N_2 + 3H_2 = 2NH_3$, which is the basis for the Haber process for the manufacture of ammonia. In order to carry out this reaction at temperatures where the equilibrium constant is sufficiently favorable special iron catalysts are used. Vanadium and other metals are added to make the catalyst more effective and to protect it from too rapid inactivation by traces of impurities in the gases. Substances which enhance the activity of catalysts are called *promoters*, and substances which inhibit catalytic activity are called *poisons*. Since only a frac-

* W. C. Bray and R. S. Livingston, *J. Am. Chem. Soc.*, *45*, 1251 (1923).

tion of the surface of the catalyst may be involved, it is easy to see how relatively small amounts of promoters and poisons may be effective. In the manufacture of sulfuric acid by the contact process, the presence of a very minute amount of arsenic completely destroys the catalytic activity of the platinum catalyst by forming platinum arsenide at the surface.

Enormous quantities of solid catalysts are used in the petroleum industry for "cracking," which increases the yield of gasoline from petroleum, and for "re-forming," which causes the rearrangement of the molecular structures and raises the octane rating of gasoline. To facilitate the regeneration of these catalysts they may be circulated as fine particles in the gas stream.

Other large-scale chemical syntheses in which solid catalysts are used include the production of methyl alcohol from carbon monoxide and hydrogen, using a zinc oxide-chromium oxide mixture as catalyst; hydrogenation of an unsaturated aliphatic acid, such as oleic acid, into a saturated acid, such as stearic acid, using nickel; and the Fischer-Tropsch synthesis of hydrocarbons from mixtures of carbon monoxide and hydrogen, using a catalyst of cobalt, iron, or nickel.

The catalytic activity of the walls of the containing vessel is a factor in many gaseous reactions. For surface reactions the temperature coefficient is usually small, because the activation energies are low and the slowest process is the diffusion of the products away from the walls. A $10°$ rise at about $300°K$ increases the diffusion rate by only about 3 per cent, whereas the rate of a chemical reaction normally increases about 300 per cent, as already explained.

Since homogeneous reactions generally have higher activation energies than the corresponding heterogeneous reactions, homogeneous reactions are favored at higher temperatures and heterogeneous reactions at lower temperatures. The presence of a heterogeneous reaction accompanying a homogeneous reaction may be detected by (1) the temperature coefficient, (2) increasing the area greatly, as by adding powdered glass to a glass vessel, or (3) changing the nature of the vessel walls. Quartz may be used instead of glass, for example, or the walls may be coated. The reaction between bromine and ethylene is catalyzed by glass, as shown by the fact that the reaction is stopped when the glass walls are covered with paraffin. When glass vessels are coated with fused halides or with nonpolar fluorocarbons or silicones, the characteristics of some gaseous reactions are changed.

The mechanisms of surface-catalyzed reactions involve a sequence of steps: (a) adsorption of the reacting gases on the surface, (b) reaction on the surface, and (c) desorption of the products. Under the influence of forces at the surface reactions occur at much higher rates than in the gas phase. The nature of the surface determines the products which are obtained, different catalysts yielding different products with the same reacting gases.

It is generally found that the rate of a surface-catalyzed reaction is directly proportional to the pressure of the reacting gas at low pressures and independent of the pressure at higher pressures. This is readily explained in terms of the Langmuir theory of adsorption (p. 609).

Acid-Base Catalysis. Acids and bases catalyze many reactions in which they are not consumed. Some reactions are catalyzed specifically by hydrogen ions and others are catalyzed by acids in general, that is, undissociated acids as well as protons. There are many possible mechanisms for the catalytic action of acids and bases. A mechanism for specific hydrogen-ion catalysis of the over-all chemical reaction $S + R \rightarrow P$ is as follows:

$$S + H^+ \underset{k_2}{\overset{k_1}{\rightleftharpoons}} SH^+ \quad \text{(fast)}$$

$$SH^+ + R \overset{k_3}{\rightarrow} P + H^+ \quad \text{(slow)}$$

The catalyst H^+ is regenerated in the second step. Since the second step is rate determining, the rate of formation of product is given by

$$\frac{d(P)}{dt} = k_3(SH^+)(R) = \frac{k_1 k_3}{k_2}(S)(H^+)(R) \tag{69}$$

where the second form is obtained by use of $(S)(H^+)/(SH^+) = k_2/k_1$. Since the concentration of SH^+ depends upon (H^+) and not upon the concentration of undissociated acids which may be present, the reaction is specifically hydrogen-ion catalyzed.

Some reactions are catalyzed by both acids and bases and may have a measurable rate in water alone (which may function as either an acid or a base). In this case the observed rate constant may be written

$$k = k_0 + k_{H^+}(H^+) + k_{OH^-}(OH^-) \tag{70}$$

where the rate constant in pure water is k_0. The so-called catalytic coefficients k_{H^+} and k_{OH^-} may be calculated from experiments at different acid and base concentrations. If the reaction is subject to general acid-base catalysis, terms of the type $k_{HA}(HA)$ and $k(B)$, where B is a base, have to be added to equation 70. The iodination of acetone is a base-catalyzed reaction, the rate being directly proportional to the concentration of base and independent of the concentration of iodine.

Enzyme Catalysis. The most amazing catalysts are the enzymes, which catalyze the multitudinous reactions in living organisms. According to thermodynamics, most organic compounds may be converted into a number of products of lower free energy. The enzymes present in the cell determine which of these reactions actually occur and the rates at which they proceed. All enzymes have been found to be proteins which are polymers of amino acids having a definite structural arrangement of the polypeptide chains. Enzymes have molecular weights as low as 15,000, but some of them are apparently attached to very large structures in the cell. To date some 150 enzymes have been isolated in crystalline form. Some of these have a high degree of specificity and catalyze only one reaction; others catalyze a large number of reactions of a given type, like ester hydrolysis. In order to operate, some enzymes require particular metal ions or coenzymes, that is, compounds which are alternately oxidized and reduced in a catalytic cycle.

The simplest enzymatic mechanism for catalyzing the reaction $S = P$ is represented by

$$E + S \underset{k_2}{\overset{k_1}{\rightleftharpoons}} X \underset{k_4}{\overset{k_3}{\rightleftharpoons}} E + P$$

where E is the enzymatic site and X is an intermediate, often referred to as the enzyme-substrate complex, since S is called the substrate. The rate equations for this mechanism are complicated and cannot be solved in general, but most enzyme kinetic studies are made in the steady state in which $d(X)/dt = 0$. If S is added initially and we consider only the period in which (P) is negligibly small, so that the reverse reaction may be neglected, the rate equations for the above mechanism are

$$\frac{d(X)}{dt} = k_1(E)(S) - (k_2 + k_3)(X) = 0 \tag{71}$$

$$\frac{d(P)}{dt} = k_3(X) \tag{72}$$

The term $-k_4(P)(E)$ is omitted in equation 72 because the concentration of P is negligible during the first part of the reaction. Since $(E) + (X) = (E)_0$, where $(E)_0$ is the initial concentration of enzymatic sites, equation 71 may be written

$$\frac{d(X)}{dt} = k_1[(E)_0 - (X)](S) - (k_2 + k_3)(X) = 0 \tag{73}$$

Solving this equation for (X), we obtain

$$(X) = \frac{(E)_0}{1 + \dfrac{(k_2 + k_3)}{k_1(S)}} \tag{74}$$

Substituting this into equation 72, we obtain the equation for the initial steady-state velocity of the enzymatic reaction:

$$\frac{d(P)}{dt} = \frac{k_3(E)_0}{1 + \dfrac{(k_2 + k_3)}{k_1(S)}} \tag{75}$$

The quantity $(k_2 + k_3)/k_1$ is called the Michaelis constant for the substrate S. The shape of the plot of the initial steady-state velocity versus substrate concentration is shown in $Fig.\ 12\text{-}8a$. If $(S) \ll$

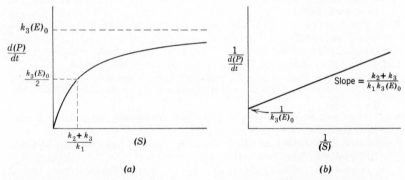

(a) (b)

Fig. 12-8. (a) Plot of initial steady-state velocity of appearance of product P at different initial concentrations of substrate S. (b) Plot of reciprocal initial velocity versus reciprocal substrate concentration.

$(k_2 + k_3)/k_1$, the steady-state rate of appearance of product is directly proportional to (S). If $(S) \gg (k_2 + k_3)/k_1$, the steady-state rate of appearance of product is independent of (S) and is equal to $k_3(E)_0$. In both cases the reaction is first order with respect to the concentration of the enzyme.

The values of $k_3(E)_0$ and $(k_2 + k_3)/k_1$ may be conveniently obtained by plotting $1/d(P)/dt$ versus $1/(S)$ as shown in $Fig.\ 12\text{-}8b$. The value of k_3 is called the *turnover number* for the enzyme. This quantity is greater than 10^8 min^{-1} for catalase, which catalyzes the decomposition of H_2O_2 to $H_2O + \frac{1}{2}O_2$, and is about 10 min^{-1} for chymotrypsin, which catalyzes the hydrolysis of a number of esters and amides.

The way in which these constants depend upon pH, salt concentration, coenzyme concentration, etc., gives further information about the enzymatic mechanism.*

Important advances have been made in biochemistry through a better understanding of enzyme kinetics. In some cases the intermediate reactions, such as those illustrated, have been followed by measuring the amount of light transmitted at a wavelength which corresponds to the absorption band of the intermediate.†

REFERENCES

E. S. Amis, *Kinetics of Chemical Change in Solution*, The Macmillan Co., New York, 1949.

R. P. Bell, *Acids and Bases, Their Quantitative Behavior*, Methuen and Co., London, 1952.

R. P. Bell, *The Proton in Chemistry*, Cornell University Press, Ithaca, 1959.

S. W. Benson, *The Foundations of Chemical Kinetics*, McGraw-Hill Book Co., New York, 1959.

P. D. Boyer, H. Lardy, and K. Myrbäck, *The Enzymes*, Vol. I, Academic Press, New York, 1958.

F. S. Dainton, *Chain Reactions*, John Wiley & Sons, New York, 1956.

F. Daniels, *Chemical Kinetics*, Cornell University Press, Ithaca, 1938.

S. L. Friess and A. Weissberger, *Technique of Organic Chemistry*, Vol. VII: *Investigation of Rates and Mechanisms of Reactions*, Interscience Publishers, New York, 1953.

A. A. Frost and R. G. Pearson, *Kinetics and Mechanism*, John Wiley & Sons, New York, 1961.

S. Glasstone, K. J. Laidler, and H. Eyring, *The Theory of Rate Processes*, McGraw-Hill Book Co., New York, 1941.

C. N. Hinshelwood, *Kinetics of Chemical Change*, Oxford University Press, Oxford, 1941.

O. A. Hougen, K. M. Watson, R. A. Ragatz, *Chemical Process Principles*, Part III. *Kinetics and Catalysis*, John Wiley & Sons, New York, 1947.

K. J. Laidler, *Chemical Kinetics*, McGraw-Hill Book Co., New York, 1950.

K. J. Laidler, *The Chemical Kinetics of Excited States*, Oxford University Press, Oxford, 1955.

N. F. Ramsey, *Molecular Beams*, Oxford Press, London, 1956.

E. W. R. Steacie, *Atomic and Free Radical Reactions*, Reinhold Publishing Corp., New York, 1954.

"Tables of Chemical Kinetics," *Natl. Bur. Standards Circ.* 510, U. S. Government Printing Office, Washington, D. C., 1951.

A. F. Trotman-Dickenson, *Gas Kinetics*, Butterworths Scientific Publications, London, 1955.

C. Walling, *Free Radicals in Solution*, John Wiley & Sons, New York, 1957.

* R. A. Alberty, *Advances in Enzymol.*, 17, 1 (1956); P. D. Boyer, H. Lardy, and K. Myrbäck, *The Enzymes*, Vol. I, Academic Press, New York, 1958.

† B. Chance in *Technique of Organic Chemistry*, Vol. VII: *Investigation of Rates and Mechanisms of Reactions*, ed. by S. L. Friess and A. Weissberger, Interscience Publishers, New York, 1953.

PROBLEMS

1. A stream of air at 10 liters min^{-1}, measured at 25° and 1 atm pressure, is passing through a catalyst tube which is 4 cm in diameter and 100 cm long, maintained throughout at 800°. Half the volume of the chamber is occupied by solid material. Approximately how many seconds is a given molecule exposed to this high temperature, if it is assumed that the gas reaches the temperature of the chamber, 800°, instantly? *Ans.* 1.05 sec.

2. The following data were obtained on the rate of hydrolysis of 17 per cent sucrose in 0.099 N HCl aqueous solution at 35°:

Time, min	9.82	59.60	93.18	142.9	294.8	589.4
Sucrose remaining, %	96.5	80.3	71.0	59.1	32.8	11.1

What is the value of the rate constant k in reciprocal seconds?

Ans. 6.34 × 10^{-5} sec^{-1}.

3. Methyl acetate is hydrolyzed in approximately 1 N HCl at 25°. Aliquots of equal volume are removed at intervals and titrated with a solution of NaOH. Calculate the first-order rate constant from the following experimental data:

Time, sec	339	1242	2745	4546	∞
Volume, ml	26.34	27.80	29.70	31.81	39.81

Ans. 1.26 × 10^{-4} sec^{-1}.

4. Prove that in a first-order reaction, where $dn/dt = -kn$, the average life, that is, the average life expectancy of the molecules, is equal to $1/k$.

$$Ans. \ \frac{1}{n_0} \int_0^\infty n \, dt = \frac{1}{k}.$$

5. The reaction between propionaldehyde and hydrocyanic acid has been studied at 25° by W. J. Svirbely and J. F. Roth [*J. Am. Chem. Soc.*, *75*, 3106 (1953)]. In a certain aqueous solution at 25° the concentrations at various times were as follows:

Time, min	2.78	5.33	8.17	15.23	19.80	∞
HCN, mole l^{-1}	0.0990	0.0906	0.0830	0.0706	0.0653	0.0424
C$_3$H$_7$CHO, mole l^{-1}	0.0566	0.0482	0.0406	0.0282	0.0229	0.0000

What is the specific reaction-rate constant k? *Ans.* 0.676 l mole^{-1} min^{-1}.

6. The reaction $CH_3CH_2NO_2 + OH^- \rightarrow H_2O + CH_3CHNO_2^-$ is of second order, and k at 0° is 39.1 liters mole^{-1} min^{-1}. An aqueous solution is made 0.004 molar in nitroethane and 0.005 molar in NaOH. How long will it take for 90 per cent of the nitroethane to react? *Ans.* 26.3 min.

7. The reaction $2NO + O_2 \rightarrow 2NO_2$ is third order. Assuming that a small amount of NO$_3$ exists in rapid reversible equilibrium with NO and O$_2$ and that the rate-determining step is the slow bimolecular reaction $NO_3 + NO \rightarrow 2NO_2$, derive the rate equation. *Ans.* $d(NO_2)/dt = k(NO)^2(O_2)$.

8. A solution of A is mixed with an equal volume of a solution of B containing the same number of moles, and the reaction $A + B = C$ occurs. At the end of 1 hr A is 75 per cent reacted. How much of A will be left unreacted at the end of 2 hr if the reaction is (a) first order in A and zero order in B; (b) first order in both A and B; (c) zero order in both A and B? *Ans.* (a) 6.25, (b) 14.3, (c) 0%.

9. Hydrogen peroxide reacts with thiosulfate ion in slightly acid solution as follows:

$$H_2O_2 + 2S_2O_3^{2-} + 2H^+ \rightarrow 2H_2O + S_4O_6^{2-}$$

This reaction rate is independent of the hydrogen-ion concentration in the pH range 4–6. The following data were obtained at 25° and pH 5.0:

Initial concentrations: (H_2O_2) = 0.03680 M; $(S_2O_3^{2-})$ = 0.02040 M

Time, min	16	36	43	52
$(S_2O_3^{2-}) \times 10^3$	10.30	5.18	4.16	3.13

(a) What is the order of the reaction?

(b) What is the rate constant?

Ans. (a) Second order. (b) 3.17×10^{-2} l mole^{-1} sec^{-1}.

10. Set up the rate expressions for the following mechanism:

$$A \underset{k_2}{\overset{k_1}{\rightleftharpoons}} B \qquad B + C \overset{k_3}{\rightarrow} D$$

Show that this reaction may follow the first-order equation at high pressures and the second-order equation at low pressures.

Ans. $d(D)/dt = k_1k_3(A)(C)/[k_2 + k_3(C)]$.

11. For the reaction $2A \underset{k_2}{\overset{k_1}{\rightleftharpoons}} B + C$ the rate law for the forward reaction is

$$-\frac{d(A)}{dt} = k_1(A)$$

Give two possible rate laws for the reverse reaction. (Cf. Appendix, p. 721).

Ans. $k(B)(C)/(A); k(B)^{1/2}(C)^{1/2}$.

12. The hydrolysis of $(CH_2)_6C\begin{smallmatrix}Cl\\/\\\backslash\\CH_3\end{smallmatrix}$ in 80 per cent ethanol follows the first-order rate equation. The values of the specific reaction-rate constants, as determined by H. C. Brown and M. Borkowski [*J. Am. Chem. Soc.*, *74*, 1896 (1952)], are as follows:

Temp., °C	0	25	35	45
k, sec^{-1}	1.06×10^{-5}	3.19×10^{-4}	9.86×10^{-4}	2.92×10^{-3}

(a) Plot log k against $1/T$; (b) calculate the activation energy; (c) calculate the frequency factor. *Ans.* (b) 21,500 cal mole^{-1}. (c) 7.5×10^{12} sec^{-1}.

13. The trichloroacetate ion in hydrogen-containing ionizing solvents decomposes into carbon dioxide and chloroform according to the reaction

$$H^+ + CCl_3COO^- \rightarrow CO_2 + CHCl_3$$

The unimolecular breaking of the carbon-carbon bond in the trichloroacetate ion is probably the rate-determining step. The reaction is first order, and the specific rate constants are $k_{90°} = 3.11 \times 10^{-4}$, $k_{80°} = 7.62 \times 10^{-5}$, and $k_{70°} = 1.71 \times 10^{-5}$ sec^{-1}. Calculate (a) the activation energy and (b) the specific rate constant at 60°. The experimentally determined value of k at 60° is 3.48×10^{-6} sec^{-1}.

Ans. (a) 35.4 kcal mole^{-1}.   (b) 3.55×10^{-6} sec^{-1}.

14. If a first-order reaction has an activation energy of 25,000 cal mole^{-1}, and, in the equation $k = se^{-E_a/RT}$, s has a value of 5×10^{13} sec^{-1}, at what temperature will the reaction have a half-life of (a) 1 min; (b) 1 month of 30 days?

Ans. (a) 76°, (b) −4°.

15. Isopropyl ether in the vapor state isomerizes to allyl acetone according to a first-order rate equation. The following equation gives the influence of temperature on the specific reaction rate (in sec^{-1}):

$$k = 5.4 \times 10^{11} e^{-29,300/RT}$$

At 150° how long will it take to build up a partial pressure of 300 mm of allyl acetone, starting with 760 mm of isopropyl ether [L. Stein and G. W. Murphy, *J. Am. Chem. Soc.*, *74*, 1041 (1952)]?   *Ans.* 1210 sec.

16. What activation energy is required to cause a reaction rate to increase by a factor of 3 for a 10° temperature rise at (a) 300°K and (b) 1000°K?

Ans. (a) 20.3, (b) 220 kcal mole^{-1}.

17. For the two parallel reactions $A \xrightarrow{k_1} B$ and $A \xrightarrow{k_2} C$ show that the activation energy E' for the disappearance of A is given in terms of the activation energies E_1 and E_2 for the two paths by

$$E' = \frac{k_1 E_1 + k_2 E_2}{k_1 + k_2}$$

18. The thermal decomposition of gaseous acetaldehyde is a second-order reaction. The value of E_a is 45,500 cal mole^{-1}, and the molecular diameter of the acetaldehyde molecule is 5×10^{-8} cm. (a) Calculate the number of molecules colliding per milliliter per second at 800°K and 760 mm pressure. (b) Calculate k in liters mole^{-1} sec^{-1} [$k = -(1/c^2)(dc/dt)$].

Ans. (a) 7.75×10^{16} molecules ml^{-1} sec^{-1}.   (b) 0.558 l mole^{-1} sec^{-1}.

19. The reaction $NO_2Cl = NO_2 + \frac{1}{2}Cl_2$ is first order and appears to follow the mechanism

$$NO_2Cl \xrightarrow{k_1} NO_2 + Cl$$

$$NO_2Cl + Cl \xrightarrow{k_2} NO_2 + Cl_2$$

(a) Assuming a steady state for the chlorine atom concentration, show that the empirical first-order rate constant can be identified with $2k_1$. (b) From the following data obtained by H. F. Cordes and H. S. Johnston [*J. Am. Chem. Soc.*, *76*, 4264 (1954)] at 180° show that the reaction is second order at these low gas pressures and calculate the second-order rate constant:

$c \times 10^8$, moles cm^{-3}	5	10	15	20
$k \times 10^4$, sec^{-1}	1.7	3.4	5.2	6.9

In a single experiment the reaction is first order, and the empirical rate constant is represented by k.   *Ans.* 3.4×10^3 (moles/cc)$^{-1}$ sec^{-1}.

20. The mutarotation of glucose is first order in glucose concentration and is catalyzed by acids (A) and bases (B). The first-order rate constant may be expressed by an equation of the type

$$k = k_w + k_{H^+}(H^+) + k_A(A) + k_B(B)$$

where k_w is the first-order rate constant in the absence of acids and bases other than water. The following data were obtained by J. N. Brönsted and E. A. Guggenheim [*J. Am. Chem. Soc.*, *49*, 2554 (1927)] at 18° in a medium containing 0.02 M sodium acetate and various concentrations of acetic acid:

(CH_3CO_2H), mole l^{-1}	0.020	0.105	0.199
$k \times 10^4$, min^{-1}	1.36	1.40	1.46

Calculate k_A. The term involving k_{H^+} is negligible under these conditions.

Ans. $k_w = 1.34 \times 10^{-4}$ min^{-1}, $k_A = 5 \times 10^{-5}$ l mole^{-1} min^{-1}.

---

21. The first-order rate constant for the reaction

$$SO_2Cl_2 = SO_2 + Cl_2$$

is 2.2×10^{-5} sec^{-1} at 320°. What percentage of SO_2Cl_2 is decomposed on heating at 320° for 2 hr?

22. The kinetics of a first-order reaction in which acid is produced is studied by periodically withdrawing a sample and titrating with standard alkali. The volumes required at various times are

Time, min	0	27	60	∞
Volume, ml	0	18.10	26.0	29.7

(*a*) Prove this reaction is first order.   (*b*) Calculate the half-life.

23. A solution of ethyl acetate and sodium hydroxide was prepared which contained (at $t = 0$) 5×10^{-3} M ethyl acetate and 8×10^{-3} M sodium hydroxide. After 400 sec at 25° a 25-ml aliquot was found to consume 33.3 ml of 5×10^{-3} M hydrochloric acid. (*a*) Calculate the rate constant for this second-order reaction. (*b*) At what time would you expect 20.0 ml of hydrochloric acid to be required?

24. The second-order rate constant for an alkaline hydrolysis of ethyl formate in 85 per cent ethanol (aqueous) at 29.86° is 4.53 liters mole^{-1} sec^{-1} [H. M. Humphreys and L. P. Hammett, *J. Am. Chem. Soc.*, *78*, 521 (1956)]. (*a*) If the reactants are both present at 0.001 M, what will be the half-life of the reaction? (*b*) If the concentration of one of the reactants is doubled and of the other is cut in half, how long will it take for half the reactant present at the lower concentration to react?

25. The rate k for the reaction $2NO + O_2 \rightarrow 2NO_2$ has a value of 7.1×10^9 mole^{-2} ml^2 sec^{-1} at 25° in $dc_{NO_2}/dt = kc_{NO}{}^2c_{O_2}$. Air blown through a certain hot chamber and cooled quickly to 25° and 760 mm contains 1 per cent by volume of nitric oxide, NO, and 20 per cent of oxygen. (*a*) How long will it take for 90 per cent of this NO to be converted into nitrogen dioxide, NO_2 (or N_2O_4)? (*b*) If the gases are blown through at the rate of 5000 ft^3 min^{-1}, how large a chamber must be constructed in order to obtain this 90 per cent conversion?

26. The following initial rates are obtained for the reaction $A + B \to AB$:

Initial Conc. of A, M	Init. Conc. of B, M	Initial Rate
1.0	1.0	0.025
0.1	1.0	0.0025
1.0	0.1	0.00025

What is the rate law for this reaction?

27. The reaction between selenious acid and iodide ion in acid solution is:

$$H_2SeO_3 + 6I^- + 4H^+ = Se(s) + 2I_3^- + 3H_2O$$

The initial reaction rates were measured at $0°$ at a variety of concentrations, as indicated in the following table, in moles per liter. These initial rates were evaluated

$(H_2SeO_3) \times 10^4$	$(H^+) \times 10^2$	$(I^-) \times 10^2$	Initial Rate $\times 10^7$
0.712	2.06	3.0	4.05
2.40	2.06	3.0	14.6
7.20	2.06	3.0	44.6
0.712	2.06	1.8	0.93
0.712	2.06	3.0	4.05
0.712	2.06	9.0	102
0.712	2.06	15.0	508
0.712	2.06	3.0	4.05
0.712	5.18	3.0	28.0
0.712	12.5	3.0	173.0

from plots of H_2SeO_3 versus time. Determine the form of the rate law. (*Note:* This rate law holds only as long as insignificant quantities of I_3^- are present.)

28. For the consecutive first-order reactions

$$A \xrightarrow[k=0.15 \text{ sec}^{-1}]{} B \xrightarrow[k=0.1 \text{ sec}^{-1}]{} C$$

plot curves which give the concentrations of A, B, and C as a function of time·

29. The initial rate of the reaction

$$BrO_3^- + 3SO_3^{2-} \rightleftharpoons Br^- + 3SO_4^{2-}$$

was found by F. S. Williamson and E. L. King [*J. Am. Chem. Soc., 79*, 5397 (1953)] to be given by $k(BrO_3^-)(SO_3^{2-})(H^+)$. Give one of the thermodynamically possible rate laws for the reverse reaction.

30. Write the equation for detailed balancing for the reaction scheme

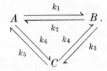

31. The following specific reaction rates were obtained by Wiig for the first-order decomposition of acetone dicarboxylic acid in aqueous solution:

Temp., °C	0	20	40	60
$k \times 10^5$, sec^{-1}	2.46	47.5	576	5480

(a) Plot $\log k$ against $1/T$, and determine the energy of activation. (b) Calculate the frequency factor s. (c) What is the half-life of this reaction at 80°?

32. Although the thermal decomposition of ethyl bromide is complex, the overall rate is first order and the specific reaction rate is given by the expression $k = 3.8 \times 10^{14} e^{-54,800/RT}$. Estimate the temperature at which (a) ethyl bromide decomposes at the rate of 1 per cent per sec and (b) the decomposition is 70 per cent complete in 1 hr.

33. Given that the first-order rate constant for the over-all decomposition of N_2O_5 is $k = 4.3 \times 10^{13} e^{-24,700/RT}$ sec^{-1}, calculate (a) the half-life at $-10°$; (b) the time required for 90 per cent reaction at 50°.

34. At 700°K what is the half-life of SiH_4? The equation for the first-order rate constant is $k = 2 \times 10^{13} e^{-51,700/RT}$.

35. A substance decomposes by two competing paths with rate constants k_1 and k_2. If, at 10°, $k_1/k_2 = 10$ and, at 40°, $k_1/k_2 = 0.1$, what is the difference in activation energy for these two reactions?

36. A reaction $A + B + C \rightarrow D$ follows the mechanism

$$A + B \rightleftharpoons AB$$

$$AB + C \rightarrow D$$

in which the first step remains essentially in equilibrium. Show that the dependence of rate upon temperature is given by

$$k = se^{-(E_a + \Delta H)/RT}$$

where ΔH is the enthalpy change for the first reaction.

37. (a) Calculate the second-order rate constant for collisions of dimethyl ether molecules with each other at 777°K. It is assumed that the molecules are spherical and have a radius of 2.5 A. If every collision was effective in producing decomposition, what would be the half-life of the reaction (b) at 1 atm pressure, (c) at a pressure of 1 micron of mercury?

38. Which of these two reactions is more likely with chlorine atoms: (a) giving a free radical, or (b) giving a hydrogen atom?

$$(a) \quad R_3C\!-\!H + Cl \rightarrow R_3C\cdot + HCl$$

$$(b) \quad R_3C\!-\!H + Cl \rightarrow R_3CCl + H$$

From a knowledge of the energies of dissociation or formation of the C—H, H—Cl, and C—Cl bonds one can estimate the heat of reaction. As a rough approximation the entropy change may be disregarded, and the sign and magnitude of the heat of reaction taken approximately as an indication of the free-energy change in the reactions. Those reactions which are highly endothermic will probably have a positive value of ΔG and will not be possible from a thermodynamic standpoint. They can then be ruled out in favor of a reaction which is highly exothermic and therefore likely to have a negative value of ΔG.

39. The initial rate v of oxidation of sodium succinate to form sodium fumarate by dissolved oxygen in the presence of the enzyme succinoxidase may be represented by

$$v = \frac{V}{1 + K_S/(S)}$$

where V is the maximum initial velocity obtainable with a given amount of enzyme, K_S is the Michaelis constant, and (S) is the concentration of sodium succinate. Calculate V and K_S from the following data. [For this calculation it is convenient to plot v^{-1} versus $(S)^{-1}$.]

$(S) \times 10^3$, M	10	2	1	0.5	0.33
$v \times 10^6$, M/sec	1.17	0.99	0.79	0.62	0.50

40. From the following data on the rate of the rearrangement of 1-cyclohexenyl allyl malonitrile at 135.7°, determine graphically the first-order rate constant. Check the graphical evaluation by calculating k from data at two different times.

Time, min	0	5	10	20	30	45
% rearranged	19.8	34.2	46.7	64.7	77.0	86.3

41. The hydrolysis of 1-chloro-1-methylcycloundecane in 80 per cent ethanol has been studied by H. C. Brown and M. Borkowoski [*J. Am. Chem. Soc.*, *74*, 1894 (1952)] at 25°. The extent of hydrolysis was measured by titrating the acid formed after measured intervals of time with a solution of NaOH. The data are as follows:

Time, hr	0	1.0	3.0	5.0	9.0	12	∞
x, ml	0.035	0.295	0.715	1.055	1.505	1.725	2.197

(a) Plot $\log (a - x)$ versus time. (b) Calculate k in sec^{-1}. (c) What fraction of the 1-chloro-1-methylcycloundecane will be left unhydrolyzed after 8 hr?

42. A 3-liter container is filled with air at atmospheric pressure. In order to replace the air with carbon dioxide, the CO_2 is forced to enter one end of the container at a rate of 2 liters min^{-1}, and gas is allowed to escape from the other end at the same rate. If instantaneous mixing of the gases is assumed, when will the partial pressure of oxygen be reduced to 0.01 mm?

43. It is found that 30 per cent of a compound decomposes in 10 hr at a certain temperature. Assuming a first-order reaction, how long will be required for 99 per cent of the compound to decompose?

44. A second-order reaction $A + B = C$, where $a = b$ is 20 per cent completed in 500 sec. How long will it take for the reaction to go to 60 per cent completion?

45. The second-order rate constant for a gas reaction is 1×10^3 liters $mole^{-1}$ sec^{-1} at 25°. Calculate the value of the rate constant when the rate equation is written in terms of pressure in atmospheres.

46. Integrate the following differential equation:

$$dx/dt = k(a - x)(b - x)(c - x)$$

47. Equal molar quantities of A and B are added to a liter of a suitable solvent. At the end of 500 sec half of A has reacted according to the reaction $A + B = C$. How much of A will be reacted at the end of 800 sec if the reaction is (a) zero order with respect to both A and B; (b) first order with respect to A and zero order with respect to B; (c) first order with respect to both A and B?

48. It is more difficult than commonly realized to differentiate between a first- and a second-order reaction by the shape of the plot of percentage reaction versus time. Make these plots for first- and second-order reactions ($a = b$) having the same half-life. By what per cent do they differ at (a) $t = t_{1/2}/2$ and (b) $t = 2t_{1/2}$?

49. The equations for (B) and (C) on p. 310 give an indeterminate result if $k_1 = k_2$. Rederive the equations, giving (B) and (C) as functions of time for the special case that $A \xrightarrow{k_1} B \xrightarrow{k_1} C$.

50. Carry out the integrations, and calculate the concentrations of A, B, and C shown in Fig. 12-4 for the three first-order reactions given by $A \xrightarrow{k_1} B \underset{k_3}{\overset{k_2}{\rightleftharpoons}} C$.

51. For a reversible second-order reaction $A + B \underset{k_2}{\overset{k_1}{\rightleftharpoons}} C$ the rate equation is $dx/dt = k_1(a - x)(b - x) - k_2 x^2$, where a and b are the initial concentrations of A and B and the concentration of C at any time is x. Integrate this equation to find the equation obeyed by the over-all reaction.

52. The rate of rearrangement of 1-ethyl propenyl allyl malonitrile to 1-ethyl-2-methyl-4-pentenylidene malonitrile, can be followed by measuring the refractive index. The following first-order constants were obtained:

Temp., °C	120.0	130.0	140.0
$k \times 10^4$, sec^{-1}	4.02	9.12	19.83

(a) What is the energy of activation? (b) What is the frequency factor?

53. In the reaction

$$N_2 + O_2 \underset{k_2}{\overset{k_1}{\rightleftharpoons}} 2NO$$

$$\frac{dx}{dt} = k_1 \left(p'_{N_2} - \frac{p_{NO}}{2} \right) \left(p'_{O_2} - \frac{p_{NO}}{2} \right) - k_2 p_{NO_2}$$

where p'_{N_2} is the original pressure of N_2, p'_{O_2} is the original pressure of O_2, and p_{NO} is the pressure of NO formed. Values of the equilibrium constant K are given in Table VI in Chapter 9. The rate constant for the reverse reaction is given in atm^{-1} sec^{-1} by

$$k_2 = 1 \times 10^9 e^{-70,000/RT}$$

(a) Calculate k_1 at 2400°K and 1900°K. (b) Calculate the time required for NO at 0.02 atm to undergo 10 per cent decomposition at 2400°K and at 1900°K, using k_2 and neglecting k_1.

54. Two different equations have been proposed for the second-order decomposition rate of nitric oxide (expressed in atm^{-1} sec^{-1}):

$$k = 1 \times 10^7 e^{-50,000/RT}$$

$$k = 1 \times 10^9 e^{-70,000/RT}$$

Calculate the values of k at 1800°K and at 2100°K, using both equations.

55. Suppose that a substance X decomposes into A and B in parallel paths with rate constants given by

$$k_A = 10^{15} e^{-30,000/RT}$$

$$k_B = 10^{13} e^{-20,000/RT}$$

(a) At what temperature will the two products be formed at the same rate? (b) At what temperature will A be formed 10 times as fast as B? (c) At what temperature will A be formed 0.1 as fast as B? (d) State a generalization concerning the effect of temperature on the relative rates of reactions with different activation energies.

56. Suppose that the over-all rate constant for a certain reaction is given by

$$k = \frac{k_1 k_2}{k_3}$$

where k_1, k_2, and k_3 are rate constants for individual steps with activation energies of E_1, E_2, and E_3 and frequency factors of s_1, s_2, and s_3. Express s and E for the over-all reaction in terms of the kinetic quantities for the individual steps.

57. For a hypothetical reaction between two gaseous molecules of $M = 100$ and $\sigma = 4 \times 10^{-8}$ cm calculate the second-order rate constant at $300°$, assuming that (a) each collision is effective, and (b) the activation energy is 30 kcal.

58. The energy of activation for the reaction $C_2H_5Br \rightarrow C_2H_4 + HBr$ is 55,000 cal mole^{-1}. From this fact and Table V in Chapter 4, show that the primary step in the dissociation cannot be the splitting off of an H atom or a CH_3 group but that it can involve the splitting off of an HBr molecule, or (considering the inaccuracy of the data) that it can involve the splitting off of a Br atom.

59. Show that the interconversion of ortho- and parahydrogen will be 3/2 order, as obtained experimentally in the range $600–750°$, if the rate-determining step is that between atoms and molecules of hydrogen

$$H + \text{para-}H_2 \underset{k_2}{\overset{k_1}{\rightleftharpoons}} \text{ortho-}H_2 + H$$
$$\uparrow\downarrow \qquad\qquad \uparrow\uparrow$$

where the arrows represent the directions of the nuclear spins (cf. p. 545).

60. The mutarotation of glucose is catalyzed by acids and bases and is first order in the concentration of glucose. When perchloric acid is used as a catalyst, the concentration of hydrogen ions may be taken to be equal to the concentration of perchloric acid, and the catalysis by perchlorate ion may be ignored since it is such a weak base. The following first-order rate constants were obtained by J. N. Brönsted and E. A. Guggenheim [*J. Am. Chem. Soc.*, *49*, 2554 (1927)] at $18°$:

$(HClO_4)$, mole l^{-1}	0.0010	0.0048	0.0099	0.0192	0.0300	0.0400
$k \times 10^4$, min^{-1}	1.25	1.38	1.53	1.090	2.15	2.59

Calculate the values of the constants in the equation $k = k_w + k_{H^+}(H^+)$.

61. Derive the steady-state rate equation for the mechanism

$$E + S \underset{k_2}{\overset{k_1}{\rightleftharpoons}} X \overset{k_3}{\rightarrow} E + P$$

$$E + I \underset{k_5}{\overset{k_4}{\rightleftharpoons}} EI$$

for the case that (S), $(I) \gg (E)_0$.

62. If a bimolecular reaction in solution occurs every time the centers of reactant molecules come within R_{12} cm, the bimolecular rate constant in M^{-1} sec^{-1} is given by

$$k = \frac{4\pi N_0}{1000} R_{12} (D_1 + D_2)$$

where D_1 and D_2 are the diffusion coefficients of the two reactants. Calculate k for the reaction of equal-sized spherical molecules, using equation 13 in Chapter 20 for the diffusion coefficients in water at $25°$. If the molecules react when they touch, the second-order rate constant is independent of size.

IRREVERSIBLE PROCESSES IN LIQUIDS

13

The properties of systems in equilibrium may be treated exactly by thermodynamics, which provides a reliable guide to the relationships between properties. For processes which are time dependent there is no such fully developed theoretical basis. The kinetic-theory expressions for the viscosity, diffusion coefficient, and thermal conductivity coefficients of dilute gases have been given on p. 290. In this chapter we will consider three irreversible processes in solution: viscosity, diffusion, and electrical conductivity. The basic theory of such rate processes * is not on as good a ground as thermodynamics, but these processes are of great importance, † and considerable has been learned empirically about the phenomena.

Viscosity. The coefficient of viscosity was defined in the discussion of the kinetic theory of gases on p. 288. The unit of viscosity, the *poise*, is the viscosity of a fluid for which a force of 1 dyne cm^{-2} will cause a plane to slide past a parallel surface 1 cm away with a velocity of 1 cm sec^{-1}. The coefficient of viscosity of a liquid may be measured by a number of methods which are illustrated in *Fig. 13-1;* these include the determination of the rate of flow through a cylindrical tube, the rate of settling of a sphere in a liquid, and the force required to turn one of two concentric cylinders at a certain angular velocity.

* S. Glasstone, K. J. Laidler, and H. Eyring, *Theory of Rate Processes*, McGraw-Hill Book Co., New York, 1940.

† R. B. Bird, W. E. Stewart, and E. N. Lightfoot, *Transport Phenomena*, John Wiley & Sons, New York, 1960.

350

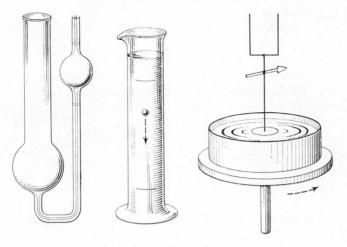

Fig. 13-1. Various types of viscometers.

The frictional coefficient f, the force in dynes required to move a sphere through a continuous liquid at a velocity of 1 cm sec^{-1} with nonturbulent flow, is given by Stokes's law

$$f = 6\pi\eta r \tag{1}$$

where r is the radius of the sphere and η the coefficient of viscosity. The force causing a sphere to settle in a liquid is equal to the mass of the sphere, minus the mass of solvent displaced, times the acceleration of gravity. If the density of the sphere is ρ and the density of the medium is ρ_0, this force is $\frac{4}{3}\pi r^3(\rho - \rho_0)g$, where g is the acceleration of gravity. When the rate of settling of the sphere in the liquid is constant, the retarding force $f(dx/dt) = 6\pi\eta r(dx/dt)$ is equal to the force due to gravity, and so

$$\frac{4}{3}\pi r^3(\rho - \rho_0)g = 6\pi\eta r\left(\frac{dx}{dt}\right) \tag{2}$$

$$\frac{dx}{dt} = \frac{2r^2(\rho - \rho_0)g}{9\eta} \tag{3}$$

Thus by measurement of the velocity dx/dt of settling of a ball bearing of known r and ρ in a liquid of known density ρ_0 the coefficient of viscosity η may be obtained. This method is especially valuable for solutions of high viscosity, such as solutions of high polymers.

The coefficient of viscosity η may also be determined by passing a liquid through a tube of small diameter and making use of the

Poiseuille equation

$$\eta = \frac{P\pi r^4 t}{8Vl} \tag{4}$$

where t is the time required for V ml of liquid to flow through a capillary tube of length l and radius r under an applied pressure P.

The quantitative measurement of absolute viscosity by this method is difficult. Accordingly, indirect measurements are usually made in which the viscosity of a liquid is determined relative to that of another liquid whose viscosity has been obtained by an absolute method. This determination of physical-chemical constants by making relative measurements and comparing them with similar measurements of a standard substance is a common procedure. The absolute measurements of the standard substance may well require years of research, whereas the relative measurements can often be made quickly and easily with a high degree of accuracy.

In a simple viscometer such as that illustrated on the left in Fig. 13-1 the pressure that causes flow through the capillary depends upon the difference in height h of liquid levels in the two tubes, the density of the liquid ρ_1, and the acceleration of gravity g. Thus, equation 4 may be rearranged to

$$\eta_1 = \left(\frac{hg\pi r^4}{8Vl}\right)\rho_1 t_1 \tag{5}$$

Then, if the same volume of a second liquid of viscosity η_2 and density ρ_2 takes t_2 seconds to flow through the same capillary,

$$\eta_2 = \left(\frac{hg\pi r^4}{8Vl}\right)\rho_2 t_2 \tag{6}$$

In taking the ratio of these equations the height h cancels if the same volume of the two liquids has been used, and so do the other constants, so that

$$\frac{\eta_1}{\eta_2} = \frac{\rho_1 t_1}{\rho_2 t_2} \tag{7}$$

From measurements of the densities and times of flow of the two liquids it is a simple matter to calculate the viscosity η_1 of the first liquid when that of the second is known. Quite commonly water is taken as the reference liquid, and at 25° η_2 has a value of 0.00895 poise.

When the coefficient of viscosity changes with the flow velocity, the fluid is said to be non-Newtonian. This phenomenon is especially encountered with colloidal systems.

The viscosity of an ideal gas increases as the temperature increases. On the other hand, the viscosities of most liquids decrease with increasing temperature. The flow of a liquid involves the shift of molecules from one layer to another. Such shifts require energy, and since more kinetic energy is available at higher temperatures, the liquid can flow more easily at higher temperatures. The viscosities of several liquids at different temperatures are shown in Table I. The variation

Table I.   Viscosity of Liquids in Poises

Liquid	0°	25°	50°	75°
Water	0.01793	0.00895	0.00549	0.00380
Ethanol	0.0179	0.0109	0.00698	...
Benzene	0.0090	0.0061	0.0044	...

of viscosity with temperature is such that it may be represented quite well by

$$\log \eta = A + \frac{B}{T} \tag{8}$$

where A and B are constants.

The viscosity of a gas is nearly independent of pressure. In contrast, the viscosity of a liquid increases as the pressure is increased.

Diffusion. Substances spontaneously diffuse from regions of high chemical potential to regions of low chemical potential, as, for example, in the diffusion of water vapor from warm water to cold water. Thus the driving force for diffusion is the gradient of chemical potential. However, the diffusion coefficient is defined in terms of the concentration gradient (dc/dx), where c is the concentration and x is the distance. According to Fick's first law, the flux J (quantity of substance diffusing per second through an area of 1 cm^2) of a substance through a plane perpendicular to the direction of diffusion is directly proportional to the concentration gradient.

$$J = -D \left(\frac{dc}{dx} \right) \tag{9}$$

where D is the diffusion coefficient (p. 286). This equation is analogous to those for the flux of electric charge (which is proportional to the potential gradient according to Ohm's law), the flux of heat (which is proportional to the temperature gradient), and the flux of momentum (which is proportional to the velocity gradient) in viscous flow.

Diffusion coefficients may be measured by a number of different methods.* The rate of diffusion of a solute from solution to solvent through a porous plate may be measured. Probably the most widely used methods are those in which a sharp boundary is formed between solution and solvent, as illustrated in *Fig. 13-2a*. Initially the plot of concentration on the horizontal axis versus height in the cell on the vertical axis has the shape indicated in *b*. At a later time this boundary

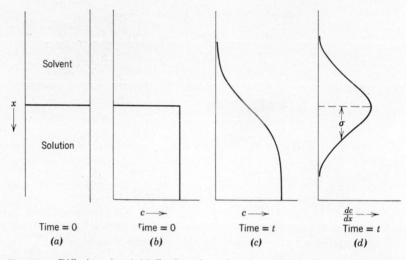

| Time = 0 | Time = 0 | Time = t | Time = t |
| (a) | (b) | (c) | (d) |

Fig. 13-2. Diffusion of an initially sharp boundary in a cell of uniform cross section.

will have become diffuse, and the concentration will vary with height as illustrated in *c*. Instead of an abrupt change in concentration there is a more gradual one. When the solute is a colored substance, its concentration may be determined as a function of height photometrically. One of the most generally useful methods for determining the diffuseness of the boundary depends upon measuring the deflection of light by the refractive-index gradient caused by the concentration gradient.† Since the bending of a light ray in such a boundary is proportional to the concentration gradient dc/dx, the curve obtained with such a system (the *schlieren* optical system, p. 584) has the shape indicated in *d*. This curve has the shape of a normal probability curve (sometimes referred to as a Gaussian curve) if D in equation 9 is independent

---

* L. J. Gosting, *Advances in Protein Chemistry*, Vol. XI, Academic Press, New York, 1956; W. Jost, *Diffusion in Solids, Liquids, and Gases*, Academic Press, New York, 1952.

† L. G. Longsworth, *Ind. Eng. Chem., Anal. Ed.*, 18, 219 (1946).

of concentration. The diffusion coefficient may be calculated from the shape of this curve in several ways. For example,

$$D = \frac{\sigma^2}{2t} \tag{10}$$

where σ is the standard deviation (half the width of the probability curve at the inflection point).

If the flow J is expressed in g cm^{-2} sec^{-1} and the concentration gradient in g cm^{-4}, it is seen that the diffusion coefficient will have the units of cm^2 sec^{-1}. The diffusion coefficient for potassium chloride in very dilute aqueous solution at 25° is 199×10^{-7} cm^2 sec^{-1}, and for sucrose it is 52.3×10^{-7} cm^2 sec^{-1}. These values may be compared with those for several proteins given on p. 586. The diffusion coefficients of salts in dilute solutions may be calculated from the mobilities of the anion and cation.

Faraday's Law. The electric current in an electrolytic solution consists of a flow of ions; in a metal, it consists of a flow of electrons. Thus, when an electric current passes from a metallic conductor to a solution, electrons must be gained or lost by ions or molecules in the solution next to the surface of the electrode. Thus chemical reactions, which involve this gain or loss of electrons, always accompany the passage of electric current from a metallic conductor to a solution. At the cathode (p. 381) electrons are supplied by the external battery or dynamo, and these electrons are transferred to the solution in a reduction reaction. At the anode electrons are withdrawn by the external battery or dynamo, and these electrons are provided by a chemical reaction at the surface of the electrode.

The removal or addition of electrons is a matter of the utmost importance, not only in electrolysis but also in many chemical reactions.

The removal of electrons is oxidation. It occurs at the anode.

The addition of electrons is reduction. It occurs at the cathode.

Thus, in electrolysis, ferric ions are reduced to ferrous ions at the cathode:

$$Fe^{3+} + e = Fe^{2+}$$

and ferrous ions are oxidized to ferric ions at the anode:

$$Fe^{2+} = Fe^{3+} + e$$

Usually there are several different kinds of ions around each electrode competing for electrons at the cathode and competing for an opportunity to give up electrons at the anode. Furthermore, it is quite likely that one or more secondary reactions will follow the primary electrode reaction in which there is a transfer of an electron. Some chemical experience is necessary in order to predict what will happen. For example, if chlorine is liberated in an alkaline solution, hypochlorite or chlorate may be formed. If chlorine is liberated on a silver anode, silver chloride is formed.

Faraday studied electrolysis quantitatively and in 1834 announced a law, which now bears his name, that 96,500 (96,493 to be exact) coulombs or ampere-seconds of electricity produces a chemical change of 1 gram-equivalent. The name *faraday* and the symbol F are given to this important quantity of electricity. In the absence of secondary reactions Faraday's law is exact since it involves a counting process, an integer number of electrons being required for each ion or molecule being oxidized or reduced. Thus, the faraday of electricity is equal to the magnitude of the charge of the electron e (1.6020×10^{-19} coulomb; see Chapter 16) times the number of atoms in a gram atom ($N_0 = 6.0235 \times 10^{23}$).

$$F = N_0 e \tag{11}$$

$F = (6.0235 \times 10^{23}$ electrons equiv$^{-1})(1.6020 \times 10^{-19}$ coulomb electron$^{-1}) = 96,493$ coulombs equiv^{-1}.

As a matter of fact, the experimental determination of the value of the faraday and the charge of the electron provides one of our best means for determining the value for Avogadro's number, 6.0235×10^{23}.

Example 1. A current of 0.1000 amp is passed through a cupric sulfate solution for 10 min, using platinum electrodes.

(a) Calculate the number of grams of copper deposited at the cathode.

$$\frac{(10 \text{ min})(60 \text{ sec min}^{-1})(0.1000 \text{ amp})(63.54 \text{ g mole}^{-1})}{(96,500 \text{ amp-sec equiv}^{-1})(2 \text{ equiv mole}^{-1})} = 0.01975 \text{ gram}$$

(b) Calculate the volume of oxygen liberated at the anode at 25° and 740 mm.

$$\frac{(10 \text{ min})(60 \text{ sec min}^{-1})(0.100 \text{ amp})(32 \text{ g mole}^{-1})}{(96,500 \text{ amp-sec equiv}^{-1})(4 \text{ equiv mole}^{-1})} = 4.98 \times 10^{-3} \text{ gram}$$

$$\frac{(4.98 \times 10^{-3} \text{ g})(0.08205 \text{ l-atm deg}^{-1} \text{ mole}^{-1})(298 \text{ deg})}{(32 \text{ g mole}^{-1})(740/760 \text{ atm})} = 0.00392 \text{ liter}$$

Electrical Units. According to Ohm's law, discovered in 1827,

$$E = IR \tag{12}$$

where I is the current in amperes, E is the difference in electrical potential in volts, and R is the resistance in ohms.

The absolute values of the ampere, volt, and ohm are based upon the fundamental mechanical units: the standard meter, the standard kilogram, and the mean solar second. Batteries and electrical resistances of certain constructions will be calibrated by the National Bureau of Standards in terms of these absolute units.

Electric energy is the product of an intensity factor, voltage, and a quantity factor, coulombs, as pointed out on p. 35. Thus

$$\text{Electric energy in joules} = EIt = I^2Rt \qquad (13)$$

Electric energy may also be separated into a power factor, the *watt* or *volt-ampere*, and a time factor, the second. One watt-second is 1 volt $\times$ 1 amp $\times$ 1 sec, or 1 joule. One kilowatt-hour is equal to 3,600,000 joules.

Electric Conductance. Electric conductance may be classified according to four types:

a. Metallic conductance, which results from the mobility of electrons. Metallic conductors become poorer conductors at higher temperatures because it is more difficult for electrons to pass through the crystal lattice when the units of the lattice are in more active thermal motion.

b. Electrolytic conductance, which results from the mobility of ions. Electrolytic conductors become better conductors as the temperature is raised because ions can move through the solution more readily at higher temperatures, where the viscosity is smaller and there is less solvation of the ions.

c. Semiconductors, solids containing ions and ion vacancies which move under the influence of an applied field. Ion vacancies in the crystal lattice are referred to as holes. When a hole is filled by an ion, a hole is created in another position, and so in effect the hole moves and thus contributes to the conductivity of the solid. Semiconductors become better conductors at higher temperatures, where more ions have the activation energy required to move to another lattice position. The conductance of semiconductors increases exponentially with the absolute temperature.

d. Electric conductance in gases by gas ions and electrons.

The resistance R of a uniform conductor is directly proportional to its length l and inversely proportional to its cross-sectional area A.

$$R = \frac{rl}{A} \quad \text{and} \quad r = \frac{RA}{l} \qquad (14)$$

The proportionality constant r is called the *specific resistance* and is the resistance of a cube of the material 1 cm on an edge. The values of

Table II.   Electrical Resistance of Typical Conductors

Material	Temperature, °C	Specific Resistance, ohm cm
Silver	0	1.468×10^{-6}
Copper	0	1.561×10^{-6}
Aluminum	0	2.564×10^{-6}
Iron	0	9.070×10^{-6}
Lead	0	20.480×10^{-6}
Mercury	0	95.85×10^{-6}
Fused sodium nitrate	500	0.568
Fused zinc chloride	500	11.93
1 M potassium chloride	25	8.93
0.001 M potassium chloride	25	6,810
1 M acetic acid	18	757.5
0.001 M acetic acid	18	24,400
Water	18	2.5×10^7
Xylene	25	7×10^{18}

the specific resistance are given for various materials in Table II. In the neighborhood of absolute zero the resistance of metals becomes extremely low. The specific resistance of mercury at 3°K, for example, is less than 10^{-8} ohm cm.

In dealing with solutions of electrolytes the *specific conductance* κ, that is, the reciprocal of the specific resistance, is generally used. Then

$$\kappa = \frac{1}{r} = \frac{l}{RA} \tag{15}$$

Measurement of the Conductance of Solutions. In the Wheatstone bridge shown in *Fig. 13-3*, R_b is the resistance of the cell containing an electrolytic solution. R_a is the resistance of the resistance box, which may be varied by turning dials to change the number of coils of resistance wire in the circuit. The ratio R_c/R_d may be changed by multiples of 10 by moving a contact.

Alternating current of about 1000 cycles per second, which gives a mosquito-like noise in the earphones, is generated by oscillator O. A dipping cell is shown in the lower right-hand corner. Cells with long paths are used for concentrated solutions, and cells with short paths and large electrodes for dilute solutions, so that the resistances to be measured will be of a convenient magnitude.

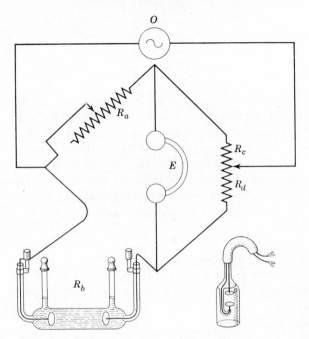

Fig. 13-3. Wheatstone bridge and cell for determining the electric conductance of a solution.

Alternating current prevents polarization (p. 411) of the electrodes, which leads to an increase in resistance. When alternating current is used and the electrodes are platinized, the electrolysis that occurs when the current passes in one direction is reversed when the current is reversed. The coating of platinum black, produced by electrolytic deposition, adsorbs gases and catalyzes their reaction. In this way the formation of a nonconducting gas film is prevented.

In making a measurement of the unknown resistance R_b, the known resistance R_a and the resistance ratio R_d/R_c are adjusted until the sound in the earphones is at a minimum. Then the two terminals of the earphones are at the same potential, and the potential drop E across the different parts of the bridge must be such that $E_b = E_a$ and $E_d = E_c$. Moreover, since according to Ohm's law the difference in potential E is equal to the current I multiplied by the resistance,

$$I_b R_b = I_a R_a \quad \text{and} \quad I_d R_d = I_c R_c \tag{16}$$

Dividing the first equation by the second gives

$$\frac{I_b R_b}{I_d R_d} = \frac{I_a R_a}{I_c R_c} \tag{17}$$

Furthermore, $I_a = I_c$ and $I_b = I_d$, since the current flowing through the two resistances in series must be the same in each resistance when no current flows through the earphones. Thus equation 17 reduces to

$$R_b = \frac{R_d R_a}{R_c} \tag{18}$$

which is the fundamental equation for the Wheatstone bridge.

It would be extremely difficult to make a conductance cell having electrodes 1 cm^2 in area and exactly 1 cm apart and enclosed by plane parallel walls in order to measure the specific conductance directly. However, it is not necessary to do this, because it is possible to determine a factor k, called the cell constant, for any conductance cell, so that the specific conductance κ may be calculated with the relation

$$\kappa = \frac{k}{R} \tag{19}$$

where R is the measured resistance for the cell. The cell constant k is determined experimentally with a standard solution of known specific conductance κ.

Example 2. When a certain conductance cell was filled with 0.0200 M potassium chloride, which has a specific conductance of 0.002768 ohm^{-1} cm^{-1}, it had a resistance of 82.4 ohms at 25° as measured with a Wheatstone bridge; when filled with 0.0050 N potassium sulfate, it had a resistance of 326.0 ohms.

(*a*) What is the cell constant?

$$k = (0.002768 \text{ ohm}^{-1} \text{ cm}^{-1})(82.4 \text{ ohms}) = 0.2281 \text{ cm}^{-1}$$

(*b*) What is the specific conductance κ of the K_2SO_4 solution?

$$\kappa = \frac{k}{R} = \frac{0.2281 \text{ cm}^{-1}}{326.0 \text{ ohm}} = 6.997 \times 10^{-4} \text{ ohm}^{-1} \text{ cm}^{-1}$$

The resistance of a 1-cm cube of electrolytic solution is $1/\kappa$ ohms. Therefore, if a difference in potential of 1 volt is applied to two opposite faces, the current density i will be, according to Ohm's law,

$$i = \frac{E}{R} = \frac{1}{(1/\kappa)} = \kappa \tag{20}$$

Thus the specific conductance κ is numerically equal to the current in amperes which will flow through a unit cube of solution across which there is a difference in potential of 1 volt.

Equivalent Conductance. In order to represent the conductance of an equivalent weight of an electrolyte it is convenient to introduce the term *equivalent conductance*.

in 1 sec if a field of 1 volt cm^{-1} is applied. Therefore $z_c c_c u_c/1000$ equivalents of cation c will be transported out of the cube per second, and $z_a c_a u_a/1000$ equivalents of anion a will be transported out of the cube in the opposite direction. To convert equivalents per second to amperes, the sum of the currents is multiplied by the faraday F.

$$\kappa = \frac{F(z_c c_c u_c + z_a c_a u_a)}{1000} \tag{29}$$

Example 7. Calculate the specific conductance of 0.100 N sodium chloride at 25° from the mobilities of sodium and chloride ions at this concentration, which are 42.6×10^{-5} and 68.0×10^{-5} cm^2 $volt^{-1}$ sec^{-1}, respectively.

$$\kappa = \frac{(96,500)\,(0.100)\,[42.6 \times 10^{-5} + 68.0 \times 10^{-5}]}{1000}$$

$$= 0.01067 \text{ ohm}^{-1} \text{ cm}^{-1}$$

The relation between the equivalent conductance and mobilities may be obtained by substituting equation 29 into equation 21 and noting that $z_c c_c = z_a c_a = C$, which is the concentration in equivalents per liter,

$$\Lambda = F(u_a + u_c) = l_a + l_c \tag{30}$$

Thus $u_a = l_a/F$ and $u_c = l_c/F$.

Transference Number. Another quantity which is frequently used in discussing electrolytic solutions is the transference number. With strong electrolytes the *transference number* T is the fraction of the current carried by a given ion. The ions that move faster carry the larger fraction of electricity through the solution. The fraction of the current carried by the cation is

$$T_c = \frac{z_c c_c u_c}{z_c c_c u_c + z_a c_a u_a} = \frac{u_c}{u_c + u_a} \tag{31}$$

since $z_c c_c = z_a c_a$.

Likewise, the transference number of the anion T_a is equal to $u_a/(u_c + u_a)$. It is obvious that

$$T_c + T_a = 1 \tag{32}$$

In a moving-boundary experiment the transference number may be calculated from the volume V in liters moved through by the boundary per faraday. If the concentration of the leading ion (that is, K^+ in Fig. 13-5) is C equivalents per liter, VC equivalents move through a fixed plane ahead of the moving boundary per faraday, and so

$$T_c = VC \tag{33}$$

Example 8. Calculate the transference numbers of potassium and chloride ions in 0.1 N potassium chloride. According to the data given in example 6, the boundary moves through $(4.64)(0.230)/(0.00521)(67)(60) = 0.0508$ ml coulomb^{-1} or $(0.0508$ ml coulomb$^{-1})(96,500$ coulombs faraday$^{-1})/(1000$ ml l$^{-1}) = 4.90$ l faraday^{-1}.

$$T_{K^+} = VC = (4.90 \text{ l faraday}^{-1})(0.1 \text{ equiv l}^{-1}) = 0.490$$

$$T_{Cl^-} = 1 - T_{K^+} = 0.510$$

Table VI gives the transference numbers of the cations of several typical electrolytes as determined by the moving-boundary method.

Table VI. Cation-Transference Numbers at 25° Determined by the Moving-Boundary Method [1]

Electrolyte	0.01 N	0.1 N	Electrolyte	0.01 N	0.1 N
HCl	0.8251	0.8314	AgNO₃	0.4648	0.4682
LiCl	0.3289	0.3168	NaC₂H₃O₂	0.5537	0.5594
NaCl	0.3918	0.3854	CaCl₂	0.4264	0.4060
KCl	0.4902	0.4898	K₂SO₄	0.4829	0.4890
KBr	0.4833	0.4833	LaCl₃	0.4625	0.4375
KNO₃	0.5084	0.5103	K₃Fe(CN)₆	0.4315	0.4410

[1] D. A. MacInnes, *The Principles of Electrochemistry*, Reinhold Publishing Corp., New York, 1939.

Hittorf Method. Transference numbers were first determined by Hittorf in 1853 by studying the concentration changes which occur in the anode and cathode compartments during an electrolysis experiment. If the cation moves faster than the anion, more cations will enter the cathode chamber during an experiment than anions enter the anode chamber. The concentration changes in the anode and cathode chambers are due not only to the unequal velocities and the difference in transference numbers but also to the chemical changes at the electrode due to electrolysis.

The transference number of the silver ion in silver nitrate may be determined by carrying out the electrolysis of silver nitrate in an apparatus having three chambers: cathode chamber, anode chamber, and connecting chamber. During an experiment the number of equivalents of silver ion formed at the silver anode (+) is equal to the number of gram atoms of metallic silver formed at the cathode $(-)$. However, the concentration of silver ions in the regions surrounding the two electrodes depends not only upon the duration of the electrolysis and the current used but also upon the fractions of the current carried by the silver and nitrate ions.

If x faradays of current pass between the electrodes, x equivalents of silver will deposit on the cathode, and x equivalents of silver ion would disappear in the cathode chamber if there were no migration of silver ion. However, the number of equivalents of silver ions y which actually do disappear from the cathode chamber is less than this because silver ions migrate toward the negative electrode. The difference $x - y$ is the number of equivalents of silver ion which have migrated into the cathode chamber during the passage of x faradays of current. The transference number of the silver ion is therefore

$$T_c = \frac{x - y}{x} \tag{34}$$

The transference number of the silver ion may also be calculated from the change in concentration in the anode chamber. Here x equivalents of silver ion are formed by the electrode reaction, but the increase in the number of equivalents of silver ion in this compartment is less than x because of the migration of silver ions away from the positive electrode. If z is the increase in the number of equivalents actually found in the anode chamber, then $x - z$ is the number of equivalents of silver ion which have migrated out of the anode chamber. The silver-ion transference number calculated from the data on the anode chamber is thus

$$T_c = \frac{x - z}{x} \tag{35}$$

Example 9. An aqueous solution of cupric sulfate was electrolyzed between copper electrodes. On the cathode 0.3000 gram of copper was deposited. The solution in the anode compartment contained 1.4300 grams of copper after electrolysis, and the same weight of water contained 1.2140 grams before electrolysis. Calculate the copper transference number. For Cu^{2+} the equivalent weight is $63.54/2 = 31.77$.

$$T_c = \frac{x - z}{x} = \frac{\dfrac{0.300}{31.77} - \dfrac{(1.4300 - 1.2140)}{31.77}}{0.300/31.77}$$

$$= (0.300 - 0.216)/0.300 = 0.28$$

$$T_a = 1 - T_c = 1 - 0.28 = 0.72$$

More accurate results may be obtained by the moving-boundary method. The moving-boundary method is also more rapid and may be used for the study of mixtures of ions, which may be colloidal ions such as proteins. The study of colloids by this method is referred to as *electrophoresis* (see p. 591).

In the case of partially dissociated electrolytes (weak electrolytes) the transference number may not be interpreted as simply the fraction of the current carried by a given ion constituent. For example, the cation-transference numbers for cadmium iodide solutions at 18° are *negative* above 0.5 equivalent per liter. This indicates the presence of ions such as CdI_3^- and CdI_4^{2-}, which cause cadmium to migrate to the anode rather than the cathode.

Relation between Transference Numbers and Ionic Conductances. Individual ionic conductances may be calculated from values of the transference number and equivalent conductance. Since the transference number is the fraction of the current carried by a given ion, it must be equal to the ratio of the ionic conductance of that ion to the equivalent conductance of the salt.

$$T = \frac{l}{\Lambda} \tag{36}$$

If Λ_0 and the value of the transference number extrapolated to zero concentration are determined, the value of the ionic conductance at infinite dilution may be calculated. The equivalent conductance of a weak electrolyte, such as acetic acid, at infinite dilution may be obtained in this way as well as by the method described on p. 364.

Example 10. Calculate Λ_0 for acetic acid at 25°, using the data of Table IV and the fact that the cation-transference numbers of hydrochloric acid and sodium acetate at infinite dilution are 0.820 and 0.550, respectively.

$$l_{0,H^+} = T_{0,H^+} \times \Lambda_{0,HCl} = 0.820 \times 426.1 = 349.4$$

$$l_{0,C_2H_3O_2^-} = T_{0,C_2H_3O_2^-} \times \Lambda_{0,NaC_2H_3O_2} = 0.450 \times 91.0 = 40.9$$

$$\Lambda_{0,HC_2H_3O_2} = l_{0,H^+} + l_{0,C_2H_3O_2^-} = 390.3$$

Ionic conductances and equivalent conductances increase with the temperature, and the temperature coefficients are very nearly the same for all ions in a given solvent and are equal to the temperature coefficient of the viscosity; for water this is 2 per cent per degree in the neighborhood of 25°.

Conductance of Nonaqueous Solutions. When electrolytes which are completely dissociated in water are dissolved in solvents of low dielectric constant, the coulombic attraction is sufficient to cause ionic association at extremely low concentrations of ions. The force between ions is inversely proportional to the dielectric constant (p. 501) of the medium. Thus all electrolytes are "weak electrolytes" in solvents of low dielectric constant. Among the solvents that have been important in studies of nonaqueous solutions of electrolytes are alcohols, liquid ammonia, dioxane, acetone, and other ketones, anhydrous formic acid and acetic acid, pyridine, and several amines and nitro compounds.

A few miscellaneous examples of conductances in nonaqueous solutions are given in Table VII.

Table VII.   Conductance of Nonaqeuous Solutions

Solvent	Temperature, °C	Electrolyte	Concentration, equivalents per liter	Specific Conductance	Equivalent Conductance
Ammonia	−33	NaI	1.14	0.28	245
Ethanol	18	NaI	1.00	0.035	35.2
Acetone	25	NaI	1.0		26.4
			0.1		64.1
			0.01		109.7
			0.0		(176.2)
Ammonia	−33	Na	0.8	1.27	2017

In water there is no detectable difference in the ionization of potassium chloride, potassium bromide, and potassium iodide, but there is a marked difference in liquid ammonia, which has a dielectric constant of 22 and a lesser tendency to solvate. At −34° in ammonia, the dissociation constants for potassium iodide and chloride are, respectively, 4.2×10^{-4} and 8.7×10^{-4}.

The degree of dissociation of electrolytes in solvents of low dielectric constant may be calculated from conductance measurements. However, this is much more difficult than for water, since Λ_0 must be determined by indirect methods.*

The conductance of metallic sodium in liquid ammonia is interesting. The neutral sodium atoms dissociate into positive Na^+ ions and electrons.

---

* C. A. Kraus, "The Present State of the Electrolyte Problem," *J. Chem. Educ.*, *35*, **324** (1958).

Salt crystals have very low conductances because the ions are held in fixed positions, but fused salts are excellent conductors. Even in the crystal form the conductance becomes appreciable at temperatures just below the melting point, a fact which shows that there is some mobility of the ions. Impurities in the salt sometimes give an abnormally large conductance. The specific conductance of many fused salts is large, sometimes exceeding the conductance of the most concentrated aqueous solutions, but the equivalent conductance is comparatively small on account of the high concentration of the electrolyte. The electrolysis of fused salts finds important technical applications in such operations as the production of sodium from fused sodium hydroxide, the production of magnesium from fused magnesium chloride, and the production of aluminum on an enormous scale by the electrolysis of fused aluminum hydroxide dissolved in molten sodium aluminum fluoride.

Diffusion of Electrolytes. The diffusion coefficient of an electrolyte at infinite dilution may be calculated from the limiting mobilities of the two ions. The two ions must diffuse with the same velocity because the solution must remain electrically neutral at every level in the diffusion cell. The force causing diffusion is equal to the negative gradient of the chemical potential. It may be shown * that for a binary electrolyte the diffusion coefficient at infinite dilution is given by

$$D_0 = \frac{2u_1u_2RT}{(u_1 + u_2)F} \tag{37}$$

where u_1 and u_2 are the mobilities of the two ions. As the electrolyte concentration is increased, the diffusion coefficient decreases because of the electrophoretic effect mentioned in the following section.

Example 11. Calculate the limiting diffusion coefficient of potassium chloride at 25°. Using the mobilities in Table V,

$$D_0 = \frac{2(76.2 \times 10^{-5})(79.0 \times 10^{-5})(8.316)(298)}{(155.2 \times 10^{-5})(96,500)}$$

$$= 1.99 \times 10^{-5} \, cm^2 \, sec^{-1}$$

The Interionic Attraction Theory of Conductance. * Whereas the decrease in equivalent conductance with increasing concentration of a weak electrolyte is largely due to the decrease in the degree of ionization, the small decrease in equivalent conductance of strong electrolytes results

* H. S. Harned and B. B. Owen, *The Physical Chemistry of Electrolytic Solutions,* Reinhold Publishing Corp., New York, 1958.

from interionic attractions. According to the Debye-Hückel theory (p. 392), interionic attractions lead to the formation of a diffuse atmosphere of oppositely charged ions around every ion in solution. This ion atmosphere has two effects, both of which tend to retard the motion of the central ion when an electric field is applied to the solution. When an ion moves in a field it tends to move out of its atmosphere, but the atmosphere re-forms. However, since the atmosphere requires a finite time for its formation, the atmosphere is no longer symmetrical about the ion and tends to hold it back by electrostatic attraction. This retarding effect is called the *relaxation effect*.

The second effect, the *electrophoretic effect*, results from the fact that the ion atmosphere tends to move in the direction opposite to that of the central ion. Since the ions of the atmosphere tend to carry along water molecules, the central ion has to move upstream against this counterflow. These effects have been treated in detail by Onsager,* who showed theoretically that the equivalent conductance of a strong electrolyte should vary with the concentration according to

$$\Lambda = \Lambda_0 - [\theta\Lambda_0 + \sigma]\sqrt{C} \qquad (38)$$

in dilute solution and was able to calculate the values of the constants θ and σ, which involve the dielectric constant of water, the absolute temperature, the viscosity of water, and the valences of the ions. For a uniunivalent electrolyte such as potassium chloride in water at 25° the constants have the values $\theta = 0.2273$ and $\sigma = 59.78$. Careful tests of this equation have shown that it gives accurately the correct limiting slope of a plot of Λ versus $\sqrt{C}$ such as Fig. 13-4.

In an alternating field each ion in solution will acquire a periodic motion. If the frequency is increased to a point where the period of oscillation of the ion becomes comparable with the time of relaxation, the dissymmetry in the ionic atmosphere will decrease, the relaxation effect will diminish, and the equivalent conductance will increase. Also, by the application of very high voltages, the ion may be forced to move fast enough to escape completely from its atmosphere, and increases in equivalent conductance of 10 per cent may be obtained at 200 kv cm^{-1}.

* L. Onsager, *Physik. Z., 28*, 277 (1927).

REFERENCES

R. B. Bird, W. E. Stewart, and E. N. Lightfoot, *Transport Phenomena*, John Wiley & Sons, New York, 1960.

B. E. Conway, *Electrochemical Data*, Elsevier Publishing Co., Amsterdam, 1952.

H. J. M. Creighton and W. A. Koehler, *Principles and Applications of Electrochemistry*, John Wiley & Sons, New York, 1935.

P. Delahay, *New Instrumental Methods in Electrochemistry*, Interscience Publishers, New York, 1954.

R. M. Fuoss and F. Accascina, *Electrolytic Conductance*, Interscience Publishers, New York, 1959.

S. Glasstone, *Introduction to Electrochemistry*, D. Van Nostrand Co., Princeton, N. J., 1942.

H. S. Harned and B. B. Owen, *The Physical Chemistry of Electrolytic Solutions*, Reinhold Publishing Corp., New York, 1958.

W. Jost, *Diffusion in Solids, Liquids, and Gases*, Academic Press, New York, 1952.

D. A. MacInnes, *The Principles of Electrochemistry*, Reinhold Publishing Corp., New York, 1939.

R. A. Robinson and R. H. Stokes, *Electrolyte Solutions*, Academic Press, New York, 1959.

PROBLEMS

1. If it takes 10 min to drain a capillary pipet at 25° when filled with water, how long will it take to drain it when filled with ethanol ($\rho = 0.789$ g cm^{-3})?

Ans. 15.4 min.

2. A steel ball ($\rho = 7.86$ g cm^{-3}) 0.2 cm in diameter falls 10 cm through a viscous liquid ($\rho_0 = 1.50$ g cm^{-3}) in 25 sec. What is the absolute viscosity in poises at this temperature? *Ans.* 34.6 poises.

3. A sharp boundary is formed between a dilute aqueous solution of sucrose and water at 25°. After 5 hr the standard deviation of the concentration gradient is 0.434 cm. (a) What is the diffusion coefficient for sucrose under these conditions? (b) What will be the standard deviation after 10 hr?

Ans. (a) 5.23×10^{-6} cm^2 sec^{-1}. (b) 0.614 cm.

4. Ten amperes of current flowed for 1 hr through water containing a little sulfuric acid. How many liters of gas were formed at each electrode at 27° and 740 mm pressure? *Ans.* 4.72 liters of H$_2$, 2.36 liters of O$_2$.

5. It is desired to use a conductance apparatus to measure the concentration of dilute solutions of sodium chloride. If the electrodes in the cell are each 1 cm^2 in area and are 0.2 cm apart, calculate the resistance which will be obtained for 1, 10, and 100 ppm NaCl at 25°. *Ans.* 92,700, 9320, and 950 ohms.

6. Determine the value of Λ_0 for lithium chloride from the following data at 25°:

Equivalents per liter	0.05	0.01	0.005	0.001	0.0005
Equivalent conductance	100.11	107.32	109.40	112.40	113.15

Ans. 114.3 cm^2 equiv^{-1} ohm^{-1}.

7. A conductance cell was calibrated by filling it with a 0.02 N solution of potassium chloride ($\kappa = 0.002768$ ohm^{-1} cm^{-1}) and measuring the resistance at

$25°$, which was found to be 457.3 ohms. The cell was then filled with a calcium chloride solution containing 0.555 gram of $CaCl_2$ per liter. The measured resistance was 1050 ohms. Calculate (a) the cell constant for the cell, (b) the specific conductance of the $CaCl_2$ solution, and (c) the equivalent conductance of $CaCl_2$ at this concentration. $Ans.$ (a) 1.266 cm^{-1}. (b) 1.206 $\times 10^{-3}$ ohm^{-1} cm^{-1}. (c) 120.5 cm^2 $equiv^{-1}$ ohm^{-1}.

8. At $25°$ the equivalent conductance of propionic acid at infinite dilution is 385.6 cm^2 $equiv^{-1}$ ohm^{-1}, and the ionization constant is 1.34 $\times 10^{-5}$. Calculate the equivalent conductance of a 0.05 N solution of propionic acid at $25°$.
$Ans.$ 6.32 cm^2 $equiv^{-1}$ ohm^{-1}.

9. At $25°$ the equivalent conductance at infinite dilution Λ_0 of sodium monochloroacetate is 89.8 cm^2 $equiv^{-1}$ ohm^{-1}. Calculate Λ_0 at $25°$ for monochloroacetic acid. $Ans.$ 389.4 cm^2 $equiv^{-1}$ ohm^{-1}.

10. A moving-boundary experiment is carried out with a 0.1 N solution of hydrochloric acid at $25°$ ($\kappa = 0.0424$ ohm^{-1} cm^{-1}). Sodium ions are caused to follow the hydrogen ions. Three milliamperes is passed through the tube of 0.3 cm^2 cross-sectional area, and it is observed that the boundary moves 3.08 cm in 1 hr. Calculate (a) the hydrogen-ion mobility, (b) the hydrogen-ion transference number, and (c) the chloride-ion mobility.
$Ans.$ (a) 363 $\times 10^{-5}$ cm^2 $volt^{-1}$ sec^{-1}. (b) 0.826.
(c) 76.6 $\times 10^{-5}$ cm^2 $volt^{-1}$ sec^{-1}.

11. A solution of hydrochloric acid was electrolyzed in a transference cell between platinum electrodes. The cathode compartment contained 0.177 gram of chloride ions before the electrolysis and 0.163 gram afterwards. A silver coulometer in series had a deposit of silver equivalent to 0.0825 gram of chloride ions. What are the transference numbers of H^+ and Cl^-? $Ans.$ 0.830 and 0.170.

12. State quantitatively what chemical changes will occur at the cathode and the anode when a current of 1 amp is passed for 20 min through the following solutions:

	(a)	(b)	(c)
Cathode	Graphite	Mercury	Silver
Solution	H_2SO_4	$ZnCl_2$	$FeCl_3$
Anode	Platinum	Zinc	Silver

13. The water flow time for a viscometer of the type illustrated on the left in Fig. 13-1 is 59.2 sec at $25°$. If 46.2 sec is required for the same volume of ethyl benzene ($\rho = 0.867$ g cm^{-3}) to flow through the capillary, calculate its absolute viscosity in poises at $25°$.

14. The effect of temperature on the viscosity of a liquid is generally given quite well by $\eta = Ae^{-E/RT}$, where A is a constant. The viscosities of water at $20°$ and $30°$ are 1.005 and 0.8007 centipoises, respectively. Calculate the activation energy E in kilocalories for this flow process.

15. (a) Calculate the time required for the half-width of a freely diffusing boundary of dilute potassium chloride in water to become 0.5 cm at $25°$ ($D = 1.77 \times 10^{-5}$ cm^2 sec^{-1}). (b) Calculate the corresponding time for serum albumin ($D = 6.15 \times 10^{-7}$ cm^2 sec^{-1}).

16. (a) How many ampere-hours of electricity are required to refine by electrolysis 453 grams (1 lb) of copper, removing it from the impure anode and depositing it in a pure state on the cathode? (b) If the potential drop across the electrolytic cell is 5 volts, how much will the electricity cost at 1 cent per kilowatt-hour?

17. One hundred grams of sodium chloride is dissolved in 10,000 liters of water at 25°, giving a solution which may be regarded in these calculations as infinitely dilute. (a) What is the equivalent conductance of the solution? (b) What is the specific conductance of the solution? (c) This dilute solution is placed in a glass tube of 4-cm diameter provided with electrodes filling the tube and placed 20 cm apart. How much current will flow if the potential drop between the electrodes is 80 volts?

18. Estimate the specific conductance at 25° of water which contains 70 ppm (parts per million) by weight of magnesium sulfate.

19. The specific conductance of a saturated solution of thallous bromide at 20° is 2.158×10^{-4}, and the specific conductance of the water used was 0.044×10^{-6} ohm^{-1} cm^{-1}. The equivalent conductance at infinite dilution is 138.3. Calculate the solubility of thallous bromide in grams per liter.

20. Given $\Lambda_0 = 391$ cm^2 $equiv^{-1}$ ohm^{-1} and $K = 1.80 \times 10^{-5}$, calculate the equivalent conductance of 0.05 N acetic acid at 25°.

21. The equivalent conductance of an infinitely dilute solution of ammonium chloride is 149.7 cm^2 $equiv^{-1}$ ohm^{-1}, and the ionic conductances of the ions OH^- and Cl^- are 198.0 and 76.3, respectively. Calculate the equivalent conductance of ammonium hydroxide at infinite dilution.

22. In 0.1 N hydrochloric acid at 0° the mobilities of hydrogen and chloride ions are 365×10^{-5} and 79×10^{-5} cm^2 $volt^{-1}$ sec^{-1}, respectively. (a) Calculate the specific conductance for this solution at 0°. (b) A moving-boundary experiment is carried out in a tube with a uniform cross-sectional area of 0.200 cm^2, and sodium ions are caused to follow the hydrogen ions. If a current of 5 ma is passed for 1 hr, how far will the hydrogen ions move?

23. In studying conductances at high electric field strengths it is found that the equivalent conductance increases slightly with increasing electric field strength. A microsecond pulse at 100,000 volts cm^{-1} may be used. Approximately how far will a sodium ion move during such a pulse at room temperature?

24. MacInnes and Dole electrolyzed 1.0 N potassium chloride at 25° between a silver anode and a silver chloride cathode and found that 121.41 grams of solution from the anode portion contained 7.9039 grams of KCl. The anode reaction is $Ag + Cl^- = AgCl + e$; the cathode reaction is $AgCl + e = Ag + Cl^-$. The middle portion, unchanged by the electrolysis, contained 7.1479 per cent by weight of KCl. Calculate the number of equivalents of potassium ion which have migrated away from the solution surrounding the anode. The coulometer in the circuit gained 2.4835 grams of silver from the deposition of silver. Calculate the transference number of potassium ion in 1.0 N KCl.

25. Calculate the ionic mobility of NO_3^- in a very dilute solution, given the following equivalent conductances at infinite dilution (in cm^2 ohm^{-1} $equiv^{-1}$, at 25°): KCl, 149.9; KNO_3, 144.9; HCl, 426.1; and the transference number of H^+ in HCl as 0.821.

26. What are the probable products of electrolysis at each electrode when a current is passed through the following cells: (a) an aqueous solution of cupric sulfate with copper electrodes, (b) an aqueous solution of ferrous sulfate with graphite electrodes, (c) an aqueous solution of lithium iodide with mercury electrodes, (d) a solution of sodium iodide in acetone with platinum electrodes?

---

27. How long will it take a spherical air bubble 0.5 mm in diameter to rise 10 cm through water at 25°?

28. Plot log of viscosity of mercury against the reciprocal of the absolute temperature from the following data, and estimate the viscosity of mercury at 50°:

t, °C	0	20	35	98	203
η	0.01661	0.01547	0.01476	0.01263	0.01079

29. A sharp boundary is formed between a solution of hemoglobin in a buffer and the buffer solution at 25°. After 10 hr the half-width of the concentration-gradient curve at the inflection point is 0.226 cm. What is the diffusion coefficient of hemoglobin under these conditions?

30. A 6-volt storage battery operates two lamps in parallel for 5 hr. Each lamp draws 4 amp. The reaction is $Pb + PbO_2 + 2H^+ + 2HSO_4^- = 2PbSO_4 + 2H_2O$ (p. 409). How many grams of lead are oxidized? If 5 per cent of the energy goes into light and 95 per cent into heat, how many calories of light are given off by the lamps?

31. A sample of water from a large pool had a resistance of 9200 ohms at 25° when placed in a certain conductance cell. When filled with 0.020 N potassium chloride the cell had a resistance of 85 ohms at 25°. Five hundred grams of sodium chloride was dissolved in the pool, which was then thoroughly stirred. A sample of this solution gave a resistance of 7600 ohms. With the help of graphical interpolation calculate the number of liters of water in the pool.

32. A glass tube 4 cm in diameter and 30 cm long is closed at each end with a sheet silver electrode and filled with 0.01 N silver nitrate. Sixty volts is applied. (a) How much current flows? (b) How many degrees will the temperature of the solution rise in 10 min, if it is assumed that the heat capacity of the solution is nearly 1 cal deg^{-1} ml^{-1} and that all the heat is retained by the solution?

33. Given that $\Lambda_0 = 126.5$ cm^2 equiv^{-1} ohm^{-1}, and using Onsager's equation (p. 375), compute the equivalent conductance of 0.005 N sodium chloride at 25° and compare the value with that in Table IV.

34. The equivalent conductance of 0.05912 N acetic acid is 20.96 cm^2 equiv^{-1} ohm^{-1}. Calculate the degree of dissociation and the ionization constant.

35. Calculate the specific conductance at 25° of a solution containing 0.001 N hydrochloric acid and 0.005 N sodium chloride. The limiting ionic mobilities at infinite dilution may be used to obtain a sufficiently good approximation.

36. Show that transference number and mobilities are related by

$$T = \frac{FCu}{1000\kappa}$$

37. In a determination of the cation-transference number of 0.05 N silver nitrate solution by use of the Hittorf apparatus, a current is passed long enough to deposit 65.3 mg of silver in a silver coulometer in series with the Hittorf apparatus. Titration of solutions from the anode compartment with KCNS showed that there was an increase of 2.84×10^{-4} equivalents of silver ion in this compartment. As expected, there was a loss of 2.84×10^{-4} equivalents of silver ion from the cathode compartment. Calculate the transference numbers of Ag^+ and NO_3^-.

ELECTROMOTIVE FORCE

14

Electrochemical cells for the production of electricity from chemical reactions have been known since 1800, when Volta described his electric pile of zinc and silver disks separated by paper moistened with salt water.

The current of an electrochemical cell results from a chemical reaction in which electrons are taken up at one electrode and released at the other. The reaction is made up of two parts, an oxidation reaction in which electrons are lost and a reduction reaction in which electrons are added to the reactant. Representing the reduced form by Red and the oxidized form by Ox, the oxidation reaction is

$$Red = Ox + e$$

as, for example, in the reaction $\frac{1}{2}H_2 = H^+ + e$. The reduction reaction at the other electrode is

$$e + Ox' = Red'$$

where Ox' and Red' represent another set of oxidized and reduced forms, as, for example, in the reaction $AgCl + e = Ag + Cl^-$. The net reaction obtained by adding together the two half-reactions is

$$Red + Ox' = Red' + Ox$$

or

$$\tfrac{1}{2}H_2 + AgCl = Ag + HCl$$

The electromotive force of the cell, or difference in electrical potential between the two electrodes, depends upon the equilibrium constant for the reaction that occurs in the cell. The larger the equilibrium constant, the greater is the tendency for the electron to be transferred and the greater is the electromotive force. Measurements of electromotive force may thus be used to obtain thermodynamic data. An electrochemical cell is a device for keeping the oxidation and reduction parts of the reaction separated, so that the current may be used to perform useful work.

A Simple Electrochemical Cell. *Figure 14-1* shows a practical cell of the simplest possible type. In this cell gaseous hydrogen is bubbled

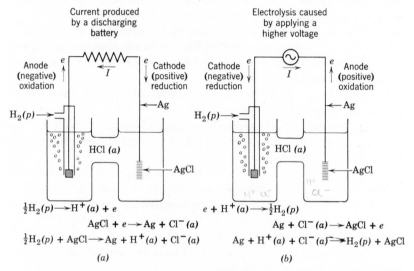

Fig. 14-1. Operation of the $H_2(p)$; $HCl(a)$; $AgCl$; Ag cell as (a) a battery or (b) an electrolysis cell.

over a piece of platinized platinum immersed in the hydrochloric acid solution to give the hydrogen electrode. The other electrode consists of a silver wire coated with a deposit of silver chloride. When the two electrodes are connected through a resistor as illustrated in the figure, a current flows. The hydrogen molecules are giving up electrons to the platinum to form hydrogen ions, and silver ions from the AgCl are reacting with electrons (coming through the wire) to produce metallic silver. The difference in electrical potential between the electrodes (the so-called electromotive force of the cell) is due to the fact that H_2 has a greater tendency to give up electrons in the presence of H^+ than Ag does in the presence of Ag^+ ions in a saturated solution of AgCl.

The electrode at which the *oxidation* half-reaction occurs is the *anode*, and the electrode at which the *reduction* half-reaction occurs is the *cathode.* Thus, when an electrochemical cell discharges spontaneously, electrons flow through the external circuit from anode to cathode as illustrated in Fig. 14-1a* by e.

The cell reaction may be reversed by applying a voltage higher than the reversible electromotive force of the cell. The chemical processes at the electrodes are then reversed: the hydrogen electrode becomes the cathode, and the Ag-AgCl electrode the anode, as shown in Fig. 14-1b. Whether a cell is operating as a discharging battery or as an electrolysis cell, "anode" is the electrode at which oxidation occurs and electrons are given up to that electrode; "cathode" is the electrode at which reduction occurs and electrons are taken up by a reactant in solution.

If in the experiment described in Fig. 14-1a the electrochemical cell were operated long enough to deliver 1 faraday of electricity, the following processes would take place:

1. One-half mole of hydrogen would be consumed with the production of one equivalent of hydrogen ion.

2. One faraday, 96,500 coulombs or ampere-seconds, which is Avogadro's number of electrons, would travel through the external circuit to the Ag-AgCl electrode.

3. One gram-equivalent of AgCl would be converted into one gram-atomic weight of silver plus one equivalent of chloride ion.

As long as the circuit is closed, these reactions go on producing hydrochloric acid and metallic silver at the expense of H_2 and AgCl. In principle the concentration of HCl would eventually become so high that the chemical reaction would no longer be spontaneous and the electromotive force would be zero.

Voltage Measurement of Cells. A voltmeter cannot be used alone for measuring the reversible electromotive force of a cell because the operation of the voltmeter causes some current to flow. If a current i flows through the cell and the resistance of the cell is R, there will be a potential drop of iR volts which will be subtracted from the voltage of the cell. The current also causes concentration changes at the electrodes which change the electromotive force. This latter effect is called *polarization*.

To avoid these difficulties the electromotive force is measured by balancing a known voltage against the cell so that practically no current flows. For this purpose a potentiometer such as that illustrated in *Fig. 14-2* is used. The potential to be measured is opposed by an equal and opposite potential which is provided by a battery C in series

---

* Conventionally the "current" I is designated as a flow of positive current from the positive electrode through the wire to the negative electrode. In this book the flow of negative electrons, which is in the opposite direction, will be emphasized.

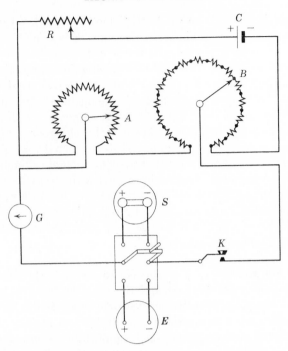

Fig. 14-2. Circuit diagram for a potentiometer, in which the voltage of an unknown cell E is compared with that of a standard cell S by balancing the resistances of the circuit in each case until no current flows, as indicated by a zero reading on the galvanometer G.

with several resistances. A galvanometer G is used to determine the setting of the potentiometer at which no current flows. The magnitude of the potential provided by the potentiometer is varied by adjusting the sliding contacts A and B on the two circular resistances. The larger resistance is usually divided into fifteen equal parts, each having the same resistance as the circular slide wire on the left which provides the fine adjustment.

In practice the double-throw switch is first connected to the standard cell S of known voltage, usually a Weston cadmium cell of 1.0186 volts at 20°. The sliding contacts A and B are rotated to read 1.0186, and the key K is tapped momentarily as the external resistance R is adjusted, until the galvanometer G reads zero, showing that the voltage at 1.0186 is equal and opposite to that of the standard cell. Then the switch is thrown to connect the potentiometer to a cell E of unknown voltage. The contacts A and B are adjusted so that the galvanometer shows no deflection when the circuit is closed by tapping the key. Then the reading of the dials on the potentiometer gives the electromotive force of the cell E directly in volts. The key K is tapped, rather than locked down, in order not to polarize the cell.

The standard cell used to calibrate a potentiometer must be a cell of very constant voltage which is accurately known at the desired temperature. The Weston cadmium cell is the one most often used. The positive electrode consists of pure mercury in contact with a paste of mercury and mercurous sulfate. The negative electrode is an amalgam of cadmium in mercury containing 10–13 per cent by weight of cadmium. The electrolyte is a concentrated solution of cadmium sulfate; in some cells a saturated solution in contact with solid $CdSO_4 \cdot \frac{8}{3} H_2O$ is used. A saturated Weston cell has a voltage of 1.0186 volts at 20°, but it is best to have the exact voltage of a cell calibrated by the National Bureau of Standards. The voltage decreases 4.06×10^{-5} volt per degree rise in temperature above 20°.

Reference Electrodes. It is *impossible* to measure the difference in potential between an electrode and the solution which is in contact with it, because another metallic electrode is required. The electric potential difference between two points in different media is a conception which therefore has no physical significance. Consequently it is impossible to measure the electromotive force of a half-reaction. However, by arbitrarily assigning a potential to one electrode (and to the corresponding half-reaction) it is possible to determine the potentials of other electrodes (and other half-reactions) with respect to this standard. The standard electrode which has been universally adopted is the hydrogen electrode. When the pressure of hydrogen is 1 atm and the activity of hydrogen ions is unity, this electrode is assigned a potential of zero at all temperatures.

One type of hydrogen electrode is illustrated in Fig. 14-1. Hydrogen is bubbled over a platinized platinum surface which catalyzes the reaction

$$\tfrac{1}{2} H_2 = H^+ + e$$

A coating of platinum black is readily deposited by electroplating from a solution of platinic chloride. The platinized electrode is arranged so that hydrogen bubbles up rapidly around the platinum and the electrode is immersed partly in solution and partly in the hydrogen. The level of the liquid is changed as the gas bubbles out from a glass hood which surrounds the electrode, and thus the electrode is bathed alternately with hydrogen and with the solution.

In accurate work the hydrogen must be at a definite known pressure and must contain no oxygen. Corrections are made for the vapor pressure of water. Several solutes may interfere with the proper operation of the hydrogen electrode, particularly oxidizing agents. Any oxidizing substances such as ferric, nitrate, and chromate ions, or unsaturated organic compounds which can be reduced by hydrogen in the presence of platinum, must be avoided. Traces of arsenic and sulfur compounds may react with platinum atoms at the surface, thus diminishing the adsorptive properties for hydrogen and giving erroneous potentials.

When the hydrochloric acid surrounding the hydrogen electrode has an activity of unity, as explained later in this chapter, and the hydrogen gas has a pressure of 1 atm, the hydrogen electrode is arbitrarily assigned a potential of zero and used as a standard to which all other potentials are referred. The potential of an electrode is therefore the voltage of a battery in which one electrode is the standard hydrogen electrode. The standard hydrogen electrode is rather difficult to prepare and maintain for high-precision work, and so it is usually replaced by the calomel electrode shown at the left in *Fig. 14-3*. The potential of the calomel electrode with respect to the hydrogen electrode is accurately known. The calomel electrode consists of mercury in the bottom of a vessel with a paste of mercury and mercurous chloride (calomel) over it in contact with a solution of potassium chloride satu-

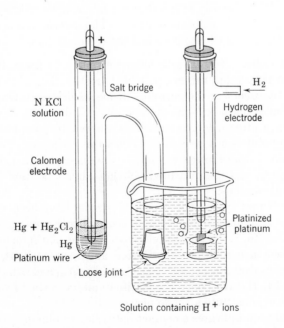

Fig. 14-3. Hydrogen electrode and normal calomel reference electrode.

rated with mercurous chloride. The half-reaction is

$$\tfrac{1}{2}Hg_2Cl_2 + e = Hg + Cl^-$$

The potassium chloride solution makes electrical contact with the other solution through a side arm provided with a porous plug or a loosely fitting ground-glass joint. Such a connecting solution is called a salt bridge. Sometimes a beaker of potassium chloride solution is placed between the calomel electrode and the electrode being measured, in order to minimize diffusion of the solutions of the two half-cells into each other.

The normal calomel electrode contains a molar solution of potassium chloride and has a potential of 0.2802 volt at 25° with reference to the standard hydrogen electrode. The saturated calomel cell contains saturated potassium chloride and has a potential of 0.2415 volt with respect to the standard hydrogen electrode. It is used sometimes in special cases where a minimization of the effect of other electrolytes is desirable, but it is inconvenient because of a larger temperature effect due in part to the change of solubility of potassium chloride with temperature.

Another reference electrode is the silver-silver chloride electrode illustrated in Fig. 14-1. A silver wire or a deposit of silver plated on a platinum wire is covered with a thin coating of silver chloride by making it the anode in a chloride solution. The determination of the potential of the Ag-AgCl electrode is discussed on p. 395.

Reversible Cells. Not all cells are reversible. In some, irreversible processes occur so that it is not possible to restore the cell to its original condition by reversing the current. If mechanical agitation produces marked unsteadiness in voltage, or if the cell does not return to the same voltage after a larger current is allowed to pass momentarily, the cell probably is not reversible. When this is the case, the electrical work obtained from the cell will not be the maximum that might have been obtained, and the measured voltages cannot be used in thermodynamic calculations.

Many different types of reversible electrodes have been studied. A metal may be immersed in a solution containing its ions, as in the zinc electrode $Zn; Zn^{2+}$. Or an inert electrode such as platinum or gold may be immersed in a solution of oxidizing and reducing ions, as in the ferrous-ferric electrode $Pt; Fe^{2+}, Fe^{3+}$. A hydrogen electrode is represented by $Pt, H_2; H^+$, since the platinum and adsorbed hydrogen are considered to constitute a single phase.

The semicolon indicates a contact between two phases such as exists between a metal and a solution, or an interface between two unmixed liquid solutions, such as a solution of zinc sulfate touching a solution of copper sulfate. A comma is used to separate different ions or molecules which exist in the same phase. At the contact between two different electrolytic solutions there is a small junction potential in addition to the potential difference due to the two electrodes. The liquid-junction potential can be rendered negligible for certain purposes by interposing a salt bridge, usually of potassium chloride, between the two solutions. The salt bridge is useful also if there is a possibility of precipitation when the two solutions are mixed.

Cells may be classified as follows:

A. Cells without liquid junctions:

Different electrodes	Pt, H_2; HCl; Cl_2, Pt
Concentration cell with amalgams	(Hg + 10% Cd); $CdCl_2$;
	(Hg + 1% Cd)

Cells without liquid junctions are required for exact thermodynamic treatment.

B. Concentration cells with liquid junctions:

Pt, H_2; HCl(c_1); HCl(c_2); H_2, Pt

The transference number of the electrolyte (p. 369) may be determined with such a cell, but this type of cell will not be discussed further here.

C. Cells with liquid junctions:

Zn; $ZnCl_2$; $CuCl_2$; Cu

The electromotive force of such cells contains an unknown liquid-junction potential.

D. Cells in which the liquid-junction potential is practically eliminated by means of a salt bridge represented by $\|$:

Different electrodes	Zn; $ZnCl_2 \parallel CuCl_2$; Cu
Concentration cells	Pt, H_2; HCl(c_1) $\parallel$ HCl(c_2); H_2, Pt

Cells in which the liquid-junction potentials have been practically eliminated by a salt bridge are used widely in practical work. A salt bridge must be used if any reaction takes place between the ions of the two solutions.

Thermodynamics of Electrochemical Cells. Electrochemical cells are often useful for the determination of the Gibbs free-energy change for a chemical reaction. The spontaneous chemical change which occurs in certain electrochemical cells may be reversed by increasing the applied potential to a value infinitesimally greater than that of the cell. If a cell is exactly balanced against an external electromotive force so that no charging or discharging of the cell is taking place, and we imagine that an infinitesimal quantity of electricity is allowed to pass through the cell, the reversible electrical work at constant temperature and pressure, or Gibbs free-energy change, is equal to the product of the voltage and the quantity of electricity. The quantity of electrical charge corresponding to the molar quantities indicated in the balanced chemical equation is nF, where n is the number of electrons transferred in the reaction and F is the faraday. If this quantity of electrical charge is transported through a potential difference of E volts, the amount of work required is given by nFE. Since this electrical change does not involve pressure-volume work and is carried out isothermally, the change in Gibbs free energy is given by

$$\Delta G = -nFE \qquad (1)$$

where E is the voltage, which by convention is taken as positive. Since ΔG is negative for a spontaneous cell reaction and E for a spontaneously discharging cell is taken as positive, the negative sign must be used in equation 1. The electromotive force of a cell does not depend upon the stoichiometric coefficients in the balanced chemical reaction, but the change in Gibbs free energy ΔG does depend upon n, which in turn depends upon how the stoichiometric equation is written.

If the faraday is expressed in coulombs $equiv^{-1}$, the electrical work calculated from equation 1 will be expressed in joules. The value of ΔG in calories is obtained by dividing by 4.184 joules cal^{-1}. Alternatively the faraday may be expressed as 96,500 coulombs/4.184 joules $cal^{-1} = 23,060$ cal $volt^{-1}$, since a joule is a volt-coulomb.

From the temperature coefficient of the electromotive force it is possible to calculate the entropy change for the cell reaction since (see p. 106)

$$\left(\frac{\partial \Delta G}{\partial T}\right)_P = -\Delta S \qquad (2)$$

Introducing equation 1,

$$nF\left(\frac{\partial E}{\partial T}\right)_P = \Delta S \qquad (3)$$

In addition the enthalpy change for the reaction may be calculated by substituting equations 1 and 3 into

$$\Delta H = \Delta G + T\,\Delta S \qquad (4)$$

$$= -nFE + nFT\left(\frac{\partial E}{\partial T}\right)_P \qquad (5)$$

Since this equation may be derived from the Gibbs-Helmholtz equation (p. 108), it is often referred to by that name.

Thus from measurements of the electromotive force of a cell at a series of temperatures it is possible to calculate ΔG, ΔS, and ΔH for the cell reaction. The great accuracy of electrical measurements often makes the determination of thermodynamic quantities by this method more exact than the direct determination of equilibrium constants or the calorimetric determination of enthalpies of reaction.

Example 1. The electromotive force of the cell

$$\text{Cd; CdCl}_2 \cdot 2\tfrac{1}{2}\text{H}_2\text{O, sat. solution; AgCl, Ag}$$

at 25° is 0.67533 volt and the temperature coefficient is -6.5×10^{-4} volt deg^{-1}. Calculate the values of ΔG, ΔS, and ΔH at 25° for the reaction

$$\text{Cd}(s) + 2\text{AgCl}(s) = 2\text{Ag}(s) + \text{CdCl}_2 \cdot 2\tfrac{1}{2}\text{H}_2\text{O}(s)$$

$$\Delta G = -(2)(23{,}060 \text{ cal volt}^{-1})(0.67533 \text{ volt})$$

$$= -31{,}150 \text{ cal}$$

$$\Delta S = (2)(23{,}060 \text{ cal volt}^{-1})(-6.5 \times 10^{-4} \text{ volt deg}^{-1})$$

$$= -30.0 \text{ cal deg}^{-1}$$

$$\Delta H = -(2)(23{,}060)(0.67533) - (2)(23{,}060)(298)(6.5 \times 10^{-4})$$

$$= -40{,}090 \text{ cal}$$

Direct calorimetric measurements give $\Delta H = -39{,}530$ cal for this reaction.

Further examples are given in Table I. The agreement between the values of ΔH obtained potentiometrically and calorimetrically is entirely satisfactory. An examination of the relative values of ΔH and

Table I.　Experimental Verification of the Gibbs-Helmholtz Equation

Cell	E, volts	$\partial E/\partial T$, volt deg^{-1}	ΔH (obs.) calorimeter, cal	ΔH (calc.) equation 5, cal	ΔG, $-\dfrac{nEF}{4.1840}$
Zn, ZnCl$_2$(0.555m), AgCl, Ag(0°)	1.015	-0.000402	$-52{,}050$	$-51{,}990$	$-46{,}830$
Cd, CdCl$_2 \cdot 2\tfrac{1}{2}$H$_2$O (sat.), AgCl, Ag(25°)	0.67533	-0.00065	$-39{,}530$	$-40{,}090$	$-31{,}150$
Cd, CdCl$_2 \cdot 2\tfrac{1}{2}$H$_2$O (sat.), PbCl$_2$, Pb(25°)	0.18806	-0.00048	$-14{,}650$	$-15{,}250$	$-8{,}670$
Pb, Pb(C$_2$H$_3$O$_2$)$_2$ (0.555m), Cu(C$_2$H$_3$O$_2$)$_2$ (sat.), Cu(0°)	0.4764	$+0.000385$	$-17{,}530$	$-16{,}900$	$-21{,}990$

ΔG is interesting. When $\partial E/\partial T$ has a positive sign, as in the case of the lead acetate-cupric acetate cell, ΔG has a larger negative value than ΔH. This means that the maximum electrical work which can be done is greater than the heat evolved when the reaction is carried out at constant temperature and pressure with no electrical work done. If $\partial E/\partial T$ has a negative sign, ΔG has a more positive value than ΔH. The heat evolved when the cell operates isothermally and reversibly may be obtained from the calculated value of the entropy change, $\Delta S = q_{rev}/T$, but it cannot be measured calorimetrically because the cell would have to be operated infinitely slowly.

Fundamental Equation for an Electromotive-Force Cell. As shown on p. 208, the Gibbs free-energy change for a reaction

$$aA + bB = gG + hH \tag{6}$$

is given by

$$\Delta G = \Delta G^\circ + RT \ln \frac{a_G{}^g a_H{}^h}{a_A{}^a a_B{}^b} \tag{7}$$

where the a's represent the activities of the reactants and products under a given set of conditions. Substituting $\Delta G = -nFE$, and $\Delta G^\circ = -nFE^\circ$ for the reactants and products in their standard states,

$$E = E^\circ - \frac{RT}{nF} \ln \frac{a_G{}^g a_H{}^h}{a_A{}^a a_B{}^b} \tag{8}$$

The standard electromotive force for the cell, E°, is the electromotive force for the cell in which the activities of the reactants and products of the cell reaction are each equal to unity. At 25°

$$E = E^\circ - \frac{(8.314)(298.1)(2.303)}{n(96,500)} \log \frac{a_G{}^g a_H{}^h}{a_A{}^a a_B{}^b} \tag{9}$$

$$E = E^\circ - \frac{0.0591}{n} \log \frac{a_G{}^g a_H{}^h}{a_A{}^a a_B{}^b} \tag{10}$$

This equation is often referred to as the Nernst equation.

Since special equations are involved in expressing the activities of electrolytes, we must now consider these expressions.

Activity of Electrolytes. When a solute does not dissociate, the activity is equal to the product of the concentration and an activity coefficient. When Convention II is used, the activity coefficient approaches unity at infinite dilution as discussed on p. 157. When the solute is an electrolyte which is considered to be completely dissociated in solution, the expression for the activity becomes more complicated.

The chemical potential of a strong, completely dissociated, electrolyte MX must be equal to the sum of the chemical potentials of the ions M^+ and X^-.

$$\mu_{MX} = \mu_{M^+} + \mu_{X^-} \tag{11}$$

$$\mu^*_{MX} + RT \ln a_{MX} = \mu^*_{M^+} + RT \ln a_{M^+} + \mu^*_{X^-} + RT \ln a_{X^-}$$

where μ^*_{MX} is the chemical potential of MX at unit activity, $\mu^*_{M^+}$ is the chemical potential of the cation at unit activity, and $\mu^*_{X^-}$ is the chemical potential of the anion at unit activity. Since $\mu^*_{MX} = \mu^*_{M^+} + \mu^*_{X^-}$, this relation shows that

$$a_{MX} = (a_{M^+})(a_{X^-}) \tag{12}$$

The activities of the cation and anion may be expressed as products of the molal concentrations m and the activity coefficients γ_+ and γ_- of the cation and anion.

$$a_{M^+} = m\gamma_+ \quad \text{and} \quad a_{X^-} = m\gamma_- \tag{13}$$

Then

$$a_{MX} = (m\gamma_+)(m\gamma_-) = m^2\gamma_\pm^2 \tag{14}$$

where $\gamma_\pm$ is the symbol which is introduced to represent the mean ionic activity coefficient for the 1–1 electrolyte (that is, one having a univalent cation and a univalent anion). It follows from equation 14 that

$$\gamma_\pm = (\gamma_+\gamma_-)^{1/2} \tag{15}$$

The mean ionic activity coefficient is of importance since it can be determined experimentally whereas the individual ion activity coefficients γ_+ and γ_- cannot. The mean ionic activity coefficient is taken to approach unity as the concentration of MX approaches zero.

The expression for the mean activity coefficient becomes more complicated for polyvalent ions. If the strong electrolyte is $M_{\nu_+}X_{\nu_-}$, where ν_+ is the number of cations and ν_- is the number of anions,

$$\mu_{M_{\nu_+}X_{\nu_-}} = \nu_+\mu_M + \nu_-\mu_X \tag{16}$$

which leads to

$$a_{M_{\nu_+}X_{\nu_-}} = (a_M)^{\nu_+}(a_X)^{\nu_-} \tag{17}$$

The activity coefficients of the cation and anion are equal to the ratios of their activities to their concentrations.

$$\gamma_+ = a_M/m_M = a_M/\nu_+m \qquad \gamma_- = a_X/m_X = a_X/\nu_-m \tag{18}$$

Then, using these relations to eliminate a_M and a_X from equation 17,

$$a_{M_{\nu_+} X_{\nu_-}} = (\nu_+ m \gamma_+)^{\nu_+} (\nu_- m \gamma_-)^{\nu_-} = (m_\pm \gamma_\pm)^{\nu_+ + \nu_-} \tag{19}$$

By rearranging terms in this equation, it is seen that the mean ionic molality $m_\pm$ and mean ionic activity coefficient $\gamma_\pm$ are given by

$$m_\pm = m(\nu_+{}^{\nu_+} \nu_-{}^{\nu_-})^{1/(\nu_+ + \nu_-)} \tag{20}$$

$$\gamma_\pm = (\gamma_+{}^{\nu_+} \gamma_-{}^{\nu_-})^{1/(\nu_+ + \nu_-)} \tag{21}$$

The mean ionic molality of a 1–1 electrolyte like NaCl is equal to m, of a 2–1 electrolyte like $CaCl_2$ is equal to $4^{\frac{1}{3}}m$, of a 2–2 electrolyte like $CuSO_4$ is equal to m, and of a 3–1 electrolyte like $LaCl_3$ is equal to $27^{\frac{1}{4}}m$, as may be deduced from equation 20. The numbers 1, 2, and 3 refer to the number of charges on the cation and anion.

In equations where the activities of electrolyte occur, these activities may be replaced by expressions involving the molality m and the mean ionic activity coefficient $\gamma_\pm$.

Example 2. Write the expressions for the activities of NaCl, $CaCl_2$, $CuSO_4$, and $LaCl_3$ in terms of their molalities and mean ionic activity coefficients.

$$a_{NaCl} = m^2 \gamma_\pm{}^2$$

$$a_{CaCl_2} = 4m^3 \gamma_\pm{}^3$$

$$a_{CuSO_4} = m^2 \gamma_\pm{}^2$$

$$a_{LaCl_3} = 27m^4 \gamma_\pm{}^4$$

Debye-Hückel Theory.* The activity coefficient of an electrolyte depends markedly upon the concentration and is due to the electrostatic interaction of ions, which extends considerably further through the solution than other intermolecular forces. At infinite dilution the distribution of ions in an electrolytic solution can be considered to be completely random because the ions are too far apart to exert any attraction on each other, and the activity coefficient of the electrolyte is unity. However, at higher concentrations where the ions are closer together, the Coulomb attractive and repulsive forces become important. According to Coulomb's law,

$$\text{Force} = \frac{e_1 e_2}{\epsilon r^2}$$

where e_1 and e_2 are the magnitudes of the charges, r is the distance between charges, and ϵ is the dielectric constant (p. 493). Because of this interaction of ions the concentration of positive ions is slightly

---

* P. Debye and E. Hückel, *Physik. Z.*, *24*, 185, 305 (1923).

higher in the neighborhood of a negative ion, and vice versa, than in the bulk solution. Because of the attractive forces between an ion and its surrounding ionic atmosphere, the activity coefficient of the electrolyte is reduced. This effect is greater for ions of high charge and is greater in solvents of lower dielectric constant where the electrostatic interactions are stronger.

The tendency of an ion to surround itself with an "atmosphere" of oppositely charged ions is opposed by the thermal motions of the ions. Debye and Hückel were able to develop a quantitative theory for this effect for dilute electrolyte solutions. Their derivation (see Appendix, p. 722) is based on the use of the Boltzmann distribution law (p. 273) to calculate the charge density in the ion atmosphere. For a 1–1 electrolyte the concentrations n_+ of positive ions and n_- of negative ions at a distance r from a positive ion in the solution are given by

$$n_+ = ne^{-e\psi/kT}$$

$$n_- = ne^{+e\psi/kT} \tag{22}$$

where n is the total number of positive or negative ions per cubic centimeter, k is the Boltzmann constant (R/N_0), e is the unit electronic charge, and ψ is the electric potential at a distance r from the central ion.

Debye and Hückel obtained

$$\ln \gamma_i = \frac{-e^3 z_i{}^2}{(\epsilon kT)^{3/2}} \sqrt{\frac{2\pi N_0 I}{1000}} \tag{23}$$

where γ_i = activity coefficient of ion species i (p. 391)
 z_i = charge on ion species i (without regard to the sign)
 e = charge of an electron = 4.803×10^{-10} electrostatic unit
 ϵ = dielectric constant of the solution = 78.56 for water at 298°K
 N_0 = Avogadro's number = 6.023×10^{23}
 k = Boltzmann constant = 1.3805×10^{-16} erg deg^{-1}
 I = ionic strength of the solution (defined in the following section)

Equation 23 shows that in dilute solution the activity coefficient of an ion depends only on its charge, the ionic strength, the dielectric constant of the medium, and the temperature. Hence, to the extent that this theory is valid, all univalent ions (both positive and negative) in the same solution will have the same activity coefficients, independent of the chemical nature of the ion.

Ionic Strength. The ionic strength I introduced in equation 23 was defined by G. N. Lewis by

$$I = \tfrac{1}{2} \sum_i m_i z_i^2 = \tfrac{1}{2}(m_1 z_1^2 + m_2 z_2^2 + \cdots + m_n z_n^2) \qquad (24)$$

where n is the total number of different ionic species in the solution and m is the molal concentration. The greater effectiveness of ions of higher charge in reducing the activity coefficient is provided for by multiplying their concentrations by the square of their valence. According to equation 24, the ionic strength of a 1–1 electrolyte is equal to its molality. The ionic strength for a 1–2 electrolyte is $3m$ and for a 2–2 electrolyte is $4m$.

Example 3. Calculate the ionic strengths of the following electrolyte solutions:

For 0.01m NaCl, $\quad I = \tfrac{1}{2}(0.01 \times 1^2 + 0.01 \times 1^2) = 0.01$

For 0.01m Li$_2$SO$_4$, $\quad I = \tfrac{1}{2}(0.02 \times 1^2 + 0.01 \times 2^2) = 0.03$

For 0.01m CuSO$_4$, $\quad I = \tfrac{1}{2}(0.01 \times 2^2 + 0.01 \times 2^2) = 0.04$

Equation 23 is in agreement with the earlier observation by Lewis that in dilute solution different electrolytes have nearly the same effect on the mean ionic activity coefficient when they are compared at the same values of the ionic strength and that the log of the mean ionic activity coefficient is a function of $I^{1/2}$.

Debye-Hückel Expression for the Mean Ionic Activity Coefficient. At 25° in water substitution of numerical values into equation 23 gives

$$\log \gamma_i = -0.509 z_i^2 \sqrt{I} \qquad (25)$$

Equation 25 gives the activity coefficient of a single ion, but the quantity which is accessible to experimental determination is the mean ionic activity coefficient, which for the electrolyte $M_{\nu_+} X_{\nu_-}$ is by equation 21

$$\gamma_\pm = (\gamma_+^{\nu_+} \gamma_-^{\nu_-})^{1/(\nu_+ + \nu_-)} \qquad (26)$$

Taking the logarithm of equation 26,

$$\log \gamma_\pm = \frac{1}{(\nu_+ + \nu_-)} (\nu_+ \log \gamma_+ + \nu_- \log \gamma_-) \qquad (27)$$

Substituting equation 25 for each activity coefficient,

$$\log \gamma_\pm = -0.509 \sqrt{I} \left(\frac{\nu_+ z_+^2 + \nu_- z_-^2}{\nu_+ + \nu_-} \right) \qquad (28)$$

Introducing $\nu_+ z_+ = \nu_- z_-$,

$$\log \gamma_\pm = -0.509 z_+ z_- \sqrt{I} \qquad (29)$$

The Debye-Hückel theory has been of great value in interpreting the properties of electrolyte solutions. It is a limiting law at low concentrations in the same sense that the ideal gas law is a limiting law at low pressures. At high values of the ionic strength the activity coefficient usually increases with increasing ionic strength. Large deviations are encountered even at low ionic strengths if the product of the valence of the highest charged ion of the salt and the valence of the oppositely charged ion of the electrolyte medium is greater than about 4.

Attempts have been made to extend the Debye-Hückel theory to higher concentrations, and forms based on the introduction of the finite sizes of ions may be used over a wider range of ionic strengths. In concentrated electrolytic solutions there are additional effects which are difficult to interpret theoretically.

Applications of the Debye-Hückel theory are illustrated in the next section and on pp. 424 and 652.

Cells without Transference. Cells that do not have a liquid junction are called cells without transference. Such cells can be given an exact thermodynamic treatment and are useful for determining activity coefficients.

Since a cell without transference contains a single electrolyte solution, the two electrodes must be chosen so that one is reversible with respect to a cation of the electrolyte and the other with respect to an anion of the electrolyte. For example, if the electrolyte is hydrochloric acid, one electrode would be the hydrogen electrode and the other a chlorine or silver chloride electrode. In the latter case the cell may be represented by

$$\text{Pt, } H_2(g); \text{ HCl}(m); \text{ AgCl, Ag}$$

The cell reaction is

$$\tfrac{1}{2}H_2(g) + \text{AgCl}(s) = \text{HCl}(m) + \text{Ag}(s)$$

According to equation 10, the electromotive force for this cell is given by

$$E = E^\circ - \frac{RT}{n} \ln \frac{a_{\text{HCl}}}{p_{H_2}^{1/2}} \tag{30}$$

assuming that H_2 may be treated as an ideal gas. If the pressure of hydrogen is 1 atm and equation 14 is introduced,

$$E = E^\circ - \frac{2.303\,RT}{n} \log m^2 \gamma_{\pm}^2 \tag{31}$$

The mean ionic activity coefficient of hydrochloric acid is represented by $\gamma_{\pm}$, and m is the molality. The electromotive force of the cell when the activity of hydrochloric acid is unity and the pressure of hydrogen is 1 atm is represented by $E°$, called the standard electromotive force of the cell.

As it stands, equation 31 contains two unknown quantities, $E°$ and $\gamma_{\pm}$. These may be obtained by determining the electromotive force of this cell over a range of hydrochloric acid concentrations, including dilute solutions. Rearranging equation 30 and substituting numerical values for 25° gives

$$E + 0.1183 \log m = E° - 0.1183 \log \gamma_{\pm} \tag{32}$$

The exponents in equation 31 have been placed in front of the logarithmic term, giving $(2)(0.05916) = 0.1183$. Since at infinite dilution $m = 0$, $\gamma_{\pm} = 1$, and $\log \gamma_{\pm} = 0$, it can be seen that, when $E + 0.1183 \log m$ is plotted against m, the extrapolation of $E + 0.1183 \log m$ to $m = 0$ will give $E°$.

In order to make a satisfactory extrapolation, use is made of the Debye-Hückel theory to furnish a function which will give nearly a straight line. The following expression is used for the mean ionic activity coefficient of a 1-1 electrolyte in dilute aqueous solutions at 25°:

$$\log \gamma_{\pm} = -0.509\sqrt{m} + bm$$

where b is an empirical constant.

Substituting in equation 32 and rearranging terms,

$$E' = E + 0.1183 \log m - 0.0602m^{\frac{1}{2}} = E° - (0.1183b)m \tag{33}$$

According to this equation, the left-hand side, which we will designate as E', will give a straight line when it is plotted against m, and the intercept at $m = 0$ is $E°$. Actually, the line will be somewhat curved, since the Debye-Hückel theory is exact only in very dilute solutions, but the extrapolation of E' to $m = 0$ can be made without difficulty.

In Table II are given the measured electromotive forces and values of E' at various molalities, and in *Fig. 14-4*, E' is plotted against m. The extrapolated value is 0.2224 volt. This is the electromotive force the cell would deliver with the hydrochloric acid at unit activity, and it is also the standard electrode potential of the silver-silver chloride electrode, since the other electrode is the standard hydrogen electrode for which the standard electrode potential is zero by definition. Similar cells have been used for determining the standard electrode potentials for other electrodes.

The value of $E°$ having been determined, the activity coefficient of hydrochloric acid at any other concentration may be calculated from the electromotive force of the cell containing hydrochloric acid at that concentration.

Table II. Electromotive Force of Concentration Cells of Hydrochloric Acid [1]

m	E	E'
0.003564	0.51527	0.22207
0.004488	0.50384	0.22204
0.006239	0.48747	0.22188
0.008636	0.47135	0.22162
0.011195	0.45861	0.22144
0.01710	0.43783	0.22092
0.02563	0.41824	0.22036
0.05391	0.38222	0.21820

[1] H. S. Harned and R. W. Ehlers, *J. Am. Chem. Soc.*, *54*, 1350 (1932).

Example 4. Calculate the mean ionic activity coefficient of 0.1 molal hydrochloric acid from the fact that the electromotive force of the cell described on p. 395 is 0.3524 volt at 25°. Substituting in equation 32,

$$0.3524 = 0.2224 - 0.1183 \log 0.1 - 0.1183 \log \gamma_\pm$$

$$\log \gamma_\pm = (-0.3524 + 0.2224 + 0.1183)/0.1183 = -0.0989$$

$$\gamma_\pm = 0.798$$

In this general manner, the activity coefficients of the electrolytes given in Table III have been determined.

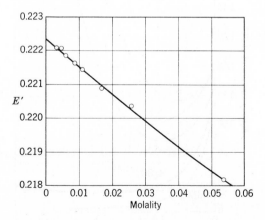

Fig. 14-4. Determination of the silver-silver chloride electrode potential by extrapolation of a function of the voltage of the cell Pt, H_2(1 atm); HCl(m); AgCl, Ag to infinite dilution.

Table III. Mean Ionic Activity Coefficients for Solutes
in Aqueous Solution at 25°

Molality	HCl	KCl	NaCl	NaOH	H_2SO_4	$CaCl_2$	$CdSO_4$
0.005	0.930	0.927	0.928	...	0.643	0.789	...
0.01	0.906	0.902	0.903	0.89	0.545	0.732	0.476
0.05	0.833	0.817	0.821	0.80	0.341	0.584	0.383
0.10	0.798	0.770	0.778	0.75	0.266	0.524	0.199
0.20	0.768	0.719	0.732	0.71	0.210	0.491	0.137
0.50	0.769	0.652	0.680	0.68	0.155	0.510	0.061
1.00	0.811	0.607	0.656	0.66	0.131	0.725	0.042
2.00	1.011	0.578	0.670	0.68	0.125	1.554	0.030
3.00	1.31	0.574	0.719	...	0.142	3.384	0.026
4.00	1.74	...	0.791	...	0.172	...	...

In *Fig. 14-5* the mean ionic activity coefficients of several electrolytes are plotted against a function of the concentration, namely, the square root of the ionic strength. It may be noted that the activity coefficients of these electrolytes pass through distinct minimum values but that the minima do not occur at the same concentration for each electrolyte.

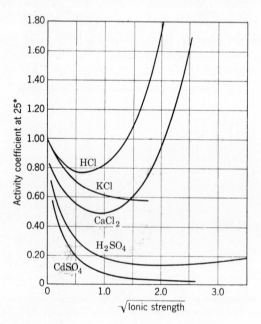

Fig. 14-5. Dependence of the mean ionic activity coefficient on $I^{1/2}$ for electrolytes.

It should also be noted that at higher concentrations of electrolytes activity coefficients may be considerably greater than unity.

The activity coefficients of a large number of electrolytes, both alone and mixed, in solutions of different concentrations have been determined with a high degree of accuracy.* Activity coefficients may be determined by a number of different types of measurements, including vapor pressure, freezing-point lowering, boiling-point elevation, osmotic pressure, distribution coefficients, equilibrium constants, solubility, and electromotive force. All different methods for determining activity coefficients must lead to the same value for a given solution.

Electrode Potentials. The relative electrode potential of any electrode may be determined by combining the electrode with a standard hydrogen electrode, preferably without a liquid junction, and measuring the voltage of the cell. If one electrode consists of a metal in contact with a solution containing its ions with charge $n+$, the cell may be represented by

$$\text{Pt, H}_2(g, 1 \text{ atm}); \text{H}^+ \parallel M^{n+}; M \tag{34}$$

The corresponding cell reaction is written according to conventions which are given shortly (p. 402).

$$\tfrac{1}{2}\text{H}_2 + \frac{1}{n} M^{+n} = \text{H}^+ + \frac{1}{n} M \tag{35}$$

The term *standard electrode potential* is used to designate the potential which would be obtained with the constituents present at unit activity. *The standard electrode potential of an electrode is given a positive value if this electrode is more positive than the standard hydrogen electrode and a negative sign if it is more negative than the standard hydrogen electrode.* The electrode with the more positive electrode potential is attached to the positive terminal of the potentiometer. Electrodes below hydrogen in the electromotive series will be positive, provided that the ions are at unit activity, and electrodes above hydrogen in the electromotive series of Table IV will be negative, provided that the ions are at unit activity. As shown earlier, the positive electrode is the one at which reduction occurs and the negative electrode is the one at which oxidation occurs.

All electrodes may be arranged in a table according to their standard electrode potentials, which are determined as described in the preceding section by means of an extrapolation to get the electromotive force at unit activity. Table IV gives standard electrode potentials E° of a

---

* H. S. Harned and B. B. Owen, *The Physical Chemistry of Electrolytic Solutions*, Reinhold Publishing Corp., New York, 1958; B. E. Conway, *Electrochemical Data*, Elsevier Publishing Co., Amsterdam, 1952.

Table IV.[1] Standard Electrode Potentials at 25°

Electrode	$E°$	Half-Cell Reaction
Li^+; Li	-3.045	$Li^+ + e = Li$
K^+; K	-2.925	$K^+ + e = K$
Rb^+; Rb	-2.925	$Rb^+ + e = Rb$
Na^+; Na	-2.714	$Na^+ + e = Na$
Mg^{2+}; Mg	-2.37	$\frac{1}{2}Mg^{2+} + e = \frac{1}{2}Mg$
Pu^{3+}; Pu	-2.07	$\frac{1}{3}Pu^{3+} + e = \frac{1}{3}Pu$
Th^{4+}; Th	-1.90	$\frac{1}{4}Th^{4+} + e = \frac{1}{4}Th$
Np^{3+}; Np	-1.86	$\frac{1}{3}Np^{3+} + e = \frac{1}{3}Np$
Al^{3+}; Al	-1.66	$\frac{1}{3}Al^{3+} + e = \frac{1}{3}Al$
Zn^{2+}; Zn	-0.763	$\frac{1}{2}Zn^{2+} + e = \frac{1}{2}Zn$
Fe^{2+}; Fe	-0.440	$\frac{1}{2}Fe^{2+} + e = \frac{1}{2}Fe$
Cr^{3+}, Cr^{2+}; Pt[3,4]	-0.41	$Cr^{3+} + e = Cr^{2+}$
Cd^{2+}; Cd	-0.403	$\frac{1}{2}Cd^{2+} + e = \frac{1}{2}Cd$
Tl^+; Tl	-0.3363	$Tl^+ + e = Tl$
Br^-; $PbBr_2(s)$, Pb	-0.280	$\frac{1}{2}PbBr_2 + e = \frac{1}{2}Pb + Br^-$
Co^{2+}; Co	-0.277	$\frac{1}{2}Co^{2+} + e = \frac{1}{2}Co$
Ni^{2+}; Ni	-0.250	$\frac{1}{2}Ni^{2+} + e = \frac{1}{2}Ni$
I^-; $AgI(s)$, Ag	-0.151	$AgI + e = Ag + I^-$
Sn^{2+}; Sn	-0.140	$\frac{1}{2}Sn^{2+} + e = \frac{1}{2}Sn$
Pb^{2+}; Pb	-0.126	$\frac{1}{2}Pb^{2+} + e = \frac{1}{2}Pb$
D^+; D_2, Pt	-0.0034	$D^+ + e = \frac{1}{2}D_2$
H^+; H_2, Pt	0.0000	$H^+ + e = \frac{1}{2}H_2$
Ti^{4+}, Ti^{3+}; Pt	0.04	$Ti^{4+} + e = Ti^{3+}$
Br^-; $AgBr(s)$, Ag	0.095	$AgBr + e = Ag + Br^-$
Sn^{4+}, Sn^{2+}; Pt	0.15	$\frac{1}{2}Sn^{4+} + e = \frac{1}{2}Sn^{2+}$
Cu^{2+}, Cu^+; Pt	0.153	$Cu^{2+} + e = Cu^+$
Cl^-; $AgCl(s)$, Ag	0.2224	$AgCl + e = Ag + Cl^-$
Cl^-; $Hg_2Cl_2(s)$, Hg [2]	0.268	$\frac{1}{2}Hg_2Cl_2 + e = Hg + Cl^-$
Cu^{2+}; Cu	0.337	$\frac{1}{2}Cu^{2+} + e = \frac{1}{2}Cu$
H^+; $C_2H_4(g)$, $C_2H_6(g)$, Pt	0.52	$H^+ + \frac{1}{2}C_2H_4(g) + e = \frac{1}{2}C_2H_6(g)$
Cu^+; Cu	0.521	$Cu^+ + e = Cu$
I^-; $I_2(s)$, Pt	0.5355	$\frac{1}{2}I_2 + e = I^-$
H^+, quinhydrone(s); Pt	0.6996	$\frac{1}{2}C_6H_4O_2 + H^+ + e = \frac{1}{2}C_6H_6O_2$
Fe^{3+}, Fe^{2+}; Pt	0.771	$Fe^{3+} + e = Fe^{2+}$
Hg_2^{2+}; Hg	0.789	$\frac{1}{2}Hg_2^{2+} + e = Hg$
Ag^+; Ag	0.7991	$Ag^+ + e = Ag$
Hg^{2+}, Hg_2^{2+}; Pt	0.920	$Hg^{2+} + e = \frac{1}{2}Hg_2^{2+}$
Pu^{4+}; Pu^{3+}; Pt	0.97	$Pu^{4+} + e = Pu^{3+}$
Br^-; $Br_2(l)$, Pt	1.0562	$\frac{1}{2}Br_2(l) + e = Br^-$
Tl^{3+}, Tl^+; Pt	1.250	$\frac{1}{2}Tl^{3+} + e = \frac{1}{2}Tl^+$
Cl^-; $Cl_2(g)$, Pt	1.3595	$\frac{1}{2}Cl_2(g) + e = Cl^-$
Pb^{2+}; PbO_2, Pb	1.455	$\frac{1}{2}PbO_2 + 2H^+ + e = \frac{1}{2}Pb^{2+} + H_2O$
Au^{3+}; Au	1.50	$\frac{1}{3}Au^{3+} + e = \frac{1}{3}Au$
Ce^{4+}, Ce^{3+}; Pt	1.61	$Ce^{4+} + e = Ce^{3+}$
Co^{3+}, Co^{2+}; Pt	1.82	$Co^{3+} + e = Co^{2+}$
$HF(aq)$; $F_2(g)$, Pt	3.06	$H^+ + \frac{1}{2}F_2 + e = HF(aq)$

[1] All ions are at unit activity in water, and all gases are at 1 atm. Additional electromotive-force data are available in W. M. Latimer, *The Oxidation States of the Elements and Their Potentials in Aqueous Solutions*, Prentice-Hall, Englewood Cliffs, N. J., 1952, but it will be noticed that the signs of the potentials in Latimer's book are the opposite of those in Table IV because there the half-cell reactions are written as oxidation reactions.

[2] The electromotive force of the normal calomel electrode is 0.2802 volt and of the calomel electrode containing saturated KCl is 0.2415 volt.

[3] The symbol Pt represents an inert electrode like platinum.

[4] The order of writing the ions in the electrolyte solution is immaterial.

400

number of electrodes at 25°. It is to be noted that these electrodes are written in the order ion-electrode and that standard electrode potentials are standard reduction potentials. The electrode reaction is written as the addition of electrons.

The magnitude of the standard electrode potential is a measure of the tendency of the half-reaction to occur in the direction of reduction, that is, the absorption of electrons. The lower a half-reaction is in Table IV, the greater is the tendency of the oxidized form to accept electrons and be reduced. The higher a half-reaction is in the table, the greater is the tendency of the reduced form to donate electrons and be oxidized. For example, the active metals sodium and potassium have very large negative standard electrode potentials and strong tendencies to donate electrons.

The reduced form of any element or ion at unit activity will reduce the oxidized form of any element or ion at unit activity which has a less negative, i.e., more positive standard, electrode potential. Table IV of standard electrode potentials may be used for calculations of the electromotive forces of electrochemical cells and the equilibrium constants of the corresponding chemical reactions.

Conventions for Electrochemical Cells and Electrode Reactions. The following three rules are convenient for calculating the standard electromotive force of a cell, relating the cell reaction to this electromotive force, and deciding whether the cell reaction is spontaneous as written. The standard electromotive force $E°$ of a cell is the electromotive force when all constituents are at unit activity.

1. *The standard electromotive force of a cell is equal to the standard electrode potential of the right-hand electrode minus the standard electrode potential of the left-hand electrode.* It is to be noted that the electrode at the right is automatically written in the order ion-electrode as it is in Table IV, and that, according to the geometry of the cell, the electrode at the left must be written in the order electrode-ion. The standard electromotive force of the cell is equal to the standard electrode potential of the electrode at the right minus the standard electrode potential of the electrode at the left.

For the cell
$$\text{Zn}; \text{Zn}^{2+} \parallel \text{Cu}^{2+}; \text{Cu} \tag{36}$$

$$E° = 0.337 - (-0.763) = 1.100 \text{ volts at } 25°$$

For the cell
$$\text{Cu}; \text{Cu}^{2+} \parallel \text{Zn}^{2+}; \text{Zn} \tag{37}$$

$$E° = -0.763 - (0.337) = -1.100 \text{ volts at } 25°$$

2. *The reaction taking place at the left electrode is written as an oxidation reaction, and the reaction taking place at the right electrode is written as a reduction reaction. The cell reaction is the sum of these two reactions.* For cell 36

$$\text{Left electrode:} \quad Zn = Zn^{2+} + 2e \quad \text{(oxidation)} \tag{38}$$

$$\text{Right electrode:} \quad Cu^{2+} + 2e = Cu \quad \text{(reduction)} \tag{39}$$

$$\text{Cell reaction:} \quad Zn + Cu^{2+} = Zn^{2+} + Cu \tag{40}$$

These equations could equally well be multiplied through by $\frac{1}{2}$ so that the cell reaction would correspond to a one-electron change and would be written

$$\tfrac{1}{2}Zn + \tfrac{1}{2}Cu^{2+} = \tfrac{1}{2}Zn^{2+} + \tfrac{1}{2}Cu \tag{41}$$

For cell 37 the cell reaction would be written

$$Cu + Zn^{2+} = Zn + Cu^{2+} \tag{42}$$

or

$$\tfrac{1}{2}Cu + \tfrac{1}{2}Zn^{2+} = \tfrac{1}{2}Zn + \tfrac{1}{2}Cu^{2+} \tag{43}$$

3. *If $E°$ for the cell calculated by rule 1 is positive, the cell reaction as written by rule 2 is a spontaneous reaction when all the reactants and products are at unit activity.* Thus reaction 40 (or 41) is thermodynamically spontaneous, but reaction 42 (or 43) is not. This rule comes from the fact that to be spontaneous the reaction must have a negative value of $\Delta G°$ (p. 103) and $\Delta G° = -nFE°$. For reaction 40,

$$\Delta G° = -(2)(96,500)(1.100)/4.184 = -50,800 \quad \text{cal}$$

Multiples of a cell reaction may be taken without changing the electromotive force $E°$, but $\Delta G°$ depends upon the way in which the chemical equation is written because of the factor n. For example, the Gibbs free-energy change for reaction 41 is $\Delta G° = -(1)(96,500)(1.100)/4.184 = -25,400$ cal. For a cell in which the reactants are not at unit activity the criterion of spontaneous reaction equilibrium is that $\Delta G = -nFE$ is negative.

Several examples will be given to illustrate the application of these conventions.

Example 5. Write the cell reaction and calculate E° at 25° for the cell

$$Cd; Cd^{2+} \parallel Cu^{2+}; Cu$$

Reduction at right	$Cu^{2+} + 2e = Cu(s)$	$E^\circ_{Cu^{2+};Cu}$ =	0.337
Oxidation at left	$Cd(s) = Cd^{2+} + 2e$	$E^\circ_{Cd^{2+};Cd}$ =	-0.403

$$Cd(s) + Cu^{2+} = Cd^{2+} + Cu(s) \quad E^\circ \qquad = \quad 0.740 \text{ volt}$$

Since E° is positive, the reaction is spontaneous as written, and $Cd(s)$ will precipitate $Cu(s)$ from a solution in which $a_{Cu^{2+}} = 1$ to produce Cd^{2+} at unit activity. What is the Gibbs free-energy change for this reaction?

$$\Delta G^\circ = -nFE^\circ = -(2)(96,500)(0.740)/4.184 = -34,200 \text{ cal}$$

Example 6. What are the cell reaction and the voltage of the cell

$$Zn; Zn^{2+} \parallel Cd^{2+}; Cd$$

Reduction at right	$Cd^{2+} + 2e = Cd(s)$	$E^\circ_{Cd^{2+};Cd}$ =	-0.403
Oxidation at left	$Zn(s) = Zn^{2+} + 2e$	$E^\circ_{Zn^{2+};Zn}$ =	-0.763

$$Zn(s) + Cd^{2+} = Cd(s) + Zn^{2+} \quad E^\circ \qquad = \quad 0.360 \text{ volt}$$

Since E° is positive, the reaction is spontaneous as written, and zinc loses electrons and cadmium ions gain them.

In the cell of example 6 cadmium is the more positive electrode, whereas in the preceding cell it was the negative electrode. The rule is that the electrode with the *more positive* standard electrode potential is attached to the positive terminal of the potentiometer when it is desired to measure the electromotive force of the cell in which the solutes are at unit activity.

The cell corresponding to a given reaction is obtained by reversing the calculations illustrated above.

Example 7. Calculate E° and ΔG° for the reaction

$$\tfrac{1}{2}Cu(s) + \tfrac{1}{2}Cl_2(g) = \tfrac{1}{2}Cu^{2+} + Cl^-$$

$$\text{Oxidation} \quad \tfrac{1}{2}Cu(s) = \tfrac{1}{2}Cu^{2+} + e$$

$$\text{Reduction} \quad \tfrac{1}{2}Cl_2(g) + e = Cl^-$$

Since the oxidation reaction is to occur at the left electrode and the reduction at the right electrode, the cell is written

$$Cu; Cu^{2+} \parallel Cl^-; Cl_2(g), Pt$$

$$E^\circ = E^\circ_{Cl^-;Cl_2,Pt} - E^\circ_{Cu^{2+};Cu} = 1.360 - 0.337 = 1.023 \text{ volts}$$

$$\Delta G^\circ = -nFE^\circ = -\frac{(96,500)(1.023)}{(4.1840)} = -23,590 \text{ cal}$$

Copper and chlorine at 1 atm will react spontaneously to give cupric ions and chloride ions at unit activity.

Calculation of the Equilibrium Constant from $E°$. Since the standard Gibbs free-energy change for a cell reaction may be calculated from $\Delta G° = -nFE°$, and since $\Delta G° = -RT \ln K$, the equilibrium constant for a cell reaction may be computed. Combining these two relations,

$$E° = \frac{RT}{nF} \ln K \tag{44}$$

At 25°

$$E° = \frac{0.0591}{n} \log K \tag{45}$$

Example 8. From electromotive-force data calculate the equilibrium constant at 25° for the reaction

$$Sn + Pb^{2+} = Pb + Sn^{2+}$$

Splitting up the reaction into the two half-cell reactions,

$$Sn = Sn^{2+} + 2e \quad \text{and} \quad Pb^{2+} + 2e = Pb$$

and putting the oxidation reaction at the left in the corresponding cell at 25°, we have

$$Sn; Sn^{2+} \parallel Pb^{2+}; Pb$$

$$E° = E°_{Pb^{2+};Pb} - E°_{Sn^{2+};Sn} = -0.126 - (-0.140) = 0.014 \text{ volt}$$

$$= (0.0591/2) \log K$$

$$K = a_{Sn^{2+}}/a_{Pb^{2+}} = 2.97$$

Carrying out a similar calculation for the addition of zinc to copper ions, we find that $E° = 1.100$, and $K = a_{Zn^{2+}}/a_{Cu^{2+}} = 10^{37}$. In other words, the removal of copper ions by zinc is quite complete.

Cells in Which the Activities Are Not Equal to Unity. Equation 10 can be used to calculate the voltage of a cell when the ions are not at unit activity. It is not possible to determine the activities of single ions. However, for some purposes it is possible to replace activities by concentrations. In other cases the activity coefficients for ions of the same charge type tend to cancel in equation 10. This is a good approximation when these ions are in the same solution, or if they are in different solutions of the same ionic strength.

Example 9. Calculate the voltage of the following cell at 25° if $m_{Sn^{2+}}/m_{Pb^{2+}} = 2$:

$$Sn; Sn^{2+} \parallel Pb^{2+}; Pb$$

The cell reaction is

$$Sn + Pb^{2+} = Sn^{2+} + Pb$$

To a good approximation, $a_{Sn^{2+}}/a_{Pb^{2+}} = 2$, and by equation 10

$$E = E° - (RT/nF) \ln (a_{Sn^{2+}}/a_{Pb^{2+}})$$

$$= 0.0140 - (0.0591/2) \log 2 \text{ (cf. example 8)}$$

$$= 0.0140 - 0.0089 = 0.0051 \text{ volt}$$

$$\Delta G = -nFE = \frac{(2)(96,500)(0.0051)}{(4.1840)} = -240 \text{ cal}$$

The Gibbs free-energy decrease ΔG for this reaction is less than $\Delta G°$ for the reaction where both reactants and products are at unit activity, because here the specified activity of the product is greater than the specified activity of the reactant.

For any cell that operates spontaneously E must be positive, and ΔG is therefore negative.

Concentration Cells. When two identical electrodes are immersed in a solution containing their ions, there is no difference in potential. However, if the electrodes are placed in two solutions of different concentrations which are connected by a liquid junction or salt bridge, a potential difference is obtained. The electrode surrounded by a higher concentration of positive ions tends to lose more electrons and become positive. The electrode in contact with more negative ions tends to gain electrons and become negative. The net reaction for such a concentration cell simply represents the transfer of a substance from the solution of higher activity at one electrode to the solution of lower activity at the other. For the cell

$$M; M^{n+}(a_1) \parallel M^{n+}(a_2); M \tag{46}$$

the reactions are

Left electrode $\quad M = M^{n+}(a_1) + ne$

Right electrode $\quad M^{n+}(a_2) + ne = M$

Cell reaction $\quad M^{n+}(a_2) = M^{n+}(a_1) \tag{47}$

Therefore, using equation 10, the electromotive force of the cell is given by

$$E = -\frac{RT}{nF} \ln \frac{a_1}{a_2} \tag{48}$$

If $a_2 > a_1$, E is positive and the cell will operate spontaneously. In this case the cell reaction represents a dilution which is a spontaneous process. This derivation is based on the assumption that the liquid-junction potential is completely eliminated by the potassium chloride salt bridge.

Example 10. Calculate the electromotive force of the cell

$$Cu; Cu^{2+}(a_1 = 0.01) \parallel Cu^{2+}(a_2 = 0.10); Cu$$

Using equation 48, we obtain

$$E = -\frac{0.0591}{2}\log\frac{0.01}{0.1} = 0.0296 \text{ volt}$$

The electrode immersed in the more concentrated solution is positive with respect to the one in the more dilute solution. Positive ions strike it more frequently.

Exercise I. Show that for the concentration cell

$$X; X^-(a_1) \parallel X^-(a_2); X$$

where X^- is a negative ion such as iodide ion, the equation for the electromotive force of the cell is

$$E = -\frac{RT}{F}\ln\frac{a_2}{a_1} \tag{49}$$

Determination of pH. The concentrations of hydrogen ions in aqueous solutions range from about 1 molar in 1 N HCl to about 10^{-14} molar in 1 N NaOH. Because of this wide range of concentrations Sorenson found it convenient in 1909 to adopt an exponential notation. He defined pH as the negative exponent of 10 which gives the hydrogen-ion concentration. Thus

$$(H^+) = 10^{-pH}$$

or

$$pH = -\log (H^+) \tag{50}$$

It will be shown on p. 427 that the product of the concentrations of the hydrogen and hydroxyl ions at 25° in dilute aqueous solution is always

$$(H^+)(OH^-) = 1 \times 10^{-14}$$

Thus, if a solution contains exactly as many hydroxyl ions as hydrogen ions, $(H^+) = (OH^-) = 10^{-7}$. The pH of a neutral solution then is 7. Addition of an acid increases the value of (H^+) and gives a pH less than 7. Addition of a base reduces the value of (H^+) and increases the pH above 7.

Electromotive-force methods are useful for studying hydrogen-ion concentrations; however, since the activity of a single ion cannot be determined, the modern definition of pH is expressed operationally in terms of the method of measuring it rather than by equation 50. A cell of the type illustrated in Fig. 14-3 may be used. This cell is represented symbolically by

$$Pt, H_2(p); H^+(a_{H^+}) \parallel Cl^-; Hg_2Cl_2; Hg$$

The electromotive force of this cell may be considered to be made up of three contributions:

$$E = 0.2802 - 0.0591 \log (a_{H^+}/p_{H_2}^{1/2}) + E_{\text{liquid junction}} \qquad (51)$$

where the contribution by the normal calomel electrode is 0.2802 volt at 25°. Although the activities of single ions cannot be determined without making some assumption, equation 51 is often used with the assumption that $E_{\text{liquid junction}} = 0$. If $p_{H_2} = 1$ atm,

$$E - 0.2802 = -0.0591 \log a_{H^+} \qquad (52)$$

Hydrogen-ion activities obtained in this way are of great practical use even though they are based upon this assumption.

Taking pH $= - \log a_{H^+}$, equation 52 becomes

$$E - 0.2802 = 0.0591 \text{ pH}$$

or

$$\text{pH} = \frac{E - 0.2802}{0.0591} \qquad (53)$$

From an actual operational viewpoint equation 53 is the definition of pH rather than equation 50.

The Glass Electrode. The glass electrode has become the most useful electrode for determining the pH of a solution. It is not affected by oxidizing or reducing agents and is not easily poisoned. It is especially useful in biochemical investigations.

A glass electrode consists of a reversible electrode, such as a calomel or Ag-AgCl electrode, in a solution of constant pH inside a thin membrane of a special glass. The thin glass bulb of this electrode is immersed in the solution to be studied along with a reference calomel electrode to form the cell indicated by

Ag, AgCl; Cl⁻, H⁺; glass membrane; solution ‖ calomel electrode

It is found experimentally that the potential of such a glass electrode varies with the activity of hydrogen ions in the same way as the hydrogen electrode, that is, 0.0591 volt per pH unit at 25°. An ordinary potentiometer cannot be used to measure the voltage of such a cell because of the high resistance of the glass membrane, and so an electronic voltmeter must be employed. Vacuum-tube circuits have been developed which make it possible to measure pH values to ±0.01 pH unit with easily portable apparatus. The pH meter, as it is often called, is calibrated by means of a buffer of known pH before it is used to measure the pH of an unknown solution. The theory and use of the glass electrode have been fully treated by Bates.*

Junction Potentials. As already mentioned, a junction between two electrolyte solutions contributes a potential to a cell. If, for example, a concentrated solution of hydrochloric acid forms a junction with a dilute solution, both hydrogen ions and chloride ions diffuse from the concentrated solution into the dilute solution. The hydrogen ion moves faster, and thus the dilute solution becomes positively charged on account of an excess of positive hydrogen ions. The more concentrated solution is left with an excess of negative chloride ions and thus acquires a negative charge. The actual separation of charge is very small, but the potential difference produced is appreciable.

In general, it may be stated that the difference of potential resulting from the junction of two solutions is caused by the difference in the rates of migration of the two ions, *the more dilute solution acquiring a charge corresponding to that of the faster-moving ion.*

The difference in potential resulting from the junction of two liquids must be eliminated or corrected for in accurate measurements of electrode potentials. The most convenient way of minimizing this potential is by means of a salt bridge of potassium chloride connecting the two solutions of different electrolytes. Potassium chloride is used because the transference numbers of the two ions are about the same, 0.49 for K^+ and 0.51 for Cl^-. Under these conditions each ion moves with nearly the same velocity, and each has the same tendency to give its charge to the more dilute solution.

Other ions than potassium and chloride are usually present at the two ends of the bridge, and it is desirable to minimize the effect of these ions by having a large excess of the potassium chloride, which tends to swamp out the slight effects due to other ions. For this purpose saturated potassium chloride is most effective in eliminating the junction potential; however, it is troublesome to use, and 1.0 N potassium chloride is generally preferred. When potassium chloride is not feasible, as, for example, in a cell containing silver nitrate, a salt bridge of ammonium nitrate is substituted.

Particularly in the electrochemistry of nonaqueous solutions, ignorance of junction potentials constitutes a serious handicap. These potentials may be quite large.

Batteries. Several cells of the same kind can be arranged in series with the anode of one cell connected to the cathode of the next to give a

---

* R. G. Bates, *Electrometric pH Determinations*, John Wiley & Sons, New York, 1954.

battery with a voltage which is equal to the sum of the voltages of the individual cells. Although electricity can be produced much more cheaply by operating a dynamo with mechanical power, batteries have the advantage of portability and are useful for storing energy in a readily available form. Two types of batteries which are widely employed are the lead storage battery and the Leclanché dry cell of zinc, ammonium chloride, and manganese dioxide.

The lead storage battery consists of an electrode of lead and an electrode of lead oxide immersed in sulfuric acid. Each plate has a rough surface exposing a large area, and the two are held close together in rigid frames. The cell reaction is

$$Pb + HSO_4^- = PbSO_4(s) + H^+ + 2e$$
$$PbO_2 + 3H^+ + HSO_4^- + 2e = PbSO_4(s) + 2H_2O$$

$$Pb + PbO_2 + 2H^+ + 2HSO_4^- \underset{\text{Charge}}{\overset{\text{Discharge}}{\rightleftharpoons}} 2PbSO_4(s) + 2H_2O$$

The important thing about this cell reaction is the fact that it is reversible. In the recharging process additional spongy lead is deposited on one electrode and lead oxide on the other. These electrically replenished electrodes are then ready to follow again the original cell reaction with the flow of electrons from the lead electrode to the lead oxide electrode, thus generating useful electricity. When the battery is discharged, the sulfuric acid is converted into lead sulfate and water; the sulfuric acid is regenerated on charging.

The Leclanché dry cell with a voltage of about 1.6 volts consists of a zinc can containing a carbon electrode surrounded by manganese dioxide and graphite immersed in a starch paste containing zinc chloride and an excess of solid ammonium chloride. The electrode reactions may be written

$$Zn + 2NH_3 = Zn(NH_3)_2^{2+} + 2e$$

$$2MnO_2 + 2NH_4^+ + 2e = Mn_2O_3 + H_2O + 2NH_3$$

where $Zn(NH_3)_2^{2+}$ represents the average of a mixture of complex ions having different numbers of ammonia molecules.

Fuel Cells.* Fuel cells are electrochemical cells in which consumable electrode material is supplied continuously to a cell to produce electricity. In the hydrogen-oxygen fuel cell

$$C(graphite), H_2; NaOH; O_2, C(graphite)$$

* G. J. Young, *Fuel Cells*, Reinhold Publishing Corp., New York, 1960.

hydrogen is bubbled through a porous carbon electrode, and oxygen is bubbled through another porous carbon electrode, the two electrodes being immersed in an aqueous solution of sodium hydroxide. The reactions are

$$2H_2 + 4OH^- = 4H_2O + 4e$$
$$O_2 + 2H_2O + 4e = 4OH^-$$

$$2H_2 + O_2 = 2H_2O$$

Such cells have produced 60–70 per cent of the maximum useful work $(-\Delta G)$. If the hydrogen and oxygen were burned to produce heat for a turbine engine, for example, a smaller amount of work would be obtained because of the relatively low thermodynamic efficiency of a heat engine.

A variety of gases has been used in fuel cells; these include methane and other hydrocarbons. Air is the cheapest material to use for the oxidizing electrode. Experimental problems include finding an electrode with a catalytic surface so that the reaction can occur rapidly, reducing the internal resistance of the cell, and removing the products of the reaction. Some fuel cells operate efficiently at high temperatures with an electrolyte of molten sodium hydroxide or sodium phosphate. Because fuel cells operate with high thermodynamic efficiency, a great deal of research effort is being devoted to the development of practical cells.

Potentiometric Titrations. Measurement of the potential of certain electrodes offers a convenient and accurate means for determining the end points of titrations. The use of a glass electrode or hydrogen electrode in studying acid-base titrations will be discussed in the next chapter. The end points in oxidation-reduction reactions may be determined by measuring the potential difference between a platinum wire, or other inert electrode, and a calomel electrode. In order to locate the end point more accurately, it is helpful to plot $\Delta E/\Delta V$ versus the volume V of the reagent used. The maximum slope occurs at the end point of the titration.

Exercise II. At the stoichiometric point in a potentiometric titration the electromotive force changes rapidly with the volume of added reagent. Using equation 49, explain why the emf changes most rapidly at the end point.

Overvoltage. The potentials at which metals plate out at appreciable rates are frequently in good agreement with the reversible electrode potentials. However, in many cases the potential required is much larger than the reversible potential. This higher voltage is required because of (a) the IR drop across the electrolytic cell, (b) the concentration polarization at the electrodes, and (c) the overvoltage. The concentration polarization is a result of the fact that changes in concentration at the electrode occur during electrolysis and produce an electromotive force which is opposite to the applied potential, according to equation 10. Vigorous stirring reduces the concentration polar-

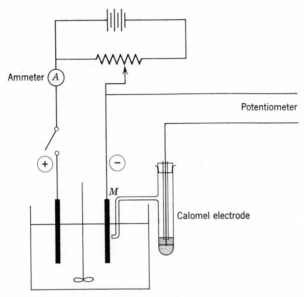

Fig. 14-6. Apparatus for measuring the overvoltage of an electrode M at various current densities.

ization, and the remaining excess voltage over the reversible electromotive force which must be applied to obtain a given current density is called the *overvoltage*.

The overvoltage may be measured with the apparatus represented in *Fig. 14-6*. While the desired current density is maintained through the surface of electrode M, the difference in potential between this electrode and a calomel electrode is measured with a potentiometer. The reversible potential of electrode M with respect to the calomel half-cell is measured when no current is flowing through the electrolysis cell.

The overvoltages for the formation of hydrogen on the surface of various metals are given in *Fig. 14-7* as a function of current density at the cathode. The fact that there is an overvoltage for hydrogen shows that some step in the discharge of hydrogen ions is slow. Oxygen evolution at a metal electrode also involves overvoltage.

An important result of the high overvoltage for hydrogen is the fact that many metals can be electroplated from aqueous solutions under conditions where hydrogen alone would be produced were it not for the hydrogen overvoltage. The reversible electrode potential for hydrogen at 1 atm and pH 7 is obtained as follows:

$$H^+(a = 10^{-7}) + e = \tfrac{1}{2}H_2(1 \text{ atm})$$

$$E = -0.0591 \log (1/10^{-7}) = -0.41 \text{ volt}$$

Thus in the absence of overvoltage only metals with more positive electrode potentials than -0.41 volt could be electroplated in aqueous solution or their electrode potentials determined. At neutral pH values cadmium and hydrogen might be expected to be produced together because they have about the same electrode potential. However, since the overvoltage of hydrogen on cadmium is about 1.2 volts at 0.01 amp cm^{-2}, no hydrogen is formed.

Since the overvoltage of hydrogen on mercury is about 1.2 to 1.4 volts, it might be expected that sodium, having an electrode potential of 2.7 volts, could not be deposited in mercury from aqueous salt solutions because hydrogen would be evolved first. However, the electrode potential of a dilute sodium amalgam against a solution containing sodium ions is only about 1.2 volts, and so metallic sodium may be deposited from aqueous solution onto a mercury cathode.

Electrodeposition is a useful technique in quantitative analysis. By control of the potential of electrolysis metal ions may be reduced one at a time, starting with the metal having the most positive electrode potential.

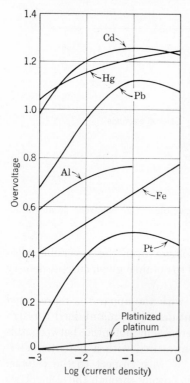

Fig. 14-7. Hydrogen overvoltage on various metals as a function of current density (amperes per square centimeter). The electrolyte solution is 1 M HCl.

Polarography.* The polarographic method of analysis developed by Heyrovsky is based upon the determination of current flow when a solution containing oxidizable or reducible substances is electrolyzed in a cell in which one electrode consists of mercury falling dropwise from a fine-bore capillary glass tube so as to give a continuously fresh surface. The other electrode is a calomel electrode. The apparatus, which automatically records the plot of current versus voltage, is called a *polarograph*. Both a qualitative and a quantitative analysis of a solution may be obtained by this method, and the volume of solution may be quite small.

As the applied potential is increased from zero, the current flowing is small and remains so until one of the components of the solution begins to be reduced at the mercury cathode. The rapid rise in current with applied potential is called a wave, and the potential at the midpoint of the wave, the *half-wave potential*, is characteristic of the substance being reduced. This potential is independent of the concentration of the reducible or oxidizable substance but may be altered by pH changes or the formation of complex ions. It is necessary to remove dissolved oxygen before an experiment by sweeping out the solution with an inert gas, since the reduction of oxygen leads to the passage of a current which masks the current of most other substances.

As an illustration, the polarogram of a solution containing two reducible species, Tl^+ and Zn^{2+}, is given in *Fig. 14-8*. As may be seen, the half-wave potentials for Tl^+ and Zn^{2+} are 0.53 volt and 1.06 volts against the saturated calomel electrode. The wave heights are proportional to the concentrations of the respective ions. The oscillations about a mean current are due to the formation and polarization of mercury droplets. Since a fresh surface is continually exposed by the growing drops, the current is solely a function of the applied potential.

As the potential is increased above the half-wave potential, a maximum value is reached which is referred to as the *diffusion current*. The diffusion current depends upon the rate with which the reducible substance diffuses to the mercury droplet and is proportional to the concentration of the reducible substance in the body of the solution. The proportionality constant for calculating the concentration of an ion from its diffusion current must be determined from experiments with known concentrations of the substance. As illustrated in Fig. 14-8, several waves are obtained for a mixture, and so it is possible to secure a quantitative analysis of a mixture of several components.

* I. M. Kolthoff and J. J. Lingane, *Polarography*, Interscience Publishers, New York, 1952.

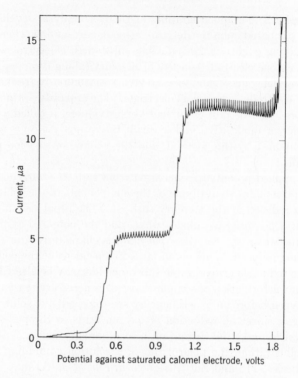

Potential against saturated calomel electrode, volts

Fig. 14-8. Polarogram of a solution containing 9×10^{-4} M Zn^{2+} and 10×10^{-4} M Tl^+ in 0.2 M KCl. (Courtesy Prof. I. Shain of the University of Wisconsin.)

REFERENCES

R. G. Bates, *Electrometric pH Determinations*, John Wiley & Sons, New York, 1954.

S. Glasstone, *Introduction to Electrochemistry*, D. Van Nostrand Co., Princeton, N. J., 1942.

H. S. Harned and B. B. Owen, *The Physical Chemistry of Electrolytic Solutions*, Reinhold Publishing Corp., New York, 1958.

G. F. A. Kortüm and J. O'M. Bockris, *Textbook of Electrochemistry*, Elsevier Publishing Co., New York, 1951.

W. M. Latimer, *Oxidation States of the Elements and Their Potentials in Aqueous Solutions*, Prentice-Hall, Englewood Cliffs, N. J., 1952.

D. A. MacInnes, *The Principles of Electrochemistry*, Reinhold Publishing Corp., New York, 1939.

J. E. Ricci, *Hydrogen Ion Concentration*, Princeton University Press, Princeton, N. J., 1952.

R. A. Robinson and R. H. Stokes, *Electrolyte Solutions*, Academic Press, New York, 1959.

PROBLEMS

1. A small dry battery of zinc and ammonium chloride weighing 85 grams will operate continuously through a 4-ohm resistance for 450 min before its voltage falls below 0.75 volt. The initial voltage is 1.60, and the effective voltage over the whole life of the battery is taken to be 1.00. Theoretically, how many miles above the earth could this battery be raised by the energy delivered under these conditions?

Ans. 5.04 miles.

2. The voltage of the cell

$$Pb; PbSO_4; Na_2SO_4 \cdot 10H_2O(sat); Hg_2SO_4; Hg$$

is 0.9647 at 25°. The temperature coefficient is 1.74×10^{-4} volt deg^{-1}. Calculate (a) the enthalpy change for the reaction and (b) the change in Gibbs free energy for the reaction

$$Pb(s) + Hg_2SO_4(s) = PbSO_4(s) + 2Hg(l)$$

Ans. (a) $-42,100$, (b) $-44,500$ cal.

3. Derive an expression for the activity of a 1–2 electrolyte (like Na_2SO_4) in terms of the mean ionic activity coefficient and the molality.

Ans. $a_{Na_2SO_4} = 4m^3\gamma_\pm^3$.

4. What is the ionic strength of each of the following solutions: (a) 0.1 M NaCl, (b) 0.1 M $Na_2C_2O_4$, (c) 0.1 M $CuSO_4$, (d) a solution containing 0.1 M Na_2HPO_4 and 0.1 M NaH_2PO_4?   *Ans.* (a) 0.1, (b) 0.3, (c) 0.4, (d) 0.4.

5. Given the mean ionic activity coefficients of HCl(aq) at 0.01 and 0.05 m as 0.906 and 0.833 at 25°, calculate the emf of the cell

$$Pt, H_2(1 \text{ atm}); HCl(m); Cl_2(1 \text{ atm}), Pt$$

where m is (a) 0.01 and (b) 0.05.   *Ans.* (a) 1.602, (b) 1.5225 volts.

6. Given the cell at 25°,

$$Pb; Pb^{2+}(a = 1) \parallel Ag^+(a = 1); Ag$$

(a) calculate the voltage; (b) write the cell reaction; and (c) calculate the Gibbs free-energy change. (d) Which electrode is positive?

Ans. (a) 0.925 volt. (b) $\frac{1}{2}Pb(s) + Ag^+(a = 1) = \frac{1}{2}Pb^{2+}(a = 1) + Ag(s)$. (c) $-21,330$ cal. (d) Silver electrode.

7. Given the cell at 25°,

$$Pt, Cl_2(1 \text{ atm}); Cl^-(a = 1) \parallel Zn^{2+}(a = 1); Zn$$

(a) Calculate $E°$. (b) Write the cell reaction. (c) Calculate $\Delta G°$.

Ans. (a) -2.123 volt. (b) $Zn^{2+} + 2Cl^- = Cl_2 + Zn$. (c) 97,900 cal.

8. Given the reaction

$$Fe^{2+}(a = 1) + Ce^{4+}(a = 1) = Fe^{3+}(a = 1) + Ce^{3+}(a = 1)$$

(a) Write the cell which corresponds to this reaction. (b) Calculate $E°$. (c) Calculate $\Delta G°$. (d) Which electrode is positive?

Ans. (a) Pt; $Fe^{2+}(a = 1)$, $Fe^{3+}(a = 1) \parallel Ce^{3+}(a = 1)$, $Ce^{4+}(a = 1)$; Pt. (b) 0.839 volt. (c) $-19,350$ cal. (d) Right electrode.

9. (a) Write the cell reaction for the cell

$$\text{Zn; ZnCl}_2(a = 0.5); \text{AgCl, Ag}$$

(b) Calculate $E°$. (c) Calculate E for the cell as written in (a). (d) Calculate ΔG. (e) Calculate $\Delta G°$.

Ans. (a) $\text{Zn} + 2\text{AgCl} = 2\text{Ag} + \text{ZnCl}_2(a = 0.5)$. (b) 0.985 volt. (c) 0.994 volt. (d) $-45,860$ cal. (e) $-45,450$ cal.

10. (a) Calculate the voltage of the following cell at 25°:

$$\text{Zn; Zn}^{2+}(a = 0.0004) \parallel \text{Cd}^{2+}(a = 0.2); \text{Cd}$$

(b) Write the cell reaction. (c) Calculate the value of the Gibbs free-energy change involved in the reaction. Ans. (a) 0.4398 volt. (b) $\text{Zn}(s) + \text{Cd}^{2+}(a = 0.2) = \text{Zn}^{2+}(a = 0.0004) + \text{Cd}(s)$. (c) $-20,287$ cal.

11. (a) Diagram the cell for the reaction

$$\text{H}_2(g, 1 \text{ atm}) + \text{I}_2(s) = 2\text{HI}(aq, a = 1)$$

(b) Calculate $E°$. (c) Calculate $\Delta G°$. (d) Calculate K. (e) What differences would there be if the reaction had been written

$$\tfrac{1}{2}\text{H}_2(g, 1 \text{ atm}) + \tfrac{1}{2}\text{I}_2(s) = \text{HI}(aq, a = 1)$$

Ans. (a) Pt, $\text{H}_2(g, 1 \text{ atm})$; $\text{HI}(aq, a = 1)$; $\text{I}_2(s)$, Pt. (b) 0.5355 volt. (c) $-24,650$ cal. (d) 1.17×10^{18}. (e) a and b are the same; $\Delta G° = -12,330$ cal; $K = 1.08 \times 10^9$.

12. (a) Calculate the equilibrium constant at 25° for the reaction

$$\text{Fe}^{2+} + \text{Ag}^+ = \text{Ag} + \text{Fe}^{3+}$$

(b) Calculate the concentration of silver ion at equilibrium (assuming that concentrations may be substituted for activities) for an experiment in which an excess of finely divided metallic silver is added to a 0.05 M solution of ferric nitrate.

Ans. (a) 3.0. (b) 0.0443 mole 1^{-1}.

13. Given the cell at 25°

$$\text{Pt, X}_2; \text{X}^-(a = 0.1) \parallel \text{X}^-(a = 0.001); \text{X}_2, \text{Pt}$$

where X is an unknown halogen. (a) Write the cell reaction. (b) Which electrode is negative? (c) What is the voltage of the cell? (d) Is the reaction spontaneous? Ans. (a) $\text{X}^-(a = 0.1) = \text{X}^-(a = 0.001)$. (b) Left. (c) 0.1182 volt. (d) Yes.

14. To what pH values are the following hydrogen-ion activities at 25° equal: (a) 0.3, (b) 10^{-12}? To what hydrogen-ion activities at 25° are the following pH values equivalent: (c) 10.6, (d) -1.1?

Ans. (a) 0.52. (b) 12. (c) 2.5×10^{-11}. (d) 12.6.

15. A cell with a solution and a hydrogen electrode and normal calomel electrode with a normal potassium chloride bridge has a potential of 0.664 volt at 25°. Calculate (a) the pH and (b) the hydrogen-ion activity.

Ans. (a) 6.50. (b) 3.16×10^{-7}.

16. Calculate the emf at 25° of the cell

$$\text{Ag; AgCl}(s); \text{ NaCl}(a = 1); \text{ Hg}_2\text{Cl}_2(s); \text{ Hg}$$

from the following Gibbs free energies of formation:

Ag^+	$+18,488$ cal mole^{-1}
$\text{AgCl}(s)$	$-26,187$
Na^+	$-62,588$
Cl^-	$-31,367$
Hg_2Cl_2	$-50,274$

17. The voltage of the standard Weston cadmium cell is 1.0186 volts at 20° and decreases 4.06×10^{-5} volt for each degree rise in temperature above 20°. (a) State these facts with a single mathematical equation, and calculate (b) ΔH for the cell reaction per mole of cadmium consumed, and (c) the change in Gibbs free energy per mole of cadmium consumed.

18. Derive an expression for the activity of a 3–1 electrolyte (like FeCl$_3$) in terms of the mean ionic activity coefficient and the molality.

19. What is the ionic strength of 0.02 M solutions of each of the following substances: (a) LiCl, (b) K$_2$SO$_4$, (c) Na$_3$PO$_4$?

20. The cell Pt, H$_2$(1 atm); HBr(m); AgBr, Ag has been studied by H. S. Harned, A. S. Keston, and J. G. Donelson [*J. Am. Chem. Soc.,* 58, 989 (1936)]. The following table gives the emf's obtained at 25°:

m	0.01	0.02	0.05	0.10
E	0.3127	0.2786	0.2340	0.2005

Calculate (a) $E°$ and (b) the activity coefficient for a 0.10 molal solution of hydrogen bromide.

21. Given the cell at 25°,

$$\text{Cd; Cd}^{2+}(a = 1) \ \| \ \text{I}^-(a = 1); \text{ I}_2(s), \text{ Pt}$$

(a) Write the cell reaction. (b) Calculate $E°$. (c) Calculate $\Delta G°$. (d) Which electrode is positive?

22. Given the cell at 25°,

$$\text{Pt, Cl}_2(g); \text{ Cl}^-(a = 1) \ \| \ \text{Tl}^{3+}(a = 1), \text{ Tl}^+(a = 1); \text{ Pt}$$

(a) Write the cell reaction. (b) Calculate $E°$. (c) Calculate $\Delta G°$. (d) Which electrode is positive?

23. (a) Design a cell in which the reaction is

$$\tfrac{1}{2}\text{Cl}_2(g, 1 \text{ atm}) + \text{Br}^-(a = 1) = \text{Cl}^-(a = 1) + \tfrac{1}{2}\text{Br}_2(l)$$

Calculate (b) the voltage at 25° and (c) the Gibbs free-energy change of the reaction at 25°.

24. (a) Write the representation for the cell for which the reaction is

$$\text{Cu} + 2\text{Ag}^+(a = 1) = \text{Cu}^{2+}(a = 1) + 2\text{Ag}$$

(b) Calculate the emf of this cell. (c) What is $\Delta G°$ for the cell reaction? (d) Which electrode is positive?

25. The value of $E°$ for the electrode Pt, $O_2(g)$; OH^- cannot be measured directly because the electrode is not reversible. Calculate $E°$ and $\Delta G°$ at $25°$ for the electrode reaction

$$\tfrac{1}{4}O_2(g) + \tfrac{1}{2}H_2O + e = OH^-(a = 1)$$

from the known Gibbs free-energy changes for the reactions

$$H_2(g) + \tfrac{1}{2}O_2(g) = H_2O(l)$$

$$H_2O(l) = H^+(a = 1) + OH^-(a = 1)$$

$$\tfrac{1}{2}H_2(g) = H^+(a = 1) + e$$

26. (a) Calculate the voltage at $25°$ of the cell

$$Pt; Ti^{3+}(a = 0.3), Ti^{4+}(a = 0.5) \parallel Ce^{3+}(a = 0.7), Ce^{4+}(a = 0.002); Pt$$

(b) Write the cell reaction. (c) Calculate ΔG for the cell reaction as written. (d) Calculate $E°$. (e) Calculate $\Delta G°$. (f) Calculate K.

27. Given the cell at $25°$

$$Cd; CdCl_2(a = 1) \parallel SnCl_2(a = 0.01); Sn$$

(a) Write the cell reaction. Calculate (b) $E°$, (c) E, (d) ΔG, (e) $\Delta G°$, (f) K.

28. H. V. Tartar, W. W. Newschwander, and A. T. Ness [*J. Am. Chem. Soc.,* *63*, 28 (1941)] found that the emf of the cell

$$Pt, H_2; H_2SO_4(m = 1.0), ZnSO_4(m = 0.5); Hg_2SO_4; Hg$$

is 0.67281 volt at $25°$. $E° = 0.61515$ volt. Calculate the activity coefficient of H_2SO_4 in a solution which is 1 molal with respect to H_2SO_4 and 0.5 molal with respect to $ZnSO_4$.

29. Using Table IV of electrode potentials, calculate the equilibrium constants at $25°$ for the following reactions in aqueous solution and give the corresponding equilibrium expressions:

$$(a) \quad Fe + 2CrCl_3 = FeCl_2 + 2CrCl_2$$

$$(b) \quad Fe(NO_3)_2 + \tfrac{1}{2}Hg_2(NO_3)_2 = Fe(NO_3)_3 + Hg$$

30. Calculate the equilibrium constant at $25°$ for the reaction

$$2H^+ + D_2(g) = H_2(g) + 2D^+$$

from the electrode potential for D^+; D_2, Pt, which is -3.4 millivolt at $25°$.

31. A thallium amalgam of 4.93 per cent Tl in mercury and another amalgam of 10.02 per cent Tl are placed in separate legs of a glass cell and covered with a solution of thallous sulfate to form a concentration cell. The voltage of the cell is 0.029480 volt at $20°$ and 0.029971 volt at $30°$. (a) Which is the negative electrode? (b) What is the heat of dilution per mole of Tl when Hg is added at $30°$ to change the concentration from 10.02 per cent to 4.93 per cent? (c) What is the voltage of the cell at $40°$?

32. (a) Convert the following hydrogen-ion activities to pH values:

$$a_{H^+} \qquad 0.150 \qquad 0.00237 \qquad 2.85 \times 10^{-7}$$

(b) Convert the following pH values to hydrogen-ion activities:

$$\text{pH} \qquad 0.78 \qquad 4.67 \qquad 9.89$$

33. A hydrogen electrode and a normal calomel cell give a voltage of 0.435 when placed in a certain solution at $25°$. (a) What is the pH of the solution? (b) What is the value of a_{H^+}?

---

34. Calculate $E°_{Zn^{2+};Zn}$ at $25°$ from the following data:

$$\begin{array}{lll}
Zn^{2+}(a = 1) & \Delta \bar{H}°_f = -36.43 \text{ kcal mole}^{-1} & \bar{S}° = -25.45 \text{ cal deg}^{-1} \text{ mole}^{-1} \\
Zn(s) & & \bar{S}° = 9.95 \text{ cal deg}^{-1} \text{ mole}^{-1} \\
H^+(a = 1) & \Delta \bar{H}°_f = 0.000 & \bar{S}° = 0.000 \\
H_2(p = 1) & & \bar{S}° = 31.211 \text{ cal deg}^{-1} \text{ mole}^{-1}
\end{array}$$

35. (a) Write the reaction which occurs when the cell

$$Zn; \; ZnCl_2(0.555 \; m); \; AgCl; \; Ag$$

delivers current and calculate (b) ΔG, (c) ΔS, and (d) ΔH at $25°$ for this reaction. At $25°$ $E = 1.015$ volts and $(\partial E/\partial T)_P = -4.02 \times 10^{-4}$ volt deg^{-1}.

36. Give the expressions for the mean ionic activity coefficients of LiCl, AlCl$_3$, and MgSO$_4$ in terms of the single ion activities and the molality.

37. What is the ionic strength of a 0.4 M solution of: (a) MnCl$_2$, (b) Na$_2$SO$_4$, (c) LaCl$_3$?

38. A solution of NaCl has an ionic strength of 0.24. (a) What is its concentration? (b) What concentration of Na$_2$SO$_4$ would have the same ionic strength? (c) What concentration of MgSO$_4$?

39. The voltage of the cell

$$Ag, \; AgBr; \; MBr(aq \; soln); \; Hg_2Br_2, \; Hg$$

has been determined accurately by T. W. Dakin and D. T. Ewing [*J. Am. Chem. Soc.*, *62*, 2280 (1940)], and the values of $E°_{Br^-;AgBr,Ag}$ have been determined by B. B. Owen and L. Foering [*J. Am. Chem. Soc.*, *58*, 1575 (1936)]. The data are as follows:

Temp., °C	E_{cell}	$E°_{Br^-;AgBr,Ag}$
15	0.06492	0.07586
25	0.06804	0.07121
35	0.07116	0.06591

(a) Calculate $E°_{Br^-;Hg_2Br_2,Hg}$ at each temperature, and find equations which give E_{cell} and $E°_{Br^-;Hg_2Br_2,Hg}$ as functions of temperature. (b) Calculate $\Delta G°$ at $25°$ for the reaction $2Ag + Hg_2Br_2 = 2AgBr + 2Hg$. (c) Calculate ΔH for this reaction. (d) Calculate ΔS for this reaction. (e) Using the Gibbs free energy of formation of silver bromide, $\Delta \bar{G}°_f = -22,935$ cal mole^{-1}, show that the free energy of formation of mercurous bromide is $-42,732$ cal mole^{-1}.

40. Calculate the voltage at $25°$ for the reaction

$$H_2O(l) = H_2(1 \text{ atm}) + \tfrac{1}{2}O_2(1 \text{ atm})$$

using (a) the Gibbs free energy of formation of water, and (b) the oxygen electrode potential calculated in problem 25.

41. Calculate the voltage for the half-cell reactions:

(a) $\quad H_2(1 \text{ atm}) = 2H^+(a = 10^{-7}) + 2e$

(b) $\quad H_2(1 \text{ atm}) + 2OH^-(a = 1) = 2H_2O(l) + 2e$

42. A small, efficient battery for hearing aids contains zinc and mercury electrodes. The mercury is mixed with mercuric oxide, and the electrolyte is potassium hydroxide. (a) Write a net reaction for the cell in which hydroxyl ions and zinc are consumed, mercury is deposited, and potassium zincate (K_2ZnO_2) is formed. (b) Write the half-cell reactions.

43. Given the cell at $25°$

$$Zn; Zn^{2+}(a = 0.001) \parallel I^-(a = 0.1); I_2(s), Pt$$

(a) Write the cell reaction. (b) Calculate the voltage of the cell. (c) Calculate the equilibrium constant for the cell reaction.

44. The Gibbs free energy of formation of Pb^{2+} at $25°$ is -5630 cal. The Gibbs free energies of formation of the elements and of the hydrogen ion at unit activity are taken as zero. Calculate the voltage of the cell at $25°$:

$$Pt, H_2(1 \text{ atm}); H^+(a = 0.2) \parallel Pb^{2+}(a = 0.001); Pb$$

45. The electromotive force of the cell

$$\text{Normal calomel electrode} \parallel \begin{pmatrix} FeCl_3(0.1 \text{ m}) \\ FeCl_2(0.1 \text{ m}) \\ HCl(0.1 \text{ m}) \end{pmatrix} ; Pt$$

is 0.446 volt at $25°$. The hydrochloric acid is added to prevent hydrolysis. Assuming that the activity coefficients of the Fe^{3+} and Fe^{2+} ions are 0.75 and 0.87 respectively, calculate the value of $E°$ for the ferrous-ferric electrode containing 0.1 m HCl.

46. Design cells without transference which could be used to determine the activity coefficients of aqueous solutions of (a) NaOH and (b) H_2SO_4. Give the equations relating voltage to mean ionic activity coefficient.

47. A solution 0.5 molal with respect to H_2SO_4 and 1.5 molal with respect to $ZnSO_4$ has a vapor pressure of 22.454 mm at $25°$. For the cell

$$Pt, H_2; H_2SO_4(m = 0.5), ZnSO_4(m = 1.5); Hg_2SO_4; Hg$$

$E = 0.69021$ volt and $E° = 0.61515$ volt. For the cell

$$Zn; H_2SO_4(m = 0.5); ZnSO_4(m = 1.5); Hg_2SO_4; Hg$$

$E = 1.44561$ volts and $E° = 1.3765$ volts. The vapor pressure of pure water at $25°$ is 23.75 mm. Calculate (a) the activity of the water, (b) the mean activity of the H_2SO_4, and (c) the mean activity of the $ZnSO_4$ [H. V. Tartar, W. W. Newschwander, and A. T. Ness, *J. Am. Chem. Soc.*, *63*, 28 (1941)].

48. (a) Calculate the equilibrium constant at $25°$ for the reaction

$$Sn^{4+} + 2Ti^{3+} = 2Ti^{4+} + Sn^{2+}$$

(b) When 0.01 mole of Sn^{2+} ion is added to 1.0 mole of Ti^{4+} ion in 1000 grams of water, what will be the concentration of Ti^{3+} ions (if it is assumed for the calculation that the activities are equal to the concentrations)?

49. (a) Diagram the cell which corresponds to the reaction $Ag^+ + Br^- = AgBr$. Calculate at 25° (b) $E°$, (c) $\Delta G°$, (d) K.

50. For the reaction

$$2Fe^{3+} + 2Hg = 2Fe^{2+} + Hg_2^{2+}$$

the equilibrium constant is 0.018 at 25° and 0.054 at 35°. Calculate the value of $E°$ at 45° for the cell which corresponds to this reaction.

51. Develop an equation for calculating the voltage of a cell consisting of two chlorine electrodes at different partial pressures immersed in a solution of a chloride. Calculate the voltage at 25° if the chlorine of one electrode is at 1 atm, and the other is at 0.70 atm with nitrogen added to bring the total pressure to 1 atm.

52. When the pH of a solution is measured by means of a hydrogen electrode against a calomel electrode, the partial pressure of the hydrogen is usually not exactly 1 atm. At 25° how low can the partial pressure of the hydrogen be before a correction is necessary, if an error of 0.01 pH unit is allowable?

53. What is the pH of a solution that has an activity of hydrogen ions of (a) 1.52, (b) 4×10^{-8}? What is the value of a_{H^+} in a solution which has a pH of (c) 15.2, (d) 0.25?

54. A hydrogen electrode and calomel cell are used to determine the pH of a solution on a mountain where the barometric pressure is 500 mm. The hydrogen is allowed to bubble out of the electrode at the atmospheric pressure prevailing there. If the pH is calculated to be 4.00, what is the correct pH of the solution?

IONIC EQUILIBRIA

15

The activity coefficients of electrolytes depend significantly upon the electrolyte concentration. This has already been illustrated by the activity coefficients obtained from electromotive-force measurements (p. 398) and will be encountered again in this chapter in connection with the solubility of electrolytes and ionic equilibria. The electrical charges of the ions produce attractions and repulsions which cause deviations from ideal behavior.

Solubility Product. The equilibrium between solid MX and its ions in solution may be represented by

$$MX(s) = M^+ + X^- \text{ (in solution)}$$

and the equilibrium relation by

$$K = \frac{a_{MX(\text{soln})}}{a_{MX(s)}}$$

The activity of the solid phase is fixed by the presence of the pure solid, and it is convenient to take $a_{MX(s)} = 1$. The solubility product K_{sp} is then written

$$K_{sp} = a_{MX(\text{soln})} = \gamma_{\pm}^2 m^2 \tag{1}$$

In general, the equilibrium between $M_{\nu_+}X_{\nu_-}(s)$ and its ions in saturated solution may be represented by

$$M_{\nu_+}X_{\nu_-}(s) = \nu_+ M + \nu_- X \text{ (in solution)}$$

and the solubility product is given by

$$K_{sp} = a_{M_{\nu_+}X^{\nu_-}}$$
$$= (\nu_+^{\nu_+}\nu_-^{\nu_-})\gamma_{\pm}^{(\nu_++\nu_-)} m^{(\nu_++\nu_-)} \tag{2}$$

422

where m is the molality of the saturated solution, and $\gamma_{\pm}$ is the mean ionic activity coefficient (p. 391). For a very slightly soluble salt $\gamma_{\pm}$ may be taken as unity if no other electrolyte is present, since $\gamma_{\pm}$ approaches unity as the concentration of the solution approaches zero. Solubility products calculated in this way are useful in many practical applications, provided that the electrolyte concentration is very low. Activity coefficients are needed for accurate calculations of the solubility in the presence of an excess of one or more of the precipitating ions or in the presence of any added electrolytes. Typical solubility products are given in Table I.

Table I.[1]   Solubility Products at 25°

AgCl	$10^{-9.7}$ mole² liter⁻²	Ag₂SO₄	$10^{-4.8}$ mole³ liter⁻³
AgBr	$10^{-12.1}$	Ag₂CO₃	$10^{-11.0}$
AgI	$10^{-16.0}$	Cu₂S	$10^{-49.4}$
		Ag₂S	$10^{-51.4}$
CaSO₄	$10^{-5.9}$	Mg(OH)₂	$10^{-10.6}$
SrSO₄	$10^{-6.6}$		
BaSO₄	$10^{-10.0}$	Fe(OH)₃	$10^{-36.4}$ mole⁴ liter⁻⁴
FeS	$10^{-17.3}$		
PbS	$10^{-29.3}$	Bi₂(SO₄)₃	10^{-97} mole⁵ liter⁻⁵
CaCO₃	$10^{-8.1}$		

[1] J. Bjerrum, G. Schwarzenbach, and L. G. Sillén, *Stability Constants*, Part II: *Inorganic Ligands*, The Chemical Society, London, 1958.

Example 1. Silver chromate is completely dissociated in solution according to

$$Ag_2CrO_4(s) = 2Ag^+ + CrO_4{}^{2-}$$

(a) Calculate the solubility product of Ag₂CrO₄ from the solubility in water at 25°, which is 8.00 × 10⁻⁵ molar. Using equation 2,

$$K_{sp} = (2^2 \cdot 1^1)(8.00 \times 10^{-5})^3 = 2.00 \times 10^{-12}$$

(b) Calculate the solubility of Ag₂CrO₄ in a solution which has an excess of AgNO₃ of 0.001 molar, assuming that the solution is sufficiently dilute so that the molarity may be taken as equal to activity.

$$K_{sp} = 2.00 \times 10^{-12} = (Ag^+)^2(CrO_4{}^{2-}) = (0.001 + 2x)^2(x)$$

$$x = 2.00 \times 10^{-6} \text{ molar, concentration of } Ag_2CrO_4$$

It is found that the solubility of a slightly soluble salt is *increased* by the addition at low concentrations of electrolytes which do not have an ion in common with the slightly soluble salt. This increase in solubility results from the smaller activity coefficient of the slightly soluble salt in the presence of the added electrolyte. This effect may be discussed quantitatively, using the expression for the solubility product involving the activity coefficient. In fact, equation 2 provides the means for determining the activity coefficient of a slightly soluble electrolyte in the presence of added electrolytes, not possessing a common ion.

Example 2. The solubility of Ag_2CrO_4 in 0.04 M $NaNO_3$ is 8.84 $\times$ 10^{-5} molar in water at 25°. Calculate the mean ionic activity coefficient. From equation 2 and example 1,

$$K_{sp} = 2.00 \times 10^{-12} = (2^2 \cdot 1^1) (8.84 \times 10^{-5})^3 \gamma_{\pm}{}^3$$

$$\gamma_{\pm} = 0.90$$

In sufficiently dilute solutions the Debye-Hückel theory (p. 392) may be used to calculate the mean ionic activity coefficient. In aqueous solutions at 25° the mean ionic activity coefficient of an electrolyte with ions of charge z_+ and z_- is given by

$$\log \gamma_{\pm} = -0.509 z_+ z_- \sqrt{I} \tag{3}$$

where I is the ionic strength.

Example 3. Calculate the mean ionic activity coefficient of Ag_2CrO_4 in an aqueous solution to which another electrolyte has been added to give an ionic strength of 0.01 at 25°.

$$\log \gamma_{\pm} = -(0.509)(2)(0.01)^{1/2} = 0.898 - 1$$

$$\gamma_{\pm} = 0.79$$

As a test of the Debye-Hückel theory, Brönsted and LaMer * determined the solubility of three types of complex cobalt ammine salts in salt solutions of various charge types. The thermodynamic solubility products of the cobalt ammine salts were determined by extrapolation to zero salt concentration. The Debye-Hückel theory indicates that for dilute salt solutions the log of the mean ionic activity coefficient is directly proportional to the square root of the ionic strength. Thus the value of K_{sp} may be obtained by plotting the logarithm of the solubility versus the square root of the ionic strength. Once the intercept at zero ionic strength has been obtained, the activity coefficient at any other strength may be calculated from the solubility. In *Fig. 15-1*, $-\log \gamma_{\pm}$ is plotted against $\sqrt{I}$. The open circle on each line gives the ionic strength of the saturated solution of the complex cobalt salt in water. The ionic strengths are increased by the

* J. N. Brönsted and V. K. LaMer, *J. Am. Chem. Soc.*, *46*, 555 (1924).

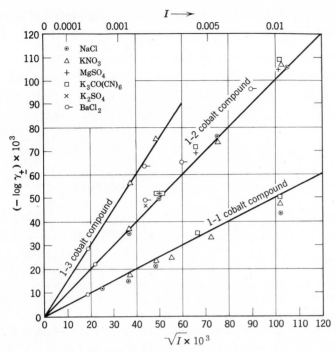

Fig. 15-1. Influence of salts of different valence types on the activity coefficients of slightly soluble cobalt ammine salts. (The various symbols indicate the salt added to increase the ionic strength. The open circles represent saturated solutions of the cobalt compounds in water.)

addition of electrolytes of various valence types. The straight lines in this figure are theoretical lines calculated with equation 3. The lowest line corresponds to a 1–1 cobalt compound, where $z_1 z_2$ is 1, and the slope is seen to be 0.5. The ionic strength of the solution rather than the specific nature of the added salt determines the value of $\gamma_\pm$. The next line corresponds to a cobalt salt of the 1–2 type, where $z_1 z_2$ has a value of 2, and the slope is $2 \times 0.5 = 1$. The steepest line in Fig. 15-1 corresponds to a 1–3 compound, where $z_1 z_2$ is 3, and the slope is 1.5. The figure emphasizes the fact that in sufficiently *dilute* solutions the activity coefficient of a given strong electrolyte is the same in all solutions of the same ionic strength, regardless of the specific electrolytes added.

Proton Theory of Acids. According to the proton theory of acids, which was developed by Brönsted and Bjerrum in Denmark and Lowry in England in 1923, an acid is a substance that yields protons and a base is a substance that accepts protons. Thus the dissociation of an acid A always produces a base B.

$$A = H^+ + B \tag{4}$$

A and B are termed a conjugate acid-base pair. Examples are:

Acid		Proton		Base
$H_2PO_4^-$	$=$	H^+	$+$	HPO_4^{2-}
NH_4^+	$=$	H^+	$+$	NH_3
H_3O^+	$=$	H^+	$+$	H_2O
H_2O	$=$	H^+	$+$	OH^-
$Cr(H_2O)_6^{3+}$	$=$	H^+	$+$	$Cr(H_2O)_5OH^{2+}$

The proton is just the nucleus of a hydrogen atom, and this small particle has a very great tendency to attach itself to molecules of the solvent. Thus the proton does not exist free in solution, but is in combination with the solvent. In water the proton may form a hydronium ion, H_3O^+, or other complex species. Since the state of the proton in aqueous solution is not exactly known, the symbol H^+ will be used to represent the hydrated hydrogen ion.

The extent to which an acid dissociates in different solvents depends upon the affinity of the solvent for protons as well as the "intrinsic" acid strength of the acid. Thus an acid may dissociate very completely in liquid ammonia and very incompletely in acetic acid, since ammonia has a much greater attraction for protons than has acetic acid. Actually the intrinsic affinity cannot be measured because the dissociation of an acid can always be represented by

$$A_1 + \text{solvent} = H^+ \cdot \text{solvent} + B_1 \tag{5}$$

A_1 is an acid because it transfers protons, but the molecule $H \cdot^+$ solvent may also be regarded as an acid A_2 because it can transfer a proton to base B_1. The solvent accepts the proton and may be regarded as a base B_2. Then, rewriting equation 5, we have

$$A_1 + B_2 = A_2 + B_1 \tag{6}$$

The solvation of protons leads to a leveling effect on the strength of all strong acids in a given solvent. Thus all acids which are completely dissociated in water have nearly the same acid strength in water because the actual acid is the hydrated hydrogen ion. On the other hand, various acids which are strong in water have quite different strengths in glacial acetic acid, which is not as basic a solvent and does not combine so strongly with protons.

The definition of an acid as a proton donor makes it possible to classify certain reactions as acid-base reactions which might not otherwise be considered from this point of view. Examples are:

$$NH_4Cl + NaNH_2 = 2NH_3 + NaCl \quad \text{(in liquid } NH_3)$$

and

$$HCl + NaC_2H_3O_2 = HC_2H_2O_3 + NaCl \quad \text{(in glacial acetic acid)}$$

A still more general theory of acids was proposed by G. N. Lewis, who pointed out that substances like SO_3, CO_2, and $SnCl_4$ behave like acids although they contain no hydrogen. According to this point of view, an acid is a molecule, radical, or ion which can accept an electron pair from some other atom to complete its stable quota of electrons, usually an octet (p. 483). A base is a substance which can share this electron pair with an acid. In other words, an acid is an electron "acceptor," and a base is an electron "donor." This definition covers all the acids included in the proton theory of acids and many additional substances also.

Ionization of Water. Water dissociates according to the reaction

$$H_2O = H^+ + OH^-$$

In the equilibrium constant expression

$$K = \frac{a_{H^+}a_{OH^-}}{a_{H_2O}}$$

the activity of water is taken as unity in dilute aqueous solutions. For pure water or aqueous solutions of quite low ionic strengths the concentrations of hydrogen and hydroxyl ions may be substituted for their activities, and the *ion product* K_w of water written as

$$K_w = (H^+)(OH^-) \tag{7}$$

The ion product of water has been determined by several methods, all of which are in excellent agreement.

Example 4. Calculate the degree of dissociation and the ion product of water at 25° from the fact that the specific conductance of the purest water has been found * to be 5.5×10^{-8} ohm^{-1} cm^{-1}. The ionic conductances at infinite dilution are $l_{H^+} = 349.8$ and $l_{OH^-} = 198.0$ cm^2 equiv^{-1} ohm^{-1}.

In pure water 18 ml contains 1 mole of H_2O. Then, the equivalent conductance Λ is given by the relation

$$\Lambda = \kappa V = (5.5 \times 10^{-8})(18.0) = 9.9 \times 10^{-7}$$

* F. Kohlrausch and A. Heydweiller, *Z. physik. Chem.*, *14*, 317 (1894); G. Jones and B. C. Bradshaw, *J. Am. Chem. Soc.*, *55*, 1800 (1933).

The equivalent conductance of a hypothetical completely ionized water is

$$\Lambda_0 = l_c + l_a = 349.8 + 198.0 = 547.8$$

$$\alpha = \frac{\Lambda}{\Lambda_0} = \frac{9.9 \times 10^{-7}}{548} = 1.81 \times 10^{-9}$$

Since there are 1000/18 or 55.5 moles of water per liter,

$$(H^+) = (OH^-) = 55.5\alpha = (55.5)(1.81 \times 10^{-9}) = 1.00 \times 10^{-7}$$

$$K_w = (H^+)(OH^-) = (1.00 \times 10^{-7})(1.00 \times 10^{-7}) = 1.00 \times 10^{-14}$$

The ion product of water may also be obtained from electromotive-force measurements of the cell.*

$$\text{Pt, } H_2(1\text{atm}); \text{ KOH, KCl; AgCl; Ag}$$

Exercise I. When the concentrations of KOH and HCl are 0.01 molal, the voltage of the cell at 25° is 1.05033. Assuming that at this dilution $\gamma_{Cl}^- = \gamma_{OH}^-$, calculate K_w for water.

The ion product of water is given at various temperatures in Table II.

Table II. Ion Product of Pure Water [1]

Temperature	0°	10°	25°	40°	50°
$K_w \times 10^{14}$	0.113	0.292	1.008	2.917	5.474

[1] H. S. Harned and W. J. Hamer, *J. Am. Chem. Soc.*, *55*, 2194 (1933).

The ion product for D_2O at 25° is 1.54×10^{-15}.

The enthalpy change for the dissociation of water may be calculated from these data as described on p. 215. The value of $\Delta H = 13.8$ kcal mole^{-1} is in agreement with the directly determined calorimetric value (p. 70) obtained from the heat of neutralization of a strong acid and a strong base.

Ionization of Weak Acids. The ionization constants of weak acids and bases may be determined in several different ways. The most important method involves potentiometric measurements with hydrogen or glass electrodes. The conductance method has already been discussed (p. 365). The equilibrium expression for the dissociation of a weak acid HA in water may be written

$$HA = H^+ + A^-$$

$$K_a = \frac{a_{H^+} a_{A^-}}{a_{HA}} = \frac{(H^+)(A^-)\gamma_\pm^2}{(HA)\gamma_{HA}} \tag{8}$$

* H. S. Harned and W. J. Hamer, *J. Am. Chem. Soc.*, *55*, 2194 (1933).

where K_a is the thermodynamic dissociation constant. For many situations where this equation is applied, the salt concentration is constant, so that it is satisfactory to assume that the activity coefficient $\gamma_\pm$ is constant. For dilute solutions γ_{HA} will also be constant and nearly equal to unity. When this is true, the activities may be placed on the other side of the equation to give

$$K_a' = K_a \frac{\gamma_{HA}}{\gamma_\pm^2} = \frac{(H^+)(A^-)}{(HA)} \tag{9}$$

The equilibrium quotient K_a' will vary with the salt concentration and is called the *apparent dissociation constant* at a particular salt concentration. The *thermodynamic dissociation constant* K_a is independent of the salt concentration and is dependent only upon the temperature and the solvent. As the electrolyte and acid concentrations approach zero, K_a' approaches K_a.

The thermodynamic ionization constants of a number of acids in water are given in Table III. The pK_a values, which are also given, are defined by $pK_a = -\log K_a$. The symbol K_1 refers to the dissociation of the first hydrogen, and K_2 to that of the second hydrogen.

Table III.[1] Ionization Constants of Acids in Water at 25°

Acid	K_a		pK_a
Formic		1.772×10^{-4}	3.75
Acetic		1.754×10^{-5}	4.76
Chloroacetic		1.379×10^{-3}	2.86
Propionic		1.336×10^{-5}	4.87
n-Butyric		1.515×10^{-5}	4.82
Lactic		1.374×10^{-4}	3.86
Sulfuric	$K_2 =$	1.01×10^{-2}	2.00
Carbonic	$K_2 =$	4.69×10^{-11}	10.33
Oxalic	$K_2 =$	5.18×10^{-5}	4.29
Malonic	$K_2 =$	2.014×10^{-6}	5.70
Phosphoric	$K_1 =$	7.516×10^{-3}	2.12
	$K_2 =$	6.226×10^{-8}	7.21
Boric	$K_1 =$	5.79×10^{-10}	9.24

[1] H. S. Harned and B. B. Owen, *The Physical Chemistry of Electrolytic Solutions,* Reinhold Publishing Corp., New York, 1950.

Example 5. Calculate the pK_a of formic acid at 25° from the fact that $K_a = 1.772 \times 10^{-4}$.

$$pK = -\log(1.772 \times 10^{-4})$$
$$= -(-4 + 0.25)$$
$$= 3.75$$

The dependence of the apparent ionization constant on ionic strength is illustrated by data for acetic acid in Table IV. The ionic strength dependence at low ionic strengths may be calculated using the Debye-Hückel theory.

Table IV. Apparent Ionization Constant of Acetic Acid in Potassium Chloride Solutions at 25°

Salt molality	0		0.01	0.05	0.10	0.20
$K_a \times 10^5$	1.75		1.86	2.19	2.69	2.95
pK_a	4.76		4.73	4.66	4.57	4.53

Example 6. Estimate the apparent ionization constant of acetic acid at 0.01 ionic strength and 25°, assuming that $\gamma_{HA} = 1$. The thermodynamic value of the ionization constant is 1.75×10^{-5}. Using equation 3,

$$\log \gamma_\pm = -0.509(0.01)^{1/2} = -0.0509$$
$$\gamma_\pm = 0.889$$

Using equation 9,

$$K_a' = 1.75 \times 10^{-5}/0.889^2 = 2.22 \times 10^{-5}$$

In working problems, apparent ionization constants will be used and will simply be represented by K. The pH will be considered to be equal to $-\log(\mathrm{H}^+)$ as a simplification.

A simple acid-dissociation problem is the calculation of the hydrogen-ion concentration in a solution of a weak acid. If $(\mathrm{H}^+) > 10^{-6}$ the following method may be used. The concentration of undissociated weak acid is given by $(HA) = c_a - (\mathrm{H}^+)$, where c_a is the total molar concentration of the weak acid, including both dissociated and undissociated forms, and $(\mathrm{H}^+) = (A^-)$. Substituting in equation 9,

$$K_a = \frac{(\mathrm{H}^+)^2}{c_a - (\mathrm{H}^+)} \tag{10}$$

The solution of a quadratic equation may be avoided if the weak acid is only slightly dissociated, so that $c_a \gg (\mathrm{H}^+)$, and equation 10 becomes

$$(\mathrm{H}^+) = (K_a c_a)^{1/2} \tag{11}$$

Example 7. Calculate the hydrogen-ion concentration and pH of an aqueous solution of acetic acid at 25° containing 0.1 mole liter^{-1}. Given: $K_a = 1.75 \times 10^{-5}$.

$$(H^+) = (K_a c_a)^{1/2} = [(1.75 \times 10^{-5})(0.1)]^{1/2}$$
$$= 1.32 \times 10^{-3} \text{ mole/l}$$
$$pH = -\log (H^+) = 2.88$$

Since $(H^+) > 10^{-6}$ and is about 1 per cent of c_a, we are justified in using equation 11.

However, to obtain an equation for the dissociation of a weak acid which is rigorously applicable it is necessary to consider all the relations which must be satisfied. These are:

(a) The equilibrium quotient expressions.
(b) The statement of electrical neutrality of the solution.
(c) The conservation of substances added to the solution.

In general the combination of these equations leads to a quadratic or higher-order equation which is difficult to solve.* Often certain approximations may be used to simplify the calculation; however, the validity of the approximations must be checked.

As an illustration let us consider the ionization of a weak acid HA in water without making the approximations of Example 7.

(a) The equilibrium expressions to be satisfied are

$$K_a = (H^+)(A^-)/(HA)$$

$$K_w = (H^+)(OH^-)$$

(b) Electrical neutrality of the solution requires that

$$(H^+) = (A^-) + (OH^-)$$

(c) Conservation of weak acid requires that

$$c_a = (HA) + (A^-)$$

where c_a is the total concentration of added weak acid.

The elimination of (HA), (A^-), and (OH^-) between these equations leads to

$$c_a = [(H^+) - K_w/(H^+)] [1 + (H^+)/K_a] \qquad (12)$$

This cubic equation may be solved for the hydrogen-ion concentration corresponding to the stoichiometric concentration c_a of added weak acid.

---

* A number of examples with suggestions for obtaining solutions are discussed by E. R. Nightingale, *J. Chem. Educ.*, *34*, 277 (1957); and E. L. King, *J. Chem. Educ.*, *31*, 183 (1954).

Under certain circumstances approximations may be introduced which simplify the numerical calculation of the hydrogen-ion concentration. For example, if $(H^+) > 10^{-6}$, then $K_w/(H^+) < 10^{-8}$ and may be neglected in the first term of equation 12. When this is done, equation 10 is obtained.

pH of a Salt Solution. A salt formed from a strong base and a strong acid gives a neutral reaction when dissolved in water, but a salt of a weak acid and a strong base gives a pH greater than 7 because the anions of the weak acid react with water molecules to produce molecules of weak acid and hydroxyl ions. Reactions of this type are referred to as hydrolysis reactions. For example

$$A^- + H_2O = HA + OH^-$$

A salt of a weak base and a strong acid gives a pH less than 7 because the cations of the weak base react with water molecules to produce molecules of weak base and protons. In order to calculate the pH of a salt solution the three types of relations just described must be considered. For a salt MA of a strong base and a weak acid:

(a) The equilibrium expressions to be satisfied are

$$K_a = (H^+)(A^-)/(HA)$$
$$K_w = (H^+)(OH^-)$$

(b) Assuming that the salt is completely dissociated, $(M^+) = c_s$, where c_s is the salt concentration. Electroneutrality of the solution requires that

$$c_s + (H^+) = (A^-) + (OH^-)$$

(c) Conservation of the salt added requires that

$$c_s = (A^-) + (HA)$$

Substitution of the conservation equation into (b) and elimination of (HA) and (OH$^-$) by use of equilibrium equations in (a) yields

$$(H^+) = \left[\frac{K_w K_a}{K_a + (A^-)} \right]^{1/2} \tag{13}$$

If K_a is negligibly small compared with (A^-), then

$$(H^+) = \left[\frac{K_w K_a}{(A^-)} \right]^{1/2} \tag{14}$$

If the concentration of the anion is practically as large as the stoichiometric concentration c_s of the salt, then

$$(H^+) = \left(\frac{K_w K_a}{c_s} \right)^{1/2} \tag{15}$$

Example 8. Calculate the hydrogen-ion concentration and pH of a 0.1 N solution of sodium acetate at 25°. The value of K_a at this ionic strength is 2.69×10^{-5}.

$$(\text{H}^+) = \left(\frac{K_w K_a}{c_s}\right)^{\frac{1}{2}} = \left[\frac{(10^{-14})(2.69 \times 10^{-5})}{0.1}\right]^{\frac{1}{2}}$$

$$= 1.64 \times 10^{-9}$$

$$\text{pH} = -\log(1.64 \times 10^{-9}) = 8.78$$

The use of equation 15 is justified, since $(A^-) \gg K_a$ and the fraction of anions reacting is very small. This is the pH at the equivalence point in a titration of 0.1 N acetic acid with a concentrated solution of a strong base; this is the point at which the number of moles of base added is equal to the number of moles of acetic acid.

If the salt solution is quite dilute, equation 15 will obviously give the wrong answer, since the hydrogen-ion concentration will not increase indefinitely as c_s is decreased. For dilute solutions it is necessary to eliminate (A^-) from equation 13 by use of the electroneutrality expression to obtain

$$(\text{H}^+) = \left[\frac{K_w K_a}{K_a + c_s + (\text{H}^+) - K_w/(\text{H}^+)}\right]^{\frac{1}{2}} \tag{16}$$

This equation may be solved for (H^+) graphically by substituting various values of (H^+) in the right side and plotting the resulting value versus (H^+). The solution is the value of (H^+) at which the plot crosses the line drawn from the origin at 45°. At this point the two sides of the equation are equal.

pH of a Solution of a Salt of a Weak Acid and the Corresponding Weak Acid. Such solutions are encountered in the titration of a weak acid with a strong base and are also useful as buffers (p. 440). In many cases, the calculation of the hydrogen-ion concentration can be greatly simplified by introducing approximations. The addition of the salt represses the ionization of the acid so that to a very good approximation the concentration of undissociated acid is equal to the molar concentration of added weak acid (c_a). Similarly the addition of the acid represses the hydrolysis of the salt so that to a very good approximation the concentration of anions of the weak acid is equal to the molar concentration of the salt c_s. Thus equation 9 becomes

$$K_a = \frac{(\text{H}^+)c_s}{c_a} \tag{17}$$

In order to make calculations of the pH it is convenient to write equation 17 in its logarithmic form:

$$-\log K_a = -\log(\text{H}^+) - \log\frac{c_s}{c_a} \tag{18}$$

Upon introduction of the definitions of pH and pK_a (p. 429), this equation becomes

$$pH = pK_a + \log \frac{c_s}{c_a} \tag{19}$$

To the approximation used in deriving equation 19, the pK_a for a weak acid is the pH of a solution containing equimolar quantities of salt and acid.

Example 9. Calculate the pH at $25°$ of a solution containing 0.10 mole liter^{-1} of sodium acetate and 0.03 mole liter^{-1} of acetic acid. Because sodium acetate and potassium chloride at the same concentration have the same ionic strength, the value of pK_a for acetic acid in 0.1 M potassium chloride, as given in Table IV, will give a much more accurate value than the pK_a at zero salt concentration.

$$pH = 4.57 + \log (0.10/0.030) = 5.09$$

Equation 19 does not give an accurate result in the case of a relatively strong acid if $c_s \ll c_a$, since (A^-) is larger than c_s and (HA) is smaller than c_a. To solve such a problem in a general way it is necessary to consider the following relations:

(a) The equilibrium expressions are

$$K_a = (\text{H}^+)(A^-)/(HA)$$

$$K_w = (\text{H}^+)(\text{OH}^-)$$

(b) Assuming that the salt is completely dissociated so that $(M^+) = c_s$, electrical neutrality of the solution requires that

$$(\text{H}^+) + c_s = (A^-) + (\text{OH}^-)$$

(c) Conservation of added weak acid and salt requires that

$$c_a + c_s = (HA) + (A^-)$$

The elimination of (HA), (A^-), and (OH^-) between these equations yields

$$(\text{H}^+) + c_s = \frac{c_a + c_s}{1 + (\text{H}^+)/K_a} + \frac{K_w}{(\text{H}^+)} \tag{20}$$

which may be solved, but with difficulty, for the hydrogen-ion concentration corresponding to the stoichiometric concentrations of added weak acid and salt.

If c_s approaches zero this equation reduces to equation 12, and if c_a approaches zero this equation reduces to equation 16.

Titration Curves of Weak Acids. The titration curve for 0.004 M acetic acid titrated with a concentrated solution of sodium hydroxide at

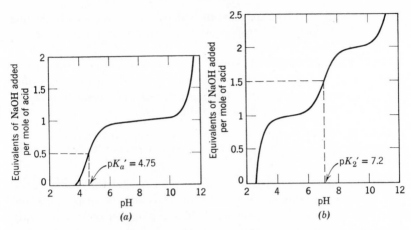

Fig. 15-2. (a) Titration of 0.004 M acetic acid with sodium hydroxide at 25°. (b) Titration of 0.004 M phosphoric acid with sodium hydroxide.

25° is given in *Fig. 15-2a.* The pH is plotted horizontally, while the number of equivalents of sodium hydroxide added to 1 equivalent of acid is plotted vertically. The pH at the midpoint of the titration is equal to the pK_a of acetic acid at this salt concentration, 4.75. The pH at any other point from about 5 to 95 per cent neutralization may be calculated with equation 19. As the end point is approached the pH changes rapidly, and the exact end point would be at the pH of a solution of sodium acetate, which may be calculated as shown in example 8.

The titration curve for 0.004 M phosphoric acid titrated with a concentrated solution of sodium hydroxide is given in *Fig. 15-2b.* The three successive ionizations of phosphoric acid are represented by

$$H_3PO_4 = H_2PO_4^- + H^+ \qquad K_1 = \frac{(H^+)(H_2PO_4^-)}{(H_3PO_4)} \qquad (21)$$

$$H_2PO_4^- = HPO_4^{2-} + H^+ \qquad K_2 = \frac{(H^+)(HPO_4^{2-})}{(H_2PO_4^-)} \qquad (22)$$

$$HPO_4^{2-} = PO_4^{3-} + H^+ \qquad K_3 = \frac{(H^+)(PO_4^{3-})}{(HPO_4^{2-})} \qquad (23)$$

For citric acid (tribasic) the values of the successive constants are enough alike so that separate steps in the titration curve are not obtained. For phosphoric acid the constants are quite different, and the third ionization is so weak that it cannot be studied in dilute aqueous solutions. The first ionization of phosphoric acid is sufficiently strong so that the shape of the titration curve in the first step cannot be calculated by means of equation 19, since the assumptions made in its derivation are not valid. However, the second ionization is sufficiently weak so that the shape of the second step is in agreement with values calculated from equation 19. The midpoint of the second step of the titration is at pH 7.2, which is the value of pK_2.

Exercise II. Sketch the titration curve for the titration of sodium carbonate with hydrochloric acid, carbon dioxide not being allowed to escape. The pK values are $pK_1 = 6.4$ and $pK_2 = 10.3$.

The determination of titration curves offers one of the most convenient means for obtaining the ionization constants of weak acids and bases. It is common practice to hold the salt concentration nearly constant by adding a neutral salt so that the salt concentration does not change with the addition of relatively small amounts of acid or base. Then the value of K_a applies at this salt concentration. Accurate thermodynamic values of ionization constants may be obtained using cells without transference (p. 395).

Relation between Ionization Constants and Structure. From the values in Table III it may be seen that replacing one of the methyl hydrogens of acetic acid with a chlorine atom leads to an increased ionization of the carboxyl group. Apparently, the attraction of chlorine for electrons pulls the electron pair in the O—H bond farther away from the hydrogen atom and permits the hydrogen ion to leave the oxygen atom with the requirement of less energy. The substitution of more hydrogen atoms by chlorine atoms in acetic acid further decreases the attraction with which the hydrogen ion is held and gives stronger acids with larger ionization constants. Trichloroacetic acid is so completely ionized that its ionization constant cannot be determined with any accuracy. The substitution of —OH, —CN, or —NO$_2$ groups for hydrogen also increases the carboxyl ionization.

The influence of one group on the reactivity of a near-by group is affected by the distance and the position, as shown in the chloro-substituted benzoic acids at 25°.

Benzoic acid	p-Chloro-benzoic acid	m-Chloro-benzoic acid	o-Chloro-benzoic acid
COOH	COOH	COOH	COOH
$K_a = 7.3 \times 10^{-5}$	$K_a = 9.3 \times 10^{-5}$	$K_a = 1.55 \times 10^{-4}$	$K_a = 1.32 \times 10^{-3}$

The interesting question as to why HF is a weak acid ($K_a = 6.7 \times 10^{-4}$), whereas HCl, HBr, and HI are strong acids, is discussed by Pauling.*

Ionization of Weak Bases. The ionization of a weak base containing a hydroxyl group is represented by

$$BOH = B^+ + OH^-$$

$$K_b = \frac{(OH^-)(B^+)}{(BOH)} \tag{24}$$

Other bases, like aniline, do not contain hydroxyl groups but are bases because they combine with protons, as represented by

$$B + H^+ = BH^+ \tag{25}$$

In discussing the ionization of a base B it is convenient to formulate the ionization in terms of the acid dissociation of BH^+. The substance BH^+ is referred to as the *conjugate* acid of B. When this is done, problems with weak bases may be handled in the same way in terms of the pH scale as problems with weak acids. The relation between K_b for the base and K_a for the conjugate acid may be found by dividing equation 24 into the expression $K_w = (H^+)(OH^-)$.

$$K_a = \frac{K_w}{K_b} = \frac{(H^+)(BOH)}{(B^+)} \tag{26}$$

which is the equilibrium constant for the ionization formulated as

$$B^+ + H_2O = H^+ + BOH$$

For a base B which does not contain a hydroxyl group

$$BH^+ = H^+ + B$$

$$K_a = \frac{(H^+)(B)}{(BH^+)} \tag{27}$$

The values of K_b and K_a for a number of bases are given in Table V. The product of K_a and K_b is equal to K_w, as shown by equation 26.

The hydrogen-ion concentrations of solutions containing weak bases may be calculated using the same methods as were described for acids earlier in the chapter.

* L. Pauling, *J. Chem. Educ.*, *33*, 16 (1956).

Table V.[1]   Ionization Constants of Bases in Water at 25°

Base	K_b	K_a	pK_a
Ammonium hydroxide	1.8×10^{-5}	5.55×10^{-10}	9.26
Aniline	3.83×10^{-10}	2.61×10^{-5}	4.58
n-Butyl amine	4.1×10^{-4}	2.4×10^{-11}	10.61
Diethyl amine	1.26×10^{-3}	7.94×10^{-12}	11.10
Ethyl amine	5.6×10^{-4}	1.78×10^{-11}	10.75
Pyridine	1.4×10^{-9}	7.1×10^{-6}	5.15
Triethyl amine	5.65×10^{-4}	1.77×10^{-11}	10.75
Urea	1.5×10^{-14}	6.7×10^{-1}	0.18

[1] N. A. Lange, *Handbook of Chemistry*, Handbook Publishers, Sandusky, Ohio.

Exercise III. Show that for a sufficiently concentrated solution of a salt of a weak base and strong acid the hydrogen-ion concentration is given by

$$(\mathrm{H}^+) = \left(\frac{K_w c_s}{K_b}\right)^{1/2} \tag{28}$$

If a solution contains c_b moles liter^{-1} of a weak base and c_s moles liter^{-1} of the salt of this weak base with a strong acid, (BOH) or $(B) = c_b$ and (B^+) or $(BH^+) = c_s$. Equation 27 may then be written

$$\mathrm{pH} = pK_a + \log \frac{c_b}{c_s} \tag{29}$$

provided that the concentrations of salt and weak base are high enough. Thus the values of pK_a or $-\log K_a$ are the pH values at which the base would be half in the basic form and half in the acidic form.

Example 10. Calculate the pH of a solution containing 0.10 N ammonium nitrate and 0.02 N ammonium hydroxide.

$$\mathrm{pH} = 9.26 + \log (0.02/0.10) = 9.26 - 0.70$$

$$= 8.56$$

Ampholytes. Glycine, $H_2NCH_2CO_2H$, is an example of a substance containing both a basic and an acidic group. In view of what has been said above it is convenient to consider an ampholyte like glycine to be a dibasic acid. The acid dissociations of glycine are represented as follows, with the most acidic form at the left and the most basic form at the right:

$$K_1 \quad \overset{-H^+}{\nearrow} \quad ^+H_3NCH_2CO_2^- \quad \overset{-H^+}{\searrow} \quad K_3$$

$$^+H_3NCH_2CO_2H \qquad\qquad H_2NCH_2CO_2^- \qquad (30)$$

$$K_2 \quad \overset{-H^+}{\searrow} \quad H_2NCH_2CO_2H \quad \overset{-H^+}{\nearrow} \quad K_4$$

Thus it can be seen that there are two intermediate ionized forms. One of these forms is a dipolar ion (p. 501), and the other a neutral molecule. The titration data do not distinguish between these two forms, and the first acid dissociation constant, K_a, is given by

$$K_a = \frac{(H^+)[(^+H_3NCH_2CO_2^-) + (H_2NCH_2CO_2H)]}{(^+H_3NCH_2CO_2H)}$$

$$= K_1 + K_2 \qquad (31)$$

where K_1 and K_2 are the equilibrium constants for the two possible dissociations of a first proton. The second acid-dissociation constant is given by

$$K_b = \frac{(H^+)(H_2NCH_2CO_2^-)}{[(^+H_3NCH_2CO_2^-) + (H_2NCH_2CO_2H)]}$$

$$= \frac{1}{(1/K_3) + (1/K_4)} \qquad (32)$$

where K_3 and K_4 are the equilibrium constants for the two possible dissociations of a second proton. This same formulation would apply to any dibasic acid. If the ionizations of the two protons from the most acidic form were independent, as would be true for $HO_2C(CH_2)_nCO_2H$ with n large, $K_1 = K_2 = K_3 = K_4$ and $K_a = 4K_b$.

The intermediate ionized form of glycine exists almost completely as the dipolar ion, $^+H_3NCH_2CO_2^-$, as shown by measurements of dipole moment (p. 501) and Raman spectra (p. 541). This is to be expected from the magnitude of the ionization constants of carboxyl and amino groups and the experimental pK values for glycine, which are 2.3 and 9.6 (cf. Tables III and V). The repulsion due to the positive amino group is largely responsible for the fact that the carboxyl group of glycine is a stronger acid group than the carboxyl group of acetic acid.

An amino acid is said to be *isoelectric* at the pH at which there are equal concentrations of the positively and negatively charged forms. Setting $(^+H_3NCH_2CO_2H) = (H_2NCH_2CO_2^-)$ and substituting from equations 31 and 32 yields

$$(H^+)^2_{\text{isoelectric}} = K_aK_b$$

which may be written

$$pH_I = \tfrac{1}{2}(pK_a + pK_b) \tag{33}$$

where pH_I is the pH of the isoelectric point. For glycine the isoelectric point is $\tfrac{1}{2}(2.3 + 9.6) = 6.0$.

Buffers. A buffer is a solution which tends to maintain a constant pH. It contains an appreciable concentration of a weak acid HA and its salt containing anion A. The addition of alkali to such a solution causes the reaction

$$OH^- + HA = H_2O + A^-$$

while the addition of acid causes the reaction

$$H^+ + A^- = HA$$

In either reaction the change in pH upon the addition of a small quantity of acid or base is small in comparison with that which would be observed if the acid or base were added to water. The buffering regions in Fig. 15-2a and b are those in which the slopes are the greatest. The optimum pH for buffering action is that equal to the pK_a of the weak acid or base in the buffer solution. At 1 pH unit away from the pK_a a buffer is about 33 per cent as effective (see problem 37). Thus, each weak acid or base listed in Table III or V could be used to prepare effective buffers from about 1 pH unit below its pK_a to about 1 pH unit above its pK_a.

Buffer solutions are important in analytical chemistry, in general laboratory work, and particularly in biochemistry, where it is desired to keep the number of variables to a minimum. Blood, milk, and various other animal fluids are highly buffered with bicarbonate ions and carbonic acid and with proteins. The pH of human blood in a normal person is approximately 7.4. Ordinarily variations are less than 0.1 of a pH unit, and an increase or decrease of as much as 0.4 is likely to be fatal. Rates of various enzymatic reactions depend markedly upon the pH.

Example 11. A buffer contains 0.04 mole of Na_2HPO_4 per liter and 0.02 mole of NaH_2PO_4 per liter. (a) Calculate the pH, using $pK_a = 6.84$, which is the pK corresponding to the ionic strength of the solution. (b) One milliliter of 1 N HCl is added to a liter of the buffer. Calculate the change in pH. (c) Calculate the pH change to be expected if this quantity of HCl is added to 1 liter of pure water which has a pH of 7.

$$(a) \qquad pH = 6.84 + \log(0.04/0.02) = 7.14$$

(b) The addition of this quantity of HCl converts 0.001 mole of Na_2HPO_4 to NaH_2PO_4.

$$pH = 6.84 + \log \frac{0.040 - 0.001}{0.020 + 0.001} = 7.11$$

$$\Delta pH = 0.03$$

(c) $$pH = -\log 10^{-3} = 3$$

$$\Delta pH = 7 - 3 = 4$$

Indicators. Indicators are acids or bases which have different colors in their acidic and basic forms, as, for example, in the reaction

$$H \, In \, (\text{color 1}) = H^+ + In^- \, (\text{color 2})$$

They are used for indicating end points in the titration of acids and bases. The pH range in which the color change occurs depends upon the ionization constant of the indicator acid, and the indicator has its intermediate color at the pH equal to the pK of the indicator acid. In the titration of an acid with a base an indicator is chosen having its color change in the range of pH of the hydrolyzed salt which is formed. With an indicator a pH change of 2 units is required to change the ratio of the two forms from 10/1 to 1/10, but the end point may be determined accurately if there is an abrupt change in pH at the end point. An indicator may be used to determine the pH of an unknown solution more accurately by comparing the color of the unknown solution with the colors obtained by adding the indicator to a series of buffer solutions.

Complex Ions. A number of metal ions combine with anions or neutral molecules to form ions which are referred to as complex ions. For example, CdI_2 is not completely dissociated in solution, and the species CdI^+, CdI_2, CdI_3^-, and CdI_4^{2-} are in equilibrium with Cd^{2+} and I^-. Other examples of complex ions are $Ag(CN)_2^-$, $Cu(NH_3)_4^{2+}$, and $FeOH^{2+}$. In general terms a substance L, called a ligand, is bound by a metal ion M to give a complex ion.

The successive association constants for the formation of ML, ML_2, $\cdots$, ML_i are

$$M + L = ML \qquad K_1 = (ML)/(M)(L)$$
$$ML + L = ML_2 \qquad K_2 = (ML_2)/(ML)(L)$$
$$\cdot \qquad\qquad\qquad \cdot$$
$$\cdot \qquad\qquad\qquad \cdot$$
$$\cdot \qquad\qquad\qquad \cdot$$
$$ML_{i-1} + L = ML_i \qquad K_i = (ML_i)/(ML_{i-1})(L)$$

$$\overline{M + iL = ML_i \qquad \beta_i = K_1K_2 \cdots K_i = (ML_i)/(M)(L)^i}$$

where β_i is the equilibrium constant for the overall reaction. The average number $\bar{n}$ of ligands L bound by the metal ion M per metal ion is given by

$$\bar{n} = \frac{(ML) + 2(ML_2) + \cdots + i(ML_i)}{(M) + (ML) + (ML_2) + \cdots + (ML_i)} \tag{34}$$

Introducing the equilibrium expressions,

$$\bar{n} = \frac{K_1(L) + 2K_1K_2(L)^2 + \cdots + iK_1K_2 \cdots K_i(L)^i}{1 + K_1(L) + K_1K_2(L)^2 + \cdots + K_1K_2 \cdots K_i(L)^i} \tag{35}$$

The values of the successive equilibrium constants may be obtained by determining $\bar{n}$ as a function of (L). If the ligand has acidic or basic properties, its concentration may be determined by means of a hydrogen electrode in solutions containing known total concentrations of the acidic or basic substance. For example, the concentration of free ammonia in solutions containing cupric nitrate and ammonium nitrate buffer has been determined by glass-electrode measurements.* If the concentration of ammonium salt is known and the hydrogen-ion concentration is measured, the concentration of ammonia may be calculated from

$$(NH_3) = \frac{K_a(NH_4^+)}{(H^+)} \tag{36}$$

Since the concentration of added ammonia, c_{NH_3}, is known, the average number $\bar{n}$ of NH_3 molecules bound per copper ion is

$$\bar{n} = \frac{c_{NH_3} - (NH_3)}{c_{Cu^{2+}}} \tag{37}$$

where $c_{Cu^{2+}}$ is the total concentration of copper ions. *Figure 15-3a* gives a plot of the number of NH_3 molecules bound per copper ion for various values of $-\log(NH_3)$. Since the equilibrium constants for the binding of successive NH_3 molecules are not greatly different, there are no steps in this plot. However, the values of the successive association constants may be calculated from these data by use of equation 35; they are $K_1 = 10^{4.15}$, $K_2 = 10^{3.50}$, $K_3 = 10^{2.89}$, and $K_4 = 10^{2.13}$.

In the formation of the tetrammine mercuric ion complex, the first two ammonia molecules are bound much more strongly than the last

* J. Bjerrum, *Metal Ammine Formation in Aqueous Solutions*, P. Haase & Son, Copenhagen, 1941.

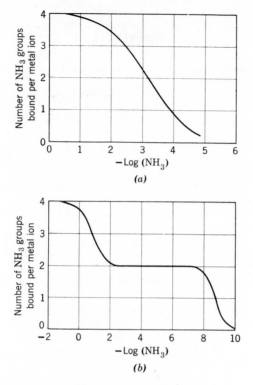

(a)

(b)

Fig. 15-3. Formation curves for ammine complexes: (a) with Cu^{2+} at $30°$ in $2\ N\ NH_4NO_3$; (b) with Hg^{2+} at $22°$ in $2\ N\ NH_4NO_3$.

two. In other words, the complex $Hg(NH_3)_2{}^{2+}$ is formed at very low ammonia concentrations, whereas $Hg(NH_3)_4{}^{2+}$ is formed only at high ammonia concentrations, as shown in *Fig. 15-3b*.

The concentrations of other colored complexes may be determined spectrophotometrically. Measurements of solubility may be used to study complex-ion equilibria in certain cases. For example, when sodium cyanide is added to silver nitrate, silver cyanide is precipitated. However, when an excess of cyanide is added, the precipitate dissolves, because of the formation of a complex ion, according to the reaction

$$AgCN + CN^- = Ag(CN)_2{}^-$$

That silver is locked up in a complex negative ion is proved by the fact that silver migrates toward the positive electrode (anode) in electrolysis.

REFERENCES

R. P. Bell, *Acids and Bases, Their Quantitative Behavior*, Methuen and Co., London, 1952.

N. J. Bjerrum, G. Schwarzenbach, and L. G. Sillén, *Stability Constants*, Parts I and II, The Chemical Society, London, 1958.

S. Glasstone, *Introduction to Electrochemistry*, D. Van Nostrand Co., Princeton, N. J., 1942.

W. J. Hamer, *Electrolytic Solutions*, John Wiley & Sons, New York, 1959.

H. S. Harned and B. B. Owen, *The Physical Chemistry of Electrolytic Solutions*, Reinhold Publishing Corp., New York, 1958.

D. A. MacInnes, *The Principles of Electrochemistry*, Reinhold Publishing Corp., New York, 1939.

J. E. Ricci, *Hydrogen Ion Concentration*, Princeton University Press, Princeton, N. J., 1952.

R. A. Robinson and R. H. Stokes, *Electrolyte Solutions*, Academic Press, New York, 1959.

PROBLEMS

1. The solubility product of AgBr at $25°$ is 7.7×10^{-13}. Calculate (a) the solubility of AgBr in pure water, (b) the solubility of AgBr in 0.01 M NaBr, utilizing the Debye-Hückel theory. *Ans.* (a) 8.8×10^{-7}, (b) 9.5×10^{-11} mole l^{-1}.

2. The solubility product of AgI is 1.2×10^{-16} at $25°$. Calculate the standard voltage of the cell

$$Ag; AgI, I^- \parallel Ag^+; Ag$$

Ans. 0.941 volt.

3. If the thermodynamic value of the solubility product of $SrSO_4$ is 2.8×10^{-7} at $25°$, estimate the solubility of $SrSO_4$ in 0.005 M NaCl. *Ans.* 7.4×10^{-4} mole l^{-1}.

4. Using the Debye-Hückel theory, estimate the apparent pK_a for acetic acid at 0.01 ionic strength. At $25°$ the thermodynamic pK_a value is 4.76. It is assumed that the activity coefficient for undissociated acetic acid is unity at this value of the ionic strength. *Ans.* 4.71.

5. Five grams of lactic acid, $CH_3CHOHCO_2H$, is diluted with water to 1 liter. What is the concentration of hydrogen ions at $25°$? The dissociation constant of $CH_3CHOHCO_2H$ is 1.36×10^{-4} at this temperature. *Ans.* 2.68×10^{-3} equiv l^{-1}.

6. In order to determine the ionization constant of the weak monobasic acid dimethyl arsinic acid, a solution was titrated with a solution of sodium hydroxide, using a pH meter. After 17.3 ml of NaOH had been added, the pH was 6.23. It was found that 27.6 ml was required to neutralize the acid solution completely. Calculate the pK_a value. *Ans.* 6.00.

7. Calculate the pH of (a) a 0.1 M solution of n-butyric acid, (b) a solution containing 0.05 M butyric acid and 0.05 M sodium butyrate, and (c) a 0.1 M solution of pure sodium butyrate. Using these data, sketch the titration curve for 0.1 M butyric acid which is titrated with a strong base so concentrated that the volume of the solution may be considered to remain constant ($K_a = 1.48 \times 10^{-5}$ at $25°$). *Ans.* (a) 2.91. (b) 4.83. (c) 8.91.

8. Calculate the concentration of (a) CO_3^{2-}, (b) HCO_3^-, and (c) H_2CO_3; and (d) the pH of a solution made up by dissolving 0.006 mole Na_2CO_3 and 0.004 mole $NaHCO_3$ in 1 liter of water.

$$K_1 = (H^+)(HCO_3^-)/(H_2CO_3) = 4.3 \times 10^{-7}$$

$$K_2 = (H^+)(CO_3^{2-})/(HCO_3^-) = 4.7 \times 10^{-11}$$

Ans. (a) 5.72×10^{-3}, (b) 4.28×10^{-3}, (c) 3.5×10^{-7} mole l^{-1}. (d) 10.45.

9. A buffer contains 0.01 mole of lactic acid ($pK_a = 3.60$) and 0.05 mole of sodium lactate per liter. (a) Calculate the pH of this buffer. (b) Five milliliters of 0.5 N hydrochloric acid is added to a liter of the buffer. Calculate the change in pH. (c) Calculate the pH change to be expected if this quantity of acid is added to 1 liter of a solution of a strong acid of the same initial pH.

Ans. (a) 4.30.   (b) 0.12.   (c) 4.4.

10. Calculate the number of moles per liter of Na_2HPO_4 and NaH_2PO_4 which should be used to prepare a 0.10 ionic strength buffer of pH 7.30. At this ionic strength the second pK_a of phosphoric acid may be taken as 6.84.

Ans. $(Na_2HPO_4) = 0.0299$ M, $(NaH_2PO_4) = 0.0104$ M.

11. At $40°$ the ionization constant of NH_4OH is 2.0×10^{-5}. (a) What is the OH^--ion concentration in 0.1 M NH_4OH? (b) What is the OH^--ion concentration of a solution 0.1 M with respect to NH_4OH which is also 0.1 M with respect to NH_4Cl?   *Ans.* (a) 1.4×10^{-3}. (b) 2.0×10^{-5}.

12. (a) What is the hydrogen-ion concentration of a 0.5 M solution of NH_4Br at $25°$? The K_a of NH_4OH is 1.8×10^{-5}. (b) What is the pH?

Ans. (a) 1.67×10^{-5}. (b) 4.78.

---

13. The specific conductance of a saturated solution of AgCl in water at $25°$ was found to be 2.28×10^{-6} ohm^{-1} cm^{-1}. The specific conductance of the water used was 1.16×10^{-6} ohm^{-1} cm^{-1}. With the information that the ionic conductance of Ag^+ is 61.9 cm^2 equiv^{-1} ohm^{-1} and of Cl^- is 76.3 cm^2 equiv^{-1} ohm^{-1} at infinite dilution, calculate: (a) the solubility of AgCl in grams per liter; (b) the solubility product of AgCl.

14. The solubility of barium sulfate at $25°$ is 1.05×10^{-5} mole liter^{-1}. (a) What is the solubility product? (b) What concentration of barium sulfate would dissolve in a solution having a sulfate-ion concentration of 0.01 gram ion liter^{-1} and an ionic strength of 0.004?

15. Calculate the solubility product of AgCl from (a) the Gibbs free energies of formation given on p. 213 and (b) the standard voltage of the cell Ag, AgCl; $Cl^- \parallel Ag^+$; Ag.

16. Using the Debye-Hückel theory, estimate the apparent pK_a for the second ionization of phosphoric acid at 0.01 ionic strength. At $25°$ the thermodynamic value for this pK_a is 7.21.

17. For benzoic acid at $25°$ the ionization constant is 7.3×10^{-5}. Calculate the pH of a 0.001 M solution of benzoic acid at $25°$.

18. The ionization constant of periodic acid (HIO_4) is 2.3×10^{-2} at $25°$. Calculate the degree of dissociation of a 0.01 M solution.

19. The ionization constants at $25°$ for acetic acid, lactic acid, and bromoacetic acid are 1.8×10^{-5}, 1.4×10^{-4}, and 1.4×10^{-3}, respectively. Calculate the degree of dissociation α for a 0.01 M solution of each of these acids (a) by the approximate method (assuming $1 - \alpha = 1$) and (b) by the exact method (see p. 365).

20. Calculate the pH of 0.1 N sodium isobutyrate at 25° $(K_a = 0.98 \times 10^{-5})$.

21. The first and second ionization constants of carbonic acid are $10^{-6.5}$ and $10^{-10.7}$. Calculate the equilibrium constant for the reaction

$$H_2CO_3 + CO_3^{2-} = 2HCO_3^-$$

22. What concentrations of sodium acetate and acetic acid should be used to prepare an acetate buffer of pH 5.10 and 0.1 ionic strength $(K_{HAc} = 1.8 \times 10^{-5})$?

23. The ionization constant of nitrous acid, HNO_2, is 4×10^{-4} at 25°. What is the pH of a solution made up with 0.1 mole HNO_2 and 0.03 mole of sodium nitrite in 1 liter?

24. Calculate the pH of a 0.1 M solution of pyridinium perchlorate in water at 25°. For pyridine $K_b = 1.6 \times 10^{-9}$.

25. The ionization constant of ammonium hydroxide is 1.4×10^{-5} at 0° and 2×10^{-5} at 40°. What is the average heat of ionization of NH_4OH in this range of temperature?

---

26. The first ionization constant of H_2S in water is 9.1×10^{-8}; the second is 1.2×10^{-15}. The solubility of H_2S in water is 3.4 g liter^{-1}. How many grams of $Pb(NO_3)_2$ added to 1 liter of saturated H_2S solution will just start precipitation of PbS?

27. Write the equations for the solubility products of AgCl, Mg(OH)$_2$, and Fe(OH)$_3$ in terms of the molalities of the saturated solutions and the mean ionic activity coefficients.

28. At 25° the potential of the cell

$$\text{Ag, AgI; KI(1 M) } \| \text{ AgNO}_3(0.001 \text{ M}); \text{Ag}$$

is 0.72 volt. The mean ionic activity coefficient of 1 M KI may be taken as 0.65, and of 0.001 M AgNO$_3$ as 0.98. (a) What is the solubility of AgI? (b) What is the solubility of AgI in pure water?

29. Calculate the energy in kilocalories per mole^{-1} required to separate a positive and negative charge from 3 angstroms to infinity in (a) a vacuum, (b) a solvent of dielectric constant 10, and (c) water at 25°, which has a dielectric constant of approximately 80.

30. The titration curve of a weak monobasic acid is plotted as equivalents of strong base added per mole of weak acid versus pH. Show by use of differentiation that the slope of this plot at the inflection point (pH $=$ pK_a) is equal to 2.303/4.

31. Calculate the pH of 10^{-5} M acetic acid in water at 25°, using the exact equation rather than the approximate form. What result would have been obtained if the approximate form had been used?

32. Calculate the pH of a 0.1 M solution of potassium cyanide at 25° $(K_a = 7.2 \times 10^{-10})$.

33. Calculate the Gibbs free energy of neutralization of a mole of strong acid in its standard state by a mole of strong base in its standard state at 25°, K_w being 1×10^{-14}.

34. (a) Calculate and record in tabular form the degree of hydrolysis α of a 1.0 N solution of a salt and a weak acid and a strong base if the ionization constant for the acid is 10^{-4}, 10^{-6}, and 10^{-10}. (b) Repeat the calculation of (a) for a 0.01 N solution.

35. Calculate the pH at 25° of a buffer solution containing 50 ml of 0.2 M potassium hydrogen phthalate and 45.45 ml of 0.2 M sodium hydroxide solution, all diluted to 200 ml. The dissociation constant for the second hydrogen of phthalic acid at 25° is 3.1×10^{-6}.

36. The pH of a 0.0312 M solution of NH_4Cl in water at 25° is 5.48. Calculate K_b for NH_4OH from this data.

37. Show that the slope of the titration curve of a monobasic weak acid is given by

$$\frac{d\alpha}{d\mathrm{pH}} = \frac{2.303 K_a(\mathrm{H}^+)}{[K_a + (\mathrm{H}^+)]^2}$$

where α is the degree of neutralization.

QUANTUM THEORY

16

In the late nineteenth century it became apparent that classical mechanics was unable to account for many experimental facts concerning the behavior of systems of atomic size. The quantum hypothesis was introduced in 1900 by Planck as a result of his theoretical study of the radiation of hot bodies. Quantum theory has been developed on the basis of many different kinds of experiments involving electrons, atoms, molecules, and other small particles. For objects of larger size quantum mechanics reduces to classical mechanics.

The Electron. The development of the theory of atomic structure began with the concept of discrete units of electric charge. The atomic nature of electricity was indicated by Faraday's experiments on the electrolysis of salts in solution, but the existence of electrons as material particles was not proved until J. J. Thomson measured the ratio of mass to charge of the electron and R. A. Millikan measured the charge.

The ratio of mass to charge of the electron was measured by accelerating a beam of electrons by an electrical potential difference and deflecting the beam with electrical and magnetic fields. At low electron velocities the ratio of mass to charge, m/e, is 5.6839×10^{-9} g coulomb^{-1}. At higher velocities approaching the velocity of light the mass increases and approaches infinity, as predicted by the theory of relativity.

The charge on the electron was measured by Millikan in the classical oil-drop experiment. A fine mist of oil was blown into a thermostated air space between two electrodes, and the radius of one particular drop was calculated from its rate of fall by means of Stokes's equation (equation 1, Chapter 13). When the electric field is turned on, the velocity of the drop is increased or decreased, depending on the sign of the charge and the direction of the field, if the drop is electrically charged. If the surrounding air is ionized by an X-ray beam, the oil drop will frequently pick up a gas ion, and hence its velocity in the electric field will change. The charge of the electron may be calculated from the observed change in velocity.

Millikan found that the change in charge of the oil drop, ne, is always a multiple of 1.602×10^{-19} coulomb, or 4.802×10^{-10} electrostatic unit, and so this is the charge of the electron. Still more accurate measurements of the charge of the electron have been made by other methods, and the value given in the Appendix is an average value.

The mass of the electron may be calculated from the value of m/e, which is 5.6839×10^{-9} g coulomb^{-1}, and the charge of the electron, 1.60186×10^{-19} coulomb:

$$(5.6839 \times 10^{-9} \text{ g coulomb}^{-1})(1.60186 \times 10^{-19} \text{ coulomb})$$

$$= 9.105 \times 10^{-28} \text{ gram}$$

This is the rest mass of the electron, the mass it possesses when it is moving slowly compared to the velocity of light. The ratio of the mass of a hydrogen atom to that of an electron is

$$\frac{(1.008)}{(6.0238 \times 10^{23})(9.105 \times 10^{-28})} = 1838$$

Example 1. When water is electrolyzed, each electron releases an atom of hydrogen at the cathode, and 96,496 coulombs releases 1.008 grams of hydrogen. What is Avogadro's number?

$$\frac{96{,}496 \text{ coulombs equiv}^{-1}}{1.601 \times 10^{-19} \text{ coulomb electron}^{-1}} = 6.024 \times 10^{23} \text{ electrons equiv}^{-1}$$

Relativistic Effects. The relativistic mass m of a particle is related to the "rest mass," m_0, and the velocity, v, by the equation

$$m = m_0 \left(1 - \frac{v^2}{c^2} \right)^{-\frac{1}{2}} \tag{1}$$

where c is the velocity of light. The kinetic energy E_{kin} of a moving particle is given by

$$E_{\text{kin}} = mc^2 - m_0 c^2 \tag{2}$$

In words, the kinetic energy is equal to the difference between the total energy, mc^2, and the rest energy, $m_0 c^2$.

Substituting equation 1 into equation 2,

$$E_{\text{kin}} = m_0 c^2 \left[\left(1 - \frac{v^2}{c^2} \right)^{-\frac{1}{2}} - 1 \right] \tag{3}$$

This equation may be used to calculate the velocity of a charged particle which has been accelerated by an electrical potential. It is apparent from this equation that the kinetic energy of a particle of finite rest mass approaches infinity as its velocity approaches that of light. By series expansion of $[1 - (v/c)^2]^{-\frac{1}{2}}$, it may be shown that for low speeds $E_{kin} = \frac{1}{2}mv^2$.

Exercise I. Show that for electrons which have been accelerated by a potential difference of 3200 volts, the expression $\frac{1}{2}m_0v^2 = Ee$ fails to give the correct kinetic energy by 1 per cent, where E is the potential difference and e is the electron charge.

For chemical problems involving electrons in atoms and molecules relativistic effects are of no importance generally, and the quantum theory in this chapter is presented from a nonrelativistic point of view.

Electromagnetic Radiation. Electromagnetic radiation consists of fluctuations of electric and magnetic field strengths propagated with the velocity c in a vacuum. These fluctuations are sinusoidal, as shown by diffraction and interference effects.

The wavelength λ of radiation is usually expressed in centimeters; microns, μ (10^{-6} meter or 10^{-4} cm); millimicrons, $m\mu$ (10^{-9} meter or 10^{-7} cm); or angstrom units, A (10^{-10} meter or 10^{-8} cm). It is readily seen that $1\ m\mu = 0.001\mu = 10$ A.

The frequency ν of radiation is the number of cycles per second and is therefore equal to the distance traversed by the radiation in 1 sec, c (3×10^{10} cm sec^{-1}), divided by the wavelength.

$$\nu = \frac{c}{\lambda} \tag{4}$$

In this equation the wavelength must of course be expressed in the same unit of distance as that used for c.

For certain purposes it is useful to express the frequency of radiation in wave numbers, $\bar{\nu}$; the wave number is the number of cycles per centimeter.

$$\bar{\nu} = \frac{1}{\lambda} \tag{5}$$

where the wavelength is given in centimeters. The wave number is thus given in cm^{-1}. In theoretical discussions it is advantageous to use frequency or wave number, since these quantities are directly proportional to the energy changes (cf. equation 12).

Example 2. What are the wavelength in centimeters and in millimicrons, the wave number, and the frequency of blue light which has a wavelength of 4500 A?

$$\lambda = (4500 \text{ A})(10^{-8} \text{ cm A}^{-1}) = 4.5 \times 10^{-5} \text{ cm}$$

$$\lambda = (4500 \text{ A})(10^{-1} \text{ m}\mu \text{ A}^{-1}) = 450 \text{ m}\mu$$

$$\tilde{\nu} = \frac{1}{4.5 \times 10^{-5} \text{ cm}} = 22,200 \text{ cm}^{-1}$$

$$\nu = \frac{3.0 \times 10^{10} \text{ cm sec}^{-1}}{4.5 \times 10^{-5} \text{ cm}} = 6.66 \times 10^{14} \text{ sec}^{-1}$$

Black-Body Radiation. The thermal radiation from different objects at the same temperature may be quite different with respect to intensity as a function of wavelengths. However, it is found that, if the radiation inside an isothermal hollow body is viewed through a small hole in its wall, the intensity of radiation and distribution of wavelengths are independent of the material and of the size and shape of the enclosure. This radiation is in equilibrium with matter and is called *black-body radiation*, since it is the external radiation that would be obtained from an ideal black body. An electrically heated furnace with a small opening serves as a convenient black body.

The spectral distribution of black-body radiation is shown at three temperatures in *Fig. 16-1*. The ordinates are proportional to the amount of energy emitted per unit wavelength interval per unit area per unit time. This curve was obtained by spreading out the radiation from a black body with a prism and measuring the energy in various wavelength ranges with a thermopile. A thermopile is a group of thermocouples in series which gives a current proportional to the difference in temperature between the hot and cold junctions. The temperature difference is directly proportional to the radiant energy received, and the current is measured with a galvanometer. It is evident that the total radiation as given by the area under the curve increases rapidly with increasing temperature. The total rate of energy emission E of a black body is given by the Stefan-Boltzmann law,

$$E = \sigma T^4 \tag{6}$$

where $\sigma = 5.69 \times 10^{-5} \text{ erg cm}^{-2} \text{ sec}^{-1} \text{ deg}^{-4}$. This law was discovered experimentally by Stefan and was derived later by Boltzmann, using the principles of thermodynamics. However, all attempts to derive the dependence of intensity on wavelength on the basis of classical physics were unsuccessful. In 1896 Wien derived an equation which represented the data in the short-wavelength region but not in the long-wavelength region. In 1900 Rayleigh derived an equation which represented only the data in the long-wavelength region.

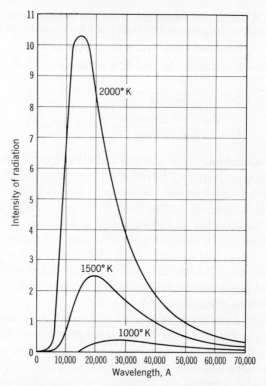

Fig. 16-1. Emission of radiation from a black body at different temperatures. The area under the curve between specified wavelengths, divided by 10^4, gives the energy in calories per second radiated from 1 cm^2 of a black body, in the range of wavelengths.

Planck's Constant. In attempting to derive the correct expression for the intensity of radiation from a black body, Planck was led in 1900 to the bold hypothesis that radiation of frequency ν cannot be emitted or absorbed in arbitrary amounts but only in quanta of energy ϵ, given by

$$\epsilon = h\nu \tag{7}$$

where h is a universal constant, Planck's constant, which has a value of 6.624×10^{-27} erg sec.

On the basis of this hypothesis Planck derived the equation

$$E_\lambda = \frac{2\pi c^2 h}{\lambda^5 (e^{ch/k\lambda T} - 1)} \tag{8}$$

where E_λ is the rate of emission of radiation of wavelength λ, c is the velocity of light, k is the Boltzmann constant.

Equation 8 can be integrated to give the Stefan-Boltzmann law; it approaches the Rayleigh law for large values of λ, and Wien's distribution law for small values of λ. Planck's equation is in excellent agreement with the various facts of radiation. In spite of these successes, Planck's equation would probably have failed to obtain general acceptance, on account of the radically new assumption concerning quanta, except for the fact that almost at once it became extremely useful in new and unrelated fields. The resulting quantum theory has revolutionized the study of spectroscopy. Resonance potentials, photoelectric effects, and specific heats have all been interpreted quantitatively with the help of the quantum theory. The understanding of photochemistry and chemical kinetics has been greatly improved by quantum mechanics.

The development of the quantum theory is one of the important milestones in science. As in many other important advances, the exact experimental facts came first, then an empirical mathematical equation to express the facts, and finally a working hypothesis to explain the terms in the equation. Then, on the basis of this hypothesis, predictions were made and new experiments planned which led to rapid progress in many different fields of science.

The Photoelectric Effect. One of the first applications of the quantum hypothesis was in the explanation of the photoelectric effect by Einstein in 1905. The photoelectric effect is the ejection of electrons from a metal surface by light. This interesting effect is the basis of the photoelectric cell, which is an extremely sensitive instrument for the detection and measurement of radiation. A diagram of a simple photoelectric cell and circuit is shown in *Fig. 16-2*.

A receiver K is coated with a thin film of potassium or other metal in a highly evacuated tube. A wire screen W placed in the tube is connected with the receiver through a battery B and a sensitive galvanometer G. The high vacuum of the tube serves as a complete insulator between W and K; but, when the receiver is exposed to light, electrons are ejected from the receiver and attracted to the posi-

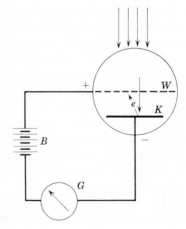

Fig. 16-2. Photoelectric cell and circuit.

tively charged screen, thus completing the circuit. The current registered by the galvanometer is directly proportional to the number of electrons ejected per second, which, in turn, is proportional to the number of photons striking the receiver, that is, to the intensity of the light.

It is found that for a given surface the frequency of the incident light must be greater than a certain value, called the *threshold frequency*, in order for any electrons to be emitted from the surface. At frequencies above the threshold frequency the electrons are ejected with excess kinetic energy. The maximum energy of the ejected electrons may be determined by reversing the polarity of the battery shown in Fig. 16-2 and determining the potential difference required to stop the current completely while the metal surface is being illuminated. It is found that the *maximum speed* of the ejected electrons is independent of the intensity of the light and depends only upon its *frequency*.

In 1906 these observations were explained by Einstein, using the quantum hypothesis. According to this explanation, when light is absorbed by a metal the total energy of a photon $h\nu$ is given to a single electron within the metal. If this quantity of energy is sufficiently large, the electron may penetrate the potential barrier at the surface of the metal and still retain some energy as kinetic energy. The kinetic energy of the ejected electrons may be determined by measuring the potential E required to stop the photoelectric current. The maximum kinetic energy is given by the equation

$$\tfrac{1}{2}mv^2 = h\nu - h\nu_0 = Ee \tag{9}$$

where m is the mass of the electron, v its velocity, ν the frequency of the incident light, and ν_0 a constant called the photoelectric threshold. The photoelectric threshold can be expressed in energy units and is referred to as the work function of the metal.

The voltage E is the potential difference necessary to retard the velocity of the electron to zero and prevent its reaching the collector W. The electrical energy eE may be calculated in ergs as shown below.

When the minimum voltage E required to prevent the production of an electron current is plotted against the frequency ν of the incident light, a straight line is obtained having a slope equal to h/e. This relation has been accurately checked with many different metals. The experimental determination of the slope offers one means of evaluating Planck's constant h.

The current from a photoelectric cell can be amplified and used for various measuring and control purposes. In a photomultiplier tube the electrons ejected by the light impinge under high voltage on a second sensitive surface, and there release additional electrons which in turn are multiplied on a third sensitive surface, etc. In this way just a few quanta can liberate many electrons and so give a large current to be measured.

The Electron Volt. In discussing the energy of electrons it is convenient to introduce the *electron volt*. The electron volt is the amount of work done in moving a unit electronic charge through a potential difference of 1 volt or, in other words, the energy acquired by an electron being accelerated by a potential difference of 1 volt. The conversion factor to ergs may be calculated as follows:

$$eE = (1.602 \times 10^{-19} \text{ coulomb}) (1 \text{ volt}) = 1.602 \times 10^{-19} \text{ joule}$$

$$= 1.602 \times 10^{-12} \text{ erg}$$

Therefore an electron volt is a very small quantity of energy. However, the energy of a mole of electrons which have been accelerated by 1 volt is of the magnitude commonly encountered for chemical reactions.

$$\frac{(1.602 \times 10^{-19} \text{ joule})(6.023 \times 10^{23} \text{ mole}^{-1})}{4.184 \text{ joules cal}^{-1}} = 23,060 \text{ cal mole}^{-1}$$

This is a useful conversion factor between the energy unit usually employed by physicists (electron volts per electron) and that used by chemists (kilocalories per mole). Further useful conversion factors are given in the Appendix (p. 728).

Spectrum of Atomic Hydrogen. In contrast with the continuous radiation of a black body it is found that the emission spectrum of a hot gas contains discrete spectral lines. If the gas contains molecules, there are families of closely spaced lines called bands. The spectrum of a gas may also be studied by passing the continuous radiation from a solid through the gas. Light of certain wavelengths is absorbed so that dark lines appear on the continuous background in the spectrograph. Although a number of relations between the wavelengths of the various spectral lines had been found empirically, these relations remained unexplained until Bohr in 1913 proposed a theory based upon the quantum hypothesis of Planck.

The simplest spectrum is that of hydrogen atoms, for which a small region is illustrated in *Fig. 16-3*. In 1885 Balmer discovered that the wavelengths (or wave numbers, $\bar{\nu}$) of the lines in the visible region of the hydrogen-atom spectrum could be expressed by a simple relation which may be written as

$$\frac{1}{\lambda} = \bar{\nu} = R \left(\frac{1}{2^2} - \frac{1}{n_2{}^2} \right) \tag{10}$$

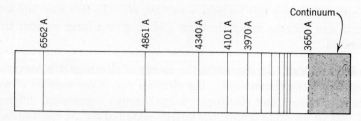

Fig. 16-3. Balmer series of lines in the spectrum of atomic hydrogen. At shorter wavelengths than the series limit there is continuous emission.

where n_2 is an integer greater than 2, and R is the Rydberg constant, $109,677.58$ cm^{-1}. The value of R may be determined very accurately because of the high precision with which the wavelengths of spectral lines can be measured.

The agreement between the wavelengths of the lines of the Balmer series and the values calculated by equation 10 is indicated by the data of Table I. It will be noticed in equation 10 that n_2 cannot be less than 2, for then $\bar{\nu}$ would be a meaningless negative number, and it cannot be 2, for then $\bar{\nu}$ becomes zero. As n_2 becomes larger than 2, the corresponding value of $\bar{\nu}$ becomes larger. However, when n_2 is already large, further increases cause $\bar{\nu}$ to increase only very slightly, and, as n_2 approaches infinity, $\bar{\nu}$ approaches $\frac{1}{4}R$ as a limit. As indicated in Fig. 16-3, there is continuous radiation at wavelengths shorter than this series limit.

Table I.   Balmer Lines in the Atomic Hydrogen Spectrum

n_2	λ_{vacuo}, calculated by equation 10	λ_{air}, calculated[1]	λ_{air}, experimental
3	6564.70	6562.89	6562.8
4	4862.74	4861.38	4861.4
5	4341.73	4340.51	4340.5
6	4102.93	4101.78	4101.8

[1] $\lambda_{air} = \lambda_{vacuo}/n$, where n is the refractive index of air. Values for n are given in the *International Critical Tables*, Vol. VII, McGraw-Hill Book Co., New York, 1930, p. 5.

The success of the Balmer formula led to further exploration, and other series of lines were discovered in the atomic hydrogen spectrum which could be represented by the equation

$$\tilde{\nu} = R \left(\frac{1}{n_1{}^2} - \frac{1}{n_2{}^2} \right) \tag{11}$$

where n_1 is also an integer. The series for which $n_1 = 1$ (Lyman series) is in the ultraviolet; the series for which $n_1 = 3$ (Paschen series), 4 (Brackett series), or 5 (Pfund series) are in the infrared region. It is important to note that every line in the spectrum can be represented as a difference of two terms, $R/n_1{}^2$ and $R/n_2{}^2$. The spectra of other atoms are more complicated, but in general it is found possible to represent the lines of the spectrum as differences between term values.

In all types of spectroscopy the energy of the photon is equal to the difference in energy between two energy levels.

$$E_2 - E_1 = \epsilon = h\nu \tag{12}$$

For example, when an electron passes from a higher energy level E_2 to a lower energy level E_1, a photon of frequency ν would be emitted.

Bohr's Theory of the Hydrogen Atom. Rutherford had deduced from the deflection of alpha particles by thin metal foils that an atom contains a small positively charged nucleus. The number of positive charges on the nucleus is defined as the *atomic number;* the number of electrons surrounding the nucleus in the neutral atom is also equal to the atomic number. The difficulty with Rutherford's theory of orbital electrons was that, according to classical physics, an electron moving around an orbit would radiate continuously. As a result of this loss of energy the electrons would spiral into the nucleus.

A successful theory of the spectrum of the hydrogen atom was developed in 1913 by Bohr * on the basis of the quantum theory. Bohr assumed that an electron in the neighborhood of a hydrogen nucleus is restricted to move along one of several allowed orbits corresponding to a discrete set of energy states. He assumed that the electron would not radiate while it followed one orbit, and so the energy of the atom would remain constant.

Bohr calculated the radii of the circular orbits on the basis that the angular momentum (mvr) of the electron was *quantized.* Instead of an infinite number of possible orbits only those occur for which mvr of an electron is an integral multiple of $h/2\pi$.

* N. Bohr, *Phil. Mag., 26,* 476, 857 (1913).

$$mvr = \frac{nh}{2\pi} \tag{13}$$

where n is an integer 1, 2, 3, 4, etc., referred to as a *quantum number*, m and v are the mass and velocity of the electron, and r is the radius of the orbit.

The radii of the Bohr orbits were calculated by equating the force of attraction of the nucleus for the electron to the centripetal force on the electron moving in the orbit. According to Coulomb's law, the force of attraction is Ze^2/r^2, where Z is the atomic number. The centripetal force is mv^2/r. Equating these forces,

$$\frac{mv^2}{r} = \frac{Ze^2}{r^2} \tag{14}$$

which makes it possible to solve for r:

$$r = \frac{Ze^2}{mv^2} \tag{15}$$

Introducing the values of v permitted by equation 13,

$$r = \frac{n^2h^2}{4\pi^2me^2Z} \tag{16}$$

For the hydrogen atom $Z = 1$, and the radius of the smallest orbit ($n = 1$) is 0.529 A. The radius of the orbit with $n = 2$ is four times larger.

The total energy E is equal to the sum of the kinetic energy E_{kin} and the potential energy E_{pot} of the orbital electron.

$$E_{kin} = \frac{1}{2}mv^2 = \frac{1}{2}\frac{Ze^2}{r} \tag{17}$$

where the second form is obtained from equation 14.

$$E_{pot} = \int_{\infty}^{r} \frac{Ze^2}{r^2}\,dr = -\frac{Ze^2}{r} \tag{18}$$

Then,

$$E = E_{kin} + E_{pot} = \frac{1}{2}\frac{Ze^2}{r} - \frac{Ze^2}{r} = -\frac{Ze^2}{2r} \tag{19}$$

The energy has a negative sign because the reference state with zero energy is taken as that state in which the electron is at infinite distance from the nucleus, and the lower limit of integration is taken as $r = \infty$.

Substituting equation 16 for the allowed radii r into equation 19 yields Bohr's equation for the energy E_n of an electron in the orbit with quantum number n:

$$E_n = \frac{-2\pi^2 m Z^2 e^4}{n^2 h^2} \tag{20}$$

where Z is the atomic number, e is the charge of the electron, and h is Planck's constant. Then, according to equation 12, the energy of a quantum of light emitted on changing from one orbit to another is given by the equation

$$\epsilon = h\nu = E_2 - E_1 = \frac{2\pi^2 m e^4 Z^2}{h^2} \left(\frac{1}{n_1^2} - \frac{1}{n_2^2} \right) \tag{21}$$

By comparison with equation 11 it can be seen that, according to the Bohr theory, the Rydberg constant R should be given by

$$R = \frac{2\pi^2 m e^4}{h^3 c} \tag{22}$$

Since for hydrogen $Z = 1$, the Z^2 term drops out. The value of R calculated from the various physical constants involved in this expression is in excellent agreement with the value obtained directly from spectroscopic measurements.

The electronic energy levels in the hydrogen atom, as calculated from equation 20 of the Bohr theory, are summarized in *Fig. 16-4*. The Lyman series of lines is produced by electrons jumping from orbits with quantum numbers 2, 3, 4, $\cdots$ into the lowest permitted orbit ($n_1 = 1$). The Balmer series of lines is produced by electrons falling from larger orbits into the second orbit ($n_1 = 2$), etc. The energies of the various orbits may be expressed in several ways. The energies in wave numbers given at the right in Fig. 16-4 are the wave numbers for radiation produced when an electron falls from an infinite distance into a given orbit with no initial kinetic energy. The wave number $\bar{\nu}$ of any line in the spectrum may be obtained by subtracting the values at the right for the two energy levels involved. Thus the second line in the Balmer series is due to an electron falling from the fourth orbit into the second, and its wave number is $27{,}420 - 6855 = 20{,}565$ cm^{-1}.

The continuous emission beyond the convergence limit of the lines shown in Fig. 16-3 is due to electrons having appreciable kinetic energy falling into an orbit of the hydrogen atom. Since for practical purposes the translational kinetic energy is not quantized, the loss in energy of the electron may have a continuous range of values, leading to the emission of continuous radiation. The convergence limit in the spectral

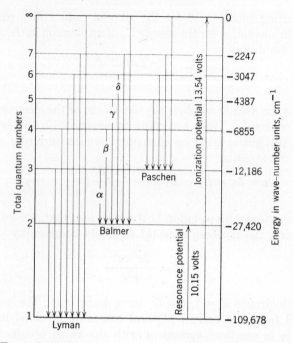

Fig. 16-4. Energy levels for the hydrogen atom as calculated from the Bohr theory.

series corresponds then to complete separation of the electron, that is, to ionization to give a free electron with no kinetic energy.

In the absorption of light the electrons are driven out to levels of higher energy by the absorption of quanta of energy.

A helium atom which has lost one of its two electrons would be expected to have a spectrum very similar to that of a hydrogen atom. Since the atomic number of helium is 2, the frequencies or wave numbers of the lines are four times as great as those for hydrogen. The spectra for Li^{2+} and Be^{3+} can also be calculated exactly, using the Bohr theory, because there is a single orbital electron.

However, the Bohr theory failed for more complicated ions and atoms, and the search for a more general theory led to quantum mechanics, which provides a rather different picture of the hydrogen atom.

Quantum Mechanics. In spite of its great success in respect to the atomic hydrogen spectrum the Bohr theory was unable to explain the spectra of other atoms, and it was felt that the definite orbits were introduced in a rather arbitrary way. Therefore means were sought for developing a general quantum theory that would give the same result as the Bohr theory for the hydrogen atom and could be applied to more general systems.

It was realized that there were a number of characteristics which a complete quantum theory would have to possess. For one thing, quantum mechanics would have to account for the wave properties of particles. In 1924 de Broglie suggested that, since photons show wave and particle properties, electrons might have wave properties and suggested that their wavelength would be given by

$$\lambda = \frac{h}{mv} = \frac{h}{p} \tag{23}$$

where h is Planck's constant, m is the mass of the electron, v is its velocity, and p is the momentum of the electron. The wavelengths of particles calculated in this way are often called de Broglie wavelengths. The wave properties of electrons suggested by de Broglie were demonstrated in 1928 by Davisson and Germer, who obtained a diffraction pattern from electrons impinging on the face of a nickel crystal.

It is interesting to note that in the Bohr theory the circumference of an orbit is such that it contains an integral number of de Broglie wavelengths for the electron. From equations 13 and 23, $2\pi r = nh/mv = n\lambda$.

The de Broglie waves are different from ordinary waves. Whereas photons always move with the speed of light, material particles move with a speed which is less than the speed of light in the medium in which they are traveling.

Another idea which is embodied in quantum mechanics is expressed by the *Heisenberg uncertainty principle*.* Whereas in classical mechanics it is assumed that a mechanical system can be specified to any desired degree of precision, Heisenberg pointed out that in studying systems of small particles an uncertainty is unavoidably introduced into the measured quantities by the measurement process itself. For example, consider the determination of the position and velocity of an electron. If it were possible to construct a microscope using rays with very short wavelength, it would be found that a single photon of light would impart a portion of its energy to the electron, causing a change in the velocity of the electron. This exchange of energy is known as the *Compton effect*. Compton † bombarded carbon and other light elements with short X rays and found, with the help of a diffracting crystal

* W. Heisenberg, Z. Physik., 43, 172 (1927).
† A. H. Compton, Phys. Rev., 21, 483 (1923).

and spectrometer, that part of the scattered radiation had a longer wavelength than the incident radiation.

The Heisenberg uncertainty principle may be expressed mathematically by

$$\Delta p \cdot \Delta x \sim h \qquad (24)$$

$$\Delta E \cdot \Delta t \sim h \qquad (25)$$

where Δp is the uncertainty in the momentum, Δx the uncertainty in position, ΔE the uncertainty in the energy, and Δt the uncertainty in time. The Heisenberg principle is more general than represented by equations 24 and 25 and may be stated in terms of further quantities. According to this principle, it will never be possible to know with exactness *both* the position *and* the momentum of an electron or other small particle. It is not a matter of physical imperfections in the measuring apparatus but a fundamental limit of nature. The position of an electron or atom may be known with exactness, but then its velocity is unknown; and in the same way the momentum can be known only at the sacrifice of information regarding the position. Similarly, a system can be said to have a precisely fixed energy only if it is in that state a long time. For macroscopic objects the Heisenberg uncertainty principle does not introduce a significant uncertainty. However, for the hydrogen atom the Heisenberg uncertainty principle means that we cannot talk about the position and momentum of the orbital electron as both having definite values. Thus in quantum theory the definite orbits of the Bohr theory are replaced by more diffuse regions in which the electrons may be found. Because of the uncertainty principle the future arrangement in an atomic system cannot be predicted with certainty, as was assumed in classical mechanics. Instead, only the *probability* that an electron will be at a given point at a given time may be predicted.

The Schrödinger Equation. The calculations of quantum mechanics are based upon the Schrödinger equation, as the calculations of classical mechanics are based upon Newton's laws of motion. The Schrödinger equation is a wave equation analogous to those describing sound waves and electromagnetic waves. Wave equations are partial differential equations involving second derivatives, and the independent variables are distance and time. The solutions of the wave equation for sound waves give pressure as a function of distance and time. The solutions of the wave equation for electromagnetic waves give the electric and magnetic field strengths as functions of distance and time. The solutions of the Schrödinger equation give wave functions ψ which are more abstract than pressure or electric field strength. However, the square * of the wave function, ψ^2, is a probability density [like $f(v)$ on p. 274]. Thus $\psi^2\ \Delta v$ is proportional to the probability that the electron will be found in the volume Δv. As summarized by the uncertainty principle, we cannot calculate the position of an electron exactly; however, we can calculate the probability that it will be in a certain element of volume.

Quantum mechanics can treat time-dependent phenomena, but we will be interested here only in the energy levels, which are independent of time. The Schrödinger equation for a single electron with a potential V is

$$-\frac{h^2}{8\pi^2 m}\left(\frac{\partial^2\psi}{\partial x^2} + \frac{\partial^2\psi}{\partial y^2} + \frac{\partial^2\psi}{\partial z^2}\right) + V\psi = E\psi \tag{26}$$

The stationary energy levels E are those for which this equation has solutions ψ which fulfill the following requirements:

$$\psi \text{ must be continuous and single valued} \tag{27}$$

$$\frac{\partial\psi}{\partial x}, \frac{\partial\psi}{\partial y}, \frac{\partial\psi}{\partial z} \text{ must be continuous} \tag{28}$$

$$\int_{-\infty}^{\infty}\psi^2\ dv \text{ must be finite} \tag{29}$$

The wave function ψ must be continuous so that there will not be a discontinuity in the probability of finding an electron in a given volume. The wave function must be single valued so that the probability will be unambiguous.

The probability of finding an electron in a small volume Δv is

$$\frac{\psi^2\ \Delta v}{\int_{-\infty}^{\infty}\psi^2\ dv} \tag{30}$$

Thus we can see that requirement 29 must be made so that the probability of finding the electron in any small volume Δv will not be zero.

In order to illustrate how the Schrödinger equation leads to definite energy levels we will consider several simple problems. These illustrations will show how the predictions of quantum mechanics differ from those of classical mechanics.

---

* If ψ is a complex quantity, as is often the case, then ψ^2 must be replaced by $\psi^*\psi$, where ψ^* is the complex conjugate of ψ. In the complex conjugate $i = \sqrt{-1}$ is replaced by $-i$.

Quantum-Mechanical Treatment of a Particle in a Box. The simplest problem which is related to that of an electron in an atom involves the calculation of the wave function for an electron which is constrained to move within a small distance of length a in the x direction. The potential energy V is taken as zero within this length a and infinite for other x values. This model is related to an atom in that the electron is bound in a small space. This simple problem illustrates many of the features of more complicated quantum-mechanical calculations.

In order to determine the wave function for the particle between $x = 0$ and $x = a$ equation 26 may be written

$$\frac{d^2\psi}{dx^2} + \frac{8\pi^2 m}{h^2} E\psi = 0 \tag{31}$$

The solution of this equation, with a constant A, is

$$\psi = A \sin \left(\frac{8\pi^2 mE}{h^2} \right)^{1/2} x \tag{32}$$

as may be shown by substitution into equation 31. A more detailed consideration * of the Schrödinger equation shows that only those wave functions which have a zero value at $x = 0$ and $x = a$ are suitable, because the others lead to an infinite probability of being outside the boundaries. The wave function in equation 32 was taken as the sine (rather than the cosine) in order to satisfy the boundary condition at $x = 0$. The sine of $n_x\pi$, where n_x is an integer, is zero. Therefore, reference to equation 32 shows that the boundary condition at $x = a$ is satisfied if

$$\left(\frac{8\pi^2 mE}{h^2} \right)^{1/2} a = n_x\pi \tag{33}$$

Thus, according to this equation, the energy of the particle in the box is given by

$$E = \frac{h^2 n_x^2}{8ma^2} \tag{34}$$

A particle moving along a line can have only the energies given by this equation for integer values of n_x, whereas a perfectly free particle can have any energy. Such definite energy levels are characteristic of solutions of the Schrödinger equation. No such definite energy levels were expected on the basis of classical mechanics.

* L. Pauling, E. B. Wilson, Jr., and M. Karplus, *Introduction to Quantum Mechanics*, McGraw-Hill Book Co., New York, in preparation.

Since n_x cannot be equal to zero, the lowest energy level is $E = h^2/8ma^2$, and the particle would necessarily have at least this much energy. This is in accord with the *uncertainty principle*, since the exact position of the particle in the box at a given time must remain uncertain.

It is apparent from equation 34 that the bigger the box or the heavier the particle the lower and more closely spaced are the energy levels. Since the energy increases with the square of the quantum number, it increases rapidly as the number of nodes in the wave function increases.

The value of the constant A in equation 32 is calculated in a process called *normalizing* the wave function. Equation 32 may be rewritten in terms of the quantum number by introducing equation 33.

$$\psi = A \sin \frac{\pi x n_x}{a} \tag{35}$$

The probability that the particle is somewhere between $x = 0$ and $x = a$ is, of course, unity, and this is expressed mathematically by integrating the square of the wave function over this distance.

$$1 = \int_0^a \psi^2 \, dx = A^2 \int_0^a \sin^2 \frac{\pi x n_x}{a} \, dx = \frac{A^2 a}{\pi} \int_0^\pi \sin^2 n_x \alpha \, d\alpha \tag{36}$$

where $\alpha = \pi x/a$. Since

$$\int_0^\pi \sin^2 n_x \alpha \, d\alpha = \frac{\pi}{2} \tag{37}$$

$A = (2/a)^{1/2}$, so that the final wave function is

$$\psi = \left(\frac{2}{a}\right)^{1/2} \sin \frac{\pi x n_x}{a} \tag{38}$$

The wave functions for $n_x = 1$, 2, and 3 are plotted in *Fig. 16-5a*, using equation 38. It can be seen that the wavelength is equal to $2a/n_x$.

The probability of finding the particle at a given x coordinate is given by the square of the wave function, and plots of probability calculated by squaring equation 38 are given in *Fig. 16-5b* for various values of the quantum number n_x.

The result for an electron in a box may be compared with the vibration of a violin string. The violin string is fixed at each end. and therefore the displacement at each end is always zero, just as the wave function for the electron is always zero at each side of the box. The violin string has a fundamental mode of vibration ($n = 1$) and a set of overtones ($n = 2, 3, \cdots$).

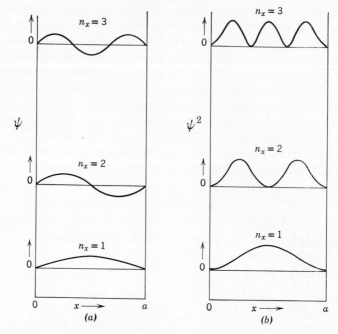

Fig. 16-5. (a) Wave functions ψ and (b) probability distribution functions ψ^2 for the lowest three energy levels for a particle in a box. The plots are placed at vertical heights which correspond to the energies of the levels.

The above treatment is readily extended to a three-dimensional rectangular box with sides of a, b, and c, and the energy levels are found to be given by

$$E = \frac{h^2}{8m}\left(\frac{n_x^2}{a^2} + \frac{n_y^2}{b^2} + \frac{n_z^2}{c^2}\right) \tag{39}$$

where n_x, n_y, and n_z are quantum numbers. If the lengths of no two edges of the box are in the ratio of integers, the energy levels will be different for all possible sets of the quantum numbers. If, however, some of the ratios are integers, several distinct combinations of the three quantum numbers give rise to the same total energy. Such an energy level is said to be *degenerate*, and the degree of degeneracy is equal to the number of independent wave functions associated with a given energy level.

If equation 39 is applied to calculating the energy levels of a baseball in a shoebox, it is found that these energy levels are so closely spaced that they are continuous by all measurements. Quantum mechanics gives the same answers as ordinary mechanics for processes with large particles, for which classical mechanics is known to be valid. This is summarized by the correspondence principle, first stated by Bohr, according to which the motion of a system described by quantum mechanics and by classical mechanics must agree in the limit that the quantum numbers involved are large.

The solutions of the Schrödinger equation for vibrating and rotating diatomic molecules are given in Chapter 17.

The Wave Mechanics of the Hydrogen Atom. The Schrödinger equation can be solved exactly for the hydrogen atom. The potential energy of the electron in the field of the nucleus is given by $V = e^2/r$, where e is the charge on the electron and r is the distance from the nucleus.

The solution of the Schrödinger equation for the hydrogen atom to obtain wave functions ψ with the desired properties involves rather complex mathematics.* It is found that the energies of the various quantum states of the hydrogen atom depend only upon the principal quantum number n. The relation between the total quantum number and the energy is the same as that obtained from the Bohr theory (equation 20), and summarized by the energy-level diagram given earlier (Fig. 16-4). The wave functions which are obtained involve quantum numbers which must have integer values. The wave functions describing single electrons are called *orbitals*. Each orbital has its associated quantum numbers. The quantum numbers which arise mathematically may be summarized as follows:

n = principal quantum number. Permissible solutions of the Schrödinger equation correspond to $n = 1, 2, 3, \cdots$.

l = angular momentum quantum number (or azimuthal quantum number). This quantum number can have only values of 0, 1, $\cdots$, $(n - 1)$, where n is the principal quantum number.

$$l = \quad 0 \quad 1 \quad 2 \quad 3$$

The corresponding symbols are $\quad s \quad p \quad d \quad f$.

Electronic orbitals in atoms are generally described by giving the principal quantum number and the symbol representing the angular momentum quantum number. Thus we speak of the $1s$, $2s$, $2p$, $3s$, $3p$, $3d$, etc., orbitals.

m = magnetic quantum number. The quantum number m may have any integer value between $+l$ and $-l$, including zero. Therefore, $2l + 1$ values of m are possible. For $l = 3$, $m = -3, -2, -1, 0, 1, 2, 3$.

---

* L. Pauling, E. B. Wilson, Jr., and M. Karplus, *Introduction to Quantum Mechanics*, McGraw-Hill Book Co., New York, in preparation.

Later we will find it necessary to introduce a fourth quantum number, the electron spin.

The equations for the $1s$ ($n = 1, l = 0, m = 0$) and $2s$ ($n = 2, l = 0, m = 0$) orbitals of the hydrogen atom are

$$\psi_{1s} = \frac{1}{\sqrt{\pi}} \left(\frac{1}{a_0}\right)^{3/2} e^{-r/a_0} \tag{40}$$

$$\psi_{2s} = \frac{1}{4\sqrt{2\pi}} \left(\frac{1}{a_0}\right)^{3/2} \left(2 - \frac{r}{a_0}\right) e^{-r/2a_0} \tag{41}$$

where $a_0 = h^2/4\pi^2\mu e^2$. The reduced mass μ is given by $mM/(m + M)$, where m is the mass of the electron and M is the mass of the proton (see p. 697). These wave functions depend only upon r, the distance from the nucleus to the electron, and so they are spherically symmetrical.

The probability of finding an electron in a volume element dv is $\psi^2 dv$, and so a plot of ψ^2 versus r, as shown in *Fig. 16-6a*, gives the probability of finding the electron in a volume dv at a distance r from the nucleus. The probability is highest for finding the electron very close to the nucleus. However, it is of greater interest to inquire as to

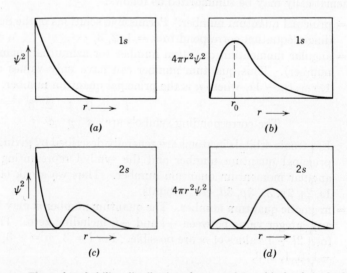

Fig. 16-6. Plots of probability distributions for $1s$ and $2s$ orbitals of the hydrogen atom.

the probability that the electron is in a spherical shell around the nucleus of radius r and thickness dr. The volume of such a shell is $4\pi r^2\, dr$. The probability of finding an electron in such a spherical shell is proportional to $4\pi r^2\psi^2$, and this probability is plotted versus r in $Fig.\ 16\text{-}6b$ for the $1s$ orbit. In contrast to Fig. 16-6a there is a maximum in this plot; the radius of the spherical shell in which the electron is most likely to be found is $r_0 = 0.529$ A. This is the same value that was obtained from the Bohr theory for $n = 1$. However, the picture of the orbital in Fig. 16-6b is quite different from that of the Bohr theory, which postulated a definite orbit like that of a planet. According to wave mechanics, the electron ranges through a large volume around the nucleus. The electron may be at a very great distance from the nucleus, but at larger values of r the probability drops off fairly rapidly.

A plot of ψ^2 for the $2s$ orbital is given in $Fig.\ 16\text{-}6c$, which was plotted from equation 41. The probability of finding the electron in a spherical shell around the nucleus is given by $Fig.\ 16\text{-}6d$. It can be seen that, when the principal quantum number is 2 rather than 1, the electron spends more of its time further from the nucleus. There are two maxima in this radial probability distribution, and both of them are spherically symmetrical with respect to the nucleus.

The probability that an electron in a hydrogen atom at room temperature will be excited to the $2s$ orbital is very small, since the energy required is much larger than kT which is available at room temperature.

The shapes of the orbitals for electrons may be represented by means of surfaces within which the electron is to be found a given fraction of the time, say 90 per cent. Such representations of the simplest types of orbitals are given in $Fig.\ 16\text{-}7$. The wave function for an s orbital is always spherically symmetrical, so that it may be respresented by a sphere around the nucleus.

The $2p$ ($n = 2$, $l = 1$) orbitals have the same energy as the $2s$ orbital, but the electron distribution is quite different and depends upon two angles as well as the radial distance from the nucleus, so that there is a directional character. The electron distribution for the $2p$ orbital with $m = 0$ is represented by p_z in Fig. 16-7. The $2p$ orbitals with $m = -1$ and $+1$ can be described in terms of closely related orbitals $2p_x$ and $2p_y$, which are illustrated in Fig. 16-7. The axes of the three types of p orbitals are mutually perpendicular. The angular dependence of these distributions is illustrated by Fig. 16-7, but it should be remembered that the electron clouds are diffuse. It will be seen in Chapter 17 that the directional character of certain chemical bonds results from the directed orientation of these and other orbitals.

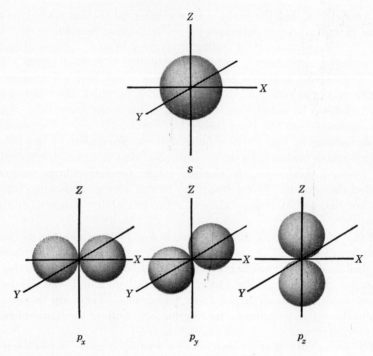

Fig. 16-7. Directional character of s and p orbitals.

Although there are three $2p$ orbitals, they all have the same energy, since all directions are equivalent unless the atom is in a magnetic field. In a magnetic field different energies are associated with the three orientations. As a result the emission spectrum of an atom in a magnetic field shows more lines, the additional lines being only slightly different in energy from the corresponding lines in the absence of the magnetic field. This splitting of lines by a magnetic field is called the *Zeeman effect*. There is a corresponding splitting of lines by an electric field which is called the *Stark effect*.

Spin. In addition to the three quantum numbers arising in the solution of the Schrödinger equation, studies of the fine structure of spectra showed that a fourth quantum number, the electron spin, is required. An electron behaves as if it were spinning about its center with a definite angular momentum. The electron-spin quantum number is represented by m_s, and two values of m_s are possible, corresponding to two possible orientations of the spin vector. The quantum numbers can change only by integers, and m_s can have only the values $+\frac{1}{2}$ and $-\frac{1}{2}$.

Pauli Exclusion Principle. Now we want to examine the way in which electrons are distributed between the various types of orbitals in atoms. We would expect electrons to go into the orbitals of lowest energy, but spectra show that only two electrons can go into the $1s$ orbital and that additional electrons must be placed in orbitals with higher quantum numbers. This restriction is referred to as the Pauli exclusion principle. According to this principle, *there can never be two electrons in a single atom or molecule with all four quantum numbers the same.* This principle cannot be derived theoretically, but it accounts for the structure of the periodic table. The ground state of an atom will be that in which the electrons are in the lowest possible energy levels consistent with the Pauli principle.

Only those combinations of quantum numbers are allowed which are in agreement with the restrictions just given. For example, if $n = 3$, l can be only 2, 1, or 0; m takes on values from $-l$ to $+l$; and m_s can be only $+\frac{1}{2}$ or $-\frac{1}{2}$. All the various combinations of the four quantum numbers permitted by the restrictions just given are recorded in Table II for values of the principal quantum number of 1, 2, 3, and 4. Re-

Table II. Quantum Numbers of Orbitals of Elements

Principal n	l	Orbital	Magnetic m_l	Spin m_s	Total Number of Different Combinations
1	0	$1s$	0	$+\frac{1}{2} -\frac{1}{2}$	2
2	0	$2s$	0	$+\frac{1}{2} -\frac{1}{2}$	2 ⎫ 8
2	1	$2p$	$+1\ 0\ -1$	$+\frac{1}{2} -\frac{1}{2}$	6 ⎭
3	0	$3s$	0	$+\frac{1}{2} -\frac{1}{2}$	2 ⎫
3	1	$3p$	$+1\ 0\ -1$	$+\frac{1}{2} -\frac{1}{2}$	6 ⎬ 18
3	2	$3d$	$+2\ +1\ 0\ -1\ -2$	$+\frac{1}{2} -\frac{1}{2}$	10 ⎭
4	0	$4s$	0	$+\frac{1}{2} -\frac{1}{2}$	2 ⎫
4	1	$4p$	$+1\ 0\ -1$	$+\frac{1}{2} -\frac{1}{2}$	6 ⎬ 32
4	2	$4d$	$+2\ +1\ 0\ -1\ -2$	$+\frac{1}{2} -\frac{1}{2}$	10 ⎬
4	3	$4f$	$+3\ +2\ +1\ 0\ -1\ -2\ -3$	$+\frac{1}{2} -\frac{1}{2}$	14 ⎭

ferring to the last column in Table II, it may be seen that 2 different combinations of quantum numbers are possible for an s electron, 6 for a p electron, 10 for a d electron, and 14 for an f electron. Now, by the Pauli principle, there can be only one kind of atom for each given combination of electronic quantum numbers. The sequence 2, 8, 18, 32, given in the last column of Table II, is thus the sequence in the number of elements found in the successive groups of the periodic table.

The periodic table is given in Table III, in which the atomic number appears over the symbol for the element. The number below the symbol is the atomic weight on the chemical scale for a naturally occurring element or (in parentheses) the mass number (p. 681) of the longest-lived isotope for a synthetic element.

The nature of the periods in the periodic table is readily explained in terms of the Pauli exclusion principle and the four quantum numbers n, l, m, and m_s. The number of orbital electrons in an atom of an element is equal to the atomic number. The lowest energy level is referred to as the $1s$ level, since the principal quantum number $n = 1$ and the orbital quantum number $l = 0$ (for which the corresponding symbol is s). The single electron of the hydrogen atom therefore goes into the $1s$ level. The two electrons of helium both go into this level and have opposite spins ($m_s = +\frac{1}{2}$ and $-\frac{1}{2}$). No more electrons are allowed in this orbital. Since considerable energy is required to remove an electron from this completed orbital, helium is a very inert substance.

Lithium has three electrons, two of which are in the $1s$ level and the third in the $2s$ level ($n = 2$, $l = 0$). Since the $2s$ electron is much farther from the nucleus and is partially shielded from the $+3$ charge of the nucleus by the two inner electrons, the outer electron is easily removed, producing an ion with the electronic structure of helium. In going from lithium to neon, there are eight elements (see Table III), ending with neon, which has a stable structure with eight electrons with $n = 2$. The next element, sodium, has one $3s$ electron ($n = 3$, $l = 0$). This electron is shielded from the $+11$ nuclear charge by ten inner electrons, so that it is loosely bound.

A description of the orbitals of an atom which are occupied is called the electron configuration. The electron configuration is given by using exponents to indicate the number of electrons in the $1s$, $2s$, $2p$, etc., orbitals. For example, hydrogen in the ground state is represented by $1s$, helium by $1s^2$, lithium by $1s^2 2s$, boron by $1s^2 2s^2 2p$, and sodium by $1s^2 2s^2 2p^6 3s$. The electron configurations are given in Table IV in tabular form for all the elements.

The distribution of electrons in an atom may be determined experimentally by electron diffraction, and the radial distribution of electrons

Table III. Periodic Table of the Elements

IA	IIA	IIIB	IVB	VB	VIB	VIIB		VIII		IB	IIB	IIIA	IVA	VA	VIA	VIIA	
																	2 He 4.003
1 H 1.0080																	
3 Li 6.940	4 Be 9.013											5 B 10.82	6 C 12.010	7 N 14.008	8 O 16.0000	9 F 19.00	10 Ne 20.183
11 Na 22.997	12 Mg 24.32											13 Al 26.98	14 Si 28.09	15 P 30.975	16 S 32.066	17 Cl 35.457	18 A 39.944
19 K 39.100	20 Ca 40.08	21 Sc 44.96	22 Ti 47.90	23 V 50.95	24 Cr 52.01	25 Mn 54.93	26 Fe 55.85	27 Co 58.94	28 Ni 58.69	29 Cu 63.54	30 Zn 65.38	31 Ga 69.72	32 Ge 72.60	33 As 74.91	34 Se 78.96	35 Br 79.916	36 Kr 83.8
37 Rb 85.48	38 Sr 87.63	39 Y 88.92	40 Zr 91.22	41 Nb 92.91	42 Mo 95.95	43 Tc (99)	44 Ru 101.7	45 Rh 102.91	46 Pd 106.7	47 Ag 107.880	48 Cd 112.41	49 In 114.76	50 Sn 118.70	51 Sb 121.76	52 Te 127.61	53 I 126.91	54 Xe 131.3
55 Cs 132.91	56 Ba 137.36	57–71 Rare Earths	72 Hf 178.6	73 Ta 180.88	74 W 183.92	75 Re 186.31	76 Os 190.2	77 Ir 193.1	78 Pt 195.23	79 Au 197.2	80 Hg 200.61	81 Tl 204.39	82 Pb 207.21	83 Bi 209.00	84 Po (210)	85 At (210)	86 Rn 222
87 Fr (223)	88 Ra 226.05	89– Acti- nides															

Rare earths (Lanthanide series)

57 La 138.92	58 Ce 140.13	59 Pr 140.92	60 Nd 144.27	61 Pm (145)	62 Sm 150.43	63 Eu 152.0	64 Gd 156.9	65 Tb 159.2	66 Dy 162.46	67 Ho 164.94	68 Er 167.2	69 Tm 169.4	70 Yb 173.04	71 Lu 174.99

Actinide series

89 Ac (227)	90 Th 232.12	91 Pa 231	92 U 238.07	93 Np (237)	94 Pu (242)	95 Am (243)	96 Cm (245)	97 Bk (249)	98 Cf (249)	99 Es (253)	100 Fm (253)	101 Md (256)	102 No

Table IV. Electron Configurations of Atoms in Their Normal States

Atomic Number	Element	$1s$	$2s\ 2p$	$3s\ 3p\ 3d$	$4s\ 4p\ 4d\ 4f$	$5s\ 5p\ 5d\ 5f$	$6s\ 6p\ 6d$	$7s$
1	H	1						
2	He	2						
3	Li	2	1					
4	Be	2	2					
5	B	2	2 1					
6	C	2	2 2					
7	N	2	2 3					
8	O	2	2 4					
9	F	2	2 5					
10	Ne	2	2 6					
11	Na			1				
12	Mg			2				
13	Al			2 1				
14	Si		Neon	2 2				
15	P		core	2 3				
16	S			2 4				
17	Cl			2 5				
18	A			2 6				
19	K				1			
20	Ca				2			
21	Sc			1	2			
22	Ti			2	2			
23	V			3	2			
24	Cr			5	1			
25	Mn			5	2			
26	Fe			6	2			
27	Co			7	2			
28	Ni		Argon core	8	2			
29	Cu			10	1			
30	Zn			10	2			
31	Ga			10	2 1			
32	Ge			10	2 2			
33	As			10	2 3			
34	Se			10	2 4			
35	Br			10	2 5			
36	Kr			10	2 6			
37	Rb					1		
38	Sr					2		
39	Y				1	2		
40	Zr				2	2		
41	Nb				4	1		
42	Mo				5	1		
43	Tc				5	2		
44	Ru		Krypton core		7	1		
45	Rh				8	1		
46	Pd				10			
47	Ag				10	1		
48	Cd				10	2		
49	In				10	2 1		
50	Sn				10	2 2		
51	Sb				10	2 3		

Table IV.   Electron Configurations of Atoms in Their Normal States (*Continued*)

Atomic Number	Element	$1s$	$2s\,2p$	$3s\,3p\,3d$	$4s\,4p\,4d\,4f$	$5s\,5p\,5d\,5f$	$6s\,6p\,6d$	$7s$
52	Te				10	2 4		
53	I			Krypton core	10	2 5		
54	Xe				10	2 6		
55	Cs						1	
56	Ba			Xenon core			2	
57	La					1	2	
58	Ce				1	1	2	
59	Pr				2	1	2	
60	Nd				4		2	
61	Pm				5		2	
62	Sm				6		2	
63	Eu				7		2	
64	Gd				7	1	2	
65	Tb				8	1	2	
66	Dy				10		2	
67	Ho				11		2	
68	Er				12		2	
69	Tm				13		2	
70	Yb				14		2	
71	Lu				14	1	2	
72	Hf				14	2	2	
73	Ta				14	3	2	
74	W				14	4	2	
75	Re				14	5	2	
76	Os				14	6	2	
77	Ir				14	9		
78	Pt				14	9	1	
79	Au				14	10	1	
80	Hg				14	10	2	
81	Tl				14	10	2 1	
82	Pb				14	10	2 2	
83	Bi				14	10	2 3	
84	Po				14	10	2 4	
85	At				14	10	2 5	
86	Rn				14	10	2 6	
87	Fr							1
88	Ra							2
89	Ac			Radon core			1	2
90	Th						2	2
91	Pa					2	1	2
92	U					3	1	2
93	Np					5		2
94	Pu					6		2
95	Am					7		2
96	Cm					7	1	2
97	Bk					8	1	2
98	Cf					9	1	2
99	Es					10	1	2
100	Fm					11	1	2
101	Md					12	1	2
102	No					13	1	2

in argon determined in this way is given in *Fig. 16-8* in comparison with the distribution calculated theoretically with the Hartree theory. The distribution function shows the existence of the diffuse orbitals with $n = 1$, 2, and 3.

It may be seen that the orbitals continue to be filled in an orderly fashion until potassium (atomic number 19) is reached. The outer electron of potassium goes into the $4s$ level rather than the $3d$ level, be-

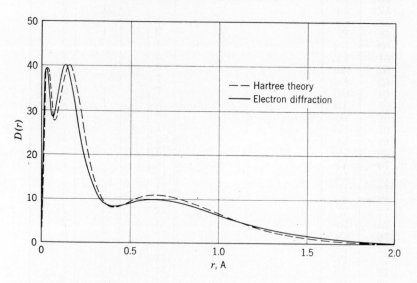

Fig. 16-8. Radial distribution of electrons in argon determined by electron diffraction [L. S. Bartell and L. O. Brockway, *Phys. Rev.*, *90*, 833 (1953)] and calculated theoretically using the Hartree theory.

cause the electron distribution for these levels is such that the $4s$ level actually has a lower energy. The reason is that s orbitals are more penetrating and have higher electron densities near the nucleus. In the transition elements which follow calcium (scandium, atomic number 21 to zinc, atomic number 30) the $3d$ shell is being filled while the number of electrons in the outer orbit is either 1 or 2.

The fifteen rare earths (lanthanum to lutetium) owe their similar properties to the fact that the $4f$ level is being completed while the outer level holds two $6s$ electrons. Because the chemical properties are largely determined by the outer valence electrons, these elements are much alike. At various times it has been suggested that at least some of the elements in the last period of the periodic table might form the beginning of a new series analogous to the rare earths. After a study of the properties of the new transuranium elements Seaborg suggested that the closely related properties of the actinide elements may be interpreted by assuming that these elements possess an incomplete shell of $5f$ electrons.

Ionization Potential. The ionization potential is the voltage corresponding with the energy required to remove an electron completely from a gaseous atom without giving the free electron any kinetic energy. The ionization potential may be determined by bombarding a gas with electrons which have been accelerated by a difference in electric potential between a grid and the hot filament which emits the electrons. If the accelerated electrons have insufficient kinetic energy to cause a shift from one energy level to another in the atoms they strike, the collisions are said to be elastic. As the potential is increased, the accelerated electrons gain sufficient energy to excite an orbital electron from one energy level to the next higher level. Light is emitted when the electron returns to the empty lower level. As the accelerating voltage is increased, new spectral lines appear. The potentials required to cause emission of light are called *resonance potentials*. At higher potentials ionization is produced. The ionization potential of an atom or ion may be calculated from spectroscopic data, since this potential is given by the series limit. The electron is quantized while in the atom and only restricted energies are allowed, thus giving discrete spectral lines. When the electron is driven outside the atom by receiving energy greater than the ionization potential, the electron can have varying amounts of kinetic energy which is not quantized. The spectrum then is not limited to definite lines and is continuous.

The relation between the accelerating potential E and the frequency of the light emitted is

$$Ee = h\nu \tag{42}$$

where e is the charge on the electron. If the accelerating potential is expressed in volts and the charge on the electron is expressed in coulombs (1.60186×10^{-19} coulomb), the product of voltage and charge must be multiplied by 10^7 to obtain the energy in ergs.

A plot of the first ionization potentials of gaseous atoms versus atomic number is given in *Fig. 16-9*. The first ionization potential is that for the removal of the first electron. The ionization potentials change in a periodic way because of the progressive filling up of shells with electrons. The principal maxima in this plot are given by the inert gases, and the principal minima by the alkali metal atoms.

The alkali metal atoms are easily ionized, since they have a single electron in the outer shell. The attraction of the nucleus for the outer-

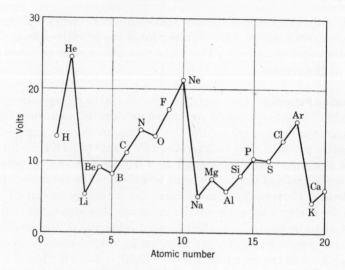

Fig. 16-9. First ionization potentials of gaseous atoms early in the periodic table.

most electron of the alkali metal atoms is quite effectively shielded by the electrons of the inner orbits. In the series lithium, sodium, potassium, rubidium, and cesium the ionization potential decreases because of the increase in size of the outer orbit containing a single electron.

In contrast, the ionization potentials of the halogens are almost as great as those of the inert gases. The electrons in the outer orbits of the halogen atoms are shielded from the nuclear charge mainly by the electrons in inner orbits, since the electrons in the outer orbits are all approximately the same distance from the nucleus. A direct result of this incomplete shielding of the nuclear charge, so far as electrons in the outer orbit are concerned, is the fact that the halogen atoms readily take on an additional electron to form negative ions. The affinities of fluorine, chlorine, bromine, and iodine for an additional electron, expressed in terms of electron volts, are 4.13, 3.72, 3.49, and 3.14. Oxygen atoms and sulfur atoms also have affinities for an additional electron (3.07 and 2.8 electron volts, respectively). The inert gases do not have affinity for electrons because an additional electron would have to go into an orbit lying further out.

The resonance potentials for atomic hydrogen may be calculated by combining equations 11 and 42 to obtain

$$Ee = h\nu = hc\bar{\nu} = hc\mathbf{R}\left(\frac{1}{n_1^2} - \frac{1}{n_2^2}\right) \tag{43}$$

or

$$E = \frac{Rhc}{e}\left(\frac{1}{n_1{}^2} - \frac{1}{n_2{}^2}\right) \tag{44}$$

where n_1 and n_2 are the quantum numbers 1, 2, 3, 4, 5, etc. The constant Rhc/e has the value of 13.539 volts.

This equation is used to calculate the resonance potentials for the Lyman series of *atomic* hydrogen, where $n_1 = 1$. The comparison with experiment is given in Table V.

Table V. Spectral Lines and Resonance Potentials in the Lyman Series

Quantum Number, n_2	Wave-length, λ_{obs}, A	Wave Number, cm^{-1}	Volts, E_{calc}	Volts, E_{obs}
2	1215	82,258	10.154	10.15
3	1026	97,491	12.034	12.05
4	973	102,823	12.692	12.70
5	950	105,291		
6	938	106,631	13.161	13.17
7	931	107,440	13.262	13.27
∞	912	109,678	13.539	13.54

X-ray Spectra. When electrons make transitions into vacancies in the inner orbits of all but the lighter elements, the quanta of radiation emitted fall in the X-ray region. In order to produce X-ray spectra electrons emitted from a hot filament are accelerated by high potentials and caused to impinge on a solid target such as copper or molybdenum. Electrons are driven out of inner orbits, and an X-ray photon is emitted when an outer electron makes a transition to this vacancy.

Moseley used different elements as targets in an X-ray tube and determined the wavelengths of the X rays, using a crystal as a diffraction grating (p. 625). The X-ray spectrum of a metal is fairly simple, involving only a few lines. These lines are all displaced in the direction of shorter wavelengths as the atomic weight of the element increases. When Moseley plotted the square root of the frequencies of the X-ray lines against the atomic number Z of the elements, he found that approximately straight lines were produced. Expressed mathematically,

$$\sqrt{\nu} = aZ - b \tag{45}$$

where a and b are constants. The explanation of this relation is that the energy of inner electrons becomes more negative approximately as the square of the atomic number Z; thus the energy $h\nu$ of the X-ray photon produced is approximately proportional to Z^2, and $\nu^{1/2}$ is approximately proportional to Z.

By means of these experiments Moseley was able to determine correctly the atomic numbers of elements for which these values were uncertain. The arrangement of elements according to their atomic numbers straightened out certain anomalies in the periodic table. Potassium follows argon, nickel follows cobalt, and iodine follows tellurium, in spite of the fact that classification by atomic weights puts them in the reverse order. The existence of nuclei with different weights but the same atomic number explains why this order is reversed and shows that the atomic number is a more fundamental property than the atomic weight. When Moseley prepared his table of atomic numbers in 1914, there were six gaps corresponding to six missing elements, but all these have since been filled.

REFERENCES

R. Daudel, R. Lefebure, and C. Moser, *Quantum Chemistry*, Interscience Publishers, New York, 1960.

G. Herzberg, *Atomic Spectra and Atomic Structure*, Prentice-Hall, Englewood Cliffs, N. J., 1937.

W. Kauzmann, *Quantum Chemistry*, Academic Press, New York, 1957.

R. B. Leighton, *Principles of Modern Physics*, McGraw-Hill Book Co., New York, 1959.

L. Pauling, *The Nature of the Chemical Bond*, Cornell University Press, Ithaca, 1960.

L. Pauling, E. B. Wilson, and M. Karplus, *Introduction to Quantum Mechanics*, McGraw-Hill Book Co., New York, in preparation.

K. S. Pitzer, *Quantum Chemistry*, Prentice-Hall, Englewood Cliffs, N. J., 1953.

F. O. Rice and E. Teller, *The Structure of Matter*, John Wiley & Sons, New York, 1949.

F. K. Richtmyer, E. H. Kennard, and T. Lauritsen, *Introduction to Modern Physics*, McGraw-Hill Book Co., New York, 1955.

G. W. Wheland, *Resonance in Organic Chemistry*, John Wiley & Sons, New York, 1955.

PROBLEMS

1. For light having a wavelength of 400 mμ calculate (a) the wavelength in angstroms, (b) the frequency, and (c) the wave number.

$\qquad$ *Ans.* (a) 4000 A.   (b) 7.50×10^{14} sec^{-1}.   (c) 2.5×10^4 cm^{-1}.

2. A hollow box with an opening of 1 cm^2 area is heated electrically. (a) What is the total energy emitted per second at 800°K? (b) How much energy is emitted per second if the temperature is 1600°K? (c) How long would it take the radiant energy emitted at this temperature, 1600°K, to melt 1000 grams of ice?

$\qquad$ *Ans.* (a) 2.33×10^7 ergs cm^{-2} sec^{-1}.

$\qquad$ (b) 3.73×10^8 ergs cm^{-2} sec^{-1}.   (c) 8950 sec.

3. Assuming that the sun radiates as a black body, calculate its surface temperature from the fact that the wavelength of maximum emission is 5000 A. The wavelength of maximum emission is given by $\lambda_{max} = ch/4.97kT$. *Ans.* 5800°K.

4. An experiment on the emission of photoelectrons from a sodium surface by light of different wavelengths gave the following values for the potentials at which the photoelectric current was reduced to zero. Plot voltage against frequency, and

λ, A	E, volts
3651	−0.950
3125	−0.382

calculate (a) the threshold frequency and (b) Planck's constant.
Ans. (a) 10.5×10^{14} sec^{-1}. (b) 6.60×10^{-27} erg sec.

5. What potential difference is required to accelerate a singly charged gas ion in a vacuum so that it has (a) a kinetic energy equal to that of an average gas molecule at 25°, (b) an energy equivalent to 20 kcal mole^{-1}? *Ans.* (a) 0.0386, (b) 0.864 volt.

6. Electrons are accelerated by a 1000-volt potential drop. (a) Calculate the de Broglie wavelength. (b) Calculate the wavelength of the X rays which could be produced when these electrons strike a solid. *Ans.* (a) 0.387, (b) 12.4 A.

7. Calculate the wavelengths (in microns) of the first three lines of the Paschen series for atomic hydrogen. *Ans.* 1.8756, 1.2822, 1.0941 μ.

8. In the Balmer series for atomic hydrogen what is the wavelength of the series limit? *Ans.* 3647 A.

9. The first ionization potential for atomic lithium is 5.39 volts (Li = Li$^+$ + e). The second ionization potential is 75.62 volts (Li$^+$ = Li^{2+} + e). Calculate the wavelengths for the convergence limits indicated by these potentials. *Ans.* 2300, 164 A.

10. What are the electron configurations for H$^-$, Li$^+$, O^{2-}, F$^-$, Na$^+$, and Mg^{2+}? *Ans.* $1s^2$, $1s^2$, $1s^22s^22p^6$, $1s^22s^22p^6$, $1s^22s^22p^6$, $1s^22s^22p^6$.

---

11. For radiation of 2000 cm^{-1} calculate (a) the wavelength in angstrom units and (b) the frequency.

12. If 10,000 cal is lost per min by radiation from the door of an electrically heated furnace at 900°K, how many more watts of electricity must be applied to offset the losses due to radiation if the furnace is heated to 1100°K?

13. Plot the intensity of black-body radiation versus wavelength for a temperature of 10,000°K. What is the wavelength of maximum emission?

14. The threshold frequency for photoelectric emission from lithium is approximately 5200 A. Calculate the velocity of electrons emitted as the result of absorption of light at 3600 A.

15. Calculate the velocity of an electron which has been accelerated by a potential difference of 1.00 volt.

16. Calculate the velocity and wavelength of (a) 1-Mev doubly charged helium atoms and (b) 1-Mev protons. (The relativistic correction may be ignored.)

17. Calculate the frequency and the wavelength in angstroms for the line in the Paschen series of the hydrogen spectrum which is due to a transition from the sixth quantum level to the third.

18. Calculate the difference in energy for $n_x = 1$ and $n_x = 2$ for a 100-gram ball in a 10-cm box.

19. The first ionization potential of atomic hydrogen is 13.54 volts. Calculate the wavelength of the light produced when a free electron without kinetic energy returns to the inner orbit.

20. Considering only the first 18 elements of the periodic table, list those whose outer electrons are in spherically symmetrical orbits and those whose outer electrons are not.

21. For copper $K\alpha$ X rays, $\lambda = 1.54$ A. Calculate (a) the frequency and (b) the wave number.

22. An electric heater of 10 cm^2 has a temperature of 800°K. How many calories of radiant heat are emitted per minute, if a perfect radiator is assumed?

23. Calculate the ratio of the intensities of light of 5000 A wavelength from black bodies of 1000°K and 5000°K.

24. What is the wavelength of light which has energy equal to the energy of electrons which have been accelerated by a potential of (a) 400 volts, (b) 3 volts?

25. Calculate the de Broglie wavelength of a hydrogen atom with a translational energy corresponding to room temperature.

26. Calculate the value of the Rydberg constant R for hydrogen, and compare it with the experimentally determined value.

27. There is a Brackett series in the hydrogen spectrum where $n_1 = 4$. Calculate the wavelengths, in angstroms, of the first two lines of this series.

28. The ionization potential of atomic sodium is 5.14 volts. Calculate the degree of ionization

$$Na \rightleftharpoons Na^+ + e$$

at 10,000°K and 0.01 atm. The pressure due to the electrons is included as well as that due to the sodium ions.

29. Using the Bohr theory, calculate the ionization potential for $Be^{3+} = Be^{4+} + e$.

30. The work function for tungsten is 4.58 volts. (a) What is the wavelength of the photoelectric threshold? (b) When light of 200 mμ is used, what potential must be applied to keep the most energetic electrons from reaching the collector? (c) What is the maximum velocity of electrons emitted by 200-mμ light?

MOLECULAR STRUCTURE

17

In 1916 G. N. Lewis described the bonding in nonpolar compounds as resulting from the sharing of pairs of electrons between atoms. Such a bond is called a *covalent bond*. The pair of electrons held jointly by two atoms was considered to be effective in completing a stable electronic configuration for each atom. It was recognized by Lewis, by Kossel, and by Langmuir that there is a tendency for an atom to lose or gain electrons in order to have an "octet" in its outer shell. Since the rare gases neon, argon, krypton, xenon, and radon have eight electrons in their outer shells, this is apparently a very stable configuration. The stable configuration of the helium atom and of hydrogen in molecular compounds has two orbital electrons.

Normal Covalent and Coordinate Covalent Bonds. A normal covalent bond is one between two atoms each of which supplies an electron to the bond. In the following representation electrons in the outer shell are represented by dots.

$$H \cdot + \cdot H = H:H$$

$$\cdot \overset{\cdot}{N}: + 3H \cdot = H:\overset{\cdot \cdot}{\underset{\overset{\cdot \cdot}{H}}{N}}:$$

A bond is referred to as a coordinate covalent bond if one atom provides both electrons for the bond. For example,

$$H:\overset{\overset{\textstyle H}{\cdot \cdot}}{\underset{\overset{\cdot \cdot}{H}}{N}}: + \overset{\overset{\textstyle F}{\cdot \cdot}}{\underset{\overset{\cdot \cdot}{F}}{B}}:F = H:\overset{\overset{\textstyle H}{}}{\underset{\overset{}{H}}{N}}:\overset{\overset{\textstyle F}{}}{\underset{\overset{}{F}}{B}}:F$$

483

Double bonds and triple bonds can be represented by the sharing of two pairs or three pairs of electrons, as shown by ethylene and acetylene.

$$\overset{H}{\underset{H}{\cdot}}\overset{\cdot}{:}C::C\overset{\cdot}{:}\overset{H}{\underset{H}{\cdot}} \qquad\qquad H:C:::C:H$$

Some molecules can be represented only by introducing one-electron or three-electron bonds. The hydrogen molecule-ion, H_2^+, is held together by a one-electron bond. There is evidence that the structure of nitric oxide may be represented by $N\overset{\cdot}{:}\overset{\cdot}{:}\overset{\cdot}{O}$ so that there is a three-electron bond in addition to the double bond.

The tendency to complete an orbit of eight electrons may also lead to an ionic bond. For example, in sodium chloride, sodium loses its single valence electron to chlorine, which has seven electrons in its outer shell.

$$Na\cdot + \cdot\overset{\cdot\cdot}{\underset{\cdot\cdot}{Cl}}: = [Na]^+ + [:\overset{\cdot\cdot}{\underset{\cdot\cdot}{Cl}}:]^-$$

The representation of chemical bonds in terms of static electron pairs is useful in explaining some properties, as shown above. However, because the electrons are not static it gives a false picture; also there are many experimental facts that cannot be accounted for by this simple theory. The explanation of the nature of chemical bonds has been one of the most important contributions of quantum mechanics to chemistry. In order to illustrate this application of quantum mechanics we will first consider an extreme type of chemical bonding, ionic bonding.

Ionic Bonding. A molecule is said to have a permanent electric dipole moment if the positive and negative charges within the molecule are partially separated so that the molecule will tend to orient in an electric field. The magnitude of this separation of charge is measured quantitatively by the magnitude of the dipole moment (p. 501). The dielectric constant of gaseous potassium chloride indicates that the molecule in the gas phase is a dipole with essentially one positive charge on the potassium atom and one negative charge on the chlorine atom. The question is whether the electrostatic attraction is sufficient to account for the stability of this molecule.

In forming a potassium chloride molecule from isolated potassium and chlorine atoms it is first necessary to remove an electron from the potassium atom and to put an electron onto the chlorine atom. Since the ionization potential (p. 478) of a potassium atom is 4.34 volts, energy in an amount of 4.34 ev is required to produce K^+. We now inquire as to the amount of energy which is evolved when an electron is added to a chlorine atom. The energy obtained when an electron is added to an atom is referred to as the electron affinity; it is usually expressed in electron volts. The electron affinity of a chlorine atom is 3.82 volts. Thus the net amount of energy required to form K^+ and Cl^- from the two atoms is $4.34 - 3.82 = 0.52$ ev. The ions have more energy than the separated atoms and are therefore not stable with respect to the separated atoms. However, when the ions are brought together, there is an electrostatic attraction. The electron distributions around K^+ and Cl^- are both spherically symmetrical, since each has the argon structure. Provided that the charge clouds due to the filled orbitals do not overlap appreciably, the energy of electrostatic attraction measured relative to the energy at infinite separation is $-e^2/r$, where r is the distance between the centers of the ions. The dashed curve in *Fig. 17-1* is a plot of the electrostatic energy plus the energy required to form the two ions from the two atoms.

As the ions are brought very close to each other, a repulsion arises as soon as the closed electron shells of the ions begin to overlap appreciably. This repulsion is readily explained on the basis of the Pauli

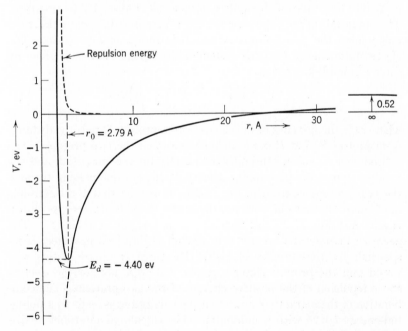

Fig. 17-1. Potential energy of the system K^+, Cl^- as a function of internuclear distance r.

exclusion principle. As the outer orbitals of the two ions begin to overlap, some of the electrons must be promoted to higher quantum states so that there will not be more than one electron per quantum state. This requires energy, and the energy required rises very rapidly as the ions begin to interpenetrate, as indicated by the dotted line in Fig. 17-1. The sum of these two potential-energy curves gives a potential-energy curve with a minimum, as shown by the solid line. The minimum occurs at the average internuclear distance for the gaseous potassium chloride molecule.

Electrostatic bonds may also be formed between an ion and a molecule having a dipole moment (page 501). Complex ions such as $[Ni(NH_3)_4]^{2+}$ contain electrostatic bonds of this *ion-dipole* type. An ion may also induce a dipole moment in a neutral molecule to form an *ion-induced dipole* bond. Such a bond is formed in the reaction

$$I^- + I_2 = I_3^-$$

The Hydrogen Molecule-Ion. When an electron is added to two protons which are about 1 A apart, a tendency to bind arises and a stable hydrogen molecule-ion H_2^+ is formed. The discussion of this binding is simpler than that of the hydrogen molecule, but is of the same type. The potential energy of an electron as a function of distance x along the line joining the two protons A and B is shown in *Fig. 17-2a*. The electrostatic energy V of the system of three point charges is given by three Coulomb-law terms.

$$V = e^2 \left(-\frac{1}{r_A} - \frac{1}{r_B} + \frac{1}{R} \right) \tag{1}$$

where r_A is the distance of the electron from proton A, r_B is the distance from proton B, and R is the distance between the two protons. The Schrödinger equation can be solved exactly for this potential, and the cross section of the probability density ψ^2 along a line passing through the two protons is given in *Fig. 17-2b*. It is seen that the electron is much more likely to be between the nuclei than elsewhere. As shown in part A of Fig. 17-2b, this region is one of low potential energy. The decrease in potential energy over that of H^+ and H separately is responsible for the stability of H_2^+. The force produced in this way would pull the protons closer together if it were not for the electrostatic repulsion of the positive charges of the two protons. The combination of the attractive- and repulsive-energy terms leads to a potential-energy curve with a minimum. The calculated internuclear distance (1.06 A) and dissociation energy (2.64 ev) are in good agreement with the values obtained from spectra.

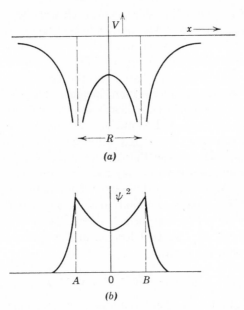

(a)

(b)

Fig. 17-2. (*a*) Potential energy of an electron along a line through the centers of two protons which are at a distance R. (*b*) Probability density for an electron moving in the potential given in *a*.

Molecular-Orbital and Valence-Bond Theories. When two or more electrons are involved, mathematical difficulties in solving the Schrödinger equation require the use of approximation methods in obtaining the wave function. These difficulties arise from the fact that the motions of the electrons are correlated; that is, they stay away from each other and affect each other's motion. There are two types of approximations for solving this problem, the molecular-orbital theory and the valence-bond theory. In the *molecular-orbital* (*MO*) *theory* we may visualize the nuclear skeleton established first. Electrons are then fed into the system one by one and go into molecular orbitals in which each electron is associated with all the nuclei. In the *valence-bond* (*VB*) *theory* complete atoms are brought together and allowed to interact. Whereas in the molecular-orbital theory all electrons are considered to belong to the whole molecule, in the valence-bond theory a pair of electrons is considered to belong to the pair of atoms which is bonded together.

It is a further useful approximation to consider the correct wave function to be a linear combination of atomic orbitals (*LCAO approximation*). The correct wave function is assumed to be made up of a summation of wave functions for atoms, each term having a coefficient which is allowed to vary. The best values of the coefficients are obtained by a *variational* method in which the coefficients are varied in such a way as to make the energy a minimum. The more closely the approximate wave function approaches the true wave function, the better will be the agreement between calculated and observed energies.

In the case of the hydrogen molecule-ion the electron would have a $1s$ wave function ψ_A centered on nucleus A if nucleus B were far away, and a $1s$ wave function ψ_B centered on nucleus B if nucleus A were far away. Thus we might expect that the wave function for the hydrogen molecule-ion could be approximately represented by some combination of ψ_A and ψ_B. According to this point of view, the wave function is considered to be a linear combination of atomic orbitals. Since the form of the $1s$ wave function for a hydrogen atom is known (p. 468), the wave function $\psi_{H_2^+}$ for the electron in the hydrogen molecule-ion may be written in the form

$$\psi_{H_2^+} = K(e^{-z'r_{a1}} + e^{-z'r_{b1}}) \tag{2}$$

where z' is a parameter which involves an effective nuclear charge and r_{a1} and r_{b1} are the distances from the two nuclei to the electron.

In equation 2 the two atomic orbitals are given equal weight because the two nuclei are identical. When the two nuclei have different charges, the two wave functions would be given different coefficients. In general, for two nuclei

$$\psi = c_1\psi_1 + c_2\psi_2 \tag{3}$$

A one-electron bond tends to be very weak unless the two nuclei are identical, because otherwise the electron tends to stay in the neighborhood of the nucleus with the stronger electron affinity and is not shared very much by the two atoms.

The probability density for the two electrons in the H_2 molecule is similar to that shown in Fig. 17-2b for H_2^+, but the curve is spread out more at $x = 0$ because of the correlation of the motion of the two electrons. In treating the hydrogen molecule, the molecular orbital theory neglects the interaction between the two electrons and considers only the interactions of the electrons with the protons. The wave function for the hydrogen molecule can then be written as a product of the two wave functions for the hydrogen molecule-ion for electrons 1 and 2.

$$\psi_{H_2} = \psi_{H_2^+}(1)\psi_{H_2^+}(2)$$

$$= K[e^{-r_{a1}-r_{a2}} + e^{-r_{a1}-r_{b2}} + e^{-r_{a2}-r_{b1}} + e^{-r_{b1}-r_{b2}}] \tag{4}$$

where r_{a1} is the distance between nucleus A and electron 1, etc. The z parameters (effective nuclear charges) are neglected here for simplicity.

The first and last terms in the wave function given in equation 4 correspond to configurations in which both electrons 1 and 2 are around nucleus a or b. These are called *ionic terms*. The middle two terms correspond to configurations in which there is one electron around each nucleus. These are called *homopolar terms*. In the molecular-orbital theory the four terms are given equal weight in the wave function. This implies that it is as probable to have two electrons around the same nucleus as to have one electron around each nucleus. This implication is not correct, since the ionic configurations are much less stable and should contribute less to the wave function. This is a weakness of the molecular-orbital theory which the valence-bond theory attempts to correct.

According to the *valence-bond theory*, the ionic terms may be neglected in equation 4, and the wave function is simply written

$$\psi_{H_2} = K(e^{-r_{a1}-r_{b2}} + e^{-r_{a2}-r_{b1}}) \tag{5}$$

This extreme is not correct either, and better wave functions may be obtained by including some ionic contributions. Although both the molecular-orbital and valence-bond theories have certain advantages, each has its limitations, and it is not possible to give exact treatments of complicated molecules at present.

The wave function for the hydrogen molecule has been obtained to a very high degree of accuracy by providing for electron correlation in the variation function. The bonding in H_2 (4.48 ev) is stronger than that in H_2^+ (2.64 ev), and the bond length in H_2 (0.74 A) is shorter than that in H_2^+ (1.06 A). If a third electron is added to the bond, it must be added to the next higher quantum level, as required by the exclusion principle. Since the next higher quantum state has a much higher energy, this leads to a repulsion. Accordingly the electron pair is the most stable configuration.

The bond between two hydrogen atoms is exceptional in that the principal source of repulsion energy is due to the repulsion of the protons. In the case of a covalent bond not involving hydrogen each nucleus is shielded by a core of inner electrons. A repulsion arises when these cores begin to interpenetrate. This repulsion is associated with the effects of the exclusion principle and has been mentioned in connection with the ionic bond in potassium chloride.

In the case of polyatomic molecules even the approximate methods (molecular-orbital and valence-bond theories) are difficult to apply quantitatively. However, these theories provide very useful qualitative pictures of molecular orbitals.

Bond Angles and Localized Molecular Orbitals. The directional nature of certain covalent bonds may be understood in terms of the orbitals which make up these bonds. As three simple examples we may consider water, which has a bond angle of 104.5°; ammonia, which has bond angles of 108°; and methane, which has bond angles of 109°28′.

The electron configuration for oxygen is $1s^2 2s^2 2p_x^2 2p_y^1 2p_z^1$, so that one p orbital is completely filled and the other two have one electron each. These half-filled p orbitals are at an angle of 90° with respect to each other (Fig. 16-7) and would tend to form covalent bonds with hydrogen with 90° bond angles. However, the actual bond angle is 104.5°. Recent theoretical considerations indicate that it is more accurate to consider that the $2s$ and $2p$ orbitals of the oxygen atom in the water molecule form a new type of orbital (a hybrid orbital) in which the four bonds have nearly tetrahedral symmetry, which would lead to a bond angle of about 109°. The combination of different types of orbitals to produce orbitals of intermediate properties is referred to as *hybridization*. The lone-pair electrons of the oxygen atom stick out in the opposite direction from the hydrogen atoms, as shown in *Fig. 17-3*.

Fig. 17-3. Representations of the H₂O and NH₃ molecules. The orbitals due to unshared electron pairs are indicated by shaded regions.

These electrons have an important effect on the properties of water because they cause the oxygen atom to be weakly bonded to the hydrogen atom of an adjacent water molecule. This type of bond is called a hydrogen bond (p. 494). In ice there is a tetrahedral arrangement with each oxygen atom bonded to four hydrogen atoms. Hydrogen bonds are formed along the axis of the lone pairs in ice, and their existence in liquid water is responsible for the high boiling point of water as compared with the boiling points of hydrides of other elements in the same column of the periodic table (H₂S, −62°; H₂Se, −42°; H₂Te, −4°).

The electron configuration of the ground state of nitrogen is $1s^2 2s^2 2p_x^1 2p_y^1 2p_z^1$, and so nitrogen can form bonds with three hydrogen atoms, using its three singly occupied $2p$ orbitals. However, the $2s$, and $2p$ orbitals are hybridized to form sp^3 orbitals in which the bonds form tetrahedral angles with each other. The actual angles in ammonia are 108°. As shown in Fig. 17-3, the ammonia molecule has a lone pair of electrons. It is because of this lone pair that ammonia forms complexes with metal ions having vacant orbitals.

The electron configuration of the ground state of carbon is $1s^2 2s^2 2p^2$, but one of the $2s$ electrons must be promoted to a p orbital in order to make available four unpaired electrons so that carbon can be bonded to four other atoms. Thus the electron configuration for a tetravalent carbon atom is $1s^2 2s 2p_x 2p_y 2p_z$. If this were an accurate representation of the carbon atom in methane or carbon tetrachloride, we would expect one of the CH or CCl bonds to be different; however, in both cases the four bonds are equivalent, and the angles are all tetrahedral (109°28'). The equivalence of the four bonds is explained in terms of the principle of *hybridization*. Hybridization of the three $2p$ orbitals and one $2s$ orbital produces four equivalent tetrahedral orbitals with an angle of 109°28' between any two bonds.

Each of the bonds described above involves only two atoms; they are called *localized molecular orbitals* and are the quantum-mechanical analog of the shared electron pair. In order to explain the stability of certain molecules, such as aromatic hydrocarbons, it is necessary to introduce *nonlocalized molecular orbitals*. These orbitals often extend over the whole molecule, and electrons are free to move in them rather than remaining fixed in bond orbitals. The energy of an electron in a large orbital is lower, since it is moving in a larger "box" (p. 464).

The structure of ethylene (C_2H_4) is best understood in terms of the hybridization of the $2s$ orbital of a carbon atom with two $2p$ orbitals to give three equivalent sp^2 orbitals which have their axes in a plane at 120° angles. In ethylene each carbon atom is bonded to the other and to two hydrogen atoms by sp^2 orbitals. This leaves $2p$ orbitals perpendicular to the plane of the molecule at each carbon atom. These unhybridized p orbitals overlap laterally to form a bond which has two regions of charge density, one above and one below the plane of the molecule. These two charge clouds belong to the same orbital and contain two electrons of opposite spin. Such a bond, which is not symmetrical about the axis, is called a π orbital to distinguish it from σ orbitals, like sp^3 and sp^2 orbitals, which are symmetrical about the axis of the bond.

Molecular-orbital theory accounts for the paramagnetism of oxygen, the stability of benzene, the bonding in complex compounds, and the structures of many substances.*

---

* E. Cartmell and G. W. A. Fowles, *Valency and Molecular Structure*, Butterworths Scientific Publications, London, 1956.

Resonance. An important contribution of the valence-bond theory to chemistry has been the concept of *resonance* of molecules among several electronic structures with an accompanying increase in stability. It is possible to formulate simple structures for many substances which account satisfactorily for their chemical properties, but for other substances no one electronic structure may be written which provides an adequate explanation for these properties. Benzene is an outstanding example. The following two Kekulé structures are the most stable valence-bond structures which can be written. Although other, less stable structures can be formulated, it is not necessary to bring them into the present discussion. These structures individually do not ac-

count for the great stability of benzene in comparison with cyclohexene. However, according to the valence-bond theory, the true state of the benzene molecule is intermediate between those represented by two or more valence-bond structures. It is not intermediate by virtue of a rapid tautomerization equilibrium, which would involve the motion of nuclei, but is a new structure which cannot be represented by any single valence-bond structure. This new structure is referred to as a *resonance hybrid structure*, and the wave function of benzene is taken to be a linear combination of wave functions representing the various valence-bond structures. This is an example of the delocalization of a set of localized molecular orbitals.

Resonance occurs only when certain conditions are met. There can be resonance only among structures that correspond to the same, or nearly the same, relative positions of the electrons. There can be resonance only among structures with the same numbers of unpaired electrons and with nearly the same energy.

The bond length of a hybrid of a single bond and double bond is intermediate between the extremes, but usually closer to the shorter bond length. For example, in the case of benzene the observed C—C distance is 1.39 A, while that for a single bond is 1.54 and for a double bond is 1.34 A. The shortening of the bond distance is associated with an increase in stability of the molecule over that which would be expected if there were normal single and double bonds. The heat of hydrogenation of cyclohexene is -29 kcal mole^{-1}, and since cyclohexene contains only one double bond it is assumed that resonance is negligible. If there were no resonance in benzene, the heat of hydrogenation of benzene to cyclohexane would be expected to be $3 \times (-29)$

$= -87$ kcal mole^{-1}. A heat of hydrogenation of -50 kcal mole^{-1} is found experimentally, and so the resonance energy of benzene is $-87 - (-50) = -37$ kcal, this being the amount that the molecule is stabilized relative to the individual Kekulé structures.

Electronegativity. Because of the difference in affinity of different atoms in a molecule for electrons, the bonding electrons are not shared equally between unlike atoms which are bonded together. As a result the molecule may have a large dipole moment or may be readily ionizable. The tendency of an atom to pull electrons toward itself is expressed by a quantity called the *electronegativity.** Fluorine is the most electronegative atom (4.0 on Pauling's scale), and cesium is the least electronegative atom (0.7 on Pauling's scale). The electronegativities of a number of elements are given in *Fig. 17-4*, which shows

		H 2.1				
Li 1.0	Be 1.5	B 2.0	C 2.5	N 3.0	O 3.5	F 4.0
Na 0.9	Mg 1.2	Al 1.5	Si 1.8	P 2.1	S 2.5	Cl 3.0
K 0.8	Ca 1.0		Ge 1.7	As 2.0	Se 2.4	Br 2.8
Rb 0.8	Sr 1.0		Sn 1.7	Sb 1.8	Te 2.1	I 2.4
Cs 0.7	Ba 0.9					

Fig. 17-4. Dependence of electronegativity on position in the periodic table.

that the electronegativity depends upon the position of the element in the periodic table. As we go down the halogen column of the periodic table, the atoms become less electronegative because of the increasingly effective screening of the charge on the nucleus by inner electrons. The alkali-metal atoms have a great tendency to lose their outer electrons and therefore have a low electronegativity. Again the electronegativity decreases as we go down a column because the distance of the outer electron from the nucleus is greater, and hence the electron is held more

* L. Pauling, *The Nature of the Chemical Bond*, Cornell University Press, Ithaca, 1960; H. O. Pritchard and H. A. Skinner, *Chem. Revs.*, **55**, 745 (1955).

loosely. Electronegativities may be estimated from bond-dissociation energies and from ionization potentials and electron affinities.

By use of electronegativities it is possible to predict which bonds will be ionic and which bonds will be covalent. Two elements of very different electronegativity, like the halogens and alkali mteals, form ionic bonds because an electron is almost completely transferred to the atom of higher electronegativity. Two elements with nearly equal electronegativities are expected to form covalent bonds. If there is a considerable difference between the electronegativities of the two elements, the bond is polar (that is, possessed of a high degree of ionic character), as in the case of hydrogen chloride, which is best described by a combination of the covalent structure $H\!:\!\overset{..}{\underset{..}{Cl}}\!:$ and the ionic structure $[H^+][:\overset{..}{\underset{..}{Cl}}\!:]^-$.

Since carbon occupies an intermediate position in the electronegativity scale, it is natural that it does not ordinarily form ionic bonds and that its bonds with other elements should be essentially covalent. In the majority of chemical bonds the sharing of the electron pair is not exactly equal, so that the bond has partial ionic character.

Hydrogen Bonds. Under certain conditions an atom of hydrogen is attracted by two atoms instead of only one, so that it may be considered to be acting as a bond between them. The hydrogen atom is unique, owing to the fact that, when its electron becomes detached, only the nucleus of very small diameter is left. Hydrogen bonds are formed only with electronegative atoms such as fluorine, oxygen, and nitrogen. Fluorine forms very strong hydrogen bonds; oxygen, weaker ones; and nitrogen, still weaker ones. The hydrogen fluoride ion, $[HF_2]^-$, is held together by a strong hydrogen bond. The unusual properties of water are due to a large extent to the formation of hydrogen bonds. When water is vaporized, these hydrogen bonds are broken, but in formic and acetic acids the hydrogen bonds are strong enough for double molecules of the type illustrated in *Fig. 17-5* to exist in the vapor. Benzoic and other carboxylic acids form dimers in certain nonpolar solvents, such as benzene and carbon tetrachloride. In salicylic

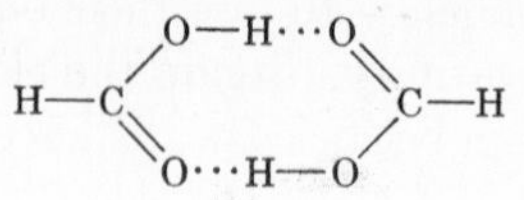

Formic acid dimer 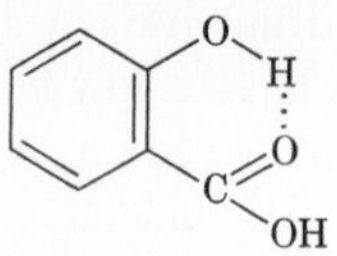　　　　　　Salicylic acid

Fig. 17-5. Examples of hydrogen bonding.

acid an intramolecular hydrogen bond can be formed, as illustrated in Fig. 17-5. This bonding tends to release the hydrogen of the carboxyl group; as a result, salicylic acid with its OH and carboxyl groups adjacent is a much stronger acid than its *meta* and *para* isomers, in which these groups are farther apart.

Hindered Internal Rotation about Bonds. The hindrance of free internal rotation about the C—C bond in ethane was discovered because its

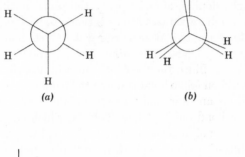

(a)   *(b)*

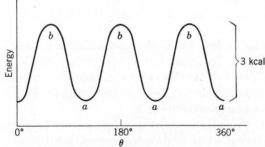

Fig. 17-6. Energy barrier for internal rotation in ethane.

experimentally determined entropy did not agree with that calculated by statistical mechanics on the basis of free internal rotation.* Two positions in the rotation of hydrogens about the C—C bond of ethane are represented in *Fig. 17-6a* and *b*, in which the C—C bond is perpendicular to the page. The dependence of this energy of interaction on the relative orientations of the CH_3 groups is shown at the bottom of the figure. The energy is high when the hydrogens are close together as in *b*, and the energy is low when they are in a staggered configuration as in *a*.

* K. S. Pitzer, *Chem. Revs.*, *27*, 39 (1940).

These ideas have had important applications in determining the structures of cyclopentane, cyclohexane, and more complicated substances derived from them, such as the steroids. This field of structural chemistry is referred to as *conformational analysis.*

Information concerning the barriers to internal rotation comes from a number of sources, particularly infrared and microwave measurements.*

Bond Radii and Molecular Models. It has been found that the distance between two kinds of atoms connected by a covalent bond of a given type (single, double, etc.) is nearly the same in different molecules. The distance between two atoms is taken to be equal to the sum of the bond radii of the two atoms. Since the C—C bond distance is 1.54 A in many compounds, the radius for a carbon single bond is taken to be 0.77 A. Since the C≡C distance in acetylene is 1.20 A, the radius for a carbon triple bond is taken to be 0.60 A. By consideration of the bond distances in many compounds it has been possible to build up tables of bond radii, such as Table I, which are useful in describing the structure of molecules. It must be realized, however, that the effective radius of an atom depends in part also on its structure and environment and on the nature of bonds that it forms with other atoms in the molecule.

As shown in Table I, the single-bond radius of carbon is 0.77 A, and the bond radius for hydrogen is 0.30 A; therefore the C—H bond length is $0.30 + 0.77 = 1.07$ A. When double bonds are present, it is found that all the adjacent bonds lie in a single plane. Thus ethylene and benzene have planar structures.

Models are available in which 1 cm represents 1 A, and the faces of the atoms are cut so as to give the correct bond angles. Models of molecules may then be built up which represent the actual relations on a large scale, and certain deductions can be drawn from these models. Models are shown in *Fig. 17-7* for the *cis* and *trans* forms of dichloroethylene, and the reasons for the difference in dipole moments, defined on page 501, are readily apparent.

Hexane, which is shown also in Fig. 17-7, has a long, snakelike structure which can move around in various positions, but the probabilities of free motions of the cyclohexane shown just below it are greatly reduced. As would be expected, the heat capacity and entropy of hexane are greater than those of cyclohexane.

---

* S. Mizushima, *Structure of Molecules and Internal Rotation,* Academic Press, New York, 1954.

Table I.   Covalent Radii for Atoms [1]

(Radii in angstroms)

	H	C	N	O	F
Single-bond radius	0.30	0.772	0.70	0.66	0.64
Double-bond radius		0.667	0.60	0.56	
Triple-bond radius		0.603			
		Si	P	S	Cl
Single-bond radius		1.17	1.10	1.04	0.99
Double-bond radius		1.07	1.00	0.94	.89
Triple-bond radius		1.00	0.93	.87	
		Ge	As	Se	Br
Single-bond radius		1.22	1.21	1.17	1.14
Double-bond radius		1.12	1.11	1.07	1.04
		Sn	Sb	Te	I
Single-bond radius		1.40	1.41	1.37	1.33
Double-bond radius		1.30	1.31	1.27	1.23

[1] Taken from L. Pauling, *The Nature of the Chemical Bond*, Cornell University Press, Ithaca, N. Y., 1960, which should be consulted for details concerning the source and constancy of these radii.

Refractive Index. The refractive index n of a medium is the ratio of the velocity of light in a vacuum to that in the medium. It is more convenient to measure the refractive index with respect to air than with respect to vacuum. Since the refractive index of air relative to vacuum is 1.00029 under standard conditions, the two types of refractive indices may be readily interconverted. To convert refractive indices measured against air to the corresponding indices measured against vacuum, it is necessary to multiply by 1.00029.

Refractive indices can be determined easily to 1 or 2 parts in 10,000 under laboratory conditions if the temperature is kept constant. Usually the angle of refraction is measured with the help of a glass prism on which is placed the liquid or solid. The refractive index depends on the wavelength of the light and on the temperature, which are usually specified with subscripts and superscripts, respectively. Thus n_D^{25} indicates a refractive index at 25° taken with the monochromatic yellow

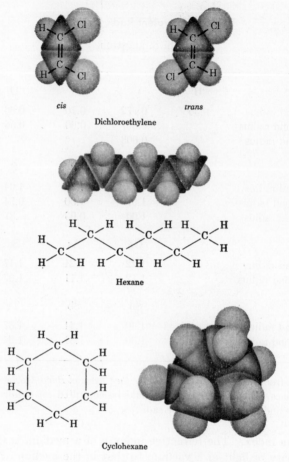

cis   trans

Dichloroethylene

Hexane

Cyclohexane

Fig. 17-7. Typical molecular models.

D light of the sodium arc. Measurements of refractive index are used to determine the concentration of solutions, to identify compounds, and to ascertain their purity.

On the basis of the electromagnetic theory of light, Lorenz and Lorentz introduced the *specific refraction r*, defined by

$$r = \frac{1}{\rho} \frac{n^2 - 1}{n^2 + 2} \tag{6}$$

where ρ is the density of the substance. The specific refraction is nearly independent of temperature, pressure, and phase. The *molar refraction* Mr is equal to the specific refraction multiplied by the molecular weight.

Example 1. The refractive index n_D^{20} of carbon tetrachloride is 1.4573, the density at 20° is 1.595 g cm^{-3}, and the molecular weight is 153.84. Calculate the molar refraction.

$$Mr_D = \frac{M(n^2 - 1)}{\rho(n^2 + 2)} = \frac{(153.84 \text{ g mole}^{-1})(1.4573^2 - 1)}{(1.595 \text{ g cm}^{-3})(1.4573^2 + 2)}$$

$$= 26.51 \text{ cm}^3 \text{ mole}^{-1}$$

The refractive index at 20°, the specific refraction, and the molar refraction are given for several common liquids in Table II.

Table II. Molar Refractions

Compound	Formula	n_D^{20}	r_D^{20}	Mr_D^{20}
Carbon tetrachloride	CCl$_4$	1.4573	0.1724	26.51
Acetone	(CH$_3$)$_2$CO	1.3571	0.2782	16.15
Benzene	C$_6$H$_6$	1.4979	0.3354	26.18
Ethanol	C$_2$H$_5$OH	1.3590	0.2775	12.78
Toluene	C$_6$H$_5$CH$_3$	1.4929	0.3356	30.92
Chloroform	CHCl$_3$	1.4426	0.1780	21.25
Acetic acid	CH$_3$COOH	1.3698	0.2154	12.93
Ethyl acetate	CH$_3$COOC$_2$H$_5$	1.3701	0.2527	22.25
Water	H$_2$O	1.3328	0.2083	3.75

The refractive indices of gases are close to unity, and as a result equation 6 may be written in a simpler way. Factoring the numerator,

$$Mr = \frac{M}{\rho} \frac{(n+1)(n-1)}{n^2 + 2} \tag{7}$$

Since n and n^2 are very close to unity, we obtain

$$Mr = \frac{M}{\rho} \frac{2(n-1)}{3} \tag{8}$$

Example 2. Calculate the molar refraction of water vapor and compare it with the molar refraction of liquid water. The refractive index of water vapor at 20° for the sodium D line is 1.000241 for a (hypothetical) pressure of 1 atm. The density of water vapor under these conditions would be 0.749 g liter^{-1}.

$$Mr_D = \frac{(18.00)(2)(0.000241)}{(0.749)(3)} = 3.85 \text{ cm}^3 \text{ mole}^{-1}$$

The value for liquid water is 3.75 cm^3 mole^{-1}. Thus we see that the molar refraction of a substance is very nearly independent of its physical state.

The molar refractions of a large number of organic and inorganic compounds have been determined, and it has been found that many atoms and groups of atoms always contribute the same definite amount to the molar refraction of any compound. Thus, in a homologous series of aliphatic compounds a difference of CH_2 in composition always produces a difference of 4.618 in the molar refraction. The molar refraction of hexane, C_6H_{14}, is 29.908; by subtracting from this value six times the effect of the CH_2 group, it is possible to obtain the atomic refraction of the hydrogen atom, namely, 1.100.

$$\frac{29.908 - (6)(4.618)}{2} = 1.100$$

From these data the atomic refraction of carbon is readily calculated.

$$4.618 - (2)(1.100) = 2.418$$

Likewise, the atomic refraction of bromine is obtained by subtracting the atomic refractions of two carbons and five hydrogens from the molar refraction of ethyl bromide. The atomic refractions are affected by structural features. A double bond between carbon atoms contributes an additional 1.733 to the molar refraction.

Table III has been built up in the manner just indicated, averaging the results for a large number of compounds.

Table III. Bond Refractions

Group	Mr_D	Group	Mr_D
CH_2	4.618	Cl	5.967
H	1.100	Br	8.865
C	2.418	I	13.900
Double bond (C=C)	1.733	N (pri-amines)	2.322
Triple bond (C≡C)	2.398	N (sec-amines)	2.499
O (carbonyl) (C=O)	2.211	N ($tert$-amines)	2.840
O (hydroxyl) (O—H)	1.525	—C≡N	5.459
O (ethers) (R—O—R)	1.643		

Dipole Moment. Two different atoms will generally have different electronegativities (p. 493). When they are bonded together, the bonding electrons spend a greater time near the atom of higher electronegativity, so that there is a net positive charge at the other atom and the molecule takes on a polar character. When the molecule consists of two identical atoms, there is no tendency of this type.

The *dipole moment* μ of a molecule with two fractional charges $+\delta e$ and $-\delta e$ separated by a distance of l is given by

$$\mu = l\, \delta e \tag{9}$$

In expressing dipole moments, distances are generally given in centimeters and charges in electrostatic units (esu). A dipole consisting of an electron separated from a unit positive charge by a distance of 1 A would have a dipole moment of $(4.80 \times 10^{-10}\text{ esu})(10^{-8}\text{ cm}) = 4.80 \times 10^{-18}$ esu cm or 4.8 debye units. Because of Debye's contribution to this field, 10^{-18} esu cm is called a debye unit.

Example 3. If gaseous HCl is considered to be a proton and a chloride ion separated by 1.27 A (internuclear distance determined from infrared spectra), a dipole moment of $(4.80 \times 10^{-10}\text{ esu})(1.27 \times 10^{-8}\text{ cm}) = 6.08 \times 10^{-18}$ esu cm would be expected. The fact that the experimental value (1.03×10^{-18}) is considerably lower indicates that the charges are not completely separated in gaseous HCl molecules.

Dipole moments may be calculated from capacitance measurements. The capacitance C of a condenser is equal to the quantity of electricity q transferred from one plate to the other, divided by the potential difference E between the plates.

$$C = \frac{q}{E} \tag{10}$$

The capacitance of a condenser is increased if a vacuum between the plates is replaced by some nonconducting substance. The ratio of the capacitance C_x of a condenser filled with medium x to the capacitance when the space between the plates is evacuated, C_{vac}, is called the dielectric constant ϵ of the medium.

$$\epsilon = \frac{C_x}{C_{\text{vac}}} \tag{11}$$

Thus the dielectric constant of a vacuum is unity. The magnitude of the dielectric constant of a substance depends upon the temperature and the frequency at which the alternating electric field varies. A few values are given in Table IV. Since water has a high dielectric constant, it is called a *polar solvent*, and benzene and hexane are referred to as *nonpolar solvents*.

When a substance is placed between the plates of a condenser, the capacitance is increased because there is a displacement of positive charge toward the negative plate and of negative charge toward the positive plate. Two phenomena contribute to this polarization of the medium, *distortion polarization* P_D and *orientation polarization* P_μ. Distortion polarization is the result of the attraction of electrons in a molecule

Table IV.[1]   Dielectric Constants of Gases and Liquids

Gas (1 atm)	Frequency, $\sec^{-1}$	ϵ at $0°$	Liquid	Frequency, $\sec^{-1}$	ϵ at $20°$
Air (CO$_2$ free)	$<3 \times 10^6$	1.000567	Acetone	Audio	21.4
Ammonia	$<1 \times 10^6$	1.0072	Ammonia	4×10^8	15.5
Argon	$<1 \times 10^6$	1.000545	Benzene	Audio	2.283
Carbon dioxide	$<1 \times 10^6$	1.00098	Chlorobenzene	Audio	5.94
Hydrogen	2×10^6	1.000272	Hexane	Audio	1.874
Hydrogen chloride	$<3 \times 10^6$	1.0046	Methanol	Audio	33.1
Water (steam at 110°)	$<3 \times 10^6$	1.0126	Toluene	Audio	2.387
			Water	1×10^8	80

[1] N. A. Lange, *Handbook of Chemistry and Physics*, Handbook Publishers, Sandusky, Ohio.

toward the positive plate, leaving an excess of positive charge in the part of the molecule closest to the negative plate. Even symmetrical molecules like H$_2$ and CCl$_4$ become polarized in this way in an electric field. Orientation polarization is the result of the lining up of molecules having permanent dipole moments with their positive poles toward the negative electrode and their negative poles toward the positive electrode.

The total molar polarization P is calculated from the dielectric constant ϵ, using the following equation, which can be derived from the electromagnetic theory of light:

$$P = \frac{\epsilon - 1}{\epsilon + 2} \frac{M}{\rho} \qquad (12)$$

If the dielectric constant is measured at optical frequencies, $\epsilon = n^2$ and so P is equal to the molar refraction (p. 498). The total molar polarization P is equal to the sum of the molar distortion polarization P_D and the molar orientation polarization P_μ.

$$P = P_D + P_\mu \qquad (13)$$

Distortion Polarization. The ease with which different molecules become polarized by distortion of the electron cloud differs greatly. The magnitude of the induced moment depends upon the orientation of the molecule in the electric field. However, because of thermal agitation the molecules pass through all possible orientations, and so the experimentally determined induced moment is an average. The *induced moment m* per unit volume is proportional to the electric field strength dE/dx.

$$m = \alpha \frac{dE}{dx} \tag{14}$$

where α is the *polarizability* of the molecule. The polarizability has the dimensions of a volume per mole. The distortion polarization is proportional to the polarizability

$$P_D = \tfrac{4}{3}\pi N_0 \alpha \tag{15}$$

where N_0 is Avogadro's number. Since α is expected to be independent of the temperature, the quantity P_D would also be expected to be independent of temperature. The total polarization is independent of temperature for a number of gases and for certain liquids, such as benzene and carbon tetrachloride. However, for many substances like water and methyl chloride, the molar polarization is large and decreases with increasing temperature.

Orientation Polarization. Debye * explained the decreasing polarization with increasing temperature as being due to molecules having permanent dipole moments. The alignment of such molecules with the field is far from complete because thermal agitation tends to produce random orientations. As the temperature is increased, the thermal agitation becomes more violent and fewer of the permanent dipoles are oriented in the direction of the field.

The contribution to the molar polarization P due to the partial alignment of dipoles in a gas by the electric field was shown by Debye to be

$$P_\mu = \frac{4\pi N_0 \mu^2}{9kT} \tag{16}$$

provided that the temperature is not too low. For a substance having a permanent dipole moment, equation 13 becomes

$$P = \frac{\epsilon - 1}{\epsilon + 2}\frac{M}{\rho} = \tfrac{4}{3}\pi N_0 \alpha + \frac{4\pi N_0 \mu^2}{9kT} \tag{17}$$

Example 4. Show from the units of the various quantities involved that the distortion polarization has the units of cm^3 $mole^{-1}$. The dipole moment is given in esu cm. Since an electrostatic unit, esu, is the charge which will repel an equal but opposite charge with a force of a dyne at a distance of a centimeter, dyne = esu^2 cm^{-2}, and an electrostatic unit has the units of $dyne^{1/2}$ cm. The dipole moment

* P. Debye, *Polar Molecules*, Chemical Catalog Co., New York, 1929; or Dover Publications, New York.

squared has the units of esu^2 cm^2, which is equivalent to dyne cm^4. Substituting units in

$$P = \frac{4\pi N_0 \mu^2}{9kT}$$

$$= \frac{(mole^{-1})(dyne\ cm^4)}{(erg\ deg^{-1})(deg)}$$

$$= cm^3\ mole^{-1}$$

Since the orientation polarization depends upon the absolute temperature, it is possible to calculate the polarizability α and the dipole moment μ of a gas from measurements of the dielectric constant ϵ at a series of temperatures. In the gaseous state the molecules are so far apart that they do not induce electric effects on each other.

To obtain the dipole moment of a gaseous molecule the dielectric constants ϵ and gas densities are obtained at several temperatures, and the corresponding total molar polarizations P are calculated with the help of equation 12. A plot of P versus $1/T$ will have an intercept a equal to $\frac{4}{3}\pi N_0 \alpha$ and a slope b of $4\pi N_0 \mu^2/9k$.

$$P = a + \frac{b}{T} \tag{18}$$

The dipole moment may be calculated from the slope b by use of the equation

$$\mu = \left(\frac{9kb}{4\pi N_0}\right)^{\frac{1}{2}} = 0.01282 \times 10^{-18} b^{\frac{1}{2}} \tag{19}$$

Plots of molar polarization P versus reciprocal absolute temperature are illustrated in *Fig. 17-8* for the chlorine-substituted compounds of

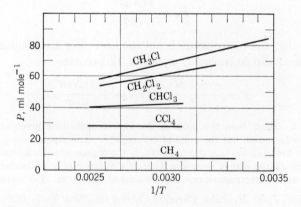

Fig. 17-8. Variation of molar polarization with absolute temperature.

methane as measured by Sanger.* It is seen that zero slopes are obtained for the symmetrical molecules CH_4 and CCl_4, and so these molecules have no permanent dipole moment. Because of the electronegative character of chlorine atoms, CH_3Cl, CH_2Cl_2, and $CHCl_3$ have permanent dipole moments with the chlorine atom the negative end of the dipole. The dipole moment of CH_3Cl is the largest of the three. When measurements may be made on a substance in the gaseous state, this method is to be preferred over the following one.

Determination of the Dipole Moment of a Solute. The dipole moment of a solute in a nonpolar solvent may be determined from dielectric-constant and density measurements on dilute solutions.† The molar polarization P_{12} of a solution is defined by

$$P_{12} = \frac{\epsilon_{12} - 1}{\epsilon_{12} + 2} \frac{(X_1M_1 + X_2M_2)}{\rho_{12}} \quad (20)$$

where ϵ_{12} is the dielectric constant of the solution, d_{12} is the density of the solution, and X_1 and X_2 are the mole fractions of solvent which has molecular weight M_1 and solute which has molecular weight M_2. Assuming that the solvent retains the properties it has when pure, the polarization P_{12} of the solution is given by

$$P_{12} = X_1 P_1{}^0 + X_2 P_2 \quad (21)$$

where $P_1{}^0$ is the molar polarization of the pure solvent, which is given by

$$P_1{}^0 = \frac{\epsilon_1 - 1}{\epsilon_1 + 2} \frac{M_1}{\rho_1} \quad (22)$$

and P_2 is the apparent molar polarization of the solute. Solving equation 21 for the apparent molar polarization of the solute,

$$P_2 = \frac{P_{12} - X_1 P_1{}^0}{X_2} \quad (23)$$

The experimental values of P_2 are extrapolated to infinite dilution to eliminate the effect of interaction between the polar-solute molecules. As infinite dilution is approached, the polarization due to the solute approaches $P_2{}^0$. The extrapolated value of the molar polarization of the solute may be interpreted by use of equation 17. If the solute is a

* R. Sanger, *Physik. Z.*, *27*, 562 (1926).

† F. Daniels, J. H. Mathews, J. W. Williams, P. Bender, and R. A. Alberty, *Experimental Physical Chemistry*, McGraw-Hill Book Co., New York, 1955.

liquid, its distortion polarization $P_{D2}{}^0$ may be calculated with adequate accuracy from the refractive index measured at optical frequencies.

$$P_{D2}{}^0 = \frac{n^2 - 1}{n^2 + 2} \frac{M_2}{\rho_2} \tag{24}$$

The distortion polarization can be calculated from the refractive index because the square of the refractive index is equal to the dielectric constant, $n^2 = \epsilon$, if both quantities are measured for electromagnetic waves of the same frequency. At optical frequencies the frequency is so great that there is not time enough for a molecule with a dipole moment to change its orientation in the field. However, distortion polarization occurs, since it involves only electrons and they can move rapidly enough to follow the high-frequency field.

The orientation polarization is obtained from

$$P_{\mu 2} = P_2{}^0 - \frac{n^2 - 1}{n^2 + 2} \frac{M_2}{\rho_2} \tag{25}$$

Once $P_{\mu 2}$ has been determined, the value of μ can be found from equation 16, using

$$\mu = 0.01282 \times 10^{-18}(P_{\mu 2}T)^{1/2} \tag{26}$$

Dipole moments of a variety of substances are given in Table V.

Experimental measurements of the dipole moment are of importance in understanding the structure of molecules. The interpretation of solubility, the properties of solutions, deviations from the laws for ideal

Table V.   Dipole Moments

(In debye units)

$AgClO_4$	4.7	C_6H_5Cl	1.55	SO_2	1.61
$C_6H_5NO_2$	3.96	C_6H_5OH	1.70	HCl	1.03
$(CH_3)_2CO$	2.8	C_2H_5OH	1.70	HBr	0.79
H_2O	1.84	$C_6H_5NH_2$	1.56	HI	0.30
CH_4	0	NH_3	1.46	N_2O	0.14
CH_3Cl	1.85	H_2S	1.10	CO	0.12
CH_3Br	1.45	H_2	0	CS_2	0
CH_3I	1.35	Cl_2	0	C_2H_4	0
CH_2Cl_2	1.59	CO_2	0	C_2H_6	0
$CHCl_3$	1.15	$C_6H_5CH_3$	0.40	C_6H_6	0
CCl_4	0				

gases and ideal solutions, and the influence of solvents on reaction rates is greatly assisted by knowledge of dipole moments.

Carbon dioxide and water might have structures corresponding to a symmetrical linear molecule, to an unsymmetrical linear molecule, or to a bent molecule. The dipole moments recorded in Table V show that carbon dioxide has zero moment; therefore, the molecule must be symmetrical and linear. If it were unsymmetrical or bent, there would be a permanent dipole moment. On the other hand, water has a pronounced dipole moment and cannot have the symmetrical linear structure.

The dipole moments of molecules having independent dipolar groups can be predicted by vector addition of group moments, in which the directions as well as the magnitudes of the moments are taken into account. The dipole moments of nitrobenzene and chlorobenzene are 3.95 and 1.55 debye units, respectively, and the negative ends of the dipoles are directed outward from the benzene ring. The way in which the dipole moments of these groups add in chloronitrobenzene is illustrated in *Fig. 17-9*. The dipole moments of the compounds calculated in this way are approximately correct, but not exact because these strongly polar groups influence each other.

Magnetic Susceptibility. The magnetic susceptibility χ is the magnetic analog of the dielectric polarization, except that it may have positive or negative values. When the magnetic susceptibility is positive, the

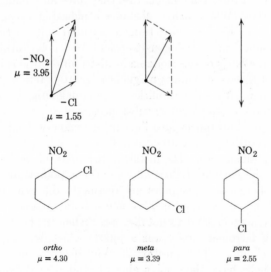

Fig. 17-9. Dipole moments of o-, m-, and p-chloronitrobenzenes in debye units.

magnetic field in the substance is greater than the applied field; when the magnetic susceptibility is negative, the magnetic field in the substance is smaller than the applied field. Substances having a negative susceptibility are said to be *diamagnetic*, and those with a positive susceptibility are said to be *paramagnetic*. Matter in general is diamagnetic, since the orbital motion of electrons is equivalent to a current and produces a magnetic field oriented perpendicular to the plane of the electronic orbit. When a diamagnetic substance is placed in a magnetic field, a magnetic moment is induced which opposes the applied field. The magnetic moment is the magnetic analog of the dipole moment. When an elongated piece of a diamagnetic substance is suspended in a magnetic field, it tends to orient itself at right angles to the field; in a nonuniform magnetic field the piece tends to move toward the weaker part of the field. This effect is weak and can be demonstrated only in delicate experiments.

Paramagnetic substances tend to be oriented parallel to a magnetic field or to move into the region of higher field strength in an inhomogeneous magnetic field. Paramagnetic behavior is shown by atoms which have permanent magnetic moments. Since electrons have a spin of $\frac{1}{2}$, they have permanent magnetic moments and tend to be oriented parallel to a magnetic field if they are not paired with electrons of opposite spin. As a result certain atoms, molecules, or ions have magnetic moments due to the spin of unpaired electrons. This property is shown by many rare-earth ions because they have an unpaired electron in an inner orbit. When such a substance is placed in a magnetic field, these magnetic moments tend to become oriented in line with the field. Thus paramagnetism is analogous to orientation polarization; and, as expected on the basis of the Boltzmann distribution, the extent of the orientation of these elementary magnets is greater at lower temperatures. The magnetic susceptibilities of paramagnetic substances are larger than those of diamagnetic substances.

Ferromagnetic substances also line up in magnetic fields, but their magnetic susceptibilities are about a million times larger than those of paramagnetic substances. The metals iron, cobalt, nickel, gadolinium, dysprosium, and certain of their alloys and compounds are ferromagnetic. Ferromagnetic substances are distinctly different from paramagnetic substances because they become strongly magnetized in weak fields, and the magnetism does not disappear when the field is removed. The origin of ferromagnetism was a puzzle which was explained by quantum mechanics. The question is, Why do so many electrons in incomplete shells have their spins aligned, and why do they remain aligned even after the applied magnetic field is removed? The explanation is that the lowest energy state for certain solids is one in which spins are parallel, rather than opposed as they are for the two electrons in a hydrogen molecule, for example. The requirements of certain atomic distances and certain radii of the orbitals for d electrons limit this phenomena to just a few elements.

Magnetic-susceptibility measurements are important for detecting unpaired electrons such as are present in free radicals (p. 325).* Since molecular oxygen is paramagnetic, it is possible to determine the oxygen partial pressure in a gas stream by measurements with a specially constructed torsion balance in the field of a magnet.

Rotation of Polarized Light. The light passing through a Nicol prism or a Polaroid film is *plane polarized*, which means that the electric vector of the emergent wave is confined to a single plane. The magnetic vector is in a perpendicular plane. A Nicol prism consists of a crystal of double-refracting Iceland spar cut and cemented in such a way that one of the two differently refracted rays is reflected to one side and the remaining one which passes through is plane polarized. Polaroid films are made by incorporating into a transparent plastic a large number of small crystals of a compound, such as iodoquinine sulfate, which possesses the property of optical dichroism, in which one of the two polarized light rays is absorbed. The crystals are treated mechanically in the plastic in such a way that they are all aligned in one direction.

When optically active substances are placed in a beam of polarized light, the plane of polarization is rotated either to the right or to the left. The extent of this rotation is measured quantitatively, using a *polarimeter*, by measuring the angle through which a second Nicol prism must be rotated in order to transmit completely, or cut off completely, the beam of polarized light.

In polarized light the fluctuation in the electric field is equivalent to two circular motions executed in opposite senses. If one of these components is transmitted through a medium more rapidly than the other (in other words, if the refractive indices are different for the two components), a rotation of the plane of polarization results.

Molecules which do not have a plane of symmetry or a center of symmetry in general rotate polarized light, although there may be no rotation at certain wavelengths or temperatures. Molecules which lack a plane of symmetry cannot be superimposed on their mirror images. The two mirror-image forms have a different effect on the two circular vibrations which we may consider make up plane-polarized light. Molecular tumbling does not affect this result, since a right-

* P. W. Selwood, *Magnetochemistry*, Interscience Publishers, New York, 1956.

handed thread remains a right-handed thread even when it is turned end for end. Certain crystalline substances like quartz rotate polarized light because of a spiral structure in the solid state.

The magnitude and direction of the optical rotation depend on several factors, including the nature of the substance; the length of the medium through which the light passes; the concentration, if the substance is dissolved in a solution; the wavelength of the light; and the temperature. The measured optical rotation α is given by

$$\alpha = [\alpha]_\lambda^t \frac{lg}{v} \tag{27}$$

where l is the length of the tube in decimeters through which the light passes, g is the number of grams of optically active material in volume v cubic centimeters, and $[\alpha]_\lambda^t$ is a proportionality constant which depends upon the wavelength of light, the temperature t, and the solvent. The proportionality constant $[\alpha]_\lambda^t$ is called the *specific rotation* and is a characteristic property of a substance.

Example 5. The value of $[\alpha]_D^{20}$ for lactose is 55.4. What is the concentration, in grams per liter, of a solution of lactose which gives a rotation of 7.24° in a 10-cm cell at 20° with sodium D light?

$$g = \frac{\alpha v}{l[\alpha]_D^{20}} = \frac{(7.24 \text{ deg})(1000 \text{ cm}^3)}{(1 \text{ dec})(55.4 \text{ deg cm}^\circ \text{ dec}^{-1} \text{ g}^{-1})}$$

$$= 131 \text{ grams}$$

The most common type of optically active molecule is one which contains an asymmetric carbon atom in which each of the four groups around the carbon atom is different. An example of such an optically active compound is lactic acid, shown in *Fig. 17-10*. The *dextro* or *d* form rotates the plane of polarized light to the right or in a clockwise direction as viewed looking toward the light source, and the *levo* or *l* form rotates it counterclockwise. If the *dextro* and *levo* forms are present together in equal amounts in the same solution, the two rotations

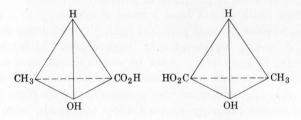

Fig. 17-10. Structures of *l*- and *d*-lactic acid.

offset each other, and no optical activity is observed. Such a mixture is called a *racemic* mixture. As a matter of fact, almost all substances capable of exhibiting optical activity are found in the racemic form when produced in the laboratory. In synthesizing lactic acid, for example, there is equal probability of obtaining either the *dextro* or the *levo* form, and the same numbers of molecules of each are formed.

Although the *dextro* and *levo* forms have nearly the same physical and chemical properties, except for the rotation of polarized light, they can be separated. Microorganisms sometimes will metabolize only one form. For example, a certain mold growing in a racemic mixture of tartaric acid will thrive at the expense of the *dextro* acid and leave the pure *levo* acid. In a second method of separating *dextro* and *levo* optical isomers, the racemic mixture is allowed to react chemically with an optically active material, such as an alkaloid. If the *dextro* form of the alkaloid is added to a racemic mixture, two compounds, *dd* and *dl*, will be formed. Since these two compounds are no longer optical isomers, they will have different properties, including solubility, so that they can be separated.

Sometimes the two optical isomers crystallize out in crystal forms which are alike except that one is the mirror image of the other. They can then be separated by hand picking, as was done first by Louis Pasteur in his brilliant researches on the optical activity of tartaric acid.

The optical rotation depends upon the wavelength of the light used and is often found to change sign when the wavelength is varied over a wide range. Large changes in optical rotation are found near certain absorption bands. The study of the dispersion of optical rotation is very useful in determining the structures of unknown compounds.*

REFERENCES

E. A. Braude and F. C. Nachod, *Determination of Organic Structures by Physical Methods*, Academic Press, New York, 1955.

E. Cartmell and G. W. A. Fowles, *Valency and Molecular Structure*, Butterworths Scientific Publications, London, 1956.

C. A. Coulson, *Valence*, Oxford University Press, Oxford, 1952.

C. Djerassi, *Optical Rotatory Dispersion*, McGraw-Hill Book Co., New York, 1959.

H. Gilman, *Organic Chemistry*, Vol. 2, Chapters 20 and 21, John Wiley & Sons, New York, 1943.

G. Herzberg, *Molecular Spectra and Molecular Structure*, D. Van Nostrand Co., Princeton, N. J., 1950.

* C. Djerassi, *Optical Rotatory Dispersion*, McGraw-Hill Book Co., New York, 1959.

J. A. A. Ketelaar, *Chemical Constitution*, D. Van Nostrand Co., Princeton, N. J., 1958.

L. Pauling, *The Nature of the Chemical Bond*, Cornell University Press, Ithaca, 1960.

G. C. Pimentel and A. L. McClellan, *The Hydrogen Bond*, W. H. Freeman and Co., San Francisco, 1960.

P. W. Selwood, *Magnetochemistry*, Interscience Publishers, New York, 1943.

A. Weissberger, *Technique of Organic Chemistry*, Vol. I, Part II (chapters on refractometry, spectrophotometry, polarimetry, electron diffraction, and dipole moments), Interscience Publishers, 1949, New York.

PROBLEMS

1. Write the following structures in terms of the electron theory of valence: (a) sulfate ion, $SO_4{}^{2-}$; (b) nitrogen, N_2; (c) ammonium chloride, NH_4Cl.

$$Ans.\ (a)\ \begin{bmatrix} \ddot{O} \\ \ddot{O}:S:\ddot{O} \\ \ddot{O} \end{bmatrix}^{2-} \quad (b)\ :N:::N: \quad (c)\ \begin{bmatrix} H \\ H:\ddot{N}:H \\ H \end{bmatrix}^+ :\ddot{Cl}:^-$$

2. Write resonance structures for benzene and naphthalene, showing the electron pairs.

3. From the atomic refractions, calculate the refractive index n_D at 20° of trimethylcarbinol, $(CH_3)_3COH$. The density is 0.7864 g cm^{-3}. The experimentally determined value of n_D is 1.3878. *Ans.* 1.385.

4. The molar refraction for liquid chloroform for the D line of sodium at 20° is 21.25 cm^3 mole^{-1}. Calculate the refractive index of chloroform vapor at a hypothetical pressure of 1 atm at 20°. The directly measured value is 1.00137.

Ans. 1.00133.

5. The molar polarization P of ammonia varies with temperature as follows:

t, °C	19.1	35.9	59.9	113.9	139.9	172.9
P, ml mole^{-1}	57.57	55.01	51.22	44.99	42.51	39.59

(a) Plot P against $1/T$ and calculate the dipole moment of ammonia. (b) If the density of ammonia gas at 59.9° and 1 atm is 0.632 g liter^{-1} (0.000632 g ml^{-1}), what is the dielectric constant of ammonia under these conditions?

Ans. (a) 1.596×10^{-18} esu cm. (b) 1.0059.

6. By extrapolation the molar polarization of pyridine oxide, C_5H_5NO, in an infinitely dilute solution in dioxane is found to be 411 ml mole^{-1} at 25°. The molar refraction of C_5H_5NO is 28 ml mole^{-1}, and this is approximately equal to P_D. Calculate the dipole moment. *Ans.* 4.33×10^{-18} esu cm.

7. The specific rotation $[\alpha]_D$ of a solution of d-ethoxysuccinic acid in water is 33.02° at 17°. Calculate the concentration of this compound in grams per liter in a solution which has a rotation of 2.02° when measured in a polarimeter at 17° in which the tube of solution is 20 cm long. *Ans.* 30.6 g/l.

8. When α-D-mannose ($[\alpha]_D^{20} = +29.3°$) is dissolved in water, the optical rotation decreases as β-D-mannose is formed until at equilibrium $[\alpha]_D^{20} = +14.2°$. This process is referred to as mutarotation. As expected, when β-D-mannose ($[\alpha]_D^{20} = -17.0°$) is dissolved in water, the optical rotation increases until $[\alpha]_D^{20} = +14.2°$ is obtained. Calculate the percentage of α form in the equilibrium mixture.

Ans. 67.4%.

9. Represent the following compounds on the basis of the electron theory of valence: (a) LiH, (b) CH$_4$, (c) HCl, (d) CO, (e) CH$_3$OH.

10. Write the electronic structure of sulfur dioxide. Since the two oxygen atoms appear to be bonded differently, explain why there is no chemical evidence for this difference.

11. The refractive index of n-heptyl fluoride, CH$_3$(CH$_2$)$_5$CH$_2$F, is 1.3861 at 20°, and the density is 0.804 g cm^{-3}. What is the refractive index of fluorotrichloromethane, CCl$_3$F, at 20° if the density is 1.494 g cm^{-3}?

12. The refractive index of benzene vapor for the D line of sodium at 20° is 1.00170, corrected to a pressure of 1 atm. Calculate the molar refraction of benzene vapor, and compare it with the value for the liquid, which is 26.18 cm^3 mole^{-1}.

13. Calculate the dipole moment of fluorobenzene, using a plot of P versus $1/T$, from the following molar polarizations measured by K. B. McAlpine and C. P. Smyth [*J. Chem. Phys.*, *3*, 55 (1935)]:

T, °K	343.6	371.4	414.1	453.2	507.0
P, ml mole^{-1}	69.9	66.8	62.5	59.3	55.8

14. The molar polarization of silicobromoform, SiHBr$_3$, is 46 ml mole^{-1} at 25°. The induced polarizability α may be taken as 1.308×10^{-23}. Calculate the dipole moment of this molecule.

15. The specific rotation of l-leucine is $[\alpha]_D^{25} = -14.0°$. If the specific rotation of a mixture of d and l forms is $[\alpha]_D^{25} = +2.3$, calculate the fraction of l form in the mixture.

16. When α-D-glucose ($[\alpha]_D^{20} = +112.2°$) is dissolved in water, the optical rotation decreases as β-D-glucose is formed until at equilibrium $[\alpha]_D^{20} = +52.7°$. As expected, when β-D-glucose ($[\alpha]_D^{20} = +18.7°$) is dissolved in water, the optical rotation increases until $[\alpha]_D^{20} = +52.7°$ is obtained. Calculate the percentage of the β form in the equilibrium mixture.

17. Write the following reactions in terms of the electron theory of valence:

(a) Zn + S = ZnS.

(b) C$_2$H$_4$ + Cl$_2$ = C$_2$H$_4$Cl$_2$.

(c) CH$_3$CO$_2$H = H$^+$ + CH$_3$CO$_2^-$.

18. Write possible resonance structures for (a) the carboxyl group and (b) nitrous oxide, N$_2$O.

19. How would molecular oxygen be represented by an electron dot formula, considering that it is paramagnetic?

20. Calculate the refractive index n_D at 20° of allyl ethyl ether, (C$_2$H$_5$)O(C$_3$H$_5$), from the atomic refractions. The density is 0.7651 g cm^{-3}. The experimental value of n_D is 1.3881.

21. The refractive index of a solution of carbon tetrachloride in benzene is a linear function of the mole fraction of either component. For benzene, $n_D^{18} = 1.5024$. For carbon tetrachloride, $n_D^{18} = 1.4618$. Calculate the per cent by weight of carbon tetrachloride in a solution of the two having a refractive index at $18°$ of 1.4807.

22. The dielectric constants and densities of germanium tetrachloride at various temperatures are tabulated. Calculate the molar plarizations at these temperatures. What do these data suggest about the dipole moment of germanium tetrachloride?

t, °C	0	20	30	40	50
ϵ	2.491	2.443	2.417	2.395	2.370
d, g ml^{-1}	1.9226	1.8762	1.8533	1.8296	1.8063

23. Using the dipole moments of toluene and chlorobenzene given in Table V, predict the dipole moments of o-, m-, and p-monochlorotoluene. In toluene the positive end of the dipole is directed outward from the benzene ring, and in chlorotoluene the negative end is directed outward. The calculation may be made with vector drawings of the type illustrated in Fig. 17-9.

24. The specific rotation for sucrose in water at $20°$ for the D line of sodium is $66.412 + 0.01267c$, where c is the concentration in grams per 100 ml of solution. Calculate the rotation for a solution containing 20 g per 100 ml in a 2-decimeter tube.

25. A solution of l-proline in water had a concentration of 23 g liter^{-1} at $20°$ and rotated polarized light (D line of sodium) $-3.05°$, as measured with a polarimeter in a cell 20 cm long. The specific rotation at $20°$ of pure l-proline is $-84.9°$. What conclusions can be drawn as to the purity of the product if it is assumed that any impurities are optically inactive?

SPECTROSCOPY

18

Spectroscopy is the study of the interactions between matter and electromagnetic radiation. The emission and absorption spectra of atoms were discussed in Chapter 16. Atomic spectra result from electrons moving from one electronic energy level in an atom to another. However, emission or absorption of electromagnetic radiation by molecules may involve transitions between rotational- and vibrational-energy levels in addition to or instead of electronic transitions. As a result, the spectra of molecules are much more complicated than those of atoms. The character of molecular spectra is determined by vibration frequencies, moments of inertia, dissocation energies, changes in size accompanying absorption, and symmetry properties of the molecule. Therefore, molecular spectra are an exceedingly important source of quantitative information about bond lengths and angles, vibration frequencies, dissociation energies, and the shapes of the potential-energy curves. The determination of electronic, vibrational, and rotational frequencies makes it possible to calculate thermodynamic properties by use of statistical mechanics. Also absorption spectra offer a means of characterizing compounds and quantitatively analyzing mixtures.

The Fundamental Equation. For both absorption and emission spectra the relation between the change in energy of the molecule and the frequency of light emitted or absorbed is given by

$$h\nu = E' - E'' = \Delta E \tag{1}$$

where E' is the energy of the higher energy state, and E'' is the energy of the lower energy state. In emission the molecules undergo transitions from states of higher energy to states of lower energy. In absorption the molecules undergo transitions to higher energy levels. Not all transitions between energy levels are permitted by the selection rules which govern various types of spectra. When a substance is irradiated by monochromatic radiation, the photons may or may not be absorbed, depending upon whether the energy for some permitted transition between energy levels corresponds to the energy of the photon.

The Electromagnetic Spectrum. The spectrum of electromagnetic radiation is continuous, but it is convenient to divide it arbitrarily into regions according to the type of transitions and the apparatus required. Typical limits of the various spectral regions are indicated in Table I.

Table I. Energy of Electromagnetic Radiation

Description	Wavelength Range	Wave Number, cm^{-1}	Frequency, sec^{-1}	Energy $kcal\ mole^{-1}$	electron volts
Radio frequency	3×10^5 cm	3.33×10^{-6}	10^5	9.51×10^{-9}	4.12×10^{-10}
Microwave	30 cm	0.0333	10^9	9.51×10^{-5}	4.12×10^{-6}
Far infrared	0.06 cm (600 μ)	16.6	4.98×10^{11}	0.0457	2.07×10^{-3}
Near infrared	30 μ	333	10^{13}	0.951	0.0412
Visible	0.8 μ (8000 A)	1.25×10^4	3.75×10^{14}	35.8	1.55
Ultraviolet	4000 A	2.5×10^4	7.5×10^{14}	71.5	3.10
Vacuum ultraviolet	1500 A	6.66×10^4	19.98×10^{14}	190	8.25
X-rays and γ rays	50 A	2×10^6	6×10^{16}	5.72×10^3	247.8
	0.001 A	10^{11}	3×10^{21}	2.86×10^8	12.4×10^6

The range of electromagnetic radiations usually referred to as light is divided into the ultraviolet, the visible, and the infrared. The visible region extends from about 4000 to 8000 A, and light within these limits may be detected by the eye, by photographic plates, and by photoelectric cells.

The chemical and physical effects of various types of radiation are quite different, and these differences can be understood in terms of the differing energies of the photons. The energy of a single photon is given by $h\nu$, and the energy of a mole of photons is obtained by multiplying by Avogadro's number. The calculation of the energy of a mole of photons in calories is illustrated in example 1.

Example 1. Calculate the energy in ergs per quantum and calories per mole of photons of wavelengths 3000 A.

$$h\nu = hc/\lambda = (6.62 \times 10^{-27} \text{ erg sec})(3 \times 10^{10} \text{ cm sec}^{-1})/(3000 \times 10^{-8} \text{ cm})$$

$$= 6.62 \times 10^{-12} \text{ erg}$$

$$N_0 h\nu = (6.02 \times 10^{23} \text{ mole}^{-1})(6.62 \times 10^{-12} \text{ erg})$$

$$= 3.98 \times 10^{12} \text{ ergs mole}^{-1}$$

$$= \frac{3.98 \times 10^{12} \text{ ergs mole}^{-1}}{(4.184 \text{ joules cal}^{-1})(10^7 \text{ ergs joule}^{-1})} = 95,300 \text{ cal mole}^{-1}$$

It is also very useful to express energies in electron volts. One electron volt is equivalent to 23,060 cal mole^{-1}, as explained on p. 455.

Example 2. Calculate the energy in electron volts which corresponds to a wavelength of 3000 A. The energy of a mole of photons of this wavelength is 95,300 cal mole^{-1}.

$$\frac{(95,300 \text{ cal mole}^{-1})}{(23,060 \text{ cal mole}^{-1} \text{ ev}^{-1})} = 4.13 \text{ electron volts}$$

Let us consider the effect on molecules of the absorption of various types of electromagnetic radiation, starting with that of lowest energy, radio waves. The quanta of radio waves are too small to produce chemical changes, but they do produce changes in the orientation of nuclear spins as shown in nuclear magnetic resonance.

Photons in the microwave region (radio waves with wavelengths of about 0.06–30 cm) are emitted by special generators, such as the klystron tube used in radar equipment. The sample, which must be gaseous, is irradiated in a long metal tube with monochromatic microwave radiation. The beam is picked up by a special receiver at the other end of the tube, and the amplified signal is plotted on a recorder as a function of frequency. Absorption occurs at certain frequencies which are determined by the moments of inertia of the gaseous molecules. In the microwave region of the spectrum the energy of a photon is so small that only rotational-energy changes occur. Microwave spectra are especially useful for determining distances between atoms and bond angles, since these distances and angles, together with the atomic masses, determine the energies of the rotational levels.

In the far infrared (30–600 μ) pure rotational spectra are also obtained, but for many molecules the energies are sufficiently great to cause vibrational changes as well. Radiation of these wavelengths is emitted by incandescent objects; Nernst glowers are a particular form of source used in infrared spectroscopy. In the far infrared region it is necessary to use gratings and focusing mirrors, rather than prisms and lenses, because glass absorbs far-infrared radiation. In this region the radiation is measured with a thermocouple which consists of a blackened bimetallic junction.

The borderline (~ 30 μ) between the near and far infrared corresponds to thermal energies at room temperature. At $300°K$ the translational kinetic energy of a gas is $\frac{3}{2}RT = 900$ cal mole^{-1}. For measurements in the near infrared, cells and prisms of single sodium chloride and potassium bromide crystals are used.

In the near infrared (30–0.8 μ) the quanta are large enough to cause vibrational transitions as well as rotational transitions. The near-infrared spectra are quite complicated because rotational transitions, involving small energies, are combined with vibrational transitions, giving rise to absorption bands. The same kinds of sources and detectors are used in this region as in the far-infrared region, but quartz optics may be preferred below about 3 μ.

In the visible region (4000–8000 A) of the spectrum the energy per quantum is sufficiently large (35–70 kcal mole^{-1}) to excite outer electrons of some molecules to higher energy levels, and chemical changes may result. A great many substances are colorless in the visible region because they lack an electronic level 35–70 kcal mole^{-1} above the ground level to which an electron can be excited. Monochromatic sources of visible light are provided by the arc spectra of atoms together with suitable filters, or by a monochromator utilizing glass prisms or gratings. Photoelectric cells and photographic plates are used as detectors.

In the ultraviolet region (4000–1800 A) the energy per quantum is still greater, and electrons are excited to higher energy levels. Sometimes ionization is produced. The energy is sufficient to bring about almost any chemical reaction because it ranges from about 70 to 200 kcal mole^{-1}. In most of this region quartz prisms and cells must be substituted for ones made of glass, and below 2000 A optical material of fluorite, CaF_2, is used. Mercury- and hydrogen-arc lamps are often employed as a source of ultraviolet radiation.

The neighboring region of shorter wavelengths is referred to as the vacuum ultraviolet (1800–50 A) because the absorption by air is sufficiently great that the spectrometer must be evacuated.

In the X-ray region of very short wavelengths (about 0.001–50 A), the electrons nearest the nucleus are displaced. Energies of thousands to millions of kilocalories per mole are required for these displacements. In this region the energy per quantum is so great that a single quantum may be detected with a Geiger-Müller counter (p. 686) by virtue of the ionization which it produces.

Spectrophotometers. When radiation containing many different wavelengths is passed into a substance, some of the radiation may be absorbed, the rest being either transmitted or reflected. A substance appears colored because part of the visible light is absorbed. For example, a solution of cupric ions appears blue because, when white light is passed through it, the red and yellow light are absorbed, and only the blue is transmitted to the eye. The intensity of absorption is characteristic of a substance, just as are the frequencies at which absorption occurs. The design of a spectrophotometer is shown schematically in *Fig. 18-1.*

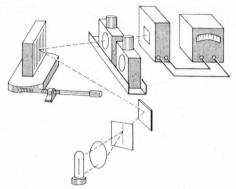

Fig. 18-1. Schematic diagram of a spectrophotometer.

A spectrophotometer is an instrument for making quantitative measurements of the transmission of light at various wavelengths. The principal parts are the source of electromagnetic radiation, the monochromator, the cell compartment, the photoelectric detector and a device for indicating the signal from the detector (electrical meter, potentiometer, or recording potentiometer). For some purposes optical filters may be used to obtain nearly monochromatic light, but in general a monochromator with a prism or grating is employed. The spread of wavelengths of the light passing through the sample depends upon the dispersion of the prism or grating (that is, the extent to which the various wavelengths are spread out) and the slit width. The narrower the slit width, the more monochromatic is the radiation, and the greater the resolution of closely spaced lines. The cell compartment contains one optical absorption cell filled with the solution to be studied and another absorption cell filled with a reference solution, usually pure solvent. One cell is placed in the optical path, and then the other. The magnitude of the electric current from the photoelectric cell is proportional to the intensity of the transmitted light, provided that a small correction is made electrically for the dark current obtained when the phototube is not illuminated.

In an experiment a cell containing solvent is put in place between the slit and phototube. The slit width or the gain of the amplifier is set so that a reading of 100 is obtained. Some light incident upon the cell is lost by reflection or by absorption due to the glass of the cell or the solvent. The loss due to reflection amounts to about 4 per cent when a perpendicular beam of light goes from air to glass or glass to air, but the exact amount lost depends on the ratio of the refractive index of glass to that of air. However, these losses will be the same for the cell containing solution, which is next put into place between the slit and phototube. Providing that the response of the meter or potentiometer is directly proportional to the light intensity, the reading now gives the percentage transmission of the solution. The percentage transmittancy determined in this way is represented by $100I/I_0$, where I/I_0 is the *transmittancy*.

By turning the prism so that light of another wavelength passes through the reference cell of solvent, adjusting the gain or slit width to obtain a reading of 100, and making a reading on the solution cell, the transmittancy I/I_0 can be determined for the different wavelengths, and the spectrum can be mapped. With some spectrophotometers such a plot is recorded automatically. When the desired absorption band is located, the monochromator can be set at some particular wavelength in this region and the transmission determined for different concentrations. The positions and intensities of the absorption bands and lines serve for identification and for criteria of purity; the percentage transmissions serve for quantitative analyses of the amount of material present.

Emission spectra of volatilized metals and compounds are readily obtained by means of an arc, a spark, or a flame; they are valuable in qualitative and quantitative analysis.

Lambert-Beer Law. The extent of absorption depends upon the probability that the energy of a photon will be absorbed by a molecule, where it can effect a chemical reaction or where it is dissipated eventually as heat. The probability of absorption is directly proportional to the concentration of absorbing molecules. This probability is expressed mathematically by the equation

$$\frac{dI}{I} = -kc \, dx \tag{2}$$

where I is the intensity of light of a particular wavelength, that is, the number of photons per square centimeter per second, and dI is the change in light intensity produced by absorption in a thin layer of thickness dx and concentration c. Distance x is measured through the cell in the direction of the beam of light which is being absorbed.

According to this equation, the fraction of light absorbed is proportional to the thickness of the absorbing solution, provided that the thickness and fraction absorbed are small. The proportionality constant k varies with the wavelength of light used, the solvent, and the temperature. A large value of k indicates that the material absorbs strongly.

The intensity of a beam of light after passing through b centimeters of solution is related to the incident intensity I_0 by equation 4, which is obtained by integrating equation 2 between the limits I_0 when $x = 0$ and I when $x = b$.

$$\int_{I_0}^{I} \frac{dI}{I} = -kc \int_0^b dx \tag{3}$$

$$\ln \frac{I}{I_0} = 2.303 \log \frac{I}{I_0} = -kcb \tag{4}$$

Since it is convenient to use logarithms to the base 10, the Lambert-Beer law is usually applied in the form

$$\log \frac{I_0}{I} = A_s = a_s bc \tag{5}$$

The quantity $\log (I_0/I)$ is referred to as the *absorbancy* A_s or optical density. It can be seen from equation 5 that the absorbancy is directly proportional to the concentration c and to the path length b. The proportionality constant is the *absorbancy index* a_s, or extinction coefficient, which is characteristic of the solute and depends upon the wavelength of the light, the solvent, and the temperature. When the concentration is expressed in moles per liter and b in centimeters, a_s becomes the *molar absorbancy index*, a_M. The Lambert-Beer law will not be obeyed unless the radiation is monochromatic. If the radiation is not monochromatic, the absorbancy index may vary significantly over the band of wavelengths used. The Lambert-Beer law will also fail if there is association or dissociation of the solute because there will be a shift of equilibrium between absorbing molecules with changing concentration.

Figure 18-2 shows an absorption spectrum from green leaves showing the two components, chlorophyll A and chlorophyll B, which have slightly different absorption maxima.

Some modern recording spectrophotometers plot absorbancy versus wavelength automatically.

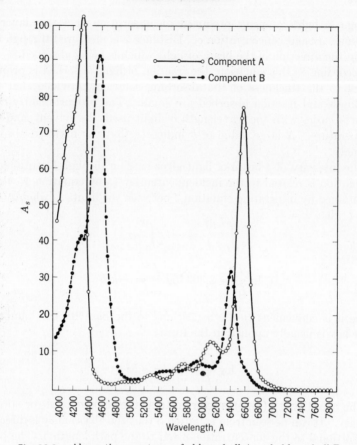

Wavelength, A

Fig. 18-2. Absorption spectrum of chlorophyll A and chlorophyll B.

Example 3. The percentage transmittancy of an aqueous solution of disodium fumarate at 250 mμ and 25° is 19.2 per cent for a 5×10^{-4} M solution in a 1-cm cell. Calculate the absorbancy and the molar absorbancy index.

$$A_s = \log (I_0/I) = \log (100/19.2) = 0.716$$

$$a_M = \frac{A_s}{bc} = \frac{0.716}{(1 \text{ cm})(5 \times 10^{-4} \text{ mole l}^{-1})} = 1.43 \times 10^3 \text{ l mole}^{-1} \text{ cm}^{-1}$$

What will be the percentage transmittancy of a 1.75×10^{-4} M solution in a 1-cm cell?

$$\log (I_0/I) = (1.43 \times 10^3 \text{ l mole}^{-1} \text{ cm}^{-1})(1 \text{ cm})(1.75 \times 10^{-4} \text{ mole l}^{-1})$$

$$= 0.250$$

$$I_0/I = 1.778 \quad \text{and} \quad 100 I/I_0 = 56.2\%$$

Example 4. When a 1.9-cm absorption cell was used, the transmittancy of 4360 A light by bromine in carbon tetrachloride solution was found to be as follows:

| c, moles per liter | 0.00546 | 0.00350 | 0.00210 | 0.00125 | 0.00066 |
| Transmittancy, I/I_0 | 0.010 | 0.050 | 0.160 | 0.343 | 0.570 |

Calculate the molar absorbancy index a_M.

In *Fig. 18-3*, log (I_0/I) is plotted against concentration, and the constant a_M is calculated from the slope of the line and the thickness of the cell to be 193 liters mole^{-1} cm^{-1}.

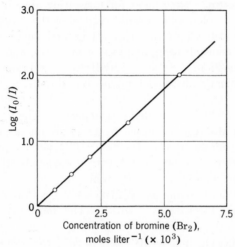

Fig. 18-3. Plot of absorbancy versus concentration for Br_2 in CCl_4 at 4360 A using a 1-cm cell.

What percentage of the incident light would be transmitted by 2 cm of solution containing 1.55×10^{-3} mole of bromine per liter of carbon tetrachloride?

$$\log (I_0/I) = a_M bc = (193 \text{ l mole}^{-1}\text{ cm}^{-1})(2 \text{ cm})(1.55 \times 10^{-3}\text{ mole l}^{-1})$$

$$= 0.599$$

$$I/I_0 = 0.252$$

or

$$100 I/I_0 = 25.2\%$$

The intensity of light absorbed is equal to the difference between the incident intensity and the transmitted intensity $(I_0 - I)$. In example 4 the absorption is $100 - 25.2 = 74.8$ per cent. Thus

$$I_0 - I = I_0(1 - 10^{-a_s bc}) \tag{6}$$

For mixtures of independently absorbing substances the absorbancy is given by the equation

$$\log (I_0/I) = A_s = (a_{s1}c_1 + a_{s2}c_2 + \cdots)b \tag{7}$$

where c_1, c_2, $\cdots$ are the concentrations of the substances having absorbancy indices of a_{s1}, a_{s2}, $\cdots$. A mixture of n components may be analyzed by measuring A_s at n wavelengths at which the absorbancy indices are known for each substance, provided that these indices are sufficiently different. The concentrations of the several substances may then be calculated by solving the n simultaneous equations.

Absorption Spectra. Equipment for measuring absorption spectra in the visible, ultraviolet, and infrared regions of the spectrum is among the chemist's most important tools. It is used for identification, determination of concentration, analysis of mixtures, and determination of molecular constants. Saturated hydrocarbons do not absorb in the visible and ordinary ultraviolet ranges but do absorb below 1800 A. Groups like C=C, C=O, —N=N—, and —N=O, which cause absorption above 1800 A, are called *chromophores*. The positions and intensities of the absorptions caused by these groups are rather characteristic. For example, double bonds C=C generally produce an absorption maximum at 1800–1900 A with a molar absorbancy index of about 10^4 liters mole^{-1} cm^{-1}. Ketone and aldehyde C=O groups usually have absorption maxima at 2700–2900 A with molar absorbancy indices of 10–30 liters mole^{-1} cm^{-1}. The most intense electronic absorption spectra are produced by certain dyes which may have molar absorbancy indices as high as 10^5 liters mole^{-1} cm^{-1} in solution. The absorption lines in the visible and ultraviolet regions for solutes are generally broad as illustrated in Fig. 18-2.

Many compounds which do not absorb light in the visible region and do not have very characteristic absorption in the ultraviolet region have very detailed and quite different spectra in the infrared region. The absorption spectrum of a compound is an identifying characteristic, just like its melting point or boiling point. For such practical applications the infrared spectra for a large number of compounds have been catalogued and are used like "fingerprints." Functional groups within the molecule also have quite characteristic absorption bands. A few such values are shown in Table II. The wavelengths at which various groups absorb vary slightly, depending upon the structure of the rest of the molecule. The principal functional groups within the molecule may frequently be determined, and such information can be used to identify positively compounds where chemical evidence permits relatively few possible structures.

Absorption spectra are frequently used in the empirical way described above, but from a physical-chemical standpoint a more important aspect of the spectra is the information they give about molecu-

Table II.[1]   Infrared Absorption Bonds for Various Functional Groups

(In wave numbers, cm^{-1})

O—H st.[2]	3800–3000
N—H st.	3500–3100
C—H st.	3100–2750
S—H st.	2600–2500
C=O (ketone) st.	1725–1650
N—H bend	1650–1550
C—H bend	1475–1375
C=C st.	1675–1575
C—C (aromatic) st.	1650–1550
C—O st.	1300–1100

[1] Courtesy of Prof. Monroe Evans, University of Wisconsin.
[2] st. = stretching frequency.

lar structure and bonding. In order to understand how this information is obtained it is necessary to consider the nature of the energy levels of molecules.

Energy Levels of Molecules. Some of the possible energy levels for a diatomic molecule may be represented by a diagram such as *Fig. 18-4.* The energy, represented by the vertical positions of the lines, is the sum of the rotational energy E_{rot}, vibrational energy E_{vib}, and electronic energy E_{el}.

$$E = E_{rot} + E_{vib} + E_{el} \qquad (8)$$

A molecule in a given electronic level must be in one of a series of vibrational levels, and in one of the rotational sublevels of that vibrational level. In contrast to our experience with larger objects the rotational or vibrational energy of a molecule may be changed only by the gain or loss of a discrete quantum of energy. Since the absorption of energy by a molecule may involve simultaneous changes in vibrational-, rotational-, and electronic-energy levels, a very complicated spectrum may result.

The differences in energy between electronic-energy levels are, as a rule, much larger than those between vibrational-energy levels, and the differences in energy between vibrational-energy levels are much larger than those between rotational levels. Thus

$$E_{el} \gg E_{vib} \gg E_{rot} \qquad (9)$$

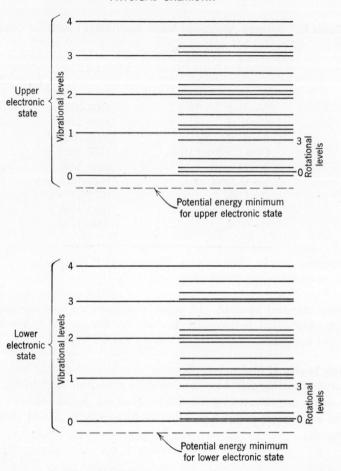

Fig. 18-4. Energy-level diagram showing two electronic levels and the various vibrational and rotational sublevels.

Actually it is not possible to separate the energy of a molecule precisely into these three terms; for example, the vibrational energy is affected by rotation because of the effect of centrifugal force on the vibration. However, the separation into electronic, vibrational, and rotational energies is often a rather good approximation.

Electronic, vibrational, and rotational changes may all occur upon the absorption or emission of a single photon, and so equation 1 may be written

$$h\nu = (E'_{el} - E''_{el}) + (E'_{vib} - E''_{vib}) + (E'_{rot} - E''_{rot}) \quad (10)$$

Each of the terms in this equation may be written as Planck's constant times a frequency.

$$\nu = (\nu'_{el} - \nu''_{el}) + (\nu'_{vib} - \nu''_{vib}) + (\nu'_{rot} - \nu''_{rot}) \qquad (11)$$

where the upper state is represented by a single prime, and the lower state by a double prime. Not all changes between energy levels are permitted by quantum theory, but only those satisfying certain selection rules. Since only small quanta of energy are required to change from one rotational-energy level to another, these changes may be studied by themselves in the far-infrared and microwave regions of the spectrum ($\lambda > 30\,\mu$). Vibrational changes result from absorption in the near-infrared region. However, for each vibrational level there are a number of rotational levels, and so bands of closely spaced lines are obtained.

Electronic changes produce absorption in the visible and ultraviolet regions. Bands of closely spaced lines or even an apparent continuum of absorption may be obtained because of the numerous superimposed lines due to vibrational and rotational changes. A *band* consists of lines associated with the same change in electronic and vibrational energy and differing only in the rotational-energy change involved in the transition. A band is distinguished by a concentration of lines at one end which is referred to as the *band head*. For different vibrational-energy changes there will be different bands, and a group of bands associated with the same electronic-energy change but different vibrational-energy changes is called a *band system*.

We will now limit our considerations to diatomic molecules, so that a detailed treatment can be made. The simplest part of the spectrum is that due to pure rotation.

Pure Rotational Spectra. In order to simplify the treatment of rotational spectra it is permissible for certain purposes to assume that the rotating molecule is rigid, although it is actually undergoing vibrational motion. Since vibrational motion takes place much more quickly than rotational motion, the internuclear distance is effectively an average distance characteristic of the vibrational state of the molecule. A rigid diatomic molecule, *Fig. 18-5a*, rotates about its center of mass, which is located so that

$$r_1 m_1 = r_2 m_2 \qquad (12)$$

where r_1 and r_2 are the distances of the nuclei of masses m_1 and m_2 from the center of mass of the molecule. Since the internuclear distance is

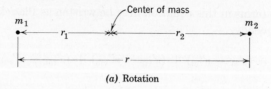

(a) Rotation

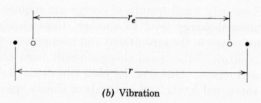

(b) Vibration

Fig. 18-5. Rotation and vibration of a diatomic molecule [cf. p. 533 for (*b*)].

$r = r_1 + r_2$, it is readily shown that

$$r_1 = \frac{m_2}{m_1 + m_2} r \tag{13}$$

$$r_2 = \frac{m_1}{m_1 + m_2} r \tag{14}$$

The moment of inertia I for a diatomic molecule is defined by

$$I = m_1 r_1^2 + m_2 r_2^2 \tag{15}$$

Substituting equations 13 and 14 yields

$$I = \frac{r^2}{\dfrac{1}{m_1} + \dfrac{1}{m_2}} = \mu r^2 \tag{16}$$

where μ, the *reduced mass*, is defined by

$$\mu = \frac{m_1 m_2}{m_1 + m_2}$$

or

$$\frac{1}{\mu} = \frac{1}{m_1} + \frac{1}{m_2} \tag{17}$$

The moment of inertia of a diatomic molecule is equivalent to that of the reduced mass revolving at a distance r from the axis.

Example 5. Calculate the reduced masses and moments of inertia of HCl^{35} and HCl^{37}, using the mean internuclear distance of 1.275 A. Using atomic weights on the physical scale (p. 678), for HCl^{35}

$$\mu = \frac{(1.008)(34.98)}{(1.008 + 34.98)(6.023 \times 10^{23})}$$

$$= 1.628 \times 10^{-24} \text{ g}$$

$$I = \mu r^2$$

$$= (1.628 \times 10^{-24} \text{ g})(1.275 \times 10^{-8} \text{ cm})^2$$

$$= 2.647 \times 10^{-40} \text{ g cm}^2$$

For HCl^{37}

$$\mu = \frac{(1.008)(36.98)}{(1.008 + 36.98)(6.023 \times 10^{23})}$$

$$= 1.630 \times 10^{-24} \text{ g}$$

$$I = (1.630 \times 10^{-23} \text{ g})(1.275 \times 10^{-8} \text{ cm})^2$$

$$= 2.650 \times 10^{-40} \text{ g cm}^2$$

The equation for the allowed rotational-energy levels of a diatomic molecule is obtained by solution of the Schrödinger equation (p. 462) for a rigid rotator. It is found that the wave functions are single valued, continuous, and finite *only* when the rotational energy E of the molecule is given by *

$$E = \frac{J(J + 1)h^2}{8\pi^2 I} \tag{18}$$

or

$$\frac{E}{hc} = \frac{h}{8\pi^2 cI} J(J + 1)$$

$$= BJ(J + 1) \tag{19}$$

where $B = h/8\pi^2 cI$ is referred to as the rotational constant. The rotational quantum number J can have only the values $0, 1, 2, 3, \cdots$. As usual only certain transitions are permitted, in this case $\Delta J = \pm 1$. Such a rule is called a *selection rule.*

Diatomic molecules can absorb or emit radiation by changes in their rotational motion only if they have permanent dipole moments (p. 501). Classically, electromagnetic radiation may be produced by a rotating dipole, since this rotation produces an alternating electric field. Since molecules like H_2 and N_2 do not have dipole moments, they do not interact with the electromagnetic field and thus do not show pure rota-

---

* W. Kauzmann, *Quantum Chemistry,* Academic Press, New York, 1957, pp. 198–200.

tional spectra as do molecules like HCl and CH_3Cl, which have dipole moments.

According to equation 1, the frequency in wave numbers for a transition from a level with quantum number J to the level $J - 1$ is given by

$$\bar{\nu} = \frac{E'}{hc} - \frac{E''}{hc}$$

$$= B\left[J(J + 1) - (J - 1)J\right] = 2BJ \qquad (20)$$

where J, the quantum number for the upper level, can only have values of 1, 2, 3, $\cdots$. Thus the frequency of the radiation absorbed is directly proportional to the quantum number of the level to which the rotating molecule is excited by the absorption of a quantum of radiation. As a result we find a series of nearly equally spaced lines in the far-infrared and microwave regions due to the rotation of a diatomic molecule. The moments of inertia of isotopically substituted molecules are appreciably different, and therefore a separate series of lines is found for each isotopically different species of a given molecule.

Example 6. Calculate the frequencies in wave numbers and the wavelengths in microns for the pure rotational lines in the spectrum of HCl^{35} corresponding to the following changes in rotational quantum number: $0 \rightarrow 1$, $1 \rightarrow 2$, $2 \rightarrow 3$, and $8 \rightarrow 9$. Using equation 20 and the moment of inertia for HCl^{35} calculated in example 5, we obtain:

$$\bar{\nu} = \frac{(6.62 \times 10^{-27} \text{ erg sec})J}{4\pi^2(2.647 \times 10^{-40} \text{ g cm}^2)(3 \times 10^{10} \text{ cm sec}^{-1})}$$

$$= 21.2J \text{ cm}^{-1}$$

Thus

J	$\bar{\nu} = 21.2J$	$\lambda = 10^4/\bar{\nu}$
1	21.2 cm^{-1}	472 μ
2	42.4	236
3	63.6	157
9	190.8	52.5

The usual experimental situation is the reverse of this example; that is, the wavelengths of the rotational lines are measured in the far-infrared or microwave region and the moment of inertia and finally the mean internuclear distance are calculated.

Microwave Spectroscopy.* Absorption in the microwave region is due to pure rotational changes. Therefore, the absorption spectrum of a gas in this region yields the moments of inertia of the molecule.

---

* W. Gordy, W. V. Smith, and R. F. Trambarulo, *Microwave Spectroscopy*, John Wiley & Sons, New York, 1953; C. H. Townes and A. L. Schawlow, *Microwave Spectroscopy*, McGraw-Hill Book Co., New York, 1955.

The rotational motion of a nonlinear (rigid) molecule is best described in terms of three axes, the principal axes, which are fixed in the molecule and rotate with it. The principal axes are oriented in such a way as to simplify the mathematical treatment. The principal axes rotate with respect to a set of axes fixed in space with their origin also at the center of mass. The moments I around the principal axes are called the principal moments and are defined by equations such as

$$I = \sum m_i r_i^2 \tag{21}$$

where m_i is the mass of a nucleus and r_i is the perpendicular distance to the chosen axis.

Molecules may be classified on the basis of their moments of inertia as follows: (1) linear molecules, for example, HCN, have two equal moments of inertia I_b and I_c; (2) spherical top molecules, like CH_4, have three moments of inertia I_a, I_b, and I_c about the axes a, b, and c, but these moments are all equal, $I_a = I_b = I_c$; (3) symmetric top molecules, for example, NH_3 and CH_3Cl, have $I_a \neq I_b = I_c$; and (4) asymmetric top molecules, for example, CH_2Cl_2 and CH_3OH, have $I_a \neq I_b \neq I_c$. Examples of these classes of molecules are shown in *Fig. 18-6a–d*. Since a molecule must have a permanent dipole moment in order to have a pure rotational spectrum, spherical top molecules have no observable rotational spectrum.

Microwave lines are very sharp, and their frequencies may generally be determined to the order of 1 part per million. Therefore, the moments of inertia of a molecule may be determined with great accuracy. As a matter of fact, this method has made possible the most precise evaluations of bond lengths and bond angles. A few interatomic distances and bond angles obtained from microwave spectra are given in Table III. In order to obtain these values for polyatomic molecules

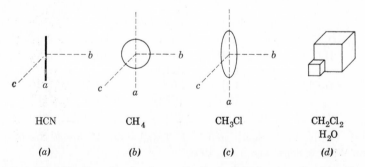

HCN	CH_4	CH_3Cl	CH_2Cl_2 H_2O
(a)	(b)	(c)	(d)

Fig. 18-6. Classification of molecules on the basis of their moments of inertia: (a) linear, (b) spherical top, (c) symmetric top, and (d) asymmetric top. These geometrical figures are purely illustrative, since other shapes have these symmetries.

Table III.[1] Interatomic Distances (A) and Bond Angles from Microwave Spectra

Substance	Bond Distance		Bond Angles	

Diatomic Molecules

CO		1.2823		
BrCl		2.138		
NaCl		2.3606		

Linear Polyatomic Molecules

HCN	CH	1.064		
	CN	1.156		
NNO	NN	1.126		
	NO	1.191		
HC≡CCN	CH	1.057		
	C—C	1.382		
	C≡C	1.203		
	CN	1.157		

Symmetric Top Molecules

CH₃Cl	CH	1.10	HCH	110°
	CCl	1.782		
CH₃C≡CH	CH₃	1.097	HCH	108°
	C≡C	1.207		
	C—C	1.460		
	≡CH	1.056		
NH₃	NH	1.016	HNH	107°

Asymmetric Top Molecules

SO₃	SO	1.433	OSO	119.33°
CH₂O	CH	1.12	HCH	118°
	CO	1.21		
CH₂Cl₂	CH	1.068	HCH	112°
	CCl	1.7724	ClCCl	111°

[1] W. Gordy, W. V. Smith, and R. F. Trambarulo, *Microwave Spectroscopy*, John Wiley & Sons, New York, 1953.

it is helpful to study the spectra of as many different isotopically substituted molecules as possible. There are small differences in the spectra of the isotopically different molecules, and these differences depend upon the bond lengths and angles. It is assumed that isotopic substitution does not alter the internuclear distance significantly.

Vibration of a Diatomic Molecule. To a first approximation a vibrating diatomic molecule is a simple harmonic oscillator. A simple harmonic oscillator is one in which the force tending to restore the particle to its equilibrium position is directly proportional to the displacement from the equilibrium position. Thus

$$\text{Force} = -k(r - r_e) \tag{22}$$

where k is the force constant. The minus sign is required because the force is in the negative r direction if the displacement from the equilibrium position r_e is positive. At the equilibrium distance there is a balance between the attractive and repulsive forces between the atoms. If the nuclei are closer together than r_e, there is repulsion. If the nuclei are further apart than r_e, there is attraction. The attraction is due to electronic bonding, and the repulsion is due to the overlapping of inner electronic shells and the repulsion between the two positively charged nuclei. The relation between r and r_e is shown in *Fig. 18-5b*.

A force of this type may be represented as the negative gradient of the potential energy V.

$$\text{Force} = -\frac{\partial V}{\partial r} = -k(r - r_e) \tag{23}$$

Integrating,

$$V = \tfrac{1}{2}k(r - r_e)^2 \tag{24}$$

if the integration constant is taken equal to zero, so that $V = 0$ when $r = r_e$. Thus a plot of potential energy versus displacement is parabolic for a simple harmonic oscillator. A small object sliding without friction in a parabolic well would execute simple harmonic motion. As it slides through the minimum, the velocity is a maximum and the potential energy is a minimum. As it slides up the other side, kinetic energy is converted to potential energy. When the particle is at either one of its two highest points in the oscillation, the total energy is stored as potential energy.

The force tending to restore the diatomic molecule to its equilibrium internuclear distance is equal to $m_1 a_1 = m_2 a_2$, where a_1 is the acceleration of nucleus 1 and a_2 is the acceleration of nucleus 2. By use of equations 13 and 14,

$$a_1 = \frac{d^2 r_1}{dt^2} = \frac{m_2}{m_1 + m_2} \frac{d^2 r}{dt^2} \tag{25}$$

$$a_2 = \frac{d^2 r_2}{dt^2} = \frac{m_1}{m_1 + m_2} \frac{d^2 r}{dt^2} \tag{26}$$

Thus

$$\text{Force} = \frac{m_1 m_2}{m_1 + m_2} \frac{d^2 r}{dt^2} = \mu \frac{d^2 r}{dt^2} = \mu \frac{d^2 (r - r_e)}{dt^2} \tag{27}$$

where μ is the reduced mass from equation 17. Equating the forces in equations 23 and 27,

$$\frac{d^2 (r - r_e)}{dt^2} = -\frac{k}{\mu} (r - r_e) \tag{28}$$

A solution of this differential equation may be written

$$r - r_e = a \sin t \left(\frac{k}{\mu} \right)^{1/2} \tag{29}$$

as may be shown by substituting it into differential equation 28. In this equation the maximum displacement from the equilibrium inter-nuclear distance is represented by a.

Equation 29 may also be written in the form

$$r - r_e = a \sin 2\pi \nu_0 t \tag{30}$$

where, ν_0, the fundamental vibration frequency in cycles per second, is given by

$$\nu_0 = \frac{1}{2\pi} \left(\frac{k}{\mu} \right)^{1/2} \tag{31}$$

Thus the fundamental vibration frequency for a diatomic molecule depends upon the force constant and the reduced mass of the molecule.

Example 7. Calculate the force constant for HCl^{35} from the fact that the fundamental vibration frequency is $8.667 \times 10^{13} \sec^{-1}$ and the reduced mass is 1.628×10^{-24} gram, as shown in example 5.

$$k = (2\pi \nu_0)^2 \mu$$

$$= (2\pi 8.667 \times 10^{13} \sec^{-1})^2 (1.628 \times 10^{-24} \text{ g})$$

$$= 4.81 \times 10^5 \text{ dynes cm}^{-1}$$

In order to obtain the quantum-mechanical solution for the vibration of a diatomic molecule, equation 24 for the potential energy of a simple harmonic oscillator is substituted into the Schrödinger equation. The solution of the resulting equation involves some mathematical complexities which it is not appropriate to discuss here. However, it is found that wave functions having the desired properties (continuous, single valued, and finite) are obtained only for energy levels given by *

$$E_n = (v + \tfrac{1}{2})h\nu_0 \tag{32}$$

where the vibrational quantum number v is 0, 1, 2, $\cdots$ and ν_0 is the fundamental vibration frequency. This equation shows that in the lowest vibrational level ($v = 0$) the molecule still has an energy of $\tfrac{1}{2}h\nu_0$, the so-called *zero-point energy*. The molecule would still possess this vibrational energy at absolute zero, and thus vibrational motion does not cease. It is evident from equation 32 that the vibrational levels are equally spaced in energy for a parabolic potential well. According to this model, we would expect to find overtones of the fundamental vibration frequency at exactly integral multiples of the fundamental. However, real molecules are not exactly simple harmonic oscillators because the potential wells are nonparabolic.

Potential-Energy Curves for Diatomic Molecules. For small displacements from the equilibrium internuclear distance the potential energy follows equation 24, and the vibration is simple harmonic according to a classical point of view. However, for larger displacements the vibration is anharmonic, and if sufficient energy is put into the vibration, the molecule may be dissociated into two atoms. These facts are represented by means of a potential-energy curve such as that shown in *Fig. 18-7.* In this plot the potential energy V is taken as zero at the equilibrium internuclear separation. As the internuclear separation is increased from this point, energy is required, and the dissociation energy D' would be needed to separate the atoms to an infinite distance. The energy required to bring the nuclei closer together than the equilibrium distance increases sharply.

It is convenient to have a mathematical expression for such a plot of potential energy V versus internuclear distance r. One of the simplest is that due to Morse.

$$V = D'[1 - e^{-\beta(r-r_e)}]^2 \tag{33}$$

The dissociation energy D' is measured from the minimum of the potential-energy curve; it is equal to the experimentally determined dissociation energy D plus the zero-point energy, *i.e.,* $D' = D + \tfrac{1}{2}h\nu_0$.

* W. Kauzmann, *Quantum Chemistry,* Academic Press, New York, 1957, pp. 201–207.

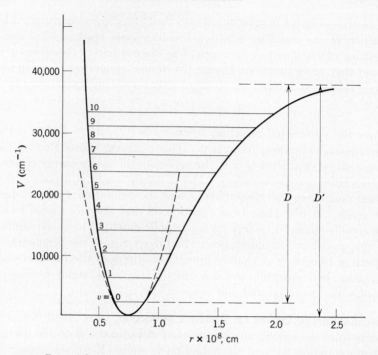

Fig. 18-7. Potential-energy diagram of the ground state of the hydrogen molecule with the first ten vibrational levels. The dashed curve shows the parabola which fits the potential-energy curve at the minimum.

Example 8. Calculate D' for H_2 from the spectroscopic dissociation energy of 4.476 ev and the fundamental vibration frequency of 4395 cm^{-1}. To calculate D' in kcal mole^{-1} we make use of the fact that 1 ev is equivalent to 23.06 kcal mole^{-1}.

$$D' = D + \tfrac{1}{2}h\nu_0$$
$$= (4.476)(23.06) + \frac{(6.62 \times 10^{-27})(3 \times 10^{10})(4395)(6.02 \times 10^{23})}{(2)(4.184 \times 10^7)(10^3)}$$
$$= 109.5 \text{ kcal mole}^{-1}$$

To calculate D' in cm^{-1} we make use of the fact that 1 ev is equivalent to 8060 cm^{-1} (p. 728).

$$D' = (4.476)(8060) + \tfrac{1}{2}(4395)$$
$$= 38,300 \text{ cm}^{-1}$$

The spectroscopic dissociation energy D is equal to the energy required to dissociate the ideal gas at absolute zero. However, it does not differ greatly from the heat of dissociation at room temperature, and it is possible to convert from one to the other by use of heat-capacity data.

The constant β, which determines the steepness of the potential-energy curve, is related to the fundamental vibrational frequency ν_0 and the reduced mass μ of the diatomic molecule by

$$\beta = \nu_0 \left(\frac{2\pi^2 c\mu}{D'h}\right)^{1/2} \tag{34}$$

Thus the potential-energy curve for a diatomic molecule may be calculated if experimental values of ν_0, r_e, and D' are available. The Morse curve for H_2 is given in Fig. 18-7. For this molecule, $\nu_0 = 4395$ cm^{-1}, $r_e = 0.7417 \times 10^{-8}$ cm, and $D' = 38{,}300$ cm^{-1}. The Morse function is an approximation which is unsatisfactory for some molecules.

It can be seen from the figure that the bottom part of a Morse curve is very closely approximated by a parabola. The vibrational levels are represented by horizontal lines in the potential-energy diagram. The vibrational levels lie more closely together as the quantum number (or energy) increases; this is illustrated in Fig. 18-7.

The fundamental vibration frequencies, spectroscopic dissociation energies, and other constants for some diatomic molecules are given in Table IV.

Table IV.[1]　Constants of Diatomic Molecules

Molecule	$N_0\mu$	$r \times 10^8$, cm	$\bar{\nu}_0$, cm^{-1}	D, ev
Br$_2$	39.958	2.283$_6$	323.2	1.971
CH	0.930024	1.1198	2861.6	3.47
Cl$_2$	17.48942	1.988	564.9	2.475
CO	6.85841	1.1282	2170.21	11.108
H$_2$	0.504066	0.7416$_6$	4395.24	4.476$_3$
H$_2^-$	0.503928	1.06	2297	2.648$_1$
HCl	0.979889	1.27460	2989.74	4.430
HBr	0.99558	1.4138	2649.67	3.75$_4$
HI	1.000187	1.604$_1$	2309.53	3.056$_4$
KCl	18.599	2.79	280	4.42
LiH	0.881506	1.5953$_5$	1405.649	2.5
Na$_2$	11.49822	3.078$_6$	159.23	0.73
NO	7.46881	1.1508	1904.03	6.487
O$_2$	8.00000	1.20739$_8$	1580.361	5.080
OH	0.94838	0.9706	3735.21	4.35

[1] From G. Herzberg, *Molecular Spectra and Molecular Structure*, D. Van Nostrand Co., Princeton, N. J., 1950. The reduced masses are for the most abundant isotopes and are on the physical atomic-weight scale (p. 678).

Vibrational Spectrum. Radiant energy may be absorbed by exciting the molecule to a higher vibrational level, and radiation is emitted when the molecule makes a transition from a higher level to a lower level. For a harmonic oscillator only transitions with $\Delta v = \pm 1$ are permitted, but for anharmonic oscillators (and real molecules are anharmonic oscillators) this selection rule does not apply. The difference in energy of two vibrational levels with quantum numbers v and v' is given by

$$\Delta E = E_v - E_{v'} = (v + \tfrac{1}{2})h\nu_0 - (v' + \tfrac{1}{2})h\nu_0 = (v - v')h\nu_0 \quad (35)$$

The fundamental vibration frequency of HCl is 8.66×10^{13} sec^{-1} (2889 cm^{-1}), and so we might expect to find absorption at integral multiples of this frequency, that is, 8.66×10^{13} sec^{-1} (2889 cm^{-1}), 17.33×10^{13} sec^{-1} (5778 cm^{-1}), 25.98×10^{13} sec^{-1} (8667 cm^{-1}), etc., or 3.46 μ, 1.73 μ, 1.15 μ, etc. However, by reference to Fig. 18-7 it can be seen that a diatomic molecule does not behave like a simple harmonic oscillator at higher vibrational energies, and as a result the overtones do not occur at exact multiples of the fundamental vibration frequency.

When the Morse function is substituted into the Schrödinger equation, the resulting expression for the first few vibrational-energy levels is

$$E = (v + \tfrac{1}{2})\nu_0 - x_e\nu_0(v + \tfrac{1}{2})^2 \quad (36)$$

where the second term is a small correction term, and

$$x_e = \frac{\nu_0}{4D'} \quad (37)$$

Vibration-Rotation Spectrum. In a transition from one vibrational level to another there must also be a change in rotational-energy level, since the selection rule is $\Delta J = \pm 1$. Thus the molecule will absorb at frequencies of $\nu_v \pm \nu_r$, where ν_v is the frequency corresponding with the vibrational change and ν_r is the frequency corresponding with a rotational change. The possible energy changes for the simplest case are given by the sum or difference of equations 19 and 35.

$$\Delta E = (v - v')h\nu_0 \pm \frac{h^2 J}{4\pi^2 I} \quad (38)$$

and the frequencies are given in terms of wave numbers by

$$\bar{\nu} = \frac{(v - v')\nu_0}{c} \pm \frac{hJ}{4\pi^2 I c} \quad (39)$$

where J, the rotational quantum number, identifies the upper level and can only have values of 1, 2, 3, $\cdots$. It is evident from this equation that the line corresponding to $\bar{\nu} = (v - v')\nu_0/c$ will be missing and there will be lines for integral values of J both above and below this missing line. This is illustrated by the infrared spectrum of HCl shown in $Fig.$ 18-8. These are the lines for the first overtone band of HCl which is due to the transition $v = 0 \rightarrow 2$. The fundamental band due to the transition $v = 0 \rightarrow 1$ is near 3.4μ (2990 cm^{-1}). The spectrum is made up of double peaks because the isotopically different molecules HCl^{35} (75% abundance) and HCl^{37} (25% abundance) have different moments of inertia and different fundamental vibration frequencies. The HCl^{37} lines occur at lower frequencies than the HCl^{35} lines, and the spacing of the rotational lines is smaller for HCl^{37} than for HCl^{35}. Detailed analysis of the data shows that the lines are not quite equally spaced on an energy scale, as would be required by equation 38, because we have ignored the anharmonicity of the vibration and the stretching of the molecule by centrifugal force.

The intensities of lines in the spectrum depend among other factors upon the populations in the energy levels from which the transitions arise. These populations depend upon the temperature, as described by the Boltzmann equation (p. 272). Since the populations decrease as J increases, the vibration-rotation lines are spread over a band of finite width.

Electronic Spectra. The electronic-energy levels in molecules differ sufficiently so that the electronic spectra are found in the visible and ultraviolet regions rather than in the infrared region. The changes from one electronic-energy level to another are accompanied by vibrational and rotational changes so that band spectra are obtained like that illustrated in Fig. 18-2 for a solute.

The dissociation energy for a molecule can frequently be determined with great accuracy from its electronic spectrum.* Dissociation of a molecule produces a region in the spectrum where there is continuous absorption. This region is separated from that in which there are discrete lines by a definite line of demarcation. The continuous absorption is due to the fact that when a molecule is dissociated the fragments are given a certain amount of kinetic energy which is not quantized, so that radiation of any wavelength below that required for dissociation may be absorbed.

Accordingly, when the energy becomes great enough (the wavelengths are short enough) to cause dissociation, the absorption becomes continuous. Just as the short-wavelength limit of continuous emission

---

* A. G. Gaydon, *Dissociation Energies and Spectra of Diatomic Molecules*, Chapman and Hall, London, 1953.

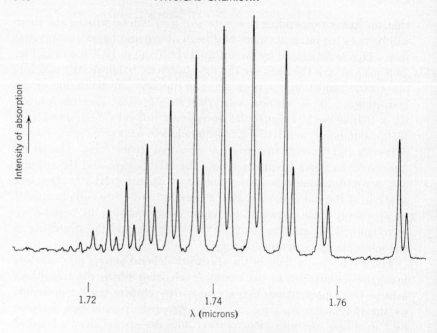

Intensity of absorption

1.72   1.74   1.76

λ (microns)

in Fig. 16-3 permitted calculation of the energy of ionization of the hydrogen atom, so also the short-wavelength limit of continuous absorption in band spectra permits calculation of the energy of dissociation of molecules.

Since dissociation of a diatomic molecule does not usually take place into unexcited atoms (p. 655), it is necessary to know the energy states of the atoms formed in order to calculate the dissociation energy from the limit of continuous emission or absorption. Some of the possible cases of excitation to higher levels are illustrated in Fig. 23-3. It is seen that a molecule may have several electronic states, and there will be a different potential-energy curve for each one of them. The energies approached by the various curves at infinite internuclear distance correspond to the different energies of excitation of the two separated atoms.

The dissociation generally takes place from the lowest vibrational level of the ground electronic state, but for heavy diatomic molecules such as I_2 the vibrational frequency is small; therefore the separation of the vibrational levels is small, and at room temperature the molecules occupy not only the lowest but also several of the lower vibrational levels of the ground electronic state. The dissociation energy of O_2 has been determined very accurately from its ultraviolet spectrum. Continuous absorption begins around 1759 A (56,877 cm^{-1}). One of the

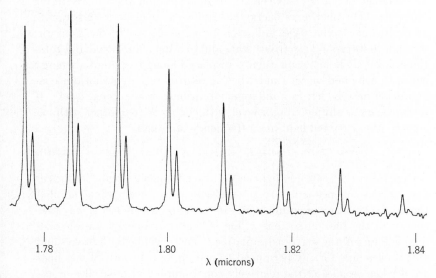

1.78   1.80   1.82   1.84

λ (microns)

Fig. 18-8. The first overtone in the infrared absorption spectrum of gaseous HCl. The double peaks are due to the presence of HCl^{35} and HCl^{37}. (Spectrum by courtesy of Prof. Monroe Evans, University of Wisconsin.)

oxygen atoms produced is in an excited state with an energy of 15,868 cm^{-1} above the ground state, and the other is in the ground electronic state. Therefore the dissociation energy is $56,877 - 15,868 = 41,009$ cm^{-1} or 5.08 ev.

Electrons in molecules move with speeds of the order of $10^7 - 10^8$ cm sec^{-1} or $10^{15} - 10^{16}$ A sec^{-1}. This is much faster than the velocity of the atoms in their vibrational motion, the vibrational frequencies being of the order of 10^{13} sec^{-1}. Thus during an electronic transition the nuclei may be considered to be a fixed distance apart. This generalization is known as the Franck-Condon principle.

Raman Spectra.* When a beam of light passes through a homogeneous medium, some of the photons are scattered in various directions without change in frequency. This scattering, known as Rayleigh scattering, is discussed in Chapter 20. In 1928 Raman discovered experimentally that there was sometimes also present in the scattered light weak radiation of frequencies not present in the incident light. The frequency dif-

---

* G. Herzberg, *Infrared and Raman Spectra of Polyatomic Molecules*, D. Van Nostrand Co., Princeton, N. J., 1945.

ferences between the weak lines and the exciting line were characteristic of the scattering substance. The light of altered frequency results from an exchange of energy between the incident photon and the scattering molecule. The photon, of energy $h\nu$ insufficient to cause a transition to an excited electronic state, induces a forced oscillation in the molecule, which is in its ground electronic state and in a low vibrational and rotational level. The molecule then is displaced along its potential-energy curve to a higher energy, and when it returns to its equilibrium configuration may be left in a different vibrational or rotational level. If the molecule is shifted from a level with energy E to another with energy E', the scattered light has a frequency of ν', and

$$h\nu + E = h\nu' + E' \tag{40}$$

Generally, the scattered light has a lower frequency (called a Stokes line) because energy is lost to the molecule. However, when the photon interacts with a molecule in an excited state, the molecule may give energy to the photon so that a line of higher frequency (anti-Stokes line) is found in the scattered radiation. There will be both Stokes and anti-Stokes lines for any permitted transition, but the anti-Stokes lines are weaker because of the relatively small number of molecules in excited energy states.

The experimental arrangement for determining Raman spectra is indicated in *Fig. 18-9*. An intense source of light is provided by a bank of mercury-vapor lamps. Liquid is circulated through a jacket around the Raman tube to remove heat produced by the lamps, and a dye is dis-

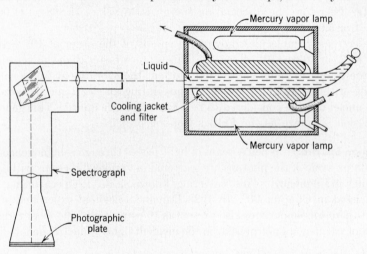

Fig. 18-9. Apparatus for obtaining Raman spectra.

solved in the liquid to filter out light of wavelengths other than the exciting line.

In *Fig. 18-10* is shown a Raman spectrum of carbon tetrachloride.

The difference in frequency between a Raman line and the incident radiation is a measure of the difference in energy between vibrational or rotational energy levels in the molecule and is independent of the frequency of the incident light. The difference in energy levels may be calculated from the Raman shift $(\nu - \nu')$ by use of

$$E' - E = h(\nu - \nu') \tag{41}$$

The shifts observed are generally of the order of 100–4000 cm^{-1} and correspond to changes in vibrational-energy levels, but rotational

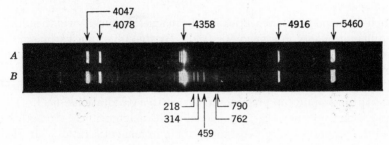

Fig. 18-10. Raman spectrum of carbon tetrachloride. A = Mercury arc. Wavelengths are given in angstroms above the spectra. B = Raman spectrum of CCl$_4$. The wave numbers of the Raman lines are given below the spectrum. (Courtesy of Prof. Paul Bender and G. J. Pontrelli, University of Wisconsin.)

Raman lines also are observed occasionally. The strongest Raman lines are ordinarily those for transitions between adjacent energy levels corresponding to a single vibrational frequency, that is, fundamental vibration frequencies. Sums and differences of several fundamental frequencies are obtained when there is a simultaneous change in the energy associated with more than one mode of vibration. Although the Raman lines may correspond to infrared lines, sometimes they correspond to transitions which are not permitted in the infrared according to the restrictions of the quantum theory. In the scattering process the electric component of the incident light wave induces a dipole moment in the molecule. In order for Raman scattering to occur there must be a change in the polarizability of the molecule attending the vibration, so that there will be a variation in the induced moment with time. Valuable information concerning molecular structure can be obtained by combining data from the Raman spectra and infrared absorption spectra.

Nuclear Magnetic Resonance (NMR) Spectroscopy.* Many nuclei have spin, and as a result they have a magnetic moment which can be thought of as a vector along the axis of spin. The only nuclei that do not have a nuclear spin are those which have an even mass number and an even number of protons in the nucleus. It can be shown quantum mechanically that in the presence of a magnetic field the component of the spin angular-momentum vector in the direction of the field can assume only certain values. Since the magnetic moment is parallel to the angular momentum, the component of the magnetic moment in the direction of the field is also quantized. If this component is called μ_z, the energy of the nucleus in a magnetic field H along the z direction is

$$E = -\mu_z H \tag{42}$$

Each of the possible orientations of the magnetic moment will then have a different energy in a magnetic field. By the use of nuclear magnetic resonance, transitions between these energy levels may be induced, and information gained about the environment of the magnetic nuclei.

The nuclear magnets precess about the direction of the magnetic field just as a spinning top precesses in the earth's gravitational field. The precession frequency ν is proportional to the magnetic field strength H, and the proportionality constant is the gyromagnetic ratio γ, divided by 2π:

$$\nu = \frac{\gamma}{2\pi} H \tag{43}$$

The gyromagnetic ratio is the ratio of the magnetic moment to the spin angular momentum of the nucleus. For protons in a magnetic field of 9400 gauss, the precession frequency is about 40 megacycles. The precession frequencies for other nuclei also fall in the radiofrequency range, as shown in Table V.

Different methods for studying nuclear magnetic resonance were developed independently by Purcell and Bloch in 1946. An experimental arrangement for studying NMR is illustrated in *Fig. 18-11*. The sample is placed in a uniform magnetic field and is surrounded by a coil from a radiofrequency transmitter so that the oscillating magnetic vector of the radiofrequency waves is perpendicular to the magnetic field. The frequency of the transmitter or the strength of the magnetic field is altered until the radiofrequency is equal to the precession frequency of the nuclei in the magnetic field. When this is the case a resonance

---

* J. D. Roberts, *Nuclear Magnetic Resonance*, McGraw-Hill Book Co., New York, 1959; J. A. Pople, W. G. Schneider, and H. J. Bernstein, *High-Resolution Nuclear Magnetic Resonance*, McGraw-Hill Book Company, New York, 1959.

Table V. Nuclear Magnetic Moments and Spins

Isotope	NMR Frequency [1]	Magnetic Moment [2]	Spin
H^1	42.57	2.79277	$\frac{1}{2}$
Li^6	6.267	0.8221	1
B^{10}	4.576	1.801	3
N^{14}	3.077	0.4037	1
F^{19}	40.07	2.628	$\frac{1}{2}$
Na^{23}	11.267	2.217	$\frac{3}{2}$
P^{31}	17.24	1.131	$\frac{1}{2}$
Free electron	28,003	-1836	$\frac{1}{2}$

[1] Frequency in megacycles for a 10,000-gauss field.
[2] In multiples of the nuclear magneton $(eh/4\pi Mc)$, where M is the mass of the proton.

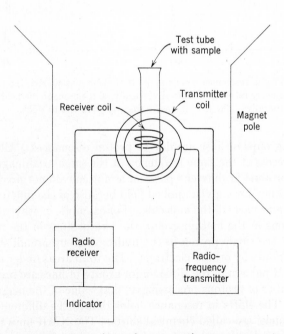

Fig. 18-11. Arrangement of a nuclear magnetic resonance spectrometer.

occurs with the result that energy is absorbed by the sample, and some of the spins are reoriented so that the nuclei are raised to higher energy states. As the nuclei return to their initial energy levels, the energy absorbed is re-emitted to the receiver coils so that a signal is obtained from the receiver.

In an NMR experiment the radiofrequency is held constant and the magnetic field strength is varied slowly through the region where resonance occurs. An example of a plot of the signal from the receiver coil versus magnetic field strength is given in *Fig. 18-12* for ethyl alcohol.

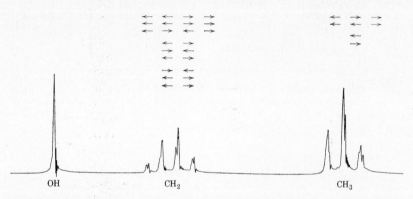

Fig. 18-12. Proton resonance spectrum of ethyl alcohol at 40 Mc. The signal from the radiofrequency receiver is plotted vertically, and the magnetic field strength is plotted horizontally. The field increases linearly from left to right.

The three groups of lines are due to proton resonances. Although all protons precess at the same frequency at the same local magnetic field strength, protons in different parts of a molecule do not precess at the same frequency for a given applied field because of the different shielding in different parts of the molecule. For example, in ethyl alcohol the three protons in the methyl group, the two protons in the methylene group, and the single proton in the hydroxyl group are all shielded to different extents by orbital electrons. The total areas under the curves in the NMR pattern of the three major groups of lines are proportional to the number of protons precessing at that value of the magnetic field strength. The shifts in resonance fields due to the different environments of nuclei are called chemical shifts. The NMR lines for a solid are much broader than those for a liquid because of direct interactions between the nuclear moments which produce widely varying local fields. In a liquid the NMR lines are much sharper because these direct interactions are averaged to zero by molecular motions.

In liquids the splitting of the NMR lines into multiplets results from the indirect interaction between chemically unlike nuclei due to coupling through the orbital electrons. Most NMR studies have been concerned with proton resonances. In the pattern for ethyl alcohol the absorption due to the methyl (CH_3) protons is split into three components because the neighboring methylene group contains two protons, each with spin $\frac{1}{2}$. Since proton-spin orientations are quantized in two directions only, the two methylene (CH_2) protons may have their spins both in one direction or both in the other or the two spins may be opposed (in either of two ways). Therefore the CH_3 protons give rise to three lines with statistical weights $1:2:1$. The three CH_3 protons can have four configurations with statistical weights $1:3:3:1$ as shown in Fig. 18-12 and the CH_2 protons therefore give rise to four lines. There is no splitting here due to the hydroxyl proton, since it is undergoing chemical exchange rapidly enough with the other protons in the medium to average out the effect. Thus important information about molecules can be obtained by radiofrequency spectroscopy from this listening post inside the atom.

Electron-Spin Resonance Spectroscopy. Electron-spin resonance is similar to nuclear magnetic resonance, but the reorientation of the magnetic moment of an unpaired electron in an externally imposed magnetic field is observed rather than the reorientation of the magnetic moment of a nucleus. It will be recalled that an electron has a spin of $\frac{1}{2}$. For the magnetic field strengths commonly used, the resonance is observed in the microwave region. Since free radicals have unpaired electrons, they may be detected and studied by electron-spin resonance. Any paramagnetic substance (p. 508) can be studied. From the width and structure of the resonance line information may be obtained about the environment of the unpaired electron. Unpaired electrons are formed in insulators and semiconductors when they are irradiated with X rays.

REFERENCES

E. R. Andrew, *Nuclear Magnetic Resonance*, Cambridge University Press, Cambridge, 1955.

B. Bak, *Elementary Introduction to Molecular Spectra*, Interscience Publishers, New York, 1954.

R. B. Barnes, R. C. Gore, V. Liddel, and V. Z. Williams, *Infrared Spectroscopy*, Reinhold Publishing Corp., New York, 1944.

W. R. Brode, *Chemical Spectroscopy*, John Wiley & Sons, New York, 1943.

A. G. Gaydon, *Dissociation Energies and Spectra of Diatomic Molecules*, Chapman and Hall, London, 1953.

G. R. Harrison, R. C. Lord, and J. R. Loofbourow, *Practical Spectroscopy*, Prentice-Hall, Englewood Cliffs, N. J., 1948.

G. Herzberg, *Atomic Spectra and Atomic Structure*, Prentice-Hall, Englewood Cliffs, N. J., 1937.

G. Herzberg, *Infrared and Raman Spectra of Polyatomic Molecules*, D. Van Nostrand Co., Princeton, N. J., 1945.

G. Herzberg, *Molecular Spectra and Molecular Structure*, D. Van Nostrand Co., Princeton, N. J., 1950.

W. Kauzmann, *Quantum Chemistry*, Academic Press, New York, 1957.

M. G. Mellon, *Analytical Absorption Spectroscopy*, John Wiley & Sons, New York, 1950.

H. W. Thompson, *Chemical Spectroscopy*, Oxford University Press, Oxford, 1938.

C. H. Townes and A. L. Schawlow, *Microwave Spectroscopy*, McGraw-Hill Book Co., New York, 1955.

A. Weissberger, *Technique of Organic Chemistry*, Vol. IX: *Chemical Applications of Spectroscopy*, ed. by W. West, Interscience Publishers, New York, 1956.

E. B. Wilson, J. C. Decius, and P. C. Cross, *Molecular Vibrations*, McGraw-Hill Book Co., New York, 1955.

PROBLEMS

1. The yellow doublet of the sodium lamp has an average wavelength of 5890 A. Calculate the energy in (a) electron volts and (b) kilocalories per mole.

Ans. (a) 2.11. (b) 48.7.

2. Most chemical reactions require activation energies ranging between 10 and 100 kcal mole^{-1}. What are the equivalents of 10 and 100 kcal mole^{-1} in terms of (a) angstroms, (b) wave numbers, (c) electron volts?

Ans. (a) 28500, 2850 A. (b) 3.50×10^3, 3.5×10^4 cm^{-1}. (c) 0.434, 4.34 ev.

3. A solution of a dye containing 1 gram per 100 ml transmits 80 per cent of the light at 4356 A in a glass cell 1 cm thick. (a) What per cent of light will be absorbed by a solution containing 2 grams per 100 ml in a cell 1 cm thick? (b) What concentration will be required to absorb 50 per cent of the light? (c) What per cent of the light will be transmitted by a solution of the dye containing 1 gram per 100 ml in a cell 5 cm thick? (d) What thickness should the cell be in order to absorb 90 per cent of the light with solution of this concentration?

Ans. (a) 36.0%. (b) 3.10 g/100 ml. (c) 32.7%. (d) 10.3 cm.

4. The absorption coefficient α for a solid is defined by $I = I_0\,e^{-\alpha x}$, where x is the thickness of the sample. The absorption coefficients for NaCl and KBr at a wavelength of 28 μ are 14 cm^{-1} and 0.25 cm^{-1}. Calculate the percentage of this infrared radiation transmitted by 0.5-cm thicknesses of these crystals.

Ans. NaCl, 0.09%; KBr, 88.3%.

5. Calculate the zero-point energies of (a) H$_2$ and (b) Cl$_2$ in kilocalories per mole. The fundamental vibration frequencies are to be found in Table IV.

Ans. (a) 6.3, (b) 0.809 kcal mole^{-1}

6. Plot the Morse curve for H$_2$ with energy units of kilocalories per mole from the fact that the fundamental vibration frequency is 4395.2 cm^{-1}, the equilibrium internuclear distance is 0.7416×10^{-8} cm, and the dissociation energy is 4.476 ev.

Ans. See Fig. 18-7.

7. According to the hypothesis of Franck, the molecules of the halogens dissociate into one normal atom and one excited atom. The wavelength of the convergence limit in the spectrum of iodine is 4995 A. (*a*) What is the energy of dissociation of iodine into one normal and one excited atom? (*b*) The lowest excitation energy of the iodine atom is 0.94 ev. What is the energy corresponding to this excitation? (*c*) Compute the heat of dissociation of the iodine molecule into two normal atoms, and compare it with the value obtained from thermochemical data, 34.5 kcal mole^{-1}. *Ans.* (*a*) 57.22, (*b*) 21.67, (*c*) 35.55 kcal mole^{-1}.

8. The fundamental vibration frequency of Br_2 given in Table IV does not appear in the simple infrared absorption spectrum because the molecule does not have a dipole moment. Calculate the energy difference between the ground and first vibrational levels in (*a*) ergs per molecule, (*b*) kilocalories per mole, and (*c*) electron volts. *Ans.* (*a*) 6.41×10^{-4} erg per molecule.

(*b*) 0.924 kcal mole^{-1}. (*c*) 4.00×10^{-2} ev.

9. (*a*) Calculate the wavelength in microns which corresponds with the fundamental vibration frequency of CO. The necessary data are in Table IV. What wavelengths correspond with the (*b*) first and (*c*) second harmonics of the fundamental vibration frequency? *Ans.* (*a*) 4.61, (*b*) 2.305, (*c*) 1.54μ.

10. Calculate (*a*) the reduced mass and (*b*) the moment of inertia for gaseous $NaCl^{35}$, which has a mean internuclear distance of 2.36 A.

Ans. (*a*) 2.31×10^{-23} g. (*b*) 12.9×10^{-39} g cm^2.

11. The moment of inertia of $C^{12}O^{16}$ is 18.75×10^{-40} g cm^2. Calculate the frequencies in wave numbers and the wavelengths in centimeters for the first four lines in the pure rotational spectrum. *Ans.* 2.98, 5.96, 8.94, 11.92 cm^{-1};

0.335, 0.167, 0.1118, 0.0839 cm.

12. Calculate the wavelengths in (*a*) wave numbers and (*b*) microns of the center two lines in the vibration-rotation spectrum of HBr for the fundamental vibration. The necessary data are to be found in Table IV.

Ans. (*a*) 2632.8, 2666.6 cm^{-1}. (*b*) 3.80, 3.76 μ.

13. The fundamental vibration frequency of HCl^{35} is 8.667×10^{13} sec^{-1}. What would be the separation in angstroms between the infrared absorption lines for HCl^{35} and HCl^{37} if the force constants of the bonds are assumed to be the same?

Ans. 10 A.

14. When CCl_4 is irradiated with the 4358 A mercury line, Raman lines are obtained at 4399, 4418, 4446, and 4507 A. Calculate the Raman frequencies of CCl_4 (expressed in wave numbers). Also calculate the wavelengths (expressed in microns) in the infrared at which absorption might be expected. In order to calculate the Raman frequencies accurately with a slide rule the equation must be rearranged as follows:

$$\bar{\nu}_{Raman} = \frac{\nu_{incid} - \nu_{scatt}}{c} = \left(\frac{1}{\lambda_{incid}} - \frac{1}{\lambda_{scatt}} \right)$$

$$= \frac{(\lambda_{scatt} - \lambda_{incid})}{\lambda_{incid}\lambda_{scatt}}$$

Ans. $\bar{\nu}_{Raman}$	213	312	454	757
λ, μ	47.0	32.0	22.0	13.2

15. Frequencies measured in nuclear magnetic resonance spectra are of the order of 10 cycles $\sec^{-1}$. Calculate the corresponding energy in kilocalories per mole.

Ans. 9.54×10^{-13} kcal mole^{-1}.

16. Absorption by the fundamental vibration of the HCl molecule occurs at 3.64μ. (*a*) What is the frequency of light of this wavelength? (*b*) What is the energy? (*c*) What is the energy in terms of electron volts?

17. (*a*) How many calories per mole are equivalent in energy to 2 ev? A lead storage battery gives about 2 volts. (*b*) How many calories per mole are equivalent to 100,000 volts? X rays have energies of about 100,000 volts. (*c*) How many calories per mole are equivalent in energy to 5 million ev? Some alpha particles have energies of about 5 million ev.

18. Commercial chlorine from electrolysis contains small amounts of chlorinated organic impurities. The concentrations of impurities may be calculated from infrared absorption spectra of liquid Cl_2. Calculate the concentration of $CHCl_3$ in grams per milliliter in a sample of liquid Cl_2 if the transmittancy at $\bar{\nu} = 1216$ cm^{-1} is 45 per cent for a 5-cm cell. At this wavelength liquid Cl_2 does not absorb, and the absorbancy index for $CHCl_3$ dissolved in liquid Cl_2 is 900 ± 80 cm^{-1} $(\text{g ml}^{-1})^{-1}$.

19. In order to test the validity of Beer's law in the determination of vitamin A, solutions of known concentration were prepared and treated by a standard procedure with antimony trichloride in chloroform to produce a blue color. The per cent transmission of the incident filtered light for each concentration, expressed in micrograms per milliliter, was as follows:

Concentration, μg ml^{-1}	Transmission, %
1.0	66.8
2.0	44.7
3.0	29.2
4.0	19.9
5.0	13.3

Plot these data so as to give a straight line. A solution, when treated in the standard manner with antimony chloride, transmitted 35 per cent of the incident light in the same cell. What was the concentration of vitamin A in the solution?

20. If the error in the measurement of per cent transmission is a constant per cent transmission, it may be shown that a concentration may be measured most accurately if it is such that the per cent transmission is 36.8. Calculate the concentration of sodium fumarate solution required to give 36.8 per cent transmission if a 2-cm cell is used. The molar absorbancy index for sodium fumarate in water at $25°$ is 1.43×10^3 cm^{-1} M^{-1} at 250 mμ.

21. Calculate the zero-point energies of gaseous HCl and KCl in electron volts. The fundamental vibration frequencies are to be found in Table IV.

22. Plot the potential-energy curve for HCl, using information in Table IV.

23. The dissociation energies of $HCl(g)$, $H_2(g)$, and $Cl_2(g)$ into normal atoms have been determined spectroscopically and are 4.431, 4.776, and 2.476 ev, respectively. Calculate the enthalpy of formation of $HCl(g)$ in kilocalories per mole from these data.

24. As explained on p. 538, there is no absorption at exactly the fundamental vibration frequency of a diatomic molecule consisting of two different kinds of atoms or exactly at the first, second, etc., harmonics. However, these frequencies are the approximate centers of vibrational-rotational bands. Calculate the wavelengths in microns of the centers of these bands for HBr and HI, including first and second harmonics. The necessary data are in Table IV.

25. The internuclear distance in CO is 1.282 A. Calculate (a) the reduced mass, and (b) the moment of inertia.

26. Calculate the wavelengths in centimeters of the first four lines in the pure rotational spectrum of $NaCl^{35}$. The moment of inertia is given in problem 10.

27. Calculate the energy difference between the $J = 0$ and $J = 1$ rotational levels of Br_2 in kilocalories per mole and electron volts for comparison with the energy difference between vibrational levels given in problem 8. The internuclear distance and reduced mass are given in Table IV.

28. The fundamental vibration frequency of HCl^{35} is 8.667×10^{13} sec^{-1}. Calculate the fundamental vibration frequency of DCl^{35} on the assumption that the force constants of the bonds are the same. About what wavelength in microns will the fundamental infrared absorption of DCl^{35} be grouped? The observed value is 4.8μ.

29. Acetylene has two C—H stretching vibrations, a symmetrical one at 3374 cm^{-1}, which is active only in the Raman spectrum, and an unsymmetrical one at 3287 cm^{-1}, which is active only in the infrared.

$$\overset{\longleftarrow\;\;\longrightarrow}{H-C\equiv C-H} \qquad \overset{\longrightarrow\;\;\longrightarrow}{H-C\equiv C-H}$$

Calculate the Raman wavelengths for the symmetrical one (for the 4358 A exciting line) and the infrared wavelength for the unsymmetrical one.

30. Sketch the expected nuclear magnetic resonance spectra for the protons in n-propyl, isopropyl, and $tert$-butyl alcohols, showing the number of components in each band. (Note that only protons on adjacent carbon atoms need to be considered in predicting the splitting.)

---

31. Convert the following wavelengths to wave numbers and megacycles per second: 10 meters, 1 meter, 10 cm, and 1 cm.

32. Since it is frequently necessary to interconvert energies in the units centimeters^{-1}, electron volts, and kilocalories per mole, calculate the factors for converting (a) electron volts to centimeters^{-1}, and (b) centimeters^{-1} to kilocalories per mole.

33. For acetone vapor at $50°$ the value of k in the expression $I = I_0 e^{-kbc}$ is 6.63 for light of 3130 A, where c is expressed in moles per liter and b is in centimeters. What per cent of light will be absorbed by acetone vapor at 100 mm pressure at $50°$ when a beam of light of 3130 A is passed through a cell 15 cm long?

34. The following absorption data are obtained for solutions of oxyhemoglobin in pH 7 buffer at 575 mμ in a 1-cm cell:

Grams per 100 ml	Transmission, %
0.03	53.5
0.05	35.1
0.10	12.3

(a) Is Beer's law obeyed? What is the molar absorbancy index? (b) Calculate the per cent transmission for a solution containing 0.01 gram per 100 ml, assuming that Beer's law is obeyed.

35. Calculate the zero-point energy of CO in kilocalories per mole and the energy difference between the zero and first vibrational-energy levels in kilocalories per mole. The fundamental vibration frequency is 2170 cm^{-1}.

36. Plot the potential-energy curve for Br$_2$ with energy units of kilocalories per mole according to the Morse function, using $D' = 45.7$ kcal, $a = 1.98$, and $r_0 = 2.28$ A.

37. The limit of continuous absorption for Br$_2$ gas occurs at a wave number of 19,570 cm^{-1}. The dissociation which occurs is

$$Br_2(normal) = Br(normal) + Br(excited)$$

The transition of a normal bromine atom to an excited one corresponds to a wave number of 3685 cm^{-1}.

$$Br(normal) = Br(excited)$$

Calculate the energy increase for the process

$$Br_2(normal) = 2Br(normal)$$

in (a) ergs per molecule and (b) electron volts.

38. Calculate the energy difference between the ground and first vibrational levels for H$_2$ in (a) ergs per molecule, (b) kilocalories per mole, and (c) electron volts. The fundamental vibration frequency is given in Table IV.

39. Assuming that the internuclear distance is 0.742 A for (a) H$_2$, (b) HD, (c) HT, and (d) D$_2$, calculate the moments of inertia of these molecules. The physical atomic weights of deuterium, D, and tritium, T, are to be found on p. 678.

40. Calculate the energy difference between the $J = 0$ and $J = 1$ rotational levels for OH radicals, in kilocalories per mole. Calculate the wavelength in centimeters at which this transition will appear. The equilibrium internuclear distance and reduced mass are given in Table IV.

41. The separation of the pure rotation lines in the spectrum of CO is 3.86 cm^{-1}. Calculate the equilibrium internuclear separation.

42. Calculate the wavelengths in (a) wave numbers and (b) microns of the center four lines in the infrared spectrum of HI at the first harmonic of the fundamental vibration frequency. The necessary data are to be found in Table IV.

43. At what temperature would the population of the first ($v = 1$) vibrational level of H (fundamental vibration frequency, ν_0, is 4395 cm^{-1}) be one-half the population of the lowest ($v = 0$) vibrational level?

44. Alkenes show a Raman frequency of 1642 cm^{-1}, which is due to the C=C stretching motion. Calculate the corresponding wavelengths in the Raman spectrum if the 4358 A exciting line is used.

45. The precession frequency of a nucleus in a magnetic field is given by $\nu = 762\mu H/I$, where μ is the magnetic moment in nuclear magnetons, H is the magnetic field strength in gauss, and I is nuclear spin. Using data from Table V, calculate the magnetic field strengths at which (a) Li^6 and (b) B^{10} will precess at 5 megacycles.

46. The following table gives the wave numbers for the lines of the HCl^{35} band at $3.46\,\mu$ [C. F. Meyer and A. A. Levin, *Phys. Rev.*, *34*, 44 (1929)]. Only a few of the lines near the center of the band are included.

	J	$\bar{\nu}$
R branch	3	2963.24
	2	2944.89
	1	2925.78
	0	2906.25
P branch	1	2865.09
	2	2843.56
	3	2821.49
	4	2798.78

The wave number of a line in the vibration-rotation spectrum may be represented by $\bar{\nu} = \bar{\nu}_0 + BJ'(J' + 1) - BJ''(J'' + 1)$ when the interaction between rotation and vibration is neglected. The rotational quantum number is represented by J' in the upper state and J'' in the lower state. The R branch in the spectrum is due to transitions from $J'' = J$ to $J' = J + 1$ (that is, $\Delta J = +1$), and the P branch in the spectrum is due to transitions from $J'' = J$ to $J' = J - 1$ (that is, $\Delta J = -1$). Derive the expressions for $\bar{\nu}_R$ and $\bar{\nu}_P$ in terms of J and calculate (a) $\bar{\nu}_0$, (b) the rotational constant B, and (c) the internuclear distance. The B value obtained by extrapolation to the center of the band should be used. In an exact calculation it would be necessary to take account of the fact that the B value is different for the excited state.

STATISTICAL MECHANICS

19

As we have seen, thermodynamics deals with properties of matter without attempting an interpretation of these properties in terms of molecules. Statistical mechanics has been developed to provide an interpretation of the properties of matter in terms of the properties of molecules, atoms, ions, and electrons. Statistical mechanics provides a practical means for predicting thermodynamic properties in certain cases from information about individual molecules. For simple molecules the calculations are not very difficult, and thermodynamic properties may be calculated from the atomic weights and quantities which may be measured spectroscopically. Because of the high precision of spectroscopic measurements, thermodynamic quantities calculated in this manner are frequently more accurate than those obtained from direct calorimetric measurements.

Statistical mechanics deals with the average behavior of a large group of molecules, with a viewpoint analogous to that of an actuary studying a large population. The classical aspects of this science were developed during the latter part of the last century by Boltzmann in Germany, Maxwell in England, and Gibbs in the United States.

Classes of States. A single molecule can exist in any one of a large number of quantum states, each of which is specified by giving its quantum numbers. Similarly, we can consider a system containing many molecules as being in a certain quantum state specified by a large number of quantum numbers. A collection of identical systems, each in a definite quantum state, is referred to as an *ensemble*. Each individual system in the ensemble might, for example, contain a mole of a given type of molecules. The concept of an ensemble of systems is important, since the thermodynamic behavior of a large group of molecules can be calculated by averaging over all the systems in an ensemble.

The state of an ensemble may be described by designating the state of each system, as has been done in Table I for an ensemble consisting of three systems, 1, 2, and 3. It is assumed that each system can be in state a, b, or c. Of course, in general the number of states is not equal

Table I.   Description of the Ensemble Consisting of Three Systems Each of Which Can Be in State a, b, or c

	Systems		
Class Specified by:	1	2	3
$N_a = 1, N_b = 1, N_c = 1$	a	b	c
	b	c	a
	c	a	b
	a	c	b
	c	b	a
	b	a	c
$N_a = 2, N_b = 1, N_c = 0$	a	a	b
	a	b	a
	b	a	a
$N_a = 1, N_b = 2, N_c = 0$	a	b	b
	b	b	a
	b	a	b
$N_a = 0, N_b = 2, N_c = 1$	b	b	c
	b	c	b
	c	b	b
$N_a = 0, N_b = 1, N_c = 2$	b	c	c
	c	c	b
	c	b	c
$N_a = 2, N_b = 0, N_c = 1$	a	a	c
	a	c	a
	c	a	a
$N_a = 1, N_b = 0, N_c = 2$	a	c	c
	c	c	a
	c	a	c
$N_a = 3, N_b = 0, N_c = 0$	a	a	a
$N_a = 0, N_b = 3, N_c = 0$	b	b	b
$N_a = 0, N_b = 0, N_c = 3$	c	c	c

to the number of systems. All the possible states of the ensemble are listed in Table 1, each line in the table representing a state. The symbols N_a, N_b, and N_c represent the numbers of systems in quantum states a, b, and c.

Now it is a fundamental postulate of statistical mechanics that *all states of the ensemble of a specified total energy are equally probable.* That is, the 27 states in Table I are equally probable if they have the same total energy. If this does not seem reasonable, it should be remembered that all completely specified bridge hands are equally probable; that is, the probability of getting 13 spades is the same as that of getting any other completely specified hand.

The complete description of an ensemble, giving the quantum state of each individual system, is more than is actually required to determine the thermodynamic properties of the system. These properties, which are averages over the ensemble, depend upon the *numbers* of systems in each quantum state and not on *which* systems are in *which* state. A description of an ensemble in terms of the *numbers* N_i of systems in the ensemble which are in state i is said to define a *class of states* of the ensemble. For the ensemble we have been considering there are 10 classes of states, as shown in Table I. The first class of states (specified by $N_a = 1$, $N_b = 1$, $N_c = 1$) consists of 6 states; thus many states of the ensemble fall in the same *class of states*, and this fact would be even more pronounced if we considered a larger number of systems.

The class of states which occurs most often will make the largest contribution to the average or thermodynamic properties of the system. The detailed theory of statistical mechanics shows that in an ensemble containing many systems there is one particular *class of states* for which there are *many, many* more states than for any other. Thus only one particular class of states contributes significantly to the average, and only it is considered in calculating thermodynamic properties.

Since the thermodynamic properties are determined by the class of states, these properties may be calculated if the characteristics of this class of states can be calculated. For averaging purposes we are interested only in the number N_i of systems in the ensemble which are in a specified state i. We let W represent the number of states in a class of states. The number of states in a class can be calculated in the same way as one calculates the number of ways in which N balls can be placed in n boxes, the first containing N_1 balls, the second containing N_2 balls, etc.

$$W = \frac{N!}{N_1! N_2! \cdots N_n!} \tag{1}$$

where the total number of balls is represented by N ($N = N_1 + N_2 + \cdots + N_n$, where n is the number of boxes) and $N!$, factorial N, is $1 \cdot 2 \cdot 3 \cdots N$.

Example 1. Calculate the number W of states in the following classes of states which are described in Table I: (1) $N_a = 1$, $N_b = 1$, $N_c = 1$, (2) $N_a = 2$, $N_b = 1$, $N_c = 0$, and (3) $N_a = 3$, $N_b = 0$, $N_c = 0$.

$$W_{abc} = \frac{3!}{1!1!1!} = 6$$

$$W_{aab} = \frac{3!}{2!1!0!} = 3$$

$$W_{aaa} = \frac{3!}{3!0!0!} = 1$$

since $0! = 1$. It is seen that these numbers are in agreement with the numbers of states in the various classes shown in Table I.

The most probable class of states is specified by the set of N_i which maximize W subject to the constraints that the total number of systems is constant, $\Sigma N_i = N$, and the total energy NE is constant.

$$NE = N_1 E_1 + N_2 E_2 + N_3 E_3 + \cdots = \sum_i N_i E_i \qquad (2)$$

where E_i is the energy of one system in state i and E is the average energy per system. It can be shown * that this set is

$$N_i = \frac{N}{Z} e^{-E_i/kT} \qquad (3)$$

where

$$Z = \sum_i e^{-E_i/kT} \qquad (4)$$

and k is the Boltzmann constant (1.38×10^{-16} erg deg^{-1}).

The Partition Function for a System. This is the way in which the Boltzmann factor, $e^{-E_i/kT}$, which we have used earlier (p. 273), arises. The summation Z defined in equation 4 is so useful in statistical mechanics that it is given a special name, *the partition function*. The partition function is important because the various thermodynamic properties of a system may be expressed in terms of this function. For example, the total energy of the system NE is given by equation 2. Substi-

* M. Dole, *Introduction to Statistical Thermodynamics*, Prentice-Hall, Englewood Cliffs, N. J., 1954, p. 48.

tuting equation 3 and equation 4 into equation 2,

$$E = \frac{1}{Z} \sum_i E_i e^{-E_i/kT}$$

$$= \frac{\sum_i E_i e^{-E_i/kT}}{\sum_i e^{-E_i/kT}} \tag{5}$$

It can be shown that this may be expressed as

$$E = kT^2 \frac{\partial \ln Z}{\partial T} \tag{6}$$

The expression for the heat capacity may be obtained by differentiating equation 6, since $C_V = (\partial E/\partial T)_V$.

$$C_V = \frac{\partial}{\partial T}\left(kT^2 \frac{\partial \ln Z}{\partial T}\right)_V = \frac{k}{T^2}\left[\frac{\partial^2 \ln Z}{\partial(1/T)^2}\right]_V \tag{7}$$

Entropy and Probability. From thermodynamics we know that the equilibrium state of an isolated system is the one of maximum entropy. According to statistical mechanics, an isolated system goes to a state of maximum probability. Since the probability and entropy both have their maximum values at equilibrium, it is reasonable to expect a relationship between entropy and probability. It turns out that the entropy is proportional to the logarithm of W, the number of states in a class of states.

$$S = \frac{k}{N} \ln W \tag{8}$$

where k is the Boltzmann constant. The greatest degree of order is represented by a perfect crystal at absolute zero; the thermodynamic probability of such a state is unity and the entropy is zero. This is the statistical mechanical explanation of the third law of thermodynamics. For a discussion of the third law and exceptions, see p. 96.

Equation 8 is consistent with the idea that, when two identical systems are combined, the entropy is twice that of either system. However, the number of states in the combined system is equal to the square of the number of states in each system, since each state of the first system can be combined with any of the states of the second system to form a state of the total system.

According to the molecular point of view, the second law of thermodynamics is a statistical law. Spontaneous changes occur because the final system is in a more probable state than the initial system. Thus gases diffuse into each other when the stopcock between the containing vessels is opened because at any later time the mixed condition is more probable than the unmixed condition. The original unmixed condition is not impossible and might actually occur at a later time, but when the number of molecules is large the probability that the system will return to its initial unmixed condition is so small that it has never been observed. In Brownian motion, where only a few particles are observed with an ultramicroscope, it is sometimes found that the tiny particles move from the region of low concentration to the region of higher concentration, but thermodynamics is concerned only with the behavior of large numbers of molecules, where the probability of a change contrary to the second law of thermodynamics is negligible.

The expression for the entropy in terms of the partition function may be obtained by substituting equation 1 into equation 8, substituting equation 3 for N_i, and rearranging.

Since N is a large number, equation 1 may be rewritten by introducing Stirling's approximation for a factorial

$$\ln N! = N \ln N - N \tag{9}$$

Taking the logarithms of both sides of equation 1 and substituting equation 9 yields

$$\ln W = N \ln N - N - \sum_i N_i \ln N_i + \sum_i N_i$$

$$= N \ln N - \sum_i N_i \ln N_i \tag{10}$$

since $\sum_i N_i = N$.

Substituting equation 10 into equation 8,

$$NS = kN \ln N - k \sum_i N_i \ln N_i \tag{11}$$

Introducing the Boltzmann equation (equation 3),

$$NS = kN \ln N - k \sum_i \left[\frac{N}{Z} e^{-E_i/kT} \ln \left(\frac{N}{Z} e^{-E_i/kT} \right) \right] \tag{12}$$

$$= kN \ln N - \frac{kN}{Z} \sum_i e^{-E_i/kT} \left(\ln N - \ln Z - \frac{E_i}{kT} \right)$$

$$= kN \ln N - kN (\ln N - \ln Z) + \frac{kN}{Z} \sum_i \frac{E_i}{kT} e^{-E_i/kT} \tag{13}$$

Introducing equation 5,

$$S = k \ln Z + \frac{E}{T} \tag{14}$$

This is a general result which permits the entropy to be calculated from the partition function. Since all the other thermodynamic functions can be expressed in terms of the internal energy and entropy, they may now be given in terms of the partition function. For example, the Helmholtz free energy $A = E - TS$ and so $A = -kT \ln Z$.

The expression for the internal energy given by equation 6 and the expression for the entropy given by equation 14 in terms of the partition function Z for the system are completely general and may be used in the study of gases, liquids, or solids, consisting of either pure substances or mixtures. The treatment of ideal gases is straightforward and will now be considered in detail.

The partition function of simple crystals can also be evaluated, and the results lead to the Debye theory of solids (p. 53). The evaluation of the partition function for dense gases or liquids is considerably more difficult and is one of the present frontiers of research.

The Partition Function of an Ideal Gas. The above equations have applied to any system, but now we will consider ideal gas molecules. The energy of a collection of ideal gas molecules is simply the sum of the energies of the individual molecules, there being no intermolecular interactions. The total energy ϵ_i' of one molecule in quantum state i may be written as

$$\epsilon_i' = \epsilon_0 + \epsilon_i \tag{15}$$

where ϵ_0 is the energy of the ground state, and ϵ_i is the energy measured above the ground state. If the molecules could be distinguished from each other, the partition function for a mole of gas molecules would be

$$Z = \left(\sum_i e^{\epsilon_i'/kT} \right)^{N_0} = e^{-N_0\epsilon_0/kT} Q^{N_0} \tag{16}$$

where N_0 is Avogadro's number and

$$Q = \sum_i e^{-\epsilon_i/kT} \tag{17}$$

is the partition function for a molecule. However, since identical molecules are indistinguishable, too many terms by the factor $N_0!$ have been included in this sum. If the energy levels are closely spaced, a good approximation to the correct partition function is obtained by dividing by $N_0!$ Thus

$$Z = \frac{Q^{N_0}}{N_0!} e^{-N_0\epsilon_0/kT} \tag{18}$$

Deviations from this result are discussed on p. 570.

The difference between the partition function Z for a system and the partition function Q for a molecule is that the former is written in terms of the energies of the states of the system, and the latter in terms of the energy of a molecule measured above the ground state.

Expressions for the Thermodynamic Properties of Ideal Gases. Substituting equation 18 into equation 6 yields the internal energy $\bar{E}$ of a mole of ideal gas.

$$\bar{E} = kT^2 \left[\frac{N_0\epsilon_0}{kT^2} + N_0 \frac{\partial \ln Q}{\partial T} \right]$$

$$\bar{E} - \bar{E}_0 = N_0 kT^2 \frac{\partial \ln Q}{\partial T} = RT^2 \frac{\partial \ln Q}{\partial T} \tag{19}$$

where $\bar{E}_0 = N_0\epsilon_0$ is the energy of Avogadro's number of molecules in the ground state.

Substituting equation 18 into equation 14 and rearranging yields the entropy of a mole of ideal gas:

$$\bar{S} = N_0 k \ln (Q/N_0) + (\bar{E} - \bar{E}_0)/T + N_0 k$$

$$= R \ln (Q/N_0) + (\bar{E} - \bar{E}_0)/T + R \tag{20}$$

Since all the molar thermodynamic functions may be expressed in terms of $\bar{S}$ and $\bar{E}$, they may also now be expressed in terms of the partition function Q for a molecule.

Since the molar Helmholtz free energy $\bar{A} = \bar{E} - T\bar{S}$,

$$\bar{A} - \bar{A}_0 = (\bar{E} - \bar{E}_0) - T\bar{S}$$

$$= -RT [\ln (Q/N_0) + 1] \tag{21}$$

where $\bar{A}_0$ and $\bar{E}_0$ are the Helmholtz free energy and internal energy in the ground state.

Since $\bar{H} = \bar{E} + P\bar{V}$, the expression for an ideal gas is given by

$$\bar{H} - \bar{H}_0 = \bar{E} - \bar{E}_0 + RT$$

$$= RT^2 \frac{\partial \ln Q}{\partial T} + RT \tag{22}$$

The free-energy function (p. 220) is given by an especially simple equation.

$$\frac{\bar{G}^\circ - \bar{H}_0}{T} = \frac{\bar{H} - \bar{H}_0}{T} - \bar{S}^\circ$$

$$= -R \ln \frac{Q}{N_0} \tag{23}$$

Evaluation of the Molecular Partition Function. As discussed in Chapter 18 on spectroscopy, a molecule has various types of energy: translational, rotational, vibrational, and electronic. To a fairly high degree of approximation it may be considered that the total energy of a molecule in a particular state is the sum of these various types of energy:

$$\epsilon = \epsilon_{tr} + \epsilon_{rot} + \epsilon_{vib} + \epsilon_{el} \tag{24}$$

In general the rotational- and vibrational-energy level schemes depend upon the electronic state. However, at normal temperatures only the ground electronic state or a group of electronic states with nearly the same energy need be considered. Substituting equation 24 into equation 17 and using $e^{a+b+c} = e^a e^b e^c$, we obtain

$$Q = \Sigma e^{-\epsilon_{tr}/kT} \Sigma e^{-\epsilon_{rot}/kT} \Sigma e^{-\epsilon_{vib}/kT} \Sigma e^{-\epsilon_{el}/kT} \tag{25}$$

or

$$Q = Q_{tr}Q_{rot}Q_{vib}Q_{el} \tag{26}$$

where

$$Q_{tr} = \Sigma e^{-\epsilon_{tr}/kT} \tag{27}$$

etc. Thus the partition function for a molecule is the product of the partition functions for the various types of energy. The thermodynamic functions themselves involve the logarithm of the partition function and may, therefore, be broken up into sums; for example, the molar enthalpy relative to the molar enthalpy at absolute zero may be written

$$(\bar{H} - \bar{H}_0) = (\bar{H} - \bar{H}_0)_{tr} + (\bar{H} - \bar{H}_0)_{rot} + (\bar{H} - \bar{H}_0)_{vib} + (\bar{H} - \bar{H}_0)_{el} \tag{28}$$

The Translational Partition Function. In Chapter 16 on quantum mechanics it is shown that the translational-energy levels for a particle in a one-dimensional box are given by

$$\epsilon_{tr} = \frac{n_x^2 h^2}{8ml^2} \tag{29}$$

where n_x is the quantum number, h is Planck's constant, m is the mass of the particle, and l is the length of the box. The translational partition function for a particle in a one-dimensional box is therefore obtained by substituting equation 29 into equation 27.

$$Q_{tr} = \Sigma e^{-n_x^2 h^2/8ml^2 kT} \tag{30}$$

Since the energy levels are so closely packed, they may be considered to be continuous and the summation may be replaced by an integration

$$Q_{tr} = \int_0^\infty e^{-n_x^2 h^2/8ml^2 kT} \, dn_x = \frac{(2\pi mkT)^{1/2} l}{h} \tag{31}$$

where the last form is obtained utilizing the definite integral given in the Appendix in equation 46:

$$\int_0^\infty e^{-x^2} \, dx = \sqrt{\frac{\pi}{2}} \tag{32}$$

The partition function for a particle in a cubic three-dimensional box is obtained by cubing equation 31:

$$Q_{tr} = \frac{(2\pi mkT)^{3/2} V}{h^3} \tag{33}$$

where $V = l^3$. If electronic excitation may be ignored, this is the only contribution to the partition function of an ideal monatomic gas.

Derivation of the Ideal Gas Law by Statistical Mechanics. Since

$$P = -\left(\frac{\partial \bar{A}}{\partial \bar{V}}\right)_T \tag{34}$$

differentiating equation 21 yields

$$P = RT \left(\frac{\partial \ln Q}{\partial \bar{V}}\right)_T \tag{35}$$

Since the internal-energy levels do not depend upon the volume of the container, only the translational contribution to the partition function needs to be considered. Taking the logarithm of equation 33 and differentiating with respect to volume at constant temperature yields

$$\left(\frac{\partial \ln Q}{\partial \bar{V}}\right)_T = \frac{1}{\bar{V}} \tag{36}$$

Substituting equation 36 into equation 35,

$$P = \frac{RT}{V} \tag{37}$$

The ideal gas equation has already been derived from kinetic theory (p. 279), and the above derivation represents still another way. The equations of state of nonideal gases may also be derived by the methods of statistical mechanics.*

The Rotational Partition Function for a Diatomic Molecule. The expression for the energy of a rigid diatomic rotator derived from the Schrödinger equation has already been discussed:

$$\epsilon_{rot} = \frac{J(J+1)h^2}{8\pi^2 I} \tag{38}$$

Here J is the rotational quantum number, and I is the moment of inertia (p. 528) of the diatomic molecule. It is assumed that the molecules are rigid and that the moment of inertia is independent of the vibrational and rotational energies. Although the energy depends only upon J, the state of a rigid rotator is specified by the quantum number J and an additional quantum number M, where M can have integer values between $-J$ and $+J$. Thus there are $2J + 1$ values of M for each value of J. The rotational partition function is thus

$$Q_{rot} = \Sigma (2J + 1)e^{-J(J+1)h^2/8\pi^2 IkT} \tag{39}$$

Since the energy levels are ordinarily so close together that they may be considered to be continuous, the summation may be replaced by an integration:

$$Q_{rot} = \frac{-8\pi^2 IkT}{h^2} \int_0^\infty (2J + 1)e^{-J(J+1)h^2/8\pi^2 IkT}\, dJ$$

Since $(2J + 1)\, dJ$ is the differential of $J(J + 1) = J^2 + J$, this equation is readily integrated to obtain

$$Q_{rot} = \frac{8\pi^2 IkT}{h^2} \tag{40}$$

If the two atoms in the diatomic molecule are identical, twice too many terms have been included in the summation, and to a good approxima-

* J. O. Hirschfelder, C. F. Curtiss, and R. B. Bird, *The Molecular Theory of Gases and Liquids*, John Wiley & Sons, New York, 1954.

tion the correct result is obtained by dividing by 2. In general

$$Q_{rot} = \frac{8\pi^2 IkT}{\sigma h^2} \tag{41}$$

where the symmetry number σ is 2 if the two atoms in the molecule are identical and is 1 if they are different.

The Vibrational Partition Function of a Diatomic Molecule. The vibrational energy of a diatomic molecule may be written

$$\epsilon_{vib} = vh\nu \tag{42}$$

where v is the vibrational quantum number. Here energy is measured above the ground state rather than above the minimum in the potential-energy curve, as it was in Chapter 18, where the corresponding equation was written $\epsilon_{vib} = (v + \frac{1}{2})h\nu$. The vibrational partition function is

$$Q_{vib} = 1 + e^{-h\nu/kT} + e^{-2h\nu/kT} + e^{-3h\nu/kT} + \cdots \tag{43}$$

When $x < 1$,

$$1 + x + x^2 + x^3 + \cdots = \frac{1}{1-x} \tag{44}$$

Since $e^{-h\nu/kT} < 1$,

$$Q_{vib} = \frac{1}{1 - e^{-h\nu/kT}} \tag{45}$$

Equations similar to those derived above for diatomic molecules may be derived for polyatomic molecules. The equations are more complicated because polyatomic molecules have larger numbers of degrees of freedom.

The Electronic Partition Function. In the electronic partition function Q_{el}, the summation must be carried out numerically. In the neighborhood of room temperature most molecules are mainly in the ground electronic state. Since the first excited electronic state often lies about 100 kcal mole^{-1} above the ground state, the temperature must be very high before there is a significant fraction of the molecules in the electronically excited state. Thus for most molecules the electronic partition function is either unity or an integer representing the number of states having the energy of the ground state.

Heat Capacity of Gases. The heat capacities of gases were discussed earlier from a classical viewpoint (p. 281). The contribution of translational motion to $\bar{C}_V$ is readily calculated from statistical mechanics by substituting equation 33 into equation 19.

Since $(\partial \ln Q_{tr}/\partial T)_V = \frac{3}{2}T$,

$$\bar{E} - \bar{E}_0 = \tfrac{3}{2}RT \tag{46}$$

Differentiating with respect to temperature at constant volume,

$$\bar{C}_{V,tr} = \left(\frac{\partial \bar{E}}{\partial T}\right)_V = \tfrac{3}{2}R = 2.98 \text{ cal deg}^{-1} \text{ mole}^{-1} \tag{47}$$

as shown earlier. The rotational contribution is obtained by substituting equation 39 into equation 19. Since $(\partial \ln Q_{rot}/\partial T)_V = 1/T$,

$$\bar{E}_{rot} - \bar{E}_0 = RT \tag{48}$$

Differentiating with respect to temperature at constant volume,

$$\bar{C}_{V,rot} = R \tag{49}$$

The rotational contribution to the heat capacity of a diatomic molecule was accounted for in classical terms on p. 282 by saying that there are two degrees of rotational freedom, each contributing $R/2$ cal deg^{-1} mole^{-1}.

The vibrational contribution to the heat capacity is obtained by substituting equation 40 into equation 19:

$$\bar{E}_{vib} - \bar{E}_0 = RT^2 \frac{\partial \ln Q_{vib}}{\partial T} \tag{50}$$

Differentiating with respect to T to obtain the contribution to $\bar{C}_V$,

$$\bar{C}_{V,vib} = \frac{R(h\nu/kT)^2 e^{-h/kT}}{(1 - e^{-h\nu/kT})^2} \tag{51}$$

At sufficiently low temperatures there is no contribution of the vibration to $\bar{C}_V$. Classical mechanics does not explain why the vibrational degree of freedom makes no contribution to $\bar{C}_V$ for most gases at room temperature but does contribute at higher temperatures and causes $\bar{C}_V$ to rise gradually as the temperature is raised. This is accounted for by the quantum-mechanical expression given in equation 51. The dependence of the heat capacity of hydrogen on absolute temperature is shown in *Fig. 19-1*.

Heat Capacity of Solids. As shown on p. 52, the heat capacities of solid elements at constant volume are about 6 cal deg^{-1} mole^{-1} at room temperature, as discovered by Dulong and Petit.

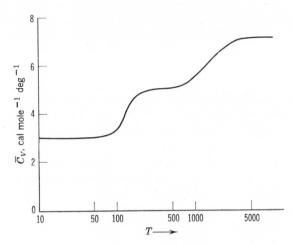

Fig. 19-1. Dependence of $\bar{C}_V$ for hydrogen on temperature. The temperature axis is on a logarithmic scale.

Boltzmann showed that this value for $\bar{C}_V$ for an atomic solid is in accord with the expectation that the atoms would have $\frac{3}{2}RT$ of kinetic energy, as do the molecules of an ideal monatomic gas, and, in addition, $\frac{3}{2}RT$ of potential energy, since the approximately simple harmonic motion of the atoms about their equilibrium positions has three degrees of freedom. Thus the total energy would be $\frac{6}{2}RT$ and $\bar{C}_V$ would be $3R$.

However, classical physics cannot account for the decrease in heat capacity of a solid which occurs when the temperature is reduced. The explanation comes from a consideration of the oscillation of the atoms, ions, or molecules of the crystal in terms of quantum mechanics.

In statistical mechanical terms a crystal is considered to be one big molecule with a large number of normal modes of vibration. The contribution of each normal mode to the heat capacity is calculated using the partition function.

Einstein made a quantitative treatment of the heat capacity of a solid by assuming that all the oscillators had the same vibration frequency. The theory was improved by Debye, who assumed a continuous frequency spectrum with an upper limit corresponding to a wavelength of the order of the distance between atoms in the lattice. The equation derived by Debye, which shows that the heat capacity at low temperatures is proportional to T^3, has already been given (p. 53). In solids with strong interatomic forces, like the diamond, the frequency spectrum of the lattice vibrations extends to higher frequencies, and these higher frequencies are not completely exited even at room temperature. Therefore the heat capacity at room temperature is less than 6 cal deg^{-1} mole^{-1}. In solids with weak interatomic forces the lattice vibrations have low frequencies which are fully excited below room temperature.

Calculation of Thermodynamic Properties. The expressions for the partition functions given earlier may be substituted into the relations between the thermodynamic properties and the partition functions. This has been done to obtain the equations in Table II for monatomic and diatomic molecules. The numerical factors have been evaluated so as to facilitate calculations. For polyatomic molecules which are not too complicated, similar equations may be derived. By use of these equations the thermodynamic properties of ideal gases may readily be calculated.

Table II.[1] Equations for Calculating the Translational, Rotational, and Vibrational Contributions to the Molar Thermodynamic Functions for Monatomic and Diatomic Molecules in the Ideal Gas State at 1 Atm Pressure

(Functions in cal deg^{-1} mole^{-1})

(a) Translational

$$(\bar{C}_P)_{\mathrm{tr}} = [(\bar{H} - \bar{H}_0)/T]_{\mathrm{tr}} = 4.9680$$
$$-[(\bar{G}^\circ - \bar{H}_0)/T]_{\mathrm{tr}} = 6.8635 \log M + 11.4392 \log T - 7.2820$$

(b) Rotational

$$(\bar{C}_P)_{\mathrm{rot}} = [(\bar{H} - \bar{H}_0)/T]_{\mathrm{rot}} = 1.9872$$
$$-[(\bar{G}^\circ - \bar{H}_0)/T]_{\mathrm{rot}} = 4.5757 \log (I \times 10^{39}) + 4.5757 \log T$$
$$- 4.5757 \log \sigma - 2.7676$$

(c) Vibrational

$$(\bar{C}_P)_{\mathrm{vib}} = \frac{1.9872x^2e^x}{(e^x - 1)^2}$$
$$[(\bar{H} - \bar{H}_0)/T]_{\mathrm{vib}} = 1.9872x/(e^x - 1)$$
$$-[(\bar{G}^\circ - \bar{H}_0)/T]_{\mathrm{vib}} = -1.9872 \ln (1 - e^{-x})$$

where $x = \bar{\nu}hc/kT$ with $\bar{\nu}$ the fundamental vibrational frequency in wave numbers, M is the molecular weight on the physical scale, and σ is the symmetry number, which is 2 if the two atoms in the molecule are identical and 1 if they are different.

---

[1] G. J. Janz, *Estimation of Thermodynamic Properties of Organic Compounds*, Academic Press, New York, 1958.

The entropy may be calculated from the enthalpy and free-energy functions, using

$$\bar{S}^\circ = \left(\frac{\bar{H} - \bar{H}_0}{T}\right) - \left(\frac{\bar{G}^\circ - \bar{H}_0}{T}\right) \tag{52}$$

where $(\bar{H} - \bar{H}_0)/T$ is referred to as the enthalpy function.

Example 2. Calculate the enthalpy function, the free-energy function, and the entropy for Cl^{35} atoms at 25° and 1 atm. There are no rotational or vibrational contributions, and so, according to Table II,

$$[(\bar{H} - \bar{H}_0)/T]_{tr} = 4.9680 \text{ cal deg}^{-1} \text{mole}^{-1}$$

$$-[(\bar{G}^\circ - \bar{H}_0)/T]_{tr} = 6.8635 \log 34.9802 + 11.4392 \log 298.2 - 7.2820$$

$$= 31.6 \text{ cal deg}^{-1} \text{mole}^{-1}$$

$$\bar{S}^\circ = \left(\frac{\bar{H} - \bar{H}_0}{T}\right) - \left(\frac{\bar{G}^\circ - \bar{H}_0}{T}\right) = 36.5 \text{ cal deg}^{-1} \text{mole}^{-1}$$

As may be seen by comparison of the value of the free-energy function on p. 220 (34.44 cal deg^{-1} mole^{-1}) and the entropy on p. 99 (39.45 cal deg^{-1} mole^{-1}), there are small electronic contributions which were neglected in the above calculation. The thermodynamic functions for Cl^{37} are only slightly different.

Example 3. Calculate the heat capacity at constant pressure, the free-energy function, the enthalpy function, and the entropy for Cl_2^{35} at 25° and 1 atm. The equilibrium internuclear distance is 1.988 A, the reduced mass is 17.4894, and the fundamental vibrational frequency is 564.9 cm^{-1}.

(a) Translational:

$$(\bar{C}_P)_{tr} = [(\bar{H} - \bar{H}_0)/T]_{tr} = 4.9680 \text{ cal deg}^{-1} \text{mole}^{-1}$$

$$-[(\bar{G}^\circ - \bar{H}_0)/T]_{tr} = 6.8635 \log (2)(34.9802) + 11.4392 \log (298.2) - 7.282$$

$$= 33.7 \text{ cal deg}^{-1} \text{mole}^{-1}$$

(b) Rotational: The moment of inertia I is equal to the product of the reduced mass μ and the square of the equilibrium internuclear distance r_e.

$$I = \mu r_e^2 = (17.4894)(1.988 \times 10^{-8})^2/(6.023 \times 10^{23}) = 11.46 \times 10^{-39} \text{ g cm}^2$$

$$(\bar{C}_P)_{rot} = [(\bar{H} - \bar{H}_0)/T]_{rot} = 1.9872 \text{ cal deg}^{-1} \text{mole}^{-1}$$

$$-[(\bar{G}^\circ - \bar{H}_0)/T]_{rot} = 4.575 \log 11.46 + 4.575 \log 298.2 - 4.5757 \log 2 - 2.7676$$

$$= 12.03 \text{ cal deg}^{-1} \text{mole}^{-1}$$

(c) Vibrational:

$$x = \bar{\nu}hc/kT = (564.9)(6.62 \times 10^{-27})(3 \times 10^{10})/(1.38 \times 10^{-16})(298)$$

$$= 2.74$$

$$(\bar{C}_P)_{vib} = 1.987x^2e^x/(e^x - 1)^2$$

$$= (1.987)(0.5540) = 1.10 \text{ cal deg}^{-1} \text{mole}^{-1}$$

$$[(\bar{H} - \bar{H}_0)/T]_{vib} = (1.9872)(0.18914) = 0.376 \text{ cal deg}^{-1} \text{mole}^{-1}$$

$$-[(\bar{G}^\circ - \bar{H}_0)/T]_{vib} = (1.9872)(0.066749) = 0.1327 \text{ cal deg}^{-1} \text{mole}^{-1}$$

(d) Total thermodynamic functions:

$$\bar{C}_P = 8.04 \text{ cal deg}^{-1} \text{ mole}^{-1} \quad (\text{cf. } 8.25 \text{ cal deg}^{-1} \text{ mole}^{-1} \text{ on p. 51})$$

$$(\bar{H} - \bar{H}_0)/T = 7.331 \text{ cal deg}^{-1} \text{ mole}^{-1}$$

$$-(\bar{G}^\circ - \bar{H}_0)/T = 45.2 \text{ cal deg}^{-1} \text{ mole}^{-1}$$

$$(\text{cf. } 45.95 \text{ cal deg}^{-1} \text{ mole}^{-1} \text{ on p. 222})$$

$$\bar{S}^\circ = \left(\frac{\bar{H} - \bar{H}_0}{T}\right) - \left(\frac{\bar{G}^\circ - \bar{H}_0}{T}\right) = 7.331 + 45.2 = 52.5 \text{ cal deg}^{-1} \text{ mole}^{-1}$$

$$(\text{cf. } 53.286 \text{ cal deg}^{-1} \text{ mole}^{-1} \text{ on p. 99})$$

Example 4. Calculate the free-energy function for HCl^{35} at $25°$ and 1 atm pressure. $N_0\mu = 0.979889$, $\bar{\nu} = 2989.74 \text{ cm}^{-1}$, and $r_e = 1.2746$ A. The electronic contributions are negligible.

(a) Translational:

$$-[(\bar{G}^\circ - \bar{H}_0)/T]_{\text{tr}} = 6.8635 \log 35.99 + 11.4392 \log 298.15 - 7.2820$$

$$= 31.4 \text{ cal deg}^{-1} \text{ mole}^{-1}$$

(b) Rotational: The symmetry number σ is unity.

$$I = (0.979889)(1.2746 \times 10^{-8})^2/6.02 \times 10^{23} = 2.65 \times 10^{-40} \text{ g cm}^2$$

$$-[(\bar{G}^\circ - \bar{H}_0)/T]_{\text{rot}} = 4.5757 \log 0.265 + 4.5757 \log 298.15 - 2.7676$$

$$= 6.26 \text{ cal deg}^{-1} \text{ mole}^{-1}$$

The vibrational frequency is so high that the vibrational contribution to the free-energy function is negligible. Therefore, the total free-energy function for HCl^{35} is 37.7 cal deg^{-1} mole^{-1}. When similar calculations are carried out for HCl^{37} and a weighted average of the results is taken based on the isotopic ratio, the free-energy function for naturally occurring HCl is 37.73 cal deg^{-1} mole^{-1} (p. 222).

The calculation of thermodynamic properties from other data is a goal that was long sought. The excellent agreement with experimental data amply confirms the basic theory. In fact, many thermodynamic properties of gases may be calculated more accurately from spectroscopic data than they may be measured calorimetrically. Much of the free-energy function data in Table V in Chapter 9 for use in calculating equilibrium constants has been calculated from spectroscopic data as described above.

Other Kinds of Statistics. When Boltzmann statistics discussed above are applied to an electron gas, a number of discrepancies between theory and experiment are found. For example, the heat capacities of metals would be expected to be greater than those of nonmetals if electrons obeyed Boltzmann statistics. Metals are good conductors because they contain electrons which may be considered to form an electron gas within the metal. The electron gas would be expected to contribute

$\frac{3}{2}R$ per mole to the heat capacity, so that the heat capacity of a metal would be expected to be $3R + \frac{3}{2}R = 9$ cal $\deg^{-1}$ mole^{-1} rather than 6 cal $\deg^{-1}$ mole^{-1}. Also, the photoelectric thresholds of metals would not be expected to be as sharp as they actually are if the electrons in the metal had a Maxwellian distribution of velocity. These discrepancies are due to the approximations arising from the introduction of $N_0!$ in the partition function in equation 18. Fermi and Dirac derived the distribution function for particles like electrons which obey the Pauli exclusion principle. By a more accurate treatment of the effect of the identity of the particles they showed that the number of molecules in a level i is given by

$$N_i = \frac{A}{Be^{\epsilon_i/kT} + 1} \tag{53}$$

where A and B are constants.

Particles, like photons, which have a spin of unity obey the Bose-Einstein distribution equation

$$N_i = \frac{A}{Be^{\epsilon_i/kT} - 1} \tag{54}$$

It can be seen that, when the factor $e^{\epsilon_i/kT}$ is very large, each of these distribution functions reduces to the Boltzmann equation.

REFERENCES

J. G. Aston and J. J. Fritz, *Thermodynamics and Statistical Thermodynamics*, John Wiley & Sons, New York, 1959.

M. Dole, *Introduction to Statistical Thermodynamics*, Prentice-Hall, Englewood Cliffs, N. J., 1954.

R. H. Fowler and E. A. Guggenheim, *Statistical Thermodynamics*, Cambridge University Press, Cambridge, 1939.

T. L. Hill, *An Introduction to Statistical Mechanics*, Addison-Wesley Publishing Co., Reading, Mass., 1960.

G. J. Janz, *Estimation of Thermodynamic Properties of Organic Compounds*, Academic Press, New York, 1958.

J. E. Mayer and M. G. Mayer, *Statistical Mechanics*, John Wiley & Sons, New York, 1940.

G. S. Rushbrooke, *Introduction to Statistical Mechanics*, Oxford University Press, Oxford, 1949.

PROBLEMS

1. Using the Boltzmann equation, calculate the ratio of populations at $25°$ of energy levels separated by (a) 2 kcal mole^{-1}, (b) 100 kcal mole^{-1}.

Ans. (a) 0.0337. (b) 3 $\times$ 10^{-74}.

2. (a) In how many different ways can two distinguishable balls be placed in two boxes? (b) In how many different ways can two distinguishable balls be placed in three boxes? (c) What are the answers to (a) and (b) if the balls are indistinguishable? *Ans.* (a) 4. (b) 9. (c) 3, 6.

3. Calculate $(\bar{H} - \bar{H}_0)/T$, the free-energy function, and the entropy of neon at $25°$ and 1 atm. *Ans.* 4.9680, -29.9790, 34.9470 cal deg^{-1} mole^{-1}.

4. Calculate $(\bar{H} - \bar{H}_0)/T$, the free-energy function, and the entropy of nitrogen gas at $25°$ and 1 atm pressure. The equilibrium separation of atoms is 1.094 A, and the vibrational wave number is 2330.7 cm^{-1}.

Ans. 6.9555, -38.7934, 45.7489 cal deg^{-1} mole^{-1}.

---

5. Calculate the ratio of populations at $25°$ of energy levels separated by (a) 1 ev and (b) 10 ev. (c) Calculate the ratios at $1000°$.

6. (a) In how many different ways can three distinguishable balls be placed in two boxes? (b) How many different ways are there if the balls are indistinguishable?

7. Calculate $(\bar{H} - \bar{H}_0)/T$, the free-energy function, and the entropy of hydrogen atoms at $25°$ and 1 atm.

8. Calculate $(\bar{H} - \bar{H}_0)/T$, the free-energy function, and the entropy of hydrogen gas at $25°$ and 1 atm. Table IV in Chapter 18 gives the values of μ, $\bar{\nu}_0$, and r_e.

9. Calculate the equilibrium constant at $25°$ for the reaction 2HD = H$_2$ + D$_2$. In addition to the data referred to in problem 8, it may be assumed that the force constant k is the same for all three molecular species, so that the additional vibrational frequencies required may be calculated from $2\pi\nu = (k/\mu)^{1/2}$. Because of the zero-point vibration, ΔE_0 for this reaction is given by

$$\Delta \bar{E}_0 = \tfrac{1}{2}N_0 h[\nu_{H_2} + \nu_{D_2} - 2\nu_{HD}]$$

---

10. The energies of the $n = 1$ and $n = 2$ orbits in the hydrogen atom are 27,420 and 109,678 cm^{-1}, respectively. What are the relative populations in these levels (a) at $25°$, (b) at $2000°$?

11. (a) In how many different ways can four distinguishable balls be placed in two boxes? (b) How many different ways are there if the balls are indistinguishable?

12. Calculate the entropy of argon at (a) $25°$ and (b) $727°$ and 1 atm pressure.

13. Calculate $(\bar{H} - \bar{H}_0)/T$, the free-energy function, and the entropy of nitrogen gas at $2000°$K and 1 atm pressure. (Compare problem 4.)

14. Calculate $\bar{C}_P$ for hydrogen gas at $300°$ and $2000°$K.

15. Calculate the value of (a) the free-energy function and (b) the entropy for chlorine gas at $25°$ and 1 atm pressure. The equilibrium separation of the atoms is 1.983 A, and the vibrational wave number is 556.9 cm^{-1}.

MACROMOLECULES

20

In the course of his investigations on diffusion in solutions in 1861, Thomas Graham drew a distinction between "colloids," such as proteins, gums, and polysaccharides, and "crystalloids," which are salts and substances of lower molecular weight. It was possible for Graham to distinguish between these two classes of substances, since colloids did not diffuse through membranes whereas crystalloids did; this separation process was called *dialysis*. The essential difference is one of size: it is generally considered that the colloidal size range extends from about 10 A to 10,000 A (or from 0.001 to 1 μ). The dimensions of simple molecules lie below about 10 A, while particles as large as 10,000 A can be seen with a microscope with visible light.

It is convenient to distinguish between colloids consisting of (1) small particles having the same internal structure as the bulk solid phase, (2) aggregates formed from smaller molecules, and (3) molecules of sufficient size that their dimensions fall in the colloid size range. A dispersion of a finely divided solid or liquid is an example of the first type. Soaps and detergents are examples of the second type. They consist of organic molecules with both hydrophobic ("water-hating") and hydrophilic ("water-loving") parts which aggregate to form *micelles*. In these micelles, which may contain as many as 100 molecules, the hydrophobic parts are together on the inside and the hydrophilic parts are on the outside. Proteins and high polymers are examples of the third type. These substances consist of molecules held together by covalent bonds; an important characteristic they have in common with colloidal particles is their size. The study of such substances has resulted in the development of new techniques which are described in this chapter.

Polymerization. Organic macromolecules may be prepared by (a) condensation reactions and (b) addition reactions. The polymerization of nylon from diamines, $H_2N(CH_2)_nNH_2$, and diacids, $HO_2C(CH_2)_n$-CO_2H, with the splitting out of water is an example of the first type; the structure of one type of nylon is indicated by

$$-(CH_2)_n-\overset{\|}{\underset{O}{C}}-\overset{|}{\underset{H}{N}}-(CH_2)_n-\overset{|}{\underset{H}{N}}-\overset{\|}{\underset{O}{C}}-(CH_2)_n-$$

The molecular weight of a condensation polymer increases continuously during the reaction. Thus the final product contains a distribution of molecular weights.

The polymerization of styrene ($C_6H_5CH{=}CH_2$) to give polystyrene

is an example of an addition polymerization.

Addition-polymerization reactions proceed by a chain mechanism. Organic peroxides are often used to initiate the polymerization. In the mechanism below it is shown that each molecule of peroxide P gives rise to two free radicals $R\cdot$. In the propagation step of the polymerization a free radical reacts with the unsaturated monomer M to form another free radical containing the initial free radical and a molecule of monomer. The chain started in this way then grows until it is terminated by reaction with another chain.

I. Initiation: $\quad P \to 2R\cdot$

II. Propagation: $\quad R\cdot + M \to M_1\cdot$

$$M_1\cdot + M \to M_2\cdot$$

$$M_i\cdot + M \to M_{i+1}\cdot$$

III. Termination: $\quad M_n\cdot + M_m\cdot \to M_{m+n} \quad$ or $\quad M_n + M_m$

The chains grow very rapidly because of the radical chain mechanism. Thus, in contrast to a condensation polymerization each molecule grows to its full size extremely rapidly, and so the molecular weight of the polymer product is independent of the extent of reaction. In order to obtain a high-molecular-weight product a small amount of initiator P is used so that the number of chains started will be small. If the rate of termination is high compared to the rate of initiation, short polymer chains will be obtained. In any case the final product contains a distribution of molecular weights.

Polymer molecules formed by free-radical chains are not necessarily linear. Branches may be introduced in several ways. One possibility is chain transfer, in which a free-radical active center is transferred to some point along the chain of a previously formed polymer molecule, and continued chain reaction leads to a branch. A branch point about four bonds from the end of a growing chain may result from a unimolecular chain transfer in which a transient ring is formed and the free radical is transferred by this ring formation from the end of the chain. This produces short side chains, which give the polymer a different character from a polymer of the same molecular weight with long side chains. The amount of long-chain branching is controlled by concentration parameters, and the amount of short-chain branching by temperature. Long-chain branching affects viscosity and other flow properties; short-chain branching influences the degree of crystallinity and all crystallite-dependent properties.

Molecular-Weight Averages. A sample of a synthetic polymer contains molecules of a range of molecular weights as illustrated in *Fig. 20-1*, and so various types of averages may be considered. The *number average molecular weight M_n* is equal to the weight of the whole sample

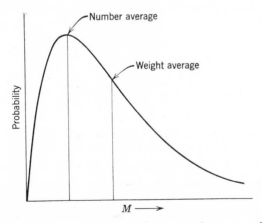

Fig. 20-1. Distribution of molecular weights and types of average molecular weight. The ordinate gives the probability of occurrence of molecules with a molecular weight of M.

divided by the number of molecules in it.

$$M_n = \frac{\sum\limits_{i} n_i M_i}{\sum\limits_{i} n_i} \tag{1}$$

Here n_i is the number of molecules of molecular weight M_i per gram of dry polymer. This type of average is obtained from the measurement of any colligative property, for example, osmotic pressure.

The *weight average molecular weight* weights molecules proportionally to their molecular weight in the averaging process; that is, the molecular weight M_i is multiplied by the weight $n_i M_i$ of material of that molecular weight rather than by the number of molecules. The weight average molecular weight M_w is defined by

$$M_w = \frac{\sum\limits_{i} n_i M_i^2}{\sum\limits_{i} n_i M_i} \tag{2}$$

This type of average is obtained by the study of light scattering (p. 578).

The weight average molecular weight must always be greater than the number average molecular weight, except for a sample in which all the molecules have the same weight, so that $M_n = M_w$. The ratio M_w/M_n is a useful measure of the breadth of the molecular-weight distribution.

Determination of the High Molecular Weights. The osmotic pressure is the only colligative property (p. 187) which offers a practical method for the determination of molecular weights in the range above 10,000. For example, an aqueous solution containing 10 g liter^{-1} of a substance of $M = 20,000$ would show a freezing-point lowering of 0.001°, a boiling-point elevation of 0.00025°, but an osmotic pressure of 128 mm of water. A slight trace of an impurity of low molecular weight might cause a larger freezing-point lowering or boiling-point elevation, but would pass through the membrane in an osmotic-pressure determination and would not contribute to the pressure.

A number of other types of methods have been developed for the determination of molecular weights greater than about 10,000. They include the measurement of the intensity of light scattered from a solution, diffusion, ultracentrifugation, and the use of the electron microscope.

Osmotic Pressure. If the molecules of the solute are very large in comparison with those of the solvent, it is not so difficult to find a membrane in which the holes are large enough to pass molecules of solvent but too small to pass molecules of solute. Cellophane is frequently used as the membrane for high-polymer solutions.

A term may be added to the simple equation (p. 186) for osmotic pressure π, so that it can be used to represent data over a wider range of concentration:

$$\frac{\pi}{c} = \frac{RT}{M} + Bc \tag{3}$$

The value of B is dependent upon polymer-polymer interactions, and for particular solvents and temperatures may be equal to zero. In using equation 3 a plot of π/c versus c is extrapolated to zero concentration. Then M is calculated from

$$\lim_{c \to 0} \frac{\pi}{c} = \frac{RT}{M} \tag{4}$$

In solutions of proteins or other colloidal electrolytes it is necessary to distinguish between the *total osmotic pressure*, which would be obtained with a membrane impermeable to both salt and protein, and the *colloid osmotic pressure*, which is obtained with a membrane permeable to salt ions but not to protein. The latter type of membrane is always used when it is desired to obtain the molecular weight of the protein or other colloidal electrolyte.

In the case of colloidal electrolytes mixed with salts, the measured osmotic pressure is greater than that expected for the colloidal ions alone. This is a result of the fact that, although the salt ions may pass through the membrane, they will not be distributed equally at equilibrium. This effect, which was explained by Donnan, may be reduced by increasing the salt concentration and, if possible, adjusting the pH to the isoelectric point (p. 593) of the colloidal electrolyte.

Example 1. The osmotic pressures of a series of solutions of a sample of polystyrene in methyl ethyl ketone are measured at $25°$. When pressure is expressed in height of the methyl ethyl ketone solution in centimeters and concentration is expressed as grams per cubic centimeter, the intercept at $c = 0$ of a graph of π/c versus c is found to be 110 cm^4 g^{-1}. Calculate the number average molecular weight of this sample of polystyrene. First, it is convenient to express π/c in literatmospheres per gram by use of the densities of methyl ethyl ketone (0.80 g cm^{-3}) and mercury (13.6 g cm^{-3}).

$$\frac{(110 \text{ cm}^4 \text{ g}^{-1})(0.80 \text{ g cm}^{-3})}{(13.6 \text{ g cm}^{-3})(76.0 \text{ cm Hg atm}^{-1})(1000 \text{ cm}^3 \, 1^{-1})} = 85 \times 10^{-6} \text{ l-atm g}^{-1}$$

$$\lim_{c \to 0} (\pi/c) = RT/M$$

$$85 \times 10^{-6} \text{ l-atm g}^{-1} = (0.082 \text{ l-atm deg}^{-1} \text{ mole}^{-1})(298 \text{ deg})/M$$

$$M = 290,000 \text{ g mole}^{-1}$$

Light Scattering. Faraday found that a narrow beam of light passing through a suspension of colloidal gold was plainly visible when viewed against a dark background, although the sol appeared quite clear. Tyndall noted that the scattered light was polarized and bluish in color and that the transmitted light was reddish although the incident light was white. Rayleigh, who investigated the theory of the scattering in 1899, showed that the intensity of light scattered by small isotropic particles (particles having the same properties in all directions) is inversely proportional to the fourth power of the wavelength of the light used. Thus, blue light is scattered to a greater extent than red light, and therefore the light transmitted through a suspension of particles is reddish. We are familiar with these effects in the blue sky and the red sunset.

The study of the intensity of light scattered by polymer or protein solutions offers an important method for the determination of molecular weight and shape of these large molecules.* Some light is scattered even by a pure liquid, because it is inhomogeneous on a molecular scale; that is, the number of molecules in a very small element of volume is not constant but fluctuates because of thermal motion. The scattering of light by a solution is greater because of local refractive-index differences due to fluctuations in concentration. The magnitude of these fluctuations is related to the osmotic work required to cause a change in concentration. Thus, Einstein was able to relate the scattering intensity of a solution to its osmotic pressure and the change in refractive index produced by the solute.

A measure of the light scattered by a solution is the turbidity τ, which is defined by

$$I = I_0 e^{-\tau l} \tag{5}$$

where I_0 is the incident intensity, and I the intensity after passing through a length l of solution. This equation is similar to Lambert's law (p. 520) but the light is scattered rather than absorbed. For a given concentration in grams per liter the turbidity is proportional to the molecular weight, whereas it will be recalled that the osmotic pressure of such a solution is inversely proportional to molecular weight. However, even for solutions of proteins or high polymers the turbidity is so small that measurements of the decrease in intensity of the transmitted light are not practical. However, the light scattered at a particular angle may be measured accurately with a relatively simple pho-

---

* P. Debye, *J. Phys. & Colloid Chem.*, *51*, 18 (1947); H. C. van de Hulst, *Light Scattering by Small Particles*, John Wiley & Sons, New York, 1957; K. A. Stacey, *Light Scattering in Physical Chemistry*, Academic Press, New York, 1956.

tometer and used to calculate τ if the dimensions of the molecules are small compared with the wavelength of the light used. Such an apparatus is shown in *Fig. 20-2*. Measurements of the intensity of light scattered at any angle may be used to obtain the molecular weight of small isotropic molecules by means of the equation

$$\frac{Hc}{\tau} = \frac{1}{M} + 2Bc \tag{6}$$

where M is the molecular weight, c is concentration, H is a constant involving a number of parameters, including the refractive-index in-

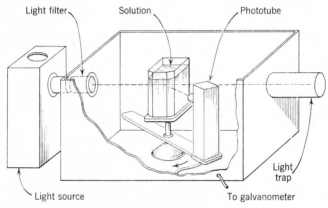

Fig. 20-2. Apparatus for measuring light scattered by a solution.

crement (dn/dc) for the high-molecular-weight component in the solvent used and the wavelength of the light, and B is the same constant as in equation 3 for osmotic pressure. Thus, Hc/τ is plotted versus c and extrapolated to $c = 0$ to obtain the value of $1/M$. Since the amount of light scattered is very small, special care must be taken to free the solution of dust particles, which would themselves scatter considerable light.

The light scattered through 90° is plane polarized if the scattering molecules are small compared with the wavelength of the light used. If one of the dimensions of a molecule is comparable to the wavelength of light, the molecule no longer acts as a single point in scattering light, and there is interference between light waves scattered from different parts of the molecule. The scattering intensity depends upon the angle of observation; it is found that large molecules scatter more light forward, in the direction of the beam, than backward. Thus for larger molecules or particles the angular dependence of the light scattering gives information as to shape.

Brownian Motion. The English botanist Robert Brown observed the motion of pollen grains and other microscopic objects suspended in a liquid. As shown by the microscope, very small particles suspended in a liquid are in a state of ceaseless erratic motion. In interpreting his results in 1827 Brown stated, "The movements arose neither from currents in the fluid nor from its gradual evaporation, but belonged to the particle itself." This motion, which is shown to an even greater extent by smoke particles, is due to the fact that the summated impacts of molecules on the sides of a small particle do not at every instant cancel exactly. Brownian motion constitutes a visual confirmation of the random kinetic motion of molecules.

The Brownian motion of particles which are too small to be seen with a microscope can be studied with an ultramicroscope. In an *ultramicroscope* a powerful beam of light is brought to a focus within the colloidal solution, and this region of the solution is viewed with a microscope at right angles to the beam of light. If the particles have a sufficiently different refractive index from the medium, it is possible to see spots of light even though the particles are below the resolving power of the microscope.

The displacements are at random, and the direction changes so fast that it is impossible to measure the velocities of the particles, but it is possible to make a quantitative study by determining the position of an individual colloid particle at regular intervals. In *Fig. 20-3* each circle represents the position of the same colloid particle at intervals of 30 sec while it moves along a path from A to B and on to P and Q. The lengths of the dashed lines give the x coordinates of the particle. The apparent displacement Δx during a 30-sec time interval is the difference between two successive x distances. For example, in going from A to B, Δx is obtained by subtracting the length of the second dashed line from that of the top one. Of course there are also displacements along the z axis, which is perpendicular to the plane of the paper.

Einstein showed that there is a relation between the Brownian displacements and the frictional coefficient of the particle. The frictional coefficient f is the force required to give the particle a steady-state velocity of 1 cm $\sec^{-1}$. This relation is

$$\frac{\overline{(\Delta x)^2}}{2\Delta t} = \frac{RT}{N_0 f} \tag{7}$$

where $\overline{(\Delta x)^2}$ is the mean value of the square of the displacements in the x direction, Δt is the time between observations, and R, T, and N_0

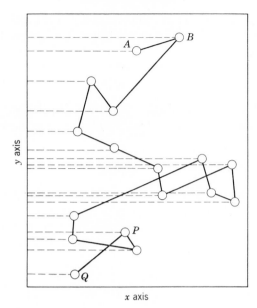

x axis

Fig. 20-3. Movement of a colloidal particle from A to Q with intermediate positions shown every 30 sec.

have their usual significance. For a spherical particle in a continuous suspension medium and nonturbulent flow, the frictional coefficient f is simply related to the radius r of the sphere by Stokes's law (p. 351).

$$f = 6\pi\eta r \tag{8}$$

In this relation η is the viscosity of the solvent. Substitution of equation 8 into equation 7 yields a relation from which the radius of a spherical particle may be calculated.

$$\frac{\overline{(\Delta x)^2}}{2\Delta t} = \frac{RT}{N_0 6\pi\eta r} \tag{9}$$

Perrin used this equation in connection with data on spherical particles of known radius r to calculate one of the early values of Avogadro's number N_0.

Diffusion. Diffusion is closely related to Brownian motion, and indeed we may consider that the molecules or particles of a substance diffuse because of their Brownian motion. The determination of the diffusion coefficient D is discussed in Chapter 13.

Diffusion coefficients are useful in determining the molecular weights of macromolecules. The diffusion coefficient is related to the frictional coefficient f by

$$D = \frac{RT}{N_0 f} \tag{10}$$

which is derived in the Appendix on p. 725. In the case of spherical particles or molecules, Stokes's law (equation 8) may be introduced.

$$D = \frac{RT}{N_0 6\pi\eta r} \tag{11}$$

Thus, in the case of spherical particles the radius may be calculated from the measured diffusion coefficient. Since it is more familiar to think of size in terms of molecular weight, the relation between D and the molecular weight of the spherical particle may be derived from equation 11 by introducing

$$\frac{M\bar{v}}{N_0} = \tfrac{4}{3}\pi r^3 \tag{12}$$

where $\bar{v}$ is the partial specific volume (that is, $\bar{v}$, divided by M).

$$D = \frac{RT}{N_0 6\pi\eta} \left(\frac{4\pi N_0}{3M\bar{v}}\right)^{\frac{1}{3}} \tag{13}$$

Thus for spherical particles the diffusion coefficient is inversely proportional to the cube root of the molecular weight. Of course if the particles or molecules are not spherical, the value of the molecular weight calculated from equation 13 will not be correct. However, this equation does give the *maximum* molecular weight that is consistent with a given D and $\bar{v}$. For a nonspherical particle the molecular weight would be smaller. The exact molecular weight may be calculated if both the diffusion coefficient and sedimentation coefficient (p. 584) are known.

Example 2. Using the diffusion coefficient and $\bar{v}$ for ovalbumin given in Table I, calculate the maximum molecular weight this protein might have. The coefficient of viscosity of water at 20° is 0.01005 poise. Using equation 13,

$$D = 7.8 \times 10^{-7} = \frac{(8.31 \times 10^7)(293)}{(6.02 \times 10^{-3})(6\pi)(0.01005)} \left[\frac{4\pi(6.02 \times 10^{23})}{3M(0.75)}\right]^{\frac{1}{3}}$$

$$M = 69,000 \text{ g mole}^{-1}$$

The ovalbumin molecule is not spherical, as shown by the fact that the actual molecular weight calculated from the sedimentation and diffusion coefficients is 44,000.

Sedimentation. If the particles of a dispersion are sufficiently large and dense, they settle out under the action of the earth's gravitational field. The steady-state velocity with which they sediment is that velocity at which the force of gravity is exactly balanced by the frictional force of the particle moving through the suspension medium.

The radius of spherical particles may be calculated from the velocity of sedimentation if their density is known. The force causing sedimentation is equal to the effective mass of the particle times the acceleration of gravity g. Since a particle of density ρ is buoyed up by the suspension medium having a density of ρ_0, the force causing sedimentation is

$$\tfrac{4}{3}\pi r^3(\rho - \rho_0)g$$

where r is the radius of the particle. The retarding force is proportional to the velocity of sedimentation dx/dt and is $f(dx/dt)$, where f is the frictional coefficient (equation 8) and is equal to $6\pi\eta r$ for a spherical particle. Since at constant velocity the retarding force is equal to the force causing sedimentation, the following equation is obtained:

$$\frac{dx}{dt} = \frac{2r^2(\rho - \rho_0)g}{9\eta} \tag{14}$$

This equation is useful in determining the particle size of finely divided solids.

Only the largest and densest colloidal particles sediment in the earth's field, and so centrifuges have been devised to produce stronger fields. Sufficiently powerful ultracentrifuges have been built to cause even molecules as small as those of sucrose to sediment at measurable rates. Svedberg* was the leader in the development of ultracentrifuges, which he defined as centrifuges adapted for quantitative measurements of convection-free and vibration-free sedimentation. There are two distinct types of ultracentrifuge experiments: (1) those in which the velocity of sedimentation of a component of the solution is measured (*sedimentation velocity*), and (2) those in which the redistribution of molecules is determined at equilibrium (*sedimentation equilibrium*).

The acceleration of a centrifugal field is equal to $\omega^2 r$, where ω is the velocity of the centrifuge in radians per second (that is, 2π times the number of revolutions per second) and r is the distance from the center of rotation. Velocity ultracentrifuges in which r is about 6 cm are commonly operated at 60,000 rpm or 1000 rps, and so the acceleration is

$$\omega^2 r = (2\pi\ 1000\ \text{sec}^{-1})^2(6\ \text{cm}) = 2.36 \times 10^8\ \text{cm sec}^{-2}$$

* T. Svedberg and K. O. Pedersen, *The Ultracentrifuge*, Oxford University Press, Oxford, 1940.

Since the acceleration of the earth's field is 980 cm sec^{-2}, the acceleration is 240,000 times greater than in the earth's field.

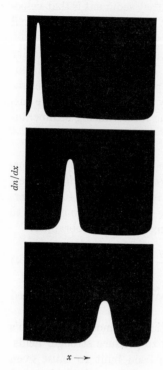

A solution to be studied in the velocity ultracentrifuge is placed in a cell with thick quartz windows. It has a sector shape when viewed at right angles to the plane of rotation of the centrifuge rotor, since the sedimentation takes place radially. As the high-molecular-weight component throughout the solution sediments, a moving boundary is formed, behind which there is only solvent. The movement of such boundaries in the cell may be followed with the schlieren optical system, as was mentioned in connection with diffusion (p. 354).

Figure 20-4 shows the schlieren patterns for an ultracentrifuge experiment with the enzyme fumarase at 50,400 rpm. The second and third photographs were taken 35 and 70 min later than the top photograph. If additional components with different rates of sedimentation had been present, additional peaks would be evident in the schlieren photograph. Thus, the ultracentrifuge is useful in analyzing complex mixtures such as blood plasma.

Fig. 20-4. Schlieren patterns for an ultracentrifuge experiment with fumarase at 50,400 rpm. The lower photographs were taken 35 and 70 min later than the top photograph. The protein is dissolved in pH 6.8 phosphate buffer.

The velocity of sedimentation, dr/dt, divided by the centrifugal acceleration $\omega^2 r$, is called the *sedimentation coefficient s*.

$$s = \frac{dr/dt}{\omega^2 r} \qquad (15)$$

The sedimentation coefficients of proteins fall in the range 10^{-13} sec to 200×10^{-13} sec, and the unit 10^{-13} sec is called a *svedberg*.

If a boundary is r_1 centimeters from the axis of the centrifuge at time t_1 and r_2 centimeters from the axis at time t_2, the sedimentation coefficient may be calculated from

$$s = \frac{1}{\omega^2(t_2 - t_1)} \ln \frac{r_2}{r_1} \qquad (16)$$

which is obtained by integrating equation 15.

Example 3.　In the ultracentrifuge experiment illustrated in Fig. 20-4 the distance from the axis of the ultracentrifuge to the boundary was 5.949 cm in the top photograph and 6.731 cm in the bottom photograph taken 70 min later. Since the speed of the rotor was 50,400 rpm, $\omega^2 = 2.82 \times 10^7$. Using equation 16,

$$s = \frac{1}{\omega^2(t_2 - t_1)} \ln \frac{r_2}{r_1} = \frac{2.303 \log (6.731/5.949)}{(2.82 \times 10^7)(60)(70)}$$

$$= 10.4 \times 10^{-13} \text{ sec}$$

This is the sedimentation coefficient at 28.2°, the temperature of the experiment. Making a correction to 20° in water, taking into account the change of viscosity and density, a value of 8.90 svedbergs is obtained.

The sedimentation coefficient by itself cannot be used to determine the molecular weight of the sedimenting component unless the molecules are spherical. However, if both the sedimentation and diffusion coefficients are measured, the molecular weight may be calculated without making any assumptions whatsoever about the shape. The equation upon which this calculation is based may be derived by equating the force of the centrifugal field on the particle to the frictional force, $f(dr/dt)$, where f is the frictional coefficient of the molecule and dr/dt is the speed of sedimentation. The force of the field on a particle of mass m and partial specific volume $\bar{v}$ suspended in a medium of density ρ is

$$m(1 - \bar{v}\rho)\omega^2 r = \frac{M}{N_0} (1 - \bar{v}\rho)\omega^2 r \tag{17}$$

where $(1 - \bar{v}\rho)$ is the buoyancy factor.

The sedimenting molecule or particle will be accelerated by the field until its velocity is such that the frictional force is equal to the force of the field

$$f\frac{dr}{dt} = \frac{M}{N_0} (1 - \bar{v}\rho)\omega^2 r \tag{18}$$

or

$$\frac{dr/dt}{\omega^2 r} = s = \frac{M(1 - \bar{v}\rho)}{N_0 f} \tag{19}$$

Since the velocity of sedimentation is so low that there is no appreciable orientation of the molecules, the frictional coefficient involved in sedimentation is taken to be the same as that involved in diffusion. Introduction of equation 10

$$f = \frac{RT}{N_0 D} \tag{20}$$

into equation 19 yields

$$M = \frac{RTs}{D(1 - \bar{v}\rho)} \tag{21}$$

In order to calculate the molecular weight from measured values of s and D it is necessary to correct sedimentation and diffusion coefficients to the same temperature, usually 20°, and, if s and D depend appreciably upon concentration, to zero concentration. Equation 21 has probably been the most widely used in the calculation of molecular weights of proteins, and the wide range of molecular weights which can be obtained by this method is indicated by Table I.

Table I. Physical Constants at 20° in Water and Molecular Weights of Certain Proteins

Protein	$s \times 10^{13}$, sec	$D \times 10^7$, $cm^2\,sec^{-1}$	$\bar{v}$, $cm^3\,g^{-1}$	M, $g\,mole^{-1}$
Beef insulin	1.7	15	0.72	12,000
Lactalbumin	1.9	10.6	0.75	17,400
Ovalbumin	3.6	7.8	0.75	44,000
Serum albumin	4.3	6.15	0.735	64,000
Serum globulin	7.1	4.0	0.75	167,000
Urease	18.6	3.4	0.73	490,000
Tobacco mosaic virus	185	0.53	0.72	40,000,000

Example 4. Using the data of Table I, the molecular weight of serum albumin may be calculated as follows (the density of water at 20° is 0.9982 g cm^{-3}):

$$M = \frac{RTs}{D(1 - \bar{v}\rho)}$$

$$M = \frac{(8.31 \times 10^7 \text{ ergs deg}^{-1}\text{ mole}^{-1})(293 \text{ deg})(4.3 \times 10^{-13} \text{ sec})}{(6.15 \times 10^{-4} \text{ cm}^2\text{ sec}^{-1})[1 - (0.735 \text{ cm}^3\text{ g}^{-1})(0.9982 \text{ g cm}^{-3})]}$$

$$= 64,000 \text{ g mole}^{-1}$$

In an equilibrium ultracentrifuge experiment the centrifugation is continued until the tendency of the molecules to sediment is balanced by the opposing tendency to diffuse into the region of lower concentration. Since this redistribution in the solution is an equilibrium phenomenon, the relation between the concentrations at two levels and the molecular weight may be derived by the methods of thermodynamics. For ideal solutions the molecular weight may be calculated from

$$M = \frac{2RT \ln (c_2/c_1)}{(1 - \bar{v}\rho)\omega^2(r_2{}^2 - r_1{}^2)} \tag{22}$$

where c_1 is the concentration at distance r_1 from the axis, c_2 is the concentration at distance r_2, ω is the angular velocity of the rotor (radians per second), and ρ is the density of the solution. Optical methods are used to determine c_2 and c_1.

Viscosity. Measurements of viscosities of high-polymer solutions are particularly important, since they offer an indirect method for determining molecular weight. The theoretical background for this method starts with Einstein's derivation, in 1906, of an equation relating the viscosity η of a dilute suspension of small rigid spheres to the volume fraction ϕ occupied by the spherical particles. Einstein derived

$$\frac{(\eta/\eta_0) - 1}{\phi} = \frac{\eta_{sp}}{\phi} = \frac{5}{2} \tag{23}$$

where η_0 is the viscosity of the solvent. The quantity $(\eta/\eta_0) - 1$ is of frequent occurrence in the theory of viscosity and is known as the specific viscosity, η_{sp}. It is interesting to note that the viscosity (for the dilute suspensions covered by this equation) is independent of the size of the spheres and is dependent only on the volume fraction ϕ that they occupy.

Since high-polymer molecules consist of chains of monomer units and are threadlike and flexible in solution, they cannot be considered to be solid spheres. Because of the difficulty of knowing the fraction of the volume occupied by high-polymer molecules in solution and the fact that the *reduced viscosity*, η_{sp}/c, is not independent of concentration, it is necessary to utilize the intrinsic viscosity $[\eta]$, defined by

$$[\eta] = \lim_{c \to 0} \frac{\eta_{sp}}{c} \tag{24}$$

where c is the concentration of the high polymer in grams per 100 ml. The intrinsic viscosity is obtained by plotting the ratio of specific viscosity to concentration against concentration for a series of solutions and extrapolating to zero concentration.

In solution certain polymer molecules have a randomly kinked and coiled configuration that is constantly changing; in other cases the molecules are not so flexible. The "size" of the molecule, measured for example by the average end-to-end distance of the chain, is not directly proportional to the molecular weight. However, the intrinsic viscosity depends upon the molecular weight. For a series of samples of the same polymer in a given solvent and at a constant temperature the following empirical relation is obeyed quite well:

$$[\eta] = KM^a \tag{25}$$

Here K and a are constants which may be determined by measuring the intrinsic viscosities of a series of samples of a polymer for which the molecular weights have been measured by another method, say osmotic-pressure determinations. Since the values of K and a are known for a large number of solvents and temperatures, this method for determining molecular weights is widely used because of the simple apparatus required. The molecular weight of a heterogeneous polymer obtained in this way is intermediate between M_n and M_w (cf. Fig. 20-1)

Example 5. The values of K and a for polystyrene dissolved in toluene at $25°$ are 3.7×10^{-4} and 0.62, respectively. Calculate the molecular weight of a sample of polystyrene having an intrinsic viscosity of 0.74.

$$0.74 = 3.7 \times 10^{-4} M^{0.62}$$

$$M = 214,000 \text{ g mole}^{-1}$$

The Mechanical Properties of Polymers. Polymeric materials display a very wide range of physical properties; they are hard or soft, leathery or rubbery, brittle or tough, and meltable or nonmeltable. These properties depend upon the molecular structure of the polymer, and the various properties are obtained by the choice of the polymer and its treatment. The physical properties depend to quite an extent on whether the polymer is (a) completely amorphous or (b) partly crystalline. In an amorphous polymer the molecular chains are coiled together in a disordered fashion like the molecules in a liquid.

Amorphous polymers may be glassy, leathery, or rubbery, depending upon the temperature. At low temperatures amorphous polymers are in the glassy state, which is like that of a supercooled liquid. As the temperature is raised, there is a transition at the "glass transition temperature" from the glassy to the leathery state. The change in properties is due to random Brownian motion of molecular chains; first short segments begin to move and then longer segments begin to move as the temperature is raised. The transition from the glassy to the rubberlike state generally extends over a range of about $50°$, but the temperature range in which it occurs depends upon the type of polymer. If there are rather long sections of the molecular chains between cross links and centers of entanglement, long segments will be in Brownian motion, and rubberlike properties will result.

The glass transition temperature is raised by vulcanization, which introduces cross linkages; that is, bonds are formed between adjacent threadlike molecules, thus restricting the molecular motions.

Rubberlike Elasticity. Rubber and certain other high polymers have the remarkable property that they may be stretched by a large factor without rupture and that they regain their original dimensions upon removal of the force. Another remarkable property of these materials is that, when they are under tension, raising the temperature causes contraction, in contrast with the usual expansion of solids and liquids. These properties are readily explained in terms of the structure of rubberlike materials. All such materials have rather long chains which have considerable freedom of movement between points where they are cross linked by chemical bonds or entanglements. Under conditions where the chains have rather weak attractions for each other the thermal motions of the chains may be very great. The effect of these motions is to force the chains apart and to draw the ends of the chain together. Rubber can be stretched to a considerable extent because these chains are normally in a randomly coiled and disordered arrangement. When tension is applied to rubber, a restriction is imposed on the arrangement of the molecular chains, and the disordered state, characteristic of the unstretched rubber, is replaced by one in which there is a higher degree of order or, in other words, a lower entropy.

For natural rubber it is found that the internal energy is independent of the length of extension. When this is true, it may be shown * that the force of contraction is entirely due to the change in entropy (cf. problem 12, p. 119). It is interesting to realize that the pressure of an ideal gas is also purely an entropy effect, the internal energy being independent of volume. The detailed theory of rubberlike elasticity predicts that the force of contraction of an elongated piece of polymer will be directly proportional to the absolute temperature. This relation exists because the thermal motions of the chains increase as the temperature is raised.

Crystallinity in Polymers. Some polymers contain regions in which the chains are arranged in an orderly, three-dimensional array. These crystalline regions typically have dimensions of the order of 100 A, and they have an important influence on the physical properties of the polymer. The extent of crystallinity increases when the polymer is stretched because this draws the chains together and reduces the random motions. For example, natural rubber is ordinarily amorphous at room temperature but becomes oriented and crystalline when stretched. The amount of crystallinity may be investigated by X-ray diffraction and by studying the volume of the polymer as a function of temperature.

Crystallites occur most frequently in polymers having a comparatively simple and symmetrical structure or polymer chains which tend

* P. J. Flory, *Principles of Polymer Chemistry*, Cornell University Press, Ithaca, 1953, p. 451.

to associate by the formation of hydrogen bonds. The presence of crystallites has an important effect on the properties of a polymer because the crystallites increase the rigidity of the solid and raise its softening temperature. The amount of crystallinity in certain polymers can be greatly increased by stereospecific methods of synthesis, using catalysts which place the side groups on one side of the chain. Polymers of monomers like styrene have asymmetric carbon atoms.

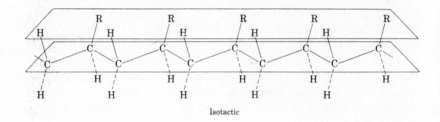

Isotactic

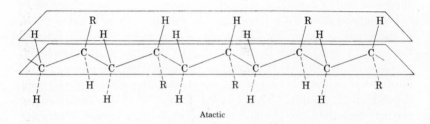

Atactic

Fig. 20-5. Steric configuration of polymer chains.

By using certain solid catalysts it is possible to prepare polymers in which all the adjacent asymmetric atoms, at least for long periods of the chain, have the same steric configuration. Natta prepared such polymers and called them isotactic. The structure of an isotactic polymer is contrasted in *Fig. 20-5* with the structure of an atactic polymer having the random orientation obtained by the usual synthetic methods. The regularity in structure of isotactic polymers makes it possible for the polymer chains to fit into a crystal lattice. This increased orderliness causes the melting point to be higher and the rigidity and toughness to be greater than those of corresponding atactic polymers.

Polyelectrolytes. High polymers may have ionizable groups which have a large effect on the properties. As a result of electrostatic repulsion of charged groups, a polyelectrolyte molecule will be more extended in solution and will show a higher viscosity than its uncharged counterpart. The properties of polyelectrolytes are therefore dependent upon the concentration of added salt which shields the charged groups from each other. Proteins are polymers of amino acids in which there is a specific folding of the molecule into a more compact shape. As a result the shapes of protein molecules in solution are not so sensitive to changes in degree of ionization and electrolyte concentration as other polyelectrolytes.

Ion-exchange resins are high polymers having negatively charged groups (in cation-exchange resins) or positively charged groups (in anion-exchange resins). Small ions of opposite charge are of course present to maintain electrical neutrality. These resins are sufficiently cross linked so that they cannot dissolve, but the particles of the resin do swell. There is a close relation between swelling equilibrium and osmotic equilibrium. The solvent flows in by osmosis because there is a greater concentration of ions inside the network structure, but this tendency is opposed by the elastic reaction of the network.

A cation-exchange resin R may be considered to be a large, insoluble and polyvalent anion. If it is treated with a great excess of sodium chloride, it is converted to the "sodium form," NaR. The sodium ions may be displaced by calcium ions.

$$2\text{NaR} + \text{Ca}^{2+} = \text{CaR}_2 + 2\text{Na}^+$$

When the resin has become saturated with calcium ions, the equilibrium may be reversed and the resin regenerated by treating it with a concentrated solution of sodium chloride. The exchange properties may be varied by the selection of the reactants for the polymerization reaction.

Electrokinetic Phenomena. If an electric field is applied to a solution containing an electrically charged colloid, the particles will move to the anode if they are negatively charged and to the cathode if they are positively charged. This motion, which is exactly like that of any ion in an electric field, is referred to as *electrophoresis*. If the particles are insoluble and form a plug or membrane, the application of an electric field causes the liquid (usually water) to move through the pores. The relative motion of solvent and solid phase is the same as if the solid particles could move; that is, the solvent moves toward the cathode if the plug or membrane is negatively charged. In this phenomenon, which is referred to as *electroösmosis*, it may be considered that the solvent is carried along by the ions in the neighborhood of the solid surface which have a sign opposite to that of the surface.

One of the most important applications of electrophoresis is in the analysis of naturally occurring mixtures of colloids, such as proteins, polysaccharides, and nucleic acids, and of the products obtained in the course of fractionations to obtain purified components. In the electrophoresis experiment sharp boundaries between protein solution and buffer are formed in a special U-tube, and the movement of boundaries is followed with a schlieren optical system (p. 354). The moving-boundary cell is placed in a thermostat near the temperature of maximum density of the buffer of about 1° to reduce the density gradient

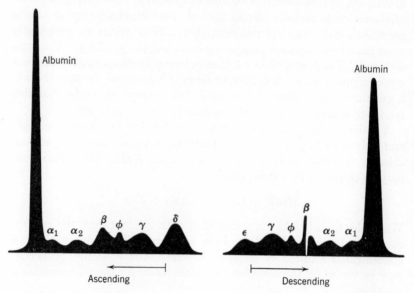

Fig. 20-6. Electrophoretic schlieren patterns for normal human blood plasma.

which accompanies the temperature gradient through the cell when the current flows.

Figure 20-6 gives an example * of an electrophoresis pattern for normal human blood plasma in 0.10 ionic strength sodium diethylbarbiturate buffer of pH 8.6 after 150 min at 6.0 volts cm^{-1} at 1°. The refractive-index gradient is plotted versus the distance in the cell, which is plotted horizontally. One pattern is obtained in the limb of the cell in which the proteins are moving downwards, and the other pattern in the limb in which the proteins are moving upwards. The positions of the initial boundaries are indicated by the rear ends of the arrows. The various proteins are represented by albumin, α_1, α_2, β, and γ globulins, and fibrinogen, ϕ. The area under a given peak is

* R. A. Alberty, "Introduction to Electrophoresis," *J. Chem. Educ.*, *25*, 426, 619 (1948).

very nearly proportional to the concentration of the protein producing that boundary. Thus the percentage of albumin, for example, may be obtained by dividing the area of the albumin peak by the total of the areas of all the protein peaks. The ϵ boundary in the descending pattern and the δ boundary in the ascending pattern are not caused by protein components, but are related to the changes in salt concentration which occur in ordinary transference experiments near the initial boundary position.

All the components of human plasma, as indicated by Fig. 20-6, have been separated by taking advantage of the differences in the solubilities of the various proteins in ethyl alcohol solutions of various pH values containing low concentrations of salts at low temperatures. Albumin, which represents about 60 per cent of the plasma proteins by weight, is largely responsible for the osmotic pressure of plasma, since it has the lowest molecular weight of the plasma proteins (see Table I).

The *isoelectric point* is the pH at which the mobility is zero for a certain salt concentration. In solutions more acid than the isoelectric point, the mobility has a positive sign because of the combination of hydrogen ions with the colloidal electrolyte; in solutions more alkaline than the isoelectric point, ionizable hydrogens are dissociated from carboxyl or other acid groups so that the molecule has a net negative charge. Proteins are generally least soluble at their isoelectric points.

Gels. A given material may be produced in either a crystalline or an amorphous form, depending on the conditions of its formation. Von Weimarn has shown that the degree of supersaturation, at the time of formation, and the viscosity of the medium largely determine the crystal size obtained. For example, when barium sulfate is precipitated from very dilute solutions, it is possible to obtain crystals. When the solutions of Ba^{2+} and SO_4^{2-} are concentrated, the state of supersaturation after mixing is greater, and the crystals are smaller. When the solutions contain about 1 equivalent per liter, an immediate precipitate is formed which is apparently amorphous. With still more concentrated solutions (3–7 equivalents per liter of barium thiocyanate and manganese sulfate), a clear jelly is produced.

A *gel* is a stiff, semirigid precipitate which retains the liquid in which it was initially dissolved. Gels may be prepared in several different ways. For example, when a 2 per cent solution of gelatin dissolved in warm water is cooled, it sets to a stiff, transparent gel. The theory of such gels has been discussed by Ferry.* Gels may be made also by

* J. D. Ferry, *Advances in Protein Chemistry*, Vol. IV, Academic Press, New York, 1948.

precipitation, as in the case of silicic acid gel, which is produced by mixing solutions of hydrochloric acid and sodium silicate. After the combined solution stands for a while, it sets to a stiff, clear gel, the time required for setting depending on the concentrations. It is this silicic acid gel which, after being dried, gives silica gel with many pores and large surface areas that are effective in the adsorption of gases.

REFERENCES

A. E. Alexander and P. Johnson, *Colloid Science*, Vols. I and II, Oxford University Press, Oxford, 1949.

F. W. Billmeyer, *Textbook of Polymer Chemistry*, Interscience Publishers, New York, 1957.

J. D. Ferry, *Viscoelastic Properties of Polymers*, John Wiley & Sons, New York, 1961.

P. J. Flory, *Principles of Polymer Chemistry*, Cornell University Press, Ithaca, 1953.

R. Kunin, *Ion Exchange Resins*, John Wiley & Sons, New York, 1958.

H. F. Mark and A. V. Tobolsky, *Physical Chemistry of High Polymeric Substances*, Interscience Publishers, New York, 1950.

K. J. Mysels, *Introduction to Colloid Chemistry*, Interscience Publishers, New York, 1959.

H. B. Weiser, *Colloid Chemistry*, John Wiley & Sons, New York, 1949.

J. W. Williams, R. A. Alberty, and E. D. Kraemer, in *Treatise on Physical Chemistry*, Vol. II, ed. by H. S. Taylor and S. Glasstone, D. Van Nostrand Co., Princeton, N. J., 1951.

PROBLEMS

1. A sample of polymer contains 0.50 mole fraction with molecular weight 100,000 and 0.50 mole fraction with molecular weight 200,000. Calculate (a) M_n and (b) M_w. *Ans.* (a) 150,000, (b) 167,000 g mole^{-1}.

2. The following osmotic pressures were measured for solutions of a sample of polyisobutylene in benzene at 25°:

c, g/100 cm^3	0.500	1.00	1.50	2.00
π, g/cm^2	0.505	1.03	1.58	2.15

Calculate the number average molecular weight from the value of π/c extrapolated to zero concentration of the polymer. (The pressures may be converted into atmospheres by dividing by $(76 \text{ cm atm}^{-1})(13.53 \text{ g cm}^{-3}) = 1028 \text{ g cm}^{-2} \text{ atm}^{-1}$.)
Ans. 256,000 g mole^{-1}.

3. The protein human plasma albumin has a molecular weight of 69,000. Calculate the osmotic pressure of a solution of this protein containing 2 grams per 100 ml at 25° in (a) millimeters of mercury and (b) millimeters of water. The experiment is carried out using a salt solution for solvent and a membrane permeable to salt. *Ans.* (a) 5.39 mm Hg. (b) 73.2 mm H$_2$O.

4. The diffusion coefficient for serum globulin at $20°$ in a dilute aqueous salt solution is 4.0×10^{-7} cm^2 sec^{-1}. If the molecules are assumed to be spherical, calculate their molecular weight. Given: $\eta_{H_2O} = 0.01005$ poise at $20°$ and $\bar{v} = 0.75$ cm^3 g^{-1} for the protein. *Ans.* 512,000 g mole^{-1}.

5. Estimate the diffusion coefficient in water at $25°$ of a spherical molecule with a molecular weight of 10^5 and $\bar{v} = 0.73$ cm^3 g^{-1}. *Ans.* $D = 7.96 \times 10^{-7}$ cm^2 sec^{-1}.

6. Calculate the time necessary for a quartz particle 10 μ in diameter to sediment 50 cm in distilled water at $25°$. The density of quartz is 2.6 g cm^{-3}. The coefficient of viscosity of water may be taken to be 0.0100 poise. *Ans.* 95.6 min.

7. Calculate the sedimentation coefficient of tobacco mosaic virus from the fact that the boundary moves with a velocity of 0.454 cm hr^{-1} in an ultracentrifuge at a speed of 10,000 rpm at a distance of 6.5 cm from the axis of the centrifuge rotor. *Ans.* 185×10^{-13} sec.

8. The sedimentation and diffusion coefficients for hemoglobin corrected to $20°$ in water are 4.41×10^{-13} sec and 6.3×10^{-7} cm^2 sec^{-1}, respectively. If $\bar{v} = 0.749$ cm^3 g^{-1} and $\rho_{H_2O} = 0.998$ g cm^{-3} at this temperature, calculate the molecular weight of the protein. If there is 1 gram atom of iron per 17,000 grams of protein, how many gram atoms of iron are there per hemoglobin molecule? *Ans.* 68,000 g mole^{-1}, 4.

9. The relative viscosities of a series of solutions of a sample of polystyrene in toluene were determined with an Ostwald viscometer at $25°$.

Concentration, g/100 ml	0.249	0.499	0.999	1.998
η/η_0	1.355	1.782	2.879	6.090

The ratio η_{sp}/c is plotted against c and extrapolated to zero concentration to obtain the intrinsic viscosity. If the constants in equation 25 are $K = 3.7 \times 10^{-4}$ and $a = 0.62$ for this polymer, calculate the molecular weight. *Ans.* 500,000 g mole^{-1}.

---

10. Calculate the (a) number and (b) weight average molecular weights for the following mixture of high-polymer fractions: 1 gram of $M = 20,000$, 2 grams of $M = 50,000$, and 0.5 gram of $M = 100,000$.

11. The following osmotic pressures of polyvinyl acetate in dioxane were measured by G. V. Browning and J. D. Ferry at $25°$:

c, g/100 cm^3	0.292	0.579	0.810	1.140
π, cm of solvent	0.73	1.76	2.73	4.68

Calculate the number average molecular weight. The density of dioxane is 1.035 g cm^{-3}.

12. Human blood plasma contains approximately 40 grams of albumin ($M = 69,000$) and 20 grams of globulin ($M = 160,000$) per liter. Calculate the colloid osmotic pressure at $37°$, ignoring the Donnan effect.

13. Using the diffusion coefficient of lactalbumin in Table I, calculate the maximum molecular weight this substance could have. The highest molecular weight is obtained by assuming that the molecules are spherical. The absolute viscosity of water at $20°$ is 0.01005 poise.

14. If only a small amount of material q is allowed to diffuse through a porous plate from a solution of concentration c'' into a solution of concentration c', Fick's law (p. 353) may be written

$$D = \frac{-q}{Kt(c' - c'')}$$

where K is the cell constant which must be determined in an experiment with a substance of known diffusion coefficient. If a 0.10 N aqueous solution of potassium chloride is allowed to diffuse into water for 12 hr and 38 min at 25°, it is found that 1.25×10^{-4} equivalent of salt diffuses through the porous plate. Calculate D if K has previously been found to be 1.5 cm.

15. Estimate the rate of sedimentation of water droplets of 1-μ diameter in air at 20°. The viscosity of air at this temperature is 180.8 micropoises.

16. The sedimentation coefficient of gamma globulin at 20° is 7.1×10^{-13} sec. Calculate how far the protein boundary will sediment in $\frac{1}{2}$ hr if the speed of the centrifuge is 60,000 rpm and the initial boundary is 6.50 cm from the axis of rotation.

17. Using data in Table I, verify the molecular weight given for urease.

18. A sample of polystyrene was dissolved in toluene, and the following flow times in an Ostwald viscometer at 25° were obtained for different concentrations:

Concentration, g/100 ml	0	0.1	0.3	0.6	0.9
Time, sec	86.0	99.5	132	194	301

If the constants in equation 25 are $K = 3.7 \times 10^{-4}$ and $a = 0.62$ for this polymer, calculate the molecular weight.

---

19. Calculate number average and weight average molecular weights for the following mixture: 1 gram of polymer of $M = 10^4$ and 1 gram of polymer of $M = 10^6$.

20. A protein solution containing 6 grams of protein per 100 ml of solution has a colloid osmotic pressure of 22 mm of water at 25° at the isoelectric point. What is the molecular weight of the protein?

21. Egg albumin has a molecular weight of 44,000. What is the osmotic pressure at 25° of a solution containing 5 grams per liter?

22. The diffusion coefficient of a certain virus having spherical particles is 0.50×10^{-7} cm^2 sec^{-1} at 0° in a solution with a viscosity of 0.0180 poise. Calculate the molecular weight of this virus, assuming that the density of the virus is 1 g cm^{-3}.

23. Using Fick's first law (p. 353), show that for diffusion in a vertical cell of constant cross section

$$\frac{\partial c}{\partial t} = D \frac{\partial^2 c}{\partial x^2}$$

if D is independent of concentration.

24. Calculate the time necessary for a spherical calcium chloride particle 40 μ in diameter to fall 1 cm in carbon tetrachloride (density = 1.595 g cm^{-3}, $\eta = 0.00975$ poise) at room temperature. The density of calcium chloride is 2.152 g cm^{-3}.

25. In an ultracentrifuge experiment with egg albumin in a buffered aqueous solution at a pH of 6, the boundary moved 6.3 mm in 105 min, as determined by measurement of the change in position of the refractive-index gradient with time. The speed of the centrifuge was 57,000 rpm. The distance from the center of rotation was 6.43 cm. Show that the sedimentation coefficient for this protein is 3.5×10^{-13} sec after multiplying by 0.81 to correct for density and viscosity.

SURFACE CHEMISTRY

21

The properties of the surface layer of a substance are different from those of the bulk phase. Previously we have considered only systems in which the surface area was sufficiently small so that the surface energy was negligible. It is evident that the effects of surfaces become greater as the degree of subdivision of matter is increased. If a cube of any substance 1 cm on an edge, having a total surface of 6 sq cm, is cut in half in the 3 directions, there will be 8 cubes having edges of 0.5 cm, and the surface will be $8 \times 6 \times 0.5^2$ or 12 sq cm. If the cube is cut into 1000 cubes 1 mm on an edge, the total surface will be 60 sq cm. If the cubes are 1 μ on an edge, the surface area will be 60,000 sq cm. If the cubes are 10 A on an edge, there will be 10^{21} cubes, and the area will be 6000 sq meters or $1\frac{1}{2}$ acres. It is obvious that surface effects which are undetected on material having an area of 6 sq cm may become very pronounced when the material is dispersed to give a total surface of many square meters. One of the most important results of this large surface is the adsorption of ions and other substances by the particles. This adsorption may lead to the accumulation of electric charges on the particles which prevent them from collecting into large aggregates because of electrostatic repulsion.

Surface Tension. A liquid surface tends to contract to the minimum area as a result of unbalanced forces of molecular attraction at the surface. The molecules at the surface are attracted into the body of the liquid because the attraction of the underlying molecules is greater than the attraction by the vapor molecules on the other side of the surface. This inward attraction causes the surface to contract if it can and gives rise to a force in the plane of the surface. Surface tension is responsible for the formation of spherical droplets, the rise of water in a capillary, and the movement of a liquid through a porous solid.

The surface tension of a liquid, γ, is the force per centimeter on the surface which opposes the expansion of the surface area. This definition is illustrated by the idealized experiment in *Fig. 21-1*, where the movable bar is pulled with force f to expand a liquid film which is stretched like a soap-bubble film on a wire frame. The surface tension can be calculated from

$$\gamma = \frac{f}{2l} \tag{1}$$

where l is the length of the bar in centimeters, and the factor 2 is introduced because there are two liquid surfaces, one at the front and one at

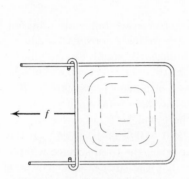

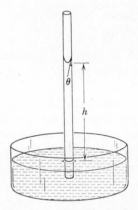

Fig. 21-1. Illustration of the surface tension of a liquid.

Fig. 21-2. Rise of a liquid in a capillary tube.

the back. The surface tension is usually expressed in dynes per centimeter.

The surface tension of a liquid may be measured by a variety of methods.* Since the surface tension affects the equilibrium shape of liquid surfaces, analysis of drop or bubble shape may be used to determine surface tension. The rise of liquid in a capillary or the pull on a thin vertical plate partially immersed in the liquid may be determined and used to calculate the surface tension quite accurately. Less accurate values of the surface tension may be obtained from measurements on moving liquid surfaces. These methods include studies of liquid jets, ripples, drop weight, maximum bubble pressure, and the force required to rupture a surface.

At a liquid-solid-gas interface there is a characteristic contact angle θ. This angle is measured in the liquid as indicated in *Fig. 21-2*. The contact angle depends upon the nature of the three phases, and it is difficult

---

* J. J. Bikerman, *Surface Chemistry*, Academic Press, New York, 1958.

to measure contact angles accurately because of the problems of surface cleanness and roughness.

Some liquids, like water, wet the walls of a glass capillary tube and so the contact angle θ is zero; others, like mercury, do not and so the contact angle θ is 180°. When a liquid wets the tube, the liquid adhering to the walls pulls the body of the liquid up; but when the liquid does not wet the tube, surface tension pulls the body of the liquid down. The most accurate method for determining the surface tension of a liquid consists in measuring the height to which it rises or is depressed in a capillary tube.

A capillary tube of radius r, as shown in Fig. 21-2, is immersed in a vessel of liquid whose density is ρ. The liquid wets the tube, and the liquid rises. It continues to rise until the force due to surface tension tending to pull the liquid upward is counterbalanced by the force of gravity pulling it downward. The height of the equivalent cylinder of liquid which is supported is represented by h. The actual meniscus is curved, but to a high degree of approximation h is equal to the height of the lowest point of the meniscus plus one-third of the radius of the capillary. Then the downward force is $\pi r^2 h \rho g$, where g is the acceleration of gravity.

The surface makes an angle θ with the walls, and only the vertical component of this force is effective in pulling the liquid upward in the capillary. The surface tension acts along the whole length of the surface. Thus, the upward force is $2\pi r\gamma \cos \theta$. At equilibrium the upward and downward forces are equal, and

$$2\pi r\gamma \cos \theta = \pi r^2 h \rho g \tag{2}$$

or

$$\gamma = \frac{h\rho g r}{2 \cos \theta} \tag{3}$$

For many liquids, including water against glass, the angle of contact is very small, θ is nearly 0, and $\cos \theta$ is practically 1. Then,

$$\gamma = \tfrac{1}{2} h \rho g r \tag{4}$$

The surface tension of a liquid decreases as the temperature rises, and becomes immeasurably small a few degrees below the critical temperature. The greater thermal agitation at the higher temperatures reduces the attractive force pulling the molecules inward.

The surface tensions of a few common liquids, measured in air, at different temperatures, are shown in Table I. The surface tensions of liquid metals and molten salts are large in comparison with those of organic liquids. For example, the surface tension of mercury at 0° is 480.3 dynes cm^{-1}, and that of silver at 800° is 800 dynes cm^{-1}.

Table I.   Surface Tension of Liquids

(In dynes per centimeter)

Temperature, °C	H_2O	CCl_4	C_6H_6	$C_6H_5NO_2$	C_2H_5OH	CH_3COOH
0	75.64	29.0	31.6	46.4	24.0	29.5
25	71.97	26.1	28.2	43.2	21.8	27.1
50	67.91	23.1	25.0	40.2	19.8	24.6
75	63.5	20.2	21.9	37.3	...	22.0

Surface Energy. Since a dyne per centimeter is equal to an erg per square centimeter, the surface tension in dynes per centimeter is also a surface energy in ergs per square centimeter. The surface energy is a Gibbs free energy, since it may in principle be completely transformed into work at constant temperature and pressure, as illustrated in Fig. 21-1. Since $H = G - T(\partial G/\partial T)_P$, the surface enthalpy is given by

$$H = \gamma - T \left(\frac{\partial \gamma}{\partial T} \right)_P \tag{5}$$

For water at $20°$, $\gamma = 72.75$ ergs cm^{-2}, $(\partial\gamma/\partial T)_P = -0.148$, and so the surface enthalpy is 116.2 ergs cm^{-2}. This is the decrease in enthalpy associated with the destruction of 1 cm^2 of liquid surface. The determination of the heat evolved when a liquid surface is destroyed forms the basis for a method * for the determination of the area of a finely divided crystalline solid. The solid is suspended in the saturated vapor of a liquid until it becomes coated with an adsorbed film. At equilibrium, when the vapor pressures of the adsorbed liquid and the bulk liquid are the same, the surface energy of the liquid on the particles becomes equal to that of the liquid in bulk. The crystals are then dropped into the liquid, and the large surface area of the liquid on the particles is destroyed. Heat is evolved, and the temperature change is measured.

The Dependence of Vapor Pressure on the Radius of Curvature. The vapor pressure over a meniscus which is concave toward the vapor phase is smaller than that over a flat surface of the liquid, and that over a meniscus which is convex toward the vapor phase is greater. As shown by equations 9 and 11, the effect is not large unless the radius of curvature is quite small. As a result of this effect very small drop-

* W. D. Harkins and G. Jura, *J. Am. Chem. Soc.*, *66*, 1362 (1944).

lets with their convex surfaces evaporate in a closed system and condensation occurs on larger droplets.

The mathematical relation may be derived by recognizing that the liquid in the meniscus of a liquid which has risen to its equilibrium height in a capillary must be in equilibrium with the vapor above the liquid. The vapor pressure at height h above a plane surface is given by (see problem 49, p. 124)

$$p = p_0 e^{-ghM/RT} \tag{6}$$

where p_0 is the vapor pressure at the plane surface ($h = 0$). The acceleration of gravity is represented by g and the molecular weight of the vapor by M. This equation may be rearranged to

$$h = \frac{RT}{gM} \ln \frac{p_0}{p} \tag{7}$$

The height of the equilibrium meniscus is

$$h = \frac{2\gamma}{\rho g r} \tag{8}$$

Eliminating h between these two equations,

$$\ln \frac{p_0}{p} = \frac{2M\gamma}{RTr\rho} \tag{9}$$

If the capillary is small, the radius of curvature of the liquid surface is equal to the radius of the capillary r. For water at 20° the vapor pressure is lowered 1 per cent when $r = 10^{-5}$ cm.

If the liquid does not wet the surface, the liquid surface is convex to the vapor and there is capillary depression. The vapor pressure at height h below the plane surface is

$$p = p_0 e^{ghM/RT} \tag{10}$$

and repeating the above derivation yields

$$\ln \frac{p}{p_0} = \frac{2M\gamma}{RTr\rho} \tag{11}$$

This equation gives the increased vapor pressure of a convex liquid surface with radius of curvature r. For water at 20° the vapor pressure is raised 1 per cent when $r = 10^{-5}$ cm.

Equation 11 is of interest in the consideration of the initial formation of liquid droplets from a supersaturated vapor. If a number of molecules come together to form a small drop, the vapor pressure of the liquid in this drop will be greater than that of the bulk liquid. Therefore, a very small droplet will evaporate rather than grow. This explains why the vapor may remain supersaturated for an extended period. Apparently in order for droplets to be formed at low degrees of supersaturation dust particles or ions must be present to give a larger mass of material and lesser convex curvature.

Interfacial Tension and Emulsions. The interface between two mutually saturated liquids tends to contract, and in principle this interfacial tension can be measured by all the methods used to measure surface tension. Interfacial tensions are even more sensitive to impurities than surface tensions. The effects of impurities and added substances on the interfacial tension are important in determining the properties of emulsions.

An *emulsion* is a system of two immiscible liquids, one of which is dispersed throughout the other in small drops. In order to prepare stable emulsions, it is usually necessary to add a small amount of an *emulsifying agent*, such as a soap, which will reduce the interfacial tension. Obviously, the introduction of a large number of small drops of a liquid within the body of another liquid increases the surface area greatly, and it is clear that the energy required for such an increase in area will be less if the interfacial tension is decreased. The interfacial tension of benzene-water, which is 35 dynes cm^{-1}, can be reduced to 2 dynes cm^{-1} by the addition of sodium oleate. By such procedures it is possible to obtain emulsions which have 100 parts of oil spread out as drops through only 1 part of water. Emulsifying agents include not only soaps and detergents, which reduce surface tensions, but also gelatin, albumin, gum arabic, and other lyophilic colloids which tend to form protective coatings around the small drops and prevent their coalescing.

The oil-in-water emulsion is a common type, but it is possible also to have water-in-oil emulsions. The liquid forming the drops is called the *dispersed liquid*, and the external liquid in which the drops are dispersed is called the *dispersion medium*. In a simple test to determine which is the dispersion medium, a drop of each liquid is added to a sample of the emulsion spread out on a plate. If water mixes with the emulsion, water is the dispersion medium; if oil mixes with it, oil is the dispersion medium.

Whether a water-in-oil or an oil-in-water emulsion is formed depends upon the ratio of the volumes of water and oil and upon the emulsifying agent used. Oil-in-water emulsions are stabilized by sodium soaps, and water-in-oil emulsions are stabilized by magnesium and calcium soaps. If a solution of calcium chloride is gradually added to an oil-in-water emulsion stabilized by a sodium soap, at some $(Ca^{2+})/(Na^+)$ ratio the emulsion changes to a water-in-oil type. The sodium soaps are soluble in water as well as in oil; but the calcium soaps are soluble only in oil, thus explaining the formation of water-in-oil emulsions.

Since emulsions are sometimes objectionable, as, for example, petroleum-water emulsions obtained from oil wells, it is of importance to be able to break them. Emulsions which are stabilized by electrostatic repulsions may be destroyed by the addition of certain electrolytes. Emulsions may often be broken by changing the oil-water ratio (by evaporation or by adding one component) or by mechanical agitation. In making butter the butterfat globules are first accumulated by centrifuging, and then the concentrated emulsion is reversed by mechanical agitation.

Surface Tension of Solutions. The addition of a third component may lower the surface tension considerably; but if the third component causes an increase in surface tension, the effect is small. Solutes are classified as "capillary active" or "capillary inactive" on the basis of their effect on the surface tension. In the case of the aqueous solution-air interface, inorganic electrolytes, salts of organic acids, bases of low molecular weight, and certain nonvolatile nonelectrolytes such as sugar and glycerin are *capillary inactive*. Solutes which are *capillary active* are organic acids, alcohols, esters, ethers, amines, ketones, etc. The effect of capillary-active substances on the surface tension of water may be very great, as illustrated in *Fig. 21-3*. Soaps and detergents are

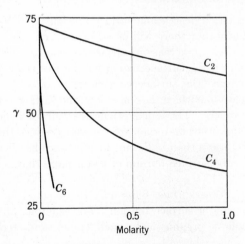

Fig. 21-3. Influence of concentration on the surface tension of aqueous solutions of fatty acids, including acetic (C_2), butyric (C_4), and hexanoic (C_6).

especially effective in lowering the surface tension or interfacial tension. They form surface films on dirt particles in washing.

Gibbs's Equation. According to thermodynamics, processes which are accompanied by a decrease in Gibbs free energy at constant temperature and pressure tend to occur spontaneously. Thus the fact that organic acids can lower the surface tension of water shows that they will spontaneously be adsorbed on the surface so that the Gibbs free energy of the system will be decreased. In 1876 Gibbs * showed that

$$\Gamma_2 = -\frac{1}{RT}\frac{\partial \gamma}{\partial \ln a_2} \tag{12}$$

where Γ_2 is the excess surface concentration of the solute, γ is the surface or interfacial tension, and a_2 is the activity of the solute. The excess surface concentration Γ_2, which is a measure of the amount adsorbed in the surface, is the difference between the total amount of a component per unit volume in the actual system and that in an imaginary system in which the two phases retain the bulk composition right up to an infinitely sharp surface. In dilute solutions in which the activity coefficient may be taken equal to unity, equation 12 written for the mole-fraction scale becomes

$$\Gamma_2 = -\frac{X_2}{RT}\frac{\partial \gamma}{\partial X_2} \tag{13}$$

If a solute causes a decrease in surface tension ($\partial \gamma/\partial X_2$ is negative), equation 13 shows that there will be adsorption on the surface.

If a solute causes an increase in surface tension ($\partial \gamma/\partial X_2$ is positive), its concentration in the surface region will be less than in the bulk of the solution. Since the surface concentration of a substance which causes an increase in surface tension is low, the surface tension will not be raised very much. These deductions are well confirmed by experiment. Soaps and other materials are known to reduce the surface tension of water by more than half, but no substance has been discovered which will raise the surface tension of water more than a few per cent.

Surface Films. Some surface films may be detected by effects other than their lowering of surface tension. For example, films formed by very slightly soluble organic acids, such as oleic and stearic acids, be-

* *The Collected Works of J. Willard Gibbs*, Yale University Press, New Haven, Conn., reprinted in 1948.

have like two-dimensional solids. The movement of the film when it is pushed or blown may be made visible by dusting the surface with some inert powder.

Langmuir devised a method for directly measuring the pressure exerted by such films. In his apparatus a horizontal tray coated with a lacquer, which is not wet by water, is filled with clean water to a level slightly higher than the edges. Movable strips laid across the tray are used to sweep impurities off the surface, and the pressure of the film against a light floating barrier is measured by use of a torsion balance. A small amount of film-forming substance is added to the surface, as, for example, a solution of stearic acid in a volatile solvent which soon evaporates. The film is then pushed toward the floating barrier with one of the movable strips.

The surface pressure may also be measured by determining the surface tension of the film-covered surface. In the Wilhelmy surface balance the downward pull on a thin vertical sheet of glass, partially immersed in the surface, is measured. The surface pressure π of a film on water is equal to the lowering of the surface tension

$$\pi = \gamma_0 - \gamma \tag{14}$$

where γ_0 is the surface tension of pure water. The pressure π measured with a Langmuir surface balance may be considered to result from the fact that the barrier is pulled toward the clean water surface with a force of γ_0 dynes cm^{-1} and toward the film-covered surface by a force of γ dynes cm^{-1}.

With a monolayer of stearic acid, no pressure is detected until the film has been confined to a certain area; then the surface pressure rises rapidly and further decreasing the area causes the film to crumple. Thus stearic acid films behave like two-dimensional solids.

The reason that stearic acid forms a surface film may be explained as follows. The carboxyl group, being a polar group, has a strong affinity for water, whereas the hydrocarbon chain does not, and as a result stearic acid is very insoluble in water. At the surface the carboxyl "heads" can be dissolved in the water phase, while the hydrocarbon "tails" stick up out of the surface. If this idea is correct and the film is really *unimolecular* in thickness, it should be possible to calculate the cross-sectional area of a molecule and its length from the measured film area, the weight and molecular weight, the density of the solid, and Avogadro's number.

Example 1. It is found that 0.106 mg of stearic acid covers 500 cm^2 of water surface. Given the molecular weight (284) and density (0.85 g cm^{-3}) of stearic acid, estimate the cross-sectional area a per stearic acid molecule, and the thickness t of the film.

$$500 \text{ cm}^2 = \frac{(0.106 \times 10^{-3} \text{ g})}{(284 \text{ g mole}^{-1})} (6.02 \times 10^{23} \text{ mole}^{-1})a$$

$$a = 22 \times 10^{-16} \text{ cm}^2 \text{ or } 22 \text{ A}^2$$

$$(500 \text{ cm}^2)t = \frac{0.106 \times 10^{-3} \text{ g}}{0.85 \text{ g cm}^{-3}}$$

$$t = 25 \times 10^{-8} \text{ cm or } 25 \text{ A}$$

It is seen that the cross-sectional area of an aliphatic chain is about 22 A^2. This was later confirmed by X-ray studies of the solid acid (p. 618). Increasing the length of the hydrocarbon chain causes a corresponding increase in the film thickness. This evidence indicates that the film is one molecule thick and closely packed, the longer axis of the molecules being nearly at right angles to the surface of the water film. The dimensions of other molecules determined from unimolecular films are given in Table II.

Table II.[1] Dimensions of Molecules in Unimolecular Films

Film	Formula	Film Thickness, A, length of molecule	Area, A^2
Palmitic acid	$C_{15}H_{31}COOH$	24	21
Stearic acid	$C_{17}H_{35}COOH$	25	22
Cerotic acid	$C_{25}H_{51}COOH$	31	25
Tristearin	$(C_{18}H_{35}O_2)_3C_3H_5$	25	66
Cetyl alcohol	$C_{16}H_{33}OH$	22	21
Myricyl alcohol	$C_{30}H_{61}OH$	41	27

[1] B. H. Ketelle and G. E. Boyd, *J. Am. Chem. Soc.*, *69*, 2808 (1947).

A unimolecular film on the surface of water considerably reduces the rate of evaporation of water. Such films are being tested for conserving water in reservoirs in arid regions.

Lower-molecular-weight fatty acids give films which behave more like two-dimensional gases; that is, the film occupies any given area and the pressure is inversely proportional to the area. At sufficiently low pressures the surface pressure π and area per molecule a are related by

$$\pi a = kT \tag{15}$$

where k is the Boltzmann constant (1.38×10^{-16} erg deg^{-1}). In some cases the behavior of monolayers resembles that of a gas in the critical region, since the film pressure is independent of area at a certain pressure corresponding to the vapor pressure of the two-dimensional liquid.

Langmuir and Blodgett have shown that unimolecular films may be transferred from the water surface to a glass or metal plate which is dipped through the surface. If the plate is drawn up through the surface so that the film is oriented on the plate with the hydrocarbon chains out, the coated plate cannot be wet by water. By depositing a large number of layers on a lens, it is possible to reduce the surface reflection by optical interference so that more light is transmitted than by the uncoated lens. Successive films are added to the surface until the total thickness of the films is equal to a quarter-wavelength of light.

Adsorption by Solids. For a given weight of adsorbent the amount of material adsorbed depends on the pressure (or concentration) of the substance being adsorbed. The higher the pressure or concentration, the greater the amount adsorbed. When an adsorbent is placed in contact with a gas or solution, the amount adsorbed increases, and the concentration of the surrounding molecules decreases until the rate of desorption becomes equal to the rate of adsorption, and thus an equilibrium is established. If the concentration of gas or solution is increased, the weight of adsorbed substance increases to a new equilibrium value; if the concentration is decreased, the adsorbent loses adsorbed substance to its surroundings until equilibrium is again established.

Adsorption occurs on the surface of a solid because of the attractive forces of the atoms or molecules in the surface of the solid. It is convenient to distinguish between *physical adsorption* and *chemisorption*. The forces causing physical adsorption are of the same type as those which cause the condensation of a gas to form a liquid and are generally referred to as van der Waals' forces. The heat evolved in the physical-adsorption process is of the order of magnitude of the heat evolved in the process of condensing the gas, and the amount adsorbed may correspond to several monolayers. Physical adsorption is readily decreased by lowering the pressure of the gas or the concentration of the solute. Chemisorption, on the other hand, is not so readily decreased, and no more than a monolayer may be adsorbed. Also, the heat evolved in chemisorption is considerably larger than in physical adsorption, and it may be assumed that a surface compound is formed.

The extent of adsorption depends greatly upon the specific nature of the solid and of the molecules being adsorbed and is a function of pressure (or concentration) and temperature. If the gas being adsorbed is below its critical point, it is customary to plot the amount adsorbed per gram of adsorbent versus $p/p°$, where $p°$ is the vapor pressure of the bulk liquid adsorbate at the temperature of the experiment. Such an adsorption isotherm is shown in *Fig. 21-4*. The amount of gas adsorbed was determined by measuring the volume v of gas taken up by the adsorbent at various pressures and at a constant temperature of $89.9°K$. As $p/p°$ approaches unity, the amount adsorbed increases rapidly because at $p/p° = 1$ bulk condensation can occur. If the temperature of the experiment is above the critical temperature of the gas, $p/p°$ cannot be calculated. When the adsorption of various gases is

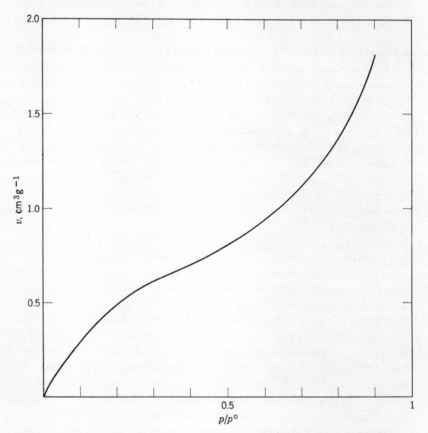

Fig. 21-4. Adsorption of nitrogen on finely divided potassium chloride at $89.9°K$. The ordinate gives the volume (at $0°C$ and 1 atm) adsorbed on 1 gram of solid adsorbent, and the abscissa gives the relative pressure of nitrogen in atmospheres [A. D. Keenan and J. M. Holmes, *J. Phys. Colloid Chem.*, *53*, 1309 (1949)].

compared above their critical temperature, it is generally found that the amount adsorbed is smaller the lower the critical temperature.

In order to discuss the theory of adsorption we will first consider an oversimplified model treated by Langmuir.

Langmuir Theory of Adsorption. Langmuir * considered the surface of a solid to be made up of elementary spaces each of which could adsorb one gas molecule. Furthermore, it was assumed that all the elementary spaces are identical in their affinity for a gas molecule and that the presence of a gas molecule on one space does not affect the properties of neighboring spaces. At adsorption equilibrium the rate of evaporation of the adsorbed gas is equal to the rate of condensation.

If θ is the fraction of the surface occupied by gas molecules, the rate of evaporation from the surface is $r\theta$, where r is the rate of evaporation from the completely covered surface at a certain temperature. The rate of adsorption of molecules on the surface is proportional to the fraction of the area that is not covered $(1 - \theta)$ and to the pressure of the gas (see p. 278). Thus, the rate of condensation is expressed by $k(1 - \theta)p$, where k is a constant at a given temperature and includes a factor to allow for the fact that not every gas molecule which strikes an unoccupied space will stick.

At equilibrium,

$$r\theta = k(1 - \theta)p \tag{16}$$

$$\theta = \frac{kp}{r + kp} = \frac{(k/r)p}{1 + (k/r)p} \tag{17}$$

Since the volume v of gas adsorbed is proportional to θ, equation 17 may be written as

$$v = \frac{abp}{1 + ap} \tag{18}$$

where a has been substituted for k/r, and b is a constant. Thus v is directly proportional to p at very low pressures where $ap \ll 1$. As the pressure is increased, the volume adsorbed increases and approaches the value b asymptotically. The dependence of v on p as given by equation 18 is the same as that shown by the plot of reaction rate versus substrate concentration shown in Fig. 12-8 for an enzymatic reaction.

It is convenient to determine the constants a and b by plotting $1/v$ versus $1/p$, since

$$\frac{1}{v} = \frac{1}{b} + \frac{1}{abp} \tag{19}$$

---

* I. Langmuir, *J. Am. Chem. Soc., 38*, 2267 (1916); *40*, 1361 (1918).

The Langmuir equation is readily derived and easily understood, and it has therefore been used to a considerable extent to interpret adsorption data. However, the Langmuir equation is not a satisfactory representation of physical-adsorption data. For example, it is found that at apparent saturation of the surface only a small percentage of the total area of the adsorbent is covered. Also it is found that the maximum adsorption does not remain constant but increases with decreasing temperature. Both these deviations from the Langmuir theory would result from a heterogeneous surface, that is, a surface on which different regions have different affinities for the substance being adsorbed. It is now believed that most surfaces are heterogeneous.

Surface-Catalyzed Reactions. Often surface-catalyzed reactions obey a rate equation which may be derived from the Langmuir adsorption isotherm. The rate of appearance of product dx/dt formed by the surface reaction is proportional to the fraction of the surface occupied by reactant molecules as given by equation 17.

$$\frac{dx}{dt} = k'\theta = \frac{k'(k/r)p}{1 + (k/r)p} \tag{20}$$

It can be seen from equation 20 that at low pressures, where $1 \gg (k/r)p$, the rate is directly proportional to the pressure.

$$\frac{dx}{dt} = k'\left(\frac{k}{r}\right)p \tag{21}$$

It can also be seen from equation 20 that at high pressures, where $1 \ll (k/r)p$, the rate is independent of the pressure of the reactant.

$$\frac{dx}{dt} = k' \tag{22}$$

Under these conditions the surface is saturated, and further increasing the pressure cannot increase the number of reactant molecules adsorbed. When ammonia is decomposed on a tungsten filament, for example, the rate of decomposition is independent of the pressure, over a wide range of pressure.

It is often found that surface-catalyzed reactions are slowed down by an accumulation of product molecules. This is a result of the adsorption of product molecules on the active sites, which may be taken into account quantitatively in the theory.

The Freundlich Equation. An equation which is sometimes more successful than the Langmuir equation from the empirical standpoint is the Freundlich equation:

$$\frac{x}{m} = kc^n \tag{23}$$

Here x is the amount adsorbed on mass m of adsorbent, and k and n are constants which can be determined using a log-log plot, since

$$\log \frac{x}{m} = \log k + n \log c \tag{24}$$

so that n is the slope of the line and k is the antilogarithm of the intercept.

The Freundlich isotherm equation may be derived,* assuming a heterogeneous surface with adsorption on each class of sites obeying the Langmuir equation. According to the Freundlich equation, the amount adsorbed increases indefinitely with increasing concentration or pressure. Therefore, this equation is unsatisfactory for high coverages.

BET Theory. In physical adsorption molecules of vapor may be adsorbed to the depth of many monolayers. An adsorption isotherm equation has been derived by Brunauer, Emmett, and Teller (BET) †
to provide for multilayer adsorption. It is assumed that the surface possesses uniform, localized sites and that adsorption at one site does not affect adsorption at neighboring sites, just as in the Langmuir theory. It is further assumed that molecules can be adsorbed in second, third, $\cdots$, and nth layers with the surface area available for the nth layer equal to the coverage of the $(n-1)$th layer. The energy of adsorption in the first layer, E_1, is assumed to be constant, and the energy of adsorption in succeeding layers is assumed to be E_L, the energy of liquefaction of the gas.

The BET equation is

$$\frac{p}{v(p^\circ - p)} = \frac{1}{v_m c} + \frac{(c-1)p}{v_m c p^\circ} \tag{25}$$

where v_m is the volume of gas adsorbed when the entire adsorbent surface is covered with a complete unimolecular layer. The volume of gas adsorbed is represented by v, and c is a constant at a given tempera-

---

* G. D. Halsey and H. S. Taylor, *J. Chem. Phys.*, *15*, 624 (1947); G. D. Halsey, in *Advances in Catalysis*, *4*, 259 (1952).

† S. Brunauer, P. H. Emmett, and E. Teller, *J. Am. Chem. Soc.*, *60*, 309 (1938).

ture. According to this equation, a plot of $p/v(p° - p)$ versus $p/p°$ should give a straight line with a slope of $(c - 1)/v_m c$ and an intercept of $1/v_m c$.

The surface area occupied by a single molecule of adsorbate on the surface may be estimated from the density of the liquefied adsorbate. For example, the area occupied by nitrogen molecules at $-195°$ is estimated to be 16.2 A^2 on the assumption that the molecules are spherical and that they are close packed in the liquid. Thus, from the measured value of v_m the surface area of the adsorbent may be calculated. This method is widely used in the determination of the surface areas of solid catalysts and adsorbents. The area values determined in this way seem, in general, to be perfectly satisfactory in spite of the rough approximations of the theory.

Example 2. The volume of nitrogen gas v_m (measured at 760 mm and 0°) required to cover a sample of silica gel with a unimolecular layer is 129 ml g^{-1} of gel. Calculate the surface area per gram of the gel if each nitrogen molecule occupies 16.2 A^2.

$$\frac{(0.129 \, l \, g^{-1})(6.02 \times 10^{23} \, mole^{-1}) \times (16.2 \, A^2)(10^{-10} \, m \, A^{-1})^2}{(22.4 \, l \, mole^{-1})} = 560 \, m^2 \, g^{-1}$$

Several of the assumptions of the BET theory are unsatisfactory. According to this theory, one molecule may be adsorbed on top of an isolated adsorbed molecule, and the energy change is assumed to be the same as when a gas is condensed to liquid in which each molecule has approximately twelve nearest neighbors. Adsorption equations have been derived with more realistic assumptions,* but the problems of surface heterogeneity and lack of an exact theory for liquids make it impossible at present to derive exact equations. The first gas molecules adsorbed are bound on the more active parts of the surface, and the less active parts are covered at higher pressures.

Adsorption isotherms are not always reversible, but show hysteresis loops in which over a considerable time interval the apparent equilibrium pressure at a certain extent of surface saturation is smaller when the pressure has been reduced than when the pressure has been increased. During the adsorption process capillaries may be filled which are not completely emptied at the same pressure on desorption.

Heat of Adsorption. Adsorption data over a range of temperature may be presented as a plot of pressure required to give a certain weight of gas adsorbed per gram of adsorbent versus temperature. Such plots

* G. Halsey, *J. Chem. Phys.*, *16*, 931 (1948); T. L. Hill, *Advances in Catalysis*, *4*, 211 (1952).

look like plots of vapor pressure versus temperature, and the heat of desorption may be calculated using the Clausius-Clapeyron equation (p. 136). The heat required to desorb a mole of gas depends upon the amount adsorbed or, in other words, on the fraction of the surface covered. A larger amount of heat is required to desorb a mole of gas when only a small fraction of the surface is covered than when a large fraction of the surface is covered. This indicates inhomogeneity of the surface, some of the sites having a higher affinity for the gas than others. For large amounts adsorbed the heat of desorption may approach the heat of vaporization for the substance being adsorbed. The nature of the adsorption can be estimated from the heats of adsorption measured in this way; large heats indicate chemisorption, and low heats physical adsorption.

Chromatography. Chromatography is the separation of materials from a flowing stream of solution or gas as it flows over the surface of solids packed in the column.

In 1906 Tswett discovered that, if a solution of chlorophyll from leaves is poured on the top of a column of a suitable adsorbent and a solvent is used to wash the pigments down the column, the colored band is resolved into a series of bands moving at different rates. Each component of the original mixture is represented by a band and may be obtained in a pure form by collecting the various solutions as they come from the column or by cutting the column into segments and eluting the pigment from the adsorbent in each segment. This method is widely used for separation of substances difficult to separate by other methods.* It has proved of great value in the detection and separation of biological materials. When used for separating substances containing radioactive materials, it is possible to detect and separate extremely small quantities of such materials.

Alumina, magnesia, charcoal, and other adsorbents may be used. Colorless materials can be separated also, and the zones may be detected by fluorescence or by chemical analysis of the eluate as it comes from the column.

Other chromatographic procedures are not based on adsorption on a solid but are very similar in operation. In partition chromatography, which is employed in both the liquid (p. 263) and gas phases, a solid is used to hold a film of liquid, and the distribution is between the liquid phase and a gas phase or an immiscible liquid phase. In ion-exchange

---

* H. H. Strain, *Chromatographic Adsorption Analysis*, Interscience Publishers, New York, 1941; L. Zechmeister and L. Cholnoky, *Principles and Practice of Chromatography*, John Wiley & Sons, New York, 1943.

chromatography (p. 263) the equilibrium is between the solution and a salt of the high-molecular-weight ion exchanger.

Precipitation of Lyophobic Colloids. The most important factors in stabilizing colloids are electric charge and hydration or solvation. Either the existence of a net electric charge which causes the particles to repel each other or a film of adsorbed solvent which prevents the particles from adhering to each other may be sufficient to keep the dispersed particles in the colloidal state. In the lyophobic colloids there is little attraction between the dispersed particles and the dispersion medium, and the stability of the colloid depends chiefly on the fact that the charged particles repel each other.*

The ability of dispersed particles to remain in the colloidal state is greatly affected by the concentration of ions. In the absence of ions a lyophobic colloid is not stable, and the material will coagulate. The presence of a few ions stabilizes the colloid because either positive or negative ions are preferentially adsorbed and give their charge to the colloidal particles. However, if there is an excess of electrolyte, the colloid particles will be coagulated by the ions of opposite charge. The concentrations of salts in milliequivalents per liter required to cause precipitation in 2 hr, as found by Freundlich, are recorded in Table III for a positive ferric hydroxide colloid (16 millimoles per liter) and for a negative arsenious sulfide colloid (8 millimoles per liter). In each case, 2 ml of the electrolyte was added to 20 ml of the colloid solution.

Table III illustrates the general principle that positive colloids are precipitated by negative ions and negative colloids are precipitated by positive ions. It is evident that the trivalent ions are much more effec-

Table III. Precipitation of Colloids by Electrolytes

Electrolyte	Concentration of Electrolyte		Electrolyte	Concentration of Electrolyte	
	$(+)$Ferric Hydroxide	$(-)$Arsenious Sulfide		$(+)$Ferric Hydroxide	$(-)$Arsenious Sulfide
NaCl	9	51	$MgSO_4$	0.2	0.8
KCl	9	50	$AlCl_3$	...	0.1
KNO_3	12	50	$Al(NO_3)_3$	...	0.1
$Ba(NO_3)_2$	14	0.7	K_2SO_4	0.2	...
$BaCl_2$	10	0.7	$K_2Cr_2O_7$	0.2	...

*E. J. W. Verwey and J. Th. G. Overbeck, *Theory of the Stability of Lyophobic Colloids*, Elsevier Publishing Co., New York, 1948.

tive in precipitating colloids of opposite sign than are the divalent ions and that the divalent ions are more effective than the univalent ions. The charge on the colloid may be determined by electrophoresis.

The action of electrolytes on lyophilic colloids is less sharply defined than their action on lyophobic colloids. Large concentrations of salts are necessary to precipitate albumins, but small amounts of the heavy metals may give precipitation on account of chemical reactions.

When a lyophilic colloid is added to a solution of a lyophobic colloid, it may form a coating around the lyophobic colloid. The lyophobic colloid surrounded by the film of lyophilic colloid then behaves as a lyophilic colloid and is thus less easily precipitated by ions. Protective coatings of this kind can be illustrated by the stabilizing effect of gelatin added to a lyophobic colloid such as sulfur or freshly precipitated silver bromide. They are found in organic colloids, and they play a part in the behavior of certain cements and even in the geology of certain sedimentary rocks.

REFERENCES

N. K. Adam, *The Physics and Chemistry of Surfaces*, Oxford University Press, Oxford, 1949.

A. W. Adamson, *The Physical Chemistry of Surfaces*, Interscience Publishers, New York, 1960.

A. E. Alexander and P. Johnson, *Colloid Science*, Oxford University Press, Oxford, 1949.

J. J. Bikerman, *Surface Chemistry*, Academic Press, New York, 1958.

S. Brunauer, *Physical Adsorption*, Princeton University Press, Princeton, N. J., 1943.

W. E. Garner, ed., *Chemisorption*, Butterworths Scientific Publications, London, 1957.

W. D. Harkins, *The Physical Chemistry of Surface Films*, Reinhold Publishing Corp., New York, 1952.

J. W. Williams, R. A. Alberty, and E. D. Kraemer, in *Treatise on Physical Chemistry*, Vol. II, ed. by H. S. Taylor and S. Glasstone, D. Van Nostrand Co., Princeton, N. J., 1951.

PROBLEMS

1. The surface tension of toluene at $20°$ is 28.4 dynes cm^{-1}, and its density at this temperature is 0.866 g cm^{-3}. What is the radius of the largest capillary that will permit the liquid to rise 2 cm? *Ans.* 0.0335 cm.

2. (a) The surface tension of water against air at 1 atm is given in the following table for various temperatures:

t, °C	20	22	25	28	30
γ, dynes cm^{-1}	72.75	72.44	71.97	71.50	71.18

Calculate the surface enthalpy at 25° in calories per square centimeter. (b) If a finely divided solid whose surface is covered with a very thin layer of water is dropped into a container of water at the same temperature, heat will be evolved. Calculate the heat evolution for 10 grams of a powder having a surface area of 200 sq meters g^{-1} [W. D. Harkins and G. Jura, *J. Am. Chem. Soc.*, *66*, 1362 (1944)]. *Ans.* 56.8 cal.

3. A solution of palmitic acid ($M = 256$) in benzene contains 4.24 grams of acid per liter. When this solution is dropped on a water surface, the benzene evaporates and the palmitic acid forms a continuous monomolecular film. If it is desired to cover an area of 500 cm^2 with a monolayer, what volume of solution should be used? The area occupied by one palmitic acid molecule may be taken to be 21 A^2. *Ans.* 0.0239 ml.

4. The following table gives the number of milliliters (v) of nitrogen (reduced to 0° and 1 atm) adsorbed per gram of active carbon at 0° at a series of pressures:

p, mm	3.93	12.98	22.94	34.01	56.23
v, ml g^{-1}	0.987	3.04	5.08	7.04	10.31

Plot the data according to the Langmuir isotherm, and determine the constants.
Ans. $a = 7.1 \times 10^{-3}$ mm^{-1}. $b = 36$ ml g^{-1}.

5. One gram of a certain activated charcoal has a surface area of 1000 sq meters. If complete surface coverage is assumed, as a limiting case, how much ammonia, at 25° and 1 atm, could be adsorbed on the surface of 45 grams of activated charcoal? The diameter of the NH_3 molecule is 3×10^{-8} cm, and it is assumed that the molecules just touch each other in a plane so that 4 adjacent spheres have their centers at the corners of a square. *Ans.* 18.6 liters at 25° and 1 atm.

6. Calculate the surface area of a catalyst which adsorbs 103 ml of nitrogen (calculated at 760 mm and 0°) per gram in order to form a monolayer. The adsorption is measured at $-195°$, and the effective area occupied by a nitrogen molecule on the surface is 16.2 A^2 at this temperature. *Ans.* 449 m^2.

---

7. Acetone has a density of 0.790 g cm^{-3} at 20° and rises to a height of 2.56 cm in a capillary tube having a radius of 0.0235 cm. What is the surface tension of the acetone at this temperature?

8. (a) If a liquid surface is expanded, will there be a heating effect or a cooling effect? (b) Given the surface-tension data for water in problem 2, calculate the latent heat of the surface per square centimeter.

9. What is the vapor pressure of water at 25° above the meniscus in a capillary 0.02 mm in diameter? The vapor pressure of a flat surface of water is 23.76 mm at 25°.

10. One hundred grams of oleic acid, $C_{17}H_{33}COOH$, is poured on the surface of a clean lake, where the spreading film can be seen if the water is rippled by a gentle wind or marked with rain drops. The cross-sectional area of the molecule is about 22 A^2. What will be the maximum diameter in meters of a circular film produced in this way?

11. The adsorption of nitrogen on mica is as follows:

p	2.8	6.1	17.3
x/m	12.0	19.0	28.2

(p is given in dynes per square centimeter, and x/m in cubic millimeters of gas at $20°$ and 760 mm adsorbed on 24.3 grams of mica, having a surface of 5750 cm^2.) (a) Determine the constants of the Langmuir equation. (b) Calculate the value of x/m at $p = 23.8$. (The experimental value is 30.8.)

12. Magnesium oxide adsorbs silica from water, and this adsorption follows the Freundlich equation. Magnesium oxide may be used to remove silica from boiler scale. Make a log-log plot of the following data, and calculate the constants of the Freundlich equation. Calculate the parts per million (ppm) of magnesium oxide needed to reduce the residual silica to 2.9 ppm.

MgO, ppm	0	75	100	200
Residual SiO$_2$, ppm	26.2	9.2	6.2	1.0
SiO$_2$ removed, ppm	0	17.0	20.0	25.2

13. The diameter of the hydrogen molecule is about 2.7 A. If an adsorbent has a surface of 850 sq meters ml^{-1} and 95 per cent of the surface is active, how much H$_2$ (measured at standard conditions) could be adsorbed by 100 ml of the adsorbent? It may be assumed that the adsorbed molecules just touch in a plane, and are arranged so that 4 adjacent spheres have their centers at the corners of a square.

14. Mercury does not wet a glass surface. Draw a figure analogous to Fig. 21-2 for mercury and glass, and calculate the relative positions of the mercury surfaces, if the diameter of the capillary is (a) 0.1 mm and (b) 2 mm. The density of mercury is 13.5 g ml^{-1}. The surface tenstion of mercury at $25°$ is 520 dynes cm^{-1}.

15. Calculate the vapor pressure of a water droplet at $25°$ that has a radius of 20 A. The vapor pressure of a flat surface of water is 23.76 mm at $25°$.

16. Derive the ideal gas law for a two-dimensional gas from the Gibbs adsorption isotherm. For dilute solutions the decrease in surface tension is proportional to concentration.

17. In a colloidal solution of silver, it is assumed that each particle is a cube $0.04\ \mu$ on an edge. (a) How many colloid particles can be produced from 0.1 gram of silver? (b) What is the total area of the silver particles? (c) What is the area of a single cube of silver weighing 0.1 gram? The density of silver is 10.5 g cm^{-3}.

18. Two gases, A and B, compete for the binding sites on the surface of an adsorbent. Show that the fraction of the surface covered by A molecules is

$$\theta_A = \frac{b_A p_A}{1 + b_A p_A + b_B p_B}$$

19. The adsorption of ammonia on charcoal is studied at $30°$ and $80°$. It is found that the pressure required to cause the adsorption of a certain amount of NH$_3$ per gram of charcoal is 106 mm at $30°$ and 560 mm at $80°$. Calculate the heat of adsorption at this extent of adsorption.

$$\log \frac{p_2}{p_1} = \frac{\Delta H_{ads}(T_2 - T_1)}{2.3RT_1T_2}$$

CRYSTALS

22

Crystalline solids are those in which the atoms are arranged in some definite arrangement constantly repeated in space. *Amorphous* solids are those which show no long-range order. Examples are pitch and glass, which may be regarded as supercooled liquids in which the force of attraction holding the molecules together is so great that the material is rigid.

Crystalline and amorphous solids differ in several respects. A pure crystalline material usually has a sharp melting point. When an amorphous solid is heated, it gradually softens and becomes fluid over a range of temperature without undergoing a sharp change from solid to liquid. The surfaces of an amorphous substance do not, in general, exhibit definite faces at definite angles, such as are displayed by crystalline solids.

The properties of a crystal, such as tensile strength, elasticity, heat conductance, electric conductance, refractive index, and rate of solution, may be different along different directions; such a crystal is called *anisotropic*. If a given property has the same value in all directions, the crystal is said to be *isotropic* with respect to that property. The characteristic color patterns of anisotropic crystals with polarized light (discussed on p. 509) are used for identification, particularly in the microscopic examination of chemicals and minerals.

Crystal Forms. The size and perfection of crystals depend to a large extent on the rate at which they are formed. The slower the rate of crystallization, the more perfect is the crystal, because the atoms or molecules have more time to find their proper positions in the crystal lattice. In order to grow large crystals the purified salt is melted in a large pot which is then allowed to cool very slowly at an automatically controlled rate. In this way sodium chloride, silver chloride, potassium bromide, lithium fluoride, and other salts have been prepared in large transparent pieces, several inches in diameter, which are valuable for infrared spectrometers. Crystals may be distinguished from each other by shapes, angles between faces, and X-ray-diffraction patterns. A given crystalline form of a chemical compound or mineral always exhibits the same angle between two given faces at a given temperature. This law was discovered by Steno in 1669. It provides an excellent means for the identification of substances by the determination of interfacial angles. Large crystals may be studied directly; small crystals may be examined with a microscope; and all crystals may be investigated by means of the diffraction of X rays.

In 1829 Miller showed that each face of a crystal may be designated by three integers which give the relation of the face to axes through the crystal. The intercepts of the plane of a face of the crystal on the three axes are expressed as ratios to unit distances a, b, and c along these axes. The Miller indices are the reciprocals of the intercepts on the axes in terms of these unit distances multiplied by a factor to eliminate fractions. For example, if a crystal face cuts the x axis at $2a$, the y axis at b, and the z axis at $c/2$, the intercepts are 2, 1, and $\frac{1}{2}$, and the reciprocals are $\frac{1}{2}$, 1, and 2. Multiplying by 2 to eliminate the fraction, the Miller indices are 1, 2, 4. It is found that the faces of crystals tend to have low Miller indices. The faces are indexed in *Fig. 22-1* for several types of crystals belonging to the cubic system. Figure 22-1b represents an octahedron, and c a tetrahedron. Intercepts in the negative direction, i.e., to the left of the origin or downward, are represented by a minus sign over the index number.

Symmetry. Crystals may have four kinds of symmetry, which are defined and then illustrated with a cube. The symmetry elements are:

(a) *Rotation axes.* If a crystal takes on the same appearance n times per 360° rotation around an axis, this is spoken of as an n-fold rotation axis; n may be 2, 3, 4, or 6, but not 5. Axes of fivefold or greater than sixfold symmetry do not occur in crystals since it is not possible to devise patterns with these symmetries which fill space. Rotation axes are represented by the symbols 2, 3, 4, and 6.

(b) *Mirror planes.* Mirror planes are imaginary planes dividing the crystal into halves which are mirror images of each other. A mirror plane is represented by m.

(c) *Center of inversion.* A crystal structure possesses a center of inversion if for every point there is another identical point at an equal distance on the other side of the center of inversion. A center of inversion is represented by i.

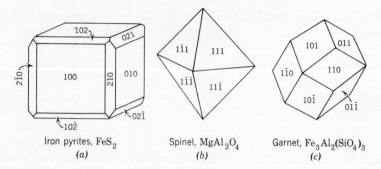

Iron pyrites, FeS$_2$
(a)

Spinel, MgAl$_2$O$_4$
(b)

Garnet, Fe$_3$Al$_2$(SiO$_4$)$_3$
(c)

Fig. 22-1. Crystals belonging to the cubic system.

(d) Rotation-inversion axes. A crystal structure has a rotation-inversion axis if after being rotated 60, 90, 120, or 180° followed by inversion of each point through a center the original appearance is restored. Two-, three-, four- and sixfold rotation-inversion axes are represented by $\bar{2}$, $\bar{3}$, $\bar{4}$, and $\bar{6}$. A $\bar{2}$ rotation-inversion axis is the same as a mirror plane.

A cubic crystal has many types of symmetry, as illustrated in *Fig. 22-2*. An axis passed through the center of a face of a cube is a fourfold axis, and a cube has three such axes.

If a cube is rotated about an axis passing through two diagonally opposite corners, the same appearance is presented three times during a revolution, and there are four such threefold axes of symmetry. An axis passing through the midpoints of two opposite edges is a twofold axis of symmetry. A cubic crystal has two types of mirror planes, those perpendicular to edges of the cube and those bisecting the angles of the upper and lower faces. The center of a cube is a center of inversion.

The crystals illustrated in Fig. 22-1 have all the kinds of symmetry

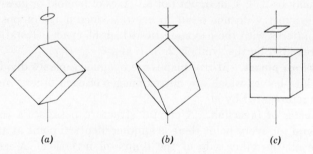

(a)   (b)   (c)

Fig. 22-2. Axes of symmetry of a cube: (a) twofold, (b) threefold, and (c) fourfold.

described for a cube, and so they belong to the cubic system. It may not be so easy to recognize the symmetry of a crystal if it has grown so that crystallographic equivalent faces are very unequal in size.

Lattices and the Unit Cell. A crystal consists of a repetition in three dimensions of a particular group of atoms. This repeating pattern is similar to a wallpaper pattern except that it is in three dimensions. For some purposes it is convenient to represent a crystal by a *space lattice*. A space lattice is an arrangement of points in space such that the environment about any particular point is the same as that about every other point. This array of points in space may be visualized as being formed from the intersections of the three sets of planes in space. The planes in each set are parallel and equally spaced. In this way space is divided into a set of identical parallelepipeds. A single one of these parallelepipeds is referred to as the *unit cell*. The size and shape of the unit cell are represented by the lengths of the three sides, a, b, and c, and the three angles between them, α, β, and γ. The whole crystal may be reproduced by the displacement of the unit cell along the directions of the three axes. The symmetry of the unit cell must be the same as that of the crystal.

There are seven different kinds of unit cells as summarized in Table I, and these are referred to as *crystal systems*. The *minimum* required symmetries for these crystal systems are also summarized in the table.

In *cubic* crystals there are four threefold axes, and there are three mutually perpendicular directions all equivalent to each other. Thus

Table I. Seven Crystal Systems

System	Angles	Axes	Minimum Symmetry
Cubic	$\alpha = \beta = \gamma = 90°$	$a = b = c$	More than one 3-fold axis
Tetragonal	$\alpha = \beta = \gamma = 90°$	$a = b \neq c$	One and only one 4-fold axis (or $\bar{4}$)
Hexagonal (trigonal)	$\alpha = \beta = 90°$; $\gamma = 120°$	$a = b \neq c$	One 6-fold axis (or $\bar{6}$)
Rhombohedral	$\alpha = \beta = \gamma \neq 90°$	$a = b = c$	One and only one 3-fold axis (or $\bar{3}$)
Orthorhombic	$\alpha = \beta = \gamma = 90°$	$a \neq b \neq c$	More than one 2 (or m); none higher
Monoclinic	$\alpha = \gamma = 90°$; $\beta \neq 90°$	$a \neq b \neq c$	Only one 2 (or m) or both
Triclinic	$\alpha \neq \beta \neq \gamma \neq 90°$	$a \neq b \neq c$	None or only i

the properties of a cubic crystal are identical along these three directions.

In *tetragonal* crystals the three axes intersect at right angles, and two of the axes are of equal length while the third is either longer or shorter.

In *hexagonal* crystals there is one sixfold axis and three equivalent directions which are at 120° to each other in a plane normal to the principal axis. Therefore four axes are required for the description of a crystal face.

In *rhombohedral* crystals there is one threefold axis.

In *orthorhombic* crystals the three axes of unequal length all intersect each other at right angles.

In *monoclinic* crystals there are three axes of unequal length, two of which intersect at right angles, while the third axis is perpendicular to one and not to the other.

In *triclinic* crystals there are no planes or axes of symmetry, although there may be a center of symmetry.

In all systems except monoclinic and triclinic the crystal will generally have more symmetry than is listed in Table I, but the symmetry listed in the table is sufficient to put the crystal in a given system. Crystals could be classified on the basis of angles and relative lengths of axes rather than symmetry. However, it can be seen that this would not be a good method of classification because it would depend upon the experimental accuracy with which, say, the actual angle could be distinguished from 90°, and the classification might change with temperature if, for example, the thermal coefficients of expansion were different in two directions. The classification of crystals according to symmetry does not have these limitations and therefore has been adopted.

By putting points at the corners of the unit cells of the seven crystal systems, seven different point lattices can be obtained. However, there are a total of fourteen ways of arranging points in space so that each point has identical surroundings. These lattices, which are shown in *Fig. 22-3*, are called Bravais lattices after the French crystallographer who showed that there are only fourteen of them. In a crystal an atom or a group of atoms may be associated with each lattice point. There are three Bravais lattices with cubic symmetry: the primitive cubic, body-centered cubic, and face-centered cubic, which we will discuss later in some detail.

The internal symmetry of crystals is revealed by X-ray and neutron diffraction. The internal symmetries of crystals may be classified according to 230 space groups. There are 230, and only 230, ways of

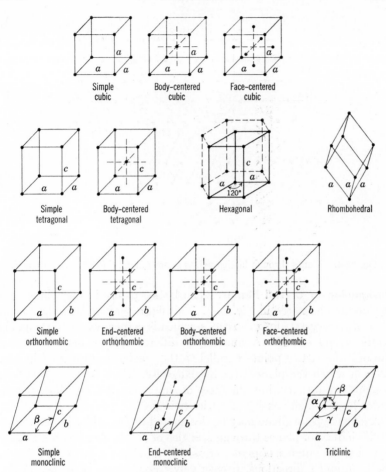

Fig. 22-3.   The fourteen Bravais lattices.

repeating a particular pattern, as, for example, a molecule, in space to give a crystalline material.

It is possible to deduce the shape of the unit cell from the crystal shape by finding the angles and relative dimensions which make it possible to describe all the faces of the crystal by the smallest whole numbers. This process is not as simple in the more complicated types of crystals as in the cubic crystals. The relative dimensions of the crystal are not a direct indication of the dimensions of the unit cell, and it is commonly found that, when a given type of crystal is grown under different conditions, the rates of growth of various faces may be quite different.

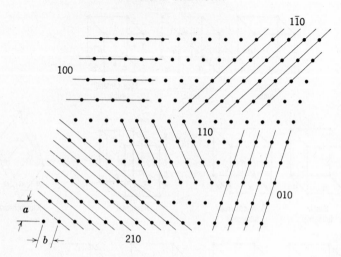

Fig. 22-4. Planes through lattice points as seen along the c axis of a crystal.

Designation of Crystal Planes. The lattice points in one plane of a crystal are illustrated in *Fig. 22-4*. This figure may be taken as an end view of the crystal along the c axis, which is perpendicular to the plane of the a and b axes. A number of different planes may be drawn through the lattice points parallel to the c axis, as illustrated in Fig. 22-4, in which the planes are seen edgewise. Each type of plane is a possible crystal face, but the faces of simple crystals are those planes which have a high density of lattice points.

A given type of plane may be designated by its Miller indices. The Miller indices of planes through a lattice of points may be obtained by counting the number of planes crossed in moving one lattice spacing in the a, b, and c directions, respectively. For the set of planes in the lower left-hand corner, two planes are crossed in going one lattice distance in the direction of the a axis, and one plane is crossed in going one lattice distance horizontally in the direction of the b axis, while no plane would be crossed in going one lattice distance into the paper, since the planes are parallel to the c axis. Thus, this set of planes is designated by the numbers 210. The indices of the planes in the upper right-hand corner are $1\bar{1}0$. The negative sign indicates that, if a plane is intercepted by going in the positive direction along a, it is necessary to go in the negative direction along b in order to intercept the same plane.

Diffraction Methods. Light waves are diffracted by gratings with closely ruled lines with a spacing of the order of magnitude of the wavelength of the light. In 1912 von Laue predicted that a crystal could act as a three-dimensional diffraction grating for X rays. X rays are electromagnetic waves having wavelengths in approximately the range 0.001–50 A. X rays are produced when electrons which have been accelerated by an electrical field strike atoms, usually in a solid target. As a result of electron bombardment of the target, electrons in inner orbits are displaced, and the energy liberated when electrons make the transition from a higher energy level to the vacancy in the inner orbit is given out in the form of an X-ray photon. These transitions produce characteristic lines in the X-ray spectrum. For example, a copper target gives an intense line at 1.54 A. In addition to the characteristic radiation, a continuous range of X-ray wavelengths is obtained; such X rays are called "white" X rays.

As a result of von Laue's suggestion Friedrich and Knipping passed a beam of X rays through a crystal and obtained a diffraction pattern on a photographic plate which proved that von Laue's prediction was correct. In the Laue method, polychromatic or "white" X rays are passed through a carefully oriented crystal which is mounted a few centimeters in front of a photographic film. A Laue photograph of beryl is shown in *Fig. 22-5.* Such photographs indicate much about the symmetry of a crystal. However, since the interpretation of these patterns is more difficult than interpretation of those obtained by use of monochromatic X rays, this method will not be discussed further.

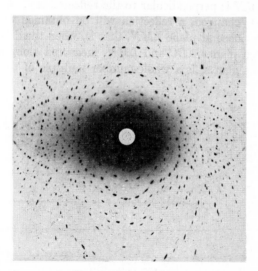

Fig. 22-5. Laue photograph of beryl. The twofold symmetry is evident. (Courtesy Prof. S. Bailey of the University of Wisconsin.)

Beams of electrons and neutrons may also be diffracted by crystals. Neutron diffraction is especially useful for determining the positions of the protons in a structure, since neutrons are strongly scattered by protons, whereas X rays, being scattered by electrons, do not generally lead to a precise determination of the position of protons. Although electrons cannot penetrate very far into solids, studies of electron diffraction by gases are very useful for determining the structures of gas molecules (p. 643), and reflections from surfaces reveal important facts about their structure.

Although X rays are diffracted by the crystal lattice just as visible light is diffracted by a grating, Bragg pointed out that it is convenient to consider that the X rays are "reflected" from planes in the crystal. X rays are reflected only at certain angles which are determined by the wavelength of the X rays and the interplanar spacing in the crystal. The intensity of reflection of X rays at various angles can be determined by the blackening of photographic film or by means of a Geiger-Müller counter, proportional counter, or scintillation counter (p. 686).

A simple relation exists between the wavelength of the X rays, the distance between planes in the crystal, and the angle of reflection. This equation, which is generally called the *Bragg equation*, may be derived by reference to *Fig. 22-6*, in which the horizontal lines represent layers in the crystal separated by the distance d. The plane ABC is perpendicular to the incident beam of parallel monochromatic X rays, and the plane LMN is perpendicular to the reflected ray. As the angle of incidence θ is changed, a reflection will be obtained only when the waves are in phase at plane LMN, that is, when the difference in distance between planes ABC and LMN, measured along rays reflected from different planes, is a whole-number multiple of the wavelength.

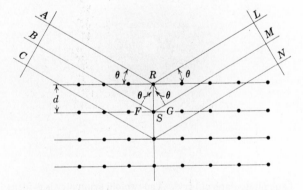

Fig. 22-6. Diagram used in proving that $n\lambda = 2d \sin \theta$.

The angle of reflection is equal to the angle of incidence. The lines RF and RG are drawn perpendicular to the beams, and it can be seen that the ray BSM travels farther than the ray ARL by an amount equal to $FS + SG$. When the difference in distance between planes ABC and LMN measured along rays reflected from different planes is an integral number of wavelengths, the rays reinforce each other and

$$FS + SG = n\lambda \tag{1}$$

Furthermore, since

$$\sin \theta = \frac{FS}{d} = \frac{SG}{d}$$

$$FS = SG = d \sin \theta$$

and

$$n\lambda = 2d \sin \theta \tag{2}$$

This important equation gives the relationship of the distance between planes in a crystal and the angle at which the reflected radiation has a maximum intensity for a given wavelength λ; that is, all the X-ray waves are in phase.

The reflection corresponding to $n = 1$ is called the first-order reflection; the reflection corresponding to $n = 2$ is the second-order reflection; and so on. Each successive order exhibits a wider angle. In discussing X-ray reflections it is customary to set $n = 1$ in equation 2 and consider that the second-order reflection is from planes separated by half the lattice distance, etc. Equation 2 may be written

$$\lambda = 2 \left(\frac{d}{n}\right) \sin \theta$$

$$= 2d_{hkl} \sin \theta \tag{3}$$

where d_{hkl} is the distance between planes having the Miller indices hkl. Thus, the second-order reflection from the 100 planes is labeled 200, the second-order reflection from the 110 planes is labeled 220, and the second-order reflection from the 111 planes is labeled 222.

In order to determine the angles at which X rays are diffracted, a single oriented crystal may be rotated in an X-ray beam and the intensity of X rays at the reflection angle determined with a counter (p. 686). Various types of X-ray cameras have been developed in which the photographic film is moved as the crystal is rotated, so that the problem of getting spots superimposed on other spots in the pattern is avoided.

Instead of scattering X rays from a single large crystal, it is convenient in some types of work to pass a collimated beam of X rays through a large number of small crystals oriented in random directions. This method was proposed originally by Hull and later by Debye and Scherrer. The reflection may be recorded on a circular photographic film as illustrated in *Fig. 22-7*. If coarse crystals are used, the powder pattern is seen to be made up of rings of spots, each spot being produced by a suitably oriented small crystal. If the crystals are very fine, a large number of spots of reflected beams are produced by the different crystal planes and continuous arcs are obtained on the film.

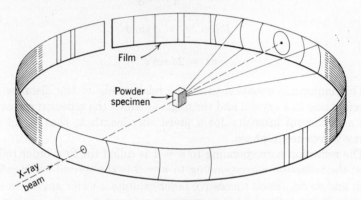

Film

Powder specimen

X-ray beam

Fig. 22-7. X-ray powder camera.

For cubic crystals, X-ray powder patterns are all that is required to differentiate between primitive, body-centered, and face-centered cubic crystals.

Cubic Lattices. Since the cubic system is the simplest, it is explored in some detail here. There are only three lattices which have all the symmetry listed on p. 621 for cubic crystals: primitive, body centered, and face centered. These are illustrated in *Fig. 22-8*. Since these lattices have the same symmetry, they cannot be distinguished by macroscopic examination of the crystals.

In the *primitive cubic lattice* in Fig. 22-8a the lattice points shown as black dots at the corners of a cube may represent atoms, ions, molecules, or any repeating structure. Three types of reflecting planes are illustrated: 100, 110, and 111. The reflections from these planes occur at the smallest angles of all the possible planes that can be imagined in a cubic crystal, since planes with higher Miller indices are closer together and θ will be larger, according to equation 2.

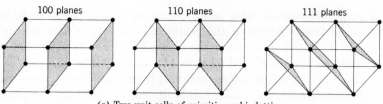

(*a*) Two unit cells of primitive cubic lattice

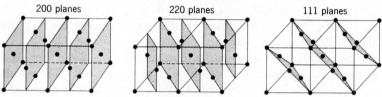

(*b*) Two unit cells of face-centered cubic lattice

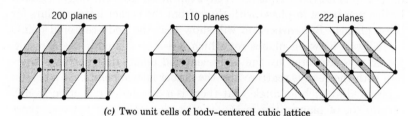

(*c*) Two unit cells of body-centered cubic lattice

Fig. 22-8. Planes through cubic lattices.

In a cubic crystal the perpendicular distance between planes with Miller indices h, k, and l is given by

$$d_{hkl} = \frac{a}{\sqrt{h^2 + k^2 + l^2}} \tag{4}$$

where a is the length of the side of the unit cell.

Exercise I. Prove equation 4, making use of the fact that the sum of the squares of the sides of a right triangle is equal to the square of the hypotenuse. Test this relation for planes with Miller indices 100, 110, and 111.

The spacings between the planes in a cubic crystal are obtained by substituting 0, 1, 2, 3, $\cdots$ for h, k, and l in equation 4. For primitive cubic crystals they may have the following values: a, $a/\sqrt{2}$, $a/\sqrt{3}$, $a/\sqrt{4}$, $a/\sqrt{5}$, $a/\sqrt{6}$, $a/\sqrt{8}$, etc., where $a/\sqrt{7}$ is missing because 7 cannot be obtained from $h^2 + k^2 + l^2$, where h, k, and l have values of 0, 1, 2, 3, $\cdots$.

In the *face-centered cubic lattice* illustrated in Fig. 22-8b there are additional lattice points in the center of each face of the unit cell. These extra lattice points lie in the planes for which the Miller indices are either all even or all odd (that is, 111, 200, 220, 311, 222, 400, 331, 420, etc.), and so reflections are obtained from these planes. However, since the face-centered lattice points lie halfway between the planes for which the Miller indices are not all even or all odd, the reflections from these planes are destroyed by interference. The spacings which will appear are $a/\sqrt{3}$, $a/\sqrt{4}$, $a/\sqrt{8}$, $a/\sqrt{11}$, $a/\sqrt{12}$, $a/\sqrt{16}$, $a/\sqrt{19}$, $a/\sqrt{20}$, etc., which are the distances between the 111, 200, 220, 311, 222, 400, 331, 420, etc., planes, respectively.

In the *body-centered cubic lattice* illustrated in Fig. 22-8c there is an additional lattice point in the center of each unit cell. These extra lattice points lie in the 110 planes, and further analysis shows that they always lie on planes for which the sum of the Miller indices $(h + k + l)$ is even. Thus the X rays diffracted from the body-centered lattice points are in phase with those from the corner lattice points for these planes. But inspection will show that the body-centered points lie halfway between planes for which $h + k + l$ is odd. As a result, the X rays scattered by the body-centered points destructively interfere with the X rays scattered by the corner lattice points. If a crystal is oriented at such an angle that there is a first-order reflection from a certain set of planes, the insertion of a plane halfway between these planes will cause destructive interference. Therefore, no 100 reflection is obtained. A similar interference destroys the reflection from the 111 planes. Thus the interplanar spacings found for a body-centered cubic lattice are $a/\sqrt{2}$, $a/\sqrt{4}$, $a/\sqrt{6}$, $a/\sqrt{8}$, etc., which are the distances between the 110, 200, 211, and 220 planes. From these considerations it is possible to determine from the missing X-ray lines to which type of cubic lattice a given crystal belongs.

The reflections for the three types of cubic crystals are summarized in *Fig. 22-9*, in which the presence of a reflection is indicated by a line at the corresponding angle of incidence. The angle of reflection for a real crystal depends upon the length of the unit cell a and the wavelength λ of the X rays used. For the purposes of this illustration, the ratio λ/a is arbitrarily taken as 0.500 for primitive cubic, 0.353 for body-centered cubic, and 0.289 for face-centered cubic. It may be seen that the various types of cubic crystals may be readily distinguished by their diffraction patterns, since the spacing of the lines is qualitatively different. In the powder pattern for primitive cubic the successive lines are closer together, and there is a gap after the sixth line. In the powder pattern for body-centered cubic this gap is filled

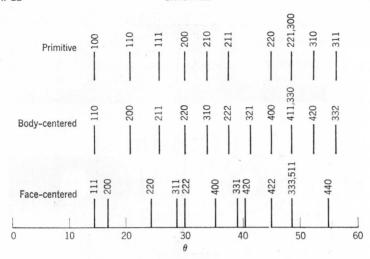

Fig. 22-9. Angles of incidence θ and Miller indices for reflections from cubic crystals. The values of λ/a have been chosen arbitrarily to cause the first reflection to fall at the same angle for each type of crystal. For primitive cubic, $\lambda/a = 0.500$; for body-centered cubic, $\lambda/a = 0.353$; for face-centered cubic, $\lambda/a = 0.289$.

in. In the powder pattern for face-centered cubic the first two lines are relatively close together, the second line is by itself, and the next two lines are close together.

Powder Patterns for Cubic Crystals. The powder patterns of three substances forming cubic crystals are shown in *Fig. 22-10*. As may be seen by comparison with Fig. 22-9, the reflections for sodium chloride are found to correspond to those expected for a face-centered cubic lattice. The Miller indices have been assigned on this basis. The 100 reflection is missing, and so none of the spacings calculated using the Bragg equation are equal to the length of the side of the unit cell a. However, a may be calculated from the angle of any reflection by use of equations 3 and 4. The value of a for sodium chloride is 5.64 A.

The structural units of the face-centered lattice which have thus been found could be sodium chloride molecules, or there might be two interpenetrating lattices, one consisting of sodium atoms or ions and the other consisting of chlorine atoms or ions. If the lattice were made up of sodium chloride molecules, all units of the lattice would be the same, and a more detailed consideration of the theory shows that the intensities of the X-ray reflections would always decrease progressively from first- to second- to third-order reflections. This is true for the 200, 400, and 600 reflections, but not for the 111, 222, 333, $\cdots$

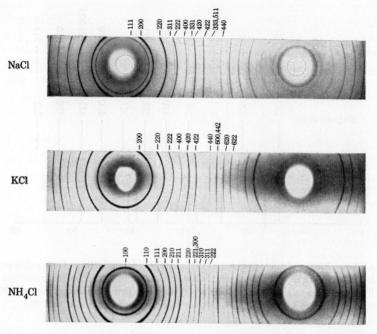

Fig. 22-10. X-ray powder patterns for cubic crystals. The X-ray beam enters through the hole at the right and leaves through the hole at the left (see Fig. 22-7). (Courtesy Prof. S. Bailey of the University of Wisconsin.)

reflections. It may be noted in Fig. 22-10 that the 111 reflection is very weak, while 222 is strong and 333 is apparently missing. This fact leads to the requirement of two interpenetrating lattices, as shown in *Fig. 22-11*, and evidence will be cited presently to show that these interpenetrating lattices are composed of ions rather than atoms.

The square connecting chloride ions is drawn in Fig. 22-11, showing that there is a face-centered chloride ion. Similar squares could be drawn on any part of the faces. A square is drawn with dashed lines for the sodium ions; it is evident that such squares can be drawn anywhere on any of the faces, showing that there are interpenetrating face-centered lattices of sodium and chloride ions. It is to be noted that these lattices overlap by half the length of the face, so as to give an interpenetrating lattice in which the corners of the sodium cube always come halfway between the corners of the chloride cube and the corners of the chloride cube come halfway between the corners of the sodium cube.

A further examination of Fig. 22-11 shows that the 111 planes which cut diagonally through the sodium chloride lattice include only sodium ions or only chloride ions. Thus the 111 planes are alternately planes of sodium and chloride ions. It may be remembered that the maximum in X-ray reflections occurs when the angle is such that the paths between successive layers of ions are equal to one wavelength of the reflected radiation. If the rays are reflected from these planes at such an angle that the rays from successive planes of chloride ions differ in path length by a distance of one wavelength, the rays coming from successive sodium-ion planes, which are spaced equally between them,

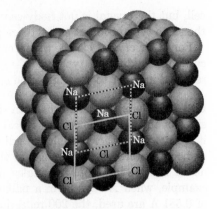

Fig. 22-11. Interpenetrating face-centered lattice of sodium chloride; small spheres, sodium ions; large spheres, chloride ions.

will then differ by half a wavelength and cause interference. The interference would be complete except for the fact that the chloride ions have more electrons and scatter X rays more efficiently than the sodium ions. In the case of the reflections from the 222 planes, however, there is a difference of a whole wavelength between the rays from the chloride and from the sodium planes, so that there is no interference, and the 222 reflection is intense. The 333 reflection again corresponds to a difference of one-half wavelength between the two sets of reflecting planes, and this interference, combined with the fact that the third-order spectrum is naturally weaker, leads to its practical disappearance.

The powder pattern for potassium chloride given in Fig. 22-10 is superficially that of a primitive cubic lattice. This appears surprising, since the structure would be expected to be face centered like that for sodium chloride, but the reflections look very much like those from a simple cubic structure because the scattering power of the potassium ion is almost exactly equal to that of the chloride ion, since both ions have the argon electronic structure. A more accurate determination of the intensities of reflection shows that potassium chloride forms a face-centered lattice.

The powder pattern for ammonium chloride given in Fig. 22-10 shows that it has a primitive cubic lattice, which can be resolved into two symmetrically interpenetrating lattices, one of chloride ions and one of ammonium ions. If the center of a chloride ion is taken as the corner of the unit cell, then the ammonium ion lies at the center of the cell, but the crystal is not body-centered cubic, since it does not have the same type of ion at each lattice point.

For other crystal classes the interpretation is very much more difficult, and additional types of X-ray-diffraction experiments may be required in order to determine the structure.

Unit-Cell Dimensions. It has been shown that the spacings and intensities of the X-ray reflections reveal the type of crystal lattice. After it is known whether a cubic crystal is of the primitive, face-centered, or body-centered type, the size of the unit cell may be calculated by use of Bragg's law from the angles at which X rays are reflected. For example, when X rays from a palladium target having a wavelength of 0.581 A are used, the 200 reflection of sodium chloride occurs at an angle of 5.9°. According to Bragg's law,

$$d_{200} = \frac{\lambda}{2 \sin \theta} = \frac{0.581 \times 10^{-8} \text{ cm}}{2 \sin 5.9} = 2.82 \times 10^{-8} \text{ cm}$$

Since the distance between 200 planes is one-half the length of the side of this unit cell, $a = 5.64 \times 10^{-8}$ cm.

If the type of crystal lattice and the number of ions or atoms per unit cell are known, the size of the unit cell may be calculated from the density of the crystal and the known atomic weights without the use of X-ray data. In the unit cell of sodium chloride there are four sodium ions and four chloride ions, as may be seen from Fig. 22-11. In the face-centered cubic lattice of chloride the ion at a corner of a unit cell is actually shared by eight adjacent unit cells, so that only one-eighth of its mass is associated with one unit cell. There are eight such corner ions per unit cell, each contributing an eighth of its mass to the unit cell, so that the corner ions together contribute one chloride ion for each unit cube of the chloride-ion lattice. In addition each unit cube of the chloride lattice has one ion on each of its six faces which is shared by an adjacent cube. Accordingly half of the six ions, or three, can be attributed to a given cube. Thus the unit cell of the sodium chloride lattice contains $(\frac{1}{8})(8) + (\frac{1}{2})(6) = 4$ chloride ions and an equal number of sodium ions.

Since the density of sodium chloride is 2.163 g cm^{-3}, the length a of the side of the unit cell which contains four sodium ions and four chlorine atoms may be calculated as follows:

$$2.163 \text{ g cm}^{-3} = \frac{(4)(58.45 \text{ g mole}^{-1})}{(6.02 \times 10^{23} \text{ mole}^{-1})a^3}$$

$$a = 5.64 \times 10^{-8} \text{ cm}$$

The wavelength of X rays may be determined from the diffraction of X rays by finely ruled gratings or by crystals for which the interplanar spacings are known. If the wavelength of the X rays and the interplanar spacings are known, Avogadro's number may be calculated from the measured angles of reflection.

Example 1. Potassium crystallizes with a body-centered cubic lattice and has a density of 0.856 g cm^{-3}. Calculate the length of the side of the unit cell a and the distance between 200, 110, and 222 planes.

$$0.856 \text{ g cm}^{-3} = \frac{(2)(39.1 \text{ g mole}^{-1})}{(6.023 \times 10^{23} \text{ mole}^{-1})a^3}$$

$$a = 5.34 \times 10^{-8} \text{ cm or } 5.34 \text{ A}$$

$$d = \frac{5.34}{\sqrt{h^2 + k^2 + l^2}}$$

For 200 planes, $d = 5.34/\sqrt{4} = 2.67$ A.
For 110 planes, $d = 5.34/\sqrt{2} = 3.77$ A.
For 222 planes, $d = 5.34/\sqrt{12} = 1.54$ A.

Ionic Radii in Crystals. In a number of inorganic crystals the binding is primarily due to electrostatic attractions between positive and negative ions. Since the coulombic force is undirected, the relative sizes of the ions largely determine how the ions are packed to form a three-dimensional array. The radius of an ion is nearly the same in different crystals because the repulsive force increases very sharply as the internuclear distance becomes smaller than a certain value. The ionic radii of the halide ions and the alkali metal ions may be calculated fairly simply from the unit-cell distances of the alkali halide crystals, since these all belong to the face-centered cubic system, except the cesium salts, which are primitive cubic.

The lengths of the sides of the unit cells of alkali halide crystals are given in Table II. Using the data in this table, it is possible to calculate the radii of the various ions.

Table II.　Unit-Cell Distances for Alkali Halide Crystals at 25°

(Face-Centered Cubic)

	Li$^+$	Na$^+$	K$^+$
Cl$^-$	5.14 A	5.62 A	6.28 A
Br$^-$	5.50	5.96	6.58
I$^-$	6.04	6.46	7.06

The unit-cell distances for all the potassium halides may be used to calculate the differences in radii of the halide ions, assuming the radius of the potassium ion remains constant. Similarly, the interatomic distances for the series of alkali chlorides indicate the differences in radii of the alkali-metal cations. Consistent values of the differences in radii for the halide ions are obtained for all the alkali halides except the lithium salts. The lithium salts are exceptional because the lithium ion is so small that it does not fill the holes between the larger halide ions. Thus the halide ions are in contact along the diagonal in a face of the lithium halide crystals, as illustrated in *Fig. 22-12*. Thus the

LiCl NaCl KCl

Fig. 22-12. Alkali halide crystal structures. The cations are represented by darker circles.

radii for the halide ions can be calculated from the size of the unit cell for the lithium halides. The ionic radii of sodium and potassium are then calculated from the unit-cell distances in the sodium and potassium salts. As may be seen in the figure, the length of the diagonal of a face of the unit cell of lithium chloride is four times the chloride-ion radius r so that:

$$a^2 + a^2 = (4r)^2 \tag{5}$$

$$r = \frac{a}{2\sqrt{2}} \tag{6}$$

Thus, using the data in Table II for lithium halides, it is found that the ionic radii for Cl^-, Br^-, and I^- are 1.81, 1.94, and 2.14 A, respectively. As may be seen from the sodium chloride structure in Fig. 22-12,

$$a = 2r_{Cl^-} + 2r_{Na^+} \tag{7}$$

The average of the three values for r_{Na^+} obtained from sodium chloride, sodium bromide, and sodium iodide is 1.03 A. The average of the three values for r_{K^+} obtained from potassium chloride, potassium bromide,

Table III.[1] Ionic Radii in Crystals

(In angstrom units)

Li^+	0.60	Be^{2+}	0.31	O^{2-}	1.40	F^-	1.36
Na^+	0.95	Mg^{2+}	0.65	S^{2-}	1.84	Cl^-	1.81
K^+	1.33	Ca^{2+}	0.99	Se^{2-}	1.98	Br^-	1.95
Rb^+	1.48	Sr^{2+}	1.13	Te^{2-}	2.21	I^-	2.16
Cs^+	1.69	Ba^{2+}	1.35				

[1] L. Pauling, *The Nature of the Chemical Bond*, Cornell University Press, Ithaca, 1960.

and potassium iodide is 1.36 A. The best values of these ionic radii in crystals, as given by Pauling and summarized in Table III, are somewhat different because further data and certain necessary corrections have been taken into account. It is seen that in each column of the periodic table the ionic radius increases with the number of orbital electrons.

Other Cubic Crystals. The X-ray-diffraction patterns of cesium chloride show that it forms primitive cubic crystals. There are interpenetrating lattices of Cs^+ and Cl^-. Each ion is surrounded by eight nearest neighbors of the opposite charge. Other salts crystallizing in this way are ammonium chloride and rubidium chloride.

The X-ray-diffraction pattern of a diamond indicates that it has the face-centered cubic structure. In this structure there are two carbon atoms associated with each lattice point, so that there are eight atoms in a unit cell (compared with four lattice points per unit cell). The carbon atoms are equidistant from their four nearest neighbors and are bonded tetrahedrally. This is a fairly open structure, only 34 per cent of the volume being filled if the carbon atoms are considered to be spheres which just touch. Silicon, germanium, and gray tin also crystallize with this structure.

Determination of the Structure of More Complicated Crystals. For more complicated crystals a different procedure is required for the determination of the structure. The procedure may be divided into the following four steps:

1. The dimensions and angles of the unit cell are determined from the angles of X-ray diffraction.

2. The number of molecules or formula units per unit cell is calculated from the unit-cell volume and the density.

3. The space group (p. 622) is determined by a study of the intensities of reflections in the X-ray-diffraction pattern, together with information on the symmetry of the lattice.

4. The positions of the atoms within the unit cell are determined from the intensities of the reflections. This last step requires mathematical methods too complicated to be discussed here. Since it is the electrons that are responsible for the scattering of X rays, the crystal structure will be completely solved if the electron density (number of electrons per unit volume) can be found throughout the unit cell. In principle the electron density may be calculated from the diffraction data. It is customary to calculate the projection of the actual three-dimensional pattern on an appropriate plane. The computation of these electron-density maps has been facilitated by the use of automatic computing equipment.

An electron-density map for crystalline maleic acid is shown in *Fig. 22-13.* In the construction of such a map it is necessary to measure the intensities of the scattered beams. If there is a heavy atom in

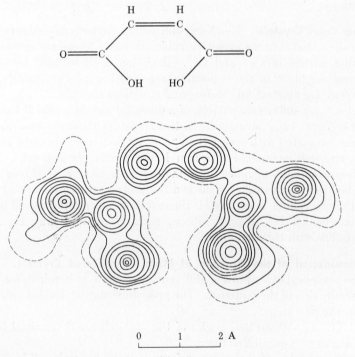

Fig. 22-13. Electron-density map for crystalline maleic acid [M. Shahat, *Acta Cryst., 5,* 763 (1952)].

the unit cell, the structure may be determined directly. Otherwise it is necessary to use a method of successive approximations, which starts with an initial assumed trial structure, in order to obtain the correct electron-density map. Once the map has been calculated from the intensities of X-ray reflections, the arrangement of atoms may be seen directly, as illustrated in Fig. 22-13. Bond distances and angles may be obtained. A number of bond distances are summarized on p. 497.

X-ray diffraction has been used to determine the positions of atoms in organic compounds of unknown structure, such as vitamin B_{12}.

Even materials not ordinarily classed as crystalline yield X-ray-diffraction patterns—for example, fibers, rubber, shellac, cellulose compounds, and asbestos. A photograph with a beam of monochromatic X rays gives symmetrical arcs for fibers.

X-ray analysis has also been of great help as a research tool in inorganic chemistry. For example, in the study of the synthetic elements neptunium, plutonium, curium, and americium it was possible to establish quickly the purity of compounds and the chemical composition with exceedingly small amounts of material and without destroying the samples.

The X-ray pattern for an unknown substance may be used to identify it, or the presence of impurities may be detected, and even measured quantitatively, in a known substance. This application is greatly facilitated by such tables as those of the American Society for Testing Materials, which give the spacings calculated from the three strongest lines for a very large number of substances.

The determination of the fluorescence of substances when exposed to X rays is also useful for identification and analysis.

Binding Forces in Crystals. A number of different types of binding forces are involved in holding crystals together. The physical properties of a crystal are very dependent upon the type of bonding. The bonding in some crystals is intermediate between the following types, and no sharp demarcation lines can be drawn.

1. Ionic crystals. There are a number of indications that in sodium chloride crystals the lattice points are occupied by ions rather than atoms. Since molten sodium chloride conducts electricity, it is reasonable to assume that the ions which produce this electric conductivity actually exist as charged ions in the crystal lattice. Another convincing argument for the ionic lattice of certain crystals depends on the lattice energies as determined from the heat of formation and heat of vaporization. The energy required to separate the ions in the crystal lattice to an infinite distance agrees with that calculated on the assumption that the units are ions held together by electrostatic forces.

In ionic crystals there is no fixed directed force of attraction. Although the ionic crystals are strong, they are likely to be brittle. They have very little elasticity and cannot easily be bent or worked. The melting points of ionic crystals are generally high (NaCl, 800°; KCl, 790°). In ionic crystals some of the atoms may be held together by covalent bonds to form ions having definite positions and orientations in the crystal lattice. For example, in the case of calcium carbonate a carbonate ion does not "belong" to a given calcium ion, but three particular oxygen atoms do belong to a given carbon atom.

2. Covalent crystals. Crystals held together by covalent bonds in three dimensions are strong and hard and have high melting points. A diamond is an example of this type. Each carbon atom is bonded to four others in a tetrahedral arrangement. This arrangement is similar to that in organic compounds, and indeed the C—C bond distance is the same as in aliphatic compounds (1.54 A). Silicon and zinc sulfide also form crystals of the diamond type.

The great difference between graphite and diamond can be understood in terms of the crystal lattice. Graphite has hexagonal networks in sheets like benzene rings. The distance between atoms in the plane is 1.34 A, but the distance between these atomic layer planes is 3.41 A. In two directions, then, the carbon atoms are tightly held as in the diamond, but in the third direction the force of attraction is much less. As a result one layer can slip over another. The crystals are flaky, and yet the material is not wholly disintegrated by a shearing action. This planar structure is part of the explanation of the lubricating action of graphite, but this action also depends upon adsorbed gases, and the coefficient of friction is much higher in a vacuum.

Covalent crystals are like ionic crystals in that there are no larger groups of atoms that differ from the fundamental units of which the lattice is made, so that the whole crystal may be regarded as the molecule.

3. Van der Waals' crystals. Crystals consisting of neutral molecules are held together by weaker forces of the same type as are involved in gases and necessitate the introduction of van der Waals' a (p. 22). Since such interactions are weak, molecular crystals are soft and possess comparatively low melting points. Examples of crystals held together by van der Waals' bonds are carbon dioxide, carbon tetrachloride, argon, and most organic compounds.

4. Hydrogen-bonded crystals. In many crystals a hydrogen atom is attracted by rather strong forces to two atoms, instead of only one, as discussed on p. 494. Hydrogen bonds are involved in many organic and inorganic crystals and in the structure of ice and water. They are comparatively weak bonds.

5. Metallic crystals. In metals the positive ions are held together by a cloud of electrons, and since the bonding does not have a strong directional nature, the arrangement of atoms frequently corresponds to closest packing of spheres. There are two ways in which spheres of equal size may be stacked with a minimum of empty space. These are referred to as *cubic close packing* and *hexagonal close packing*. In *Fig. 22-14a* it can be seen that the densest packing of spheres can be ac-

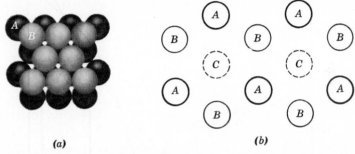

(a)   (b)

Fig. 22-14. (a) Two layers of close-packed spheres. (b) Centers of spheres in successive planes.

complished when a sphere in the second layer rests simultaneously and symmetrically on three spheres in the first layer. Referring to spheres in the first layer by A, it can be seen from *Fig. 22-14b* that there are two kinds of positions, B and C, for the second and further layers. The common sequences of layers in metals are $ABABAB\cdots$, which is the close-packed hexagonal structure, and $ABCABC\cdots$, which is face-centered cubic (cubic close packing). The fact that these regular sequences are common, whereas faulted close-packed structures, such as $ABABCAB\cdots$, are not, indicates some directional nature of the bonding.

In each of these close-packed arrangements there are twelve equidistant nearest neighbors surrounding each atom; there are six in the same plane and three in each of the adjacent planes. Although the majority of metallic elements crystallize with hexagonal close packing or cubic close packing, some crystallize with the body-centered cubic arrangement. This later structure is not a close-packed structure, and there are only eight equidistant nearest neighbors surrounding each atom. Copper, silver, and lead crystallize in cubic close packing (face-centered cubic), and zinc and magnesium in hexagonal close packing.

The alkali metals and tungsten crystallize in a body-centered cubic lattice.

A characteristic of metals is that the electrons are held loosely in the crystal so that they are good conductors of electricity. In contrast to the other types, metallic crystals can be bent and worked and are strong.

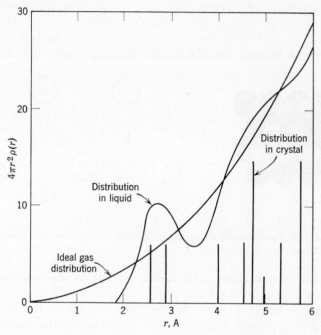

Fig. 22-15. Atomic distribution for liquid Zn at 460°. (Adapted from L. S. Darken and R. W. Gurry, *Physical Chemistry of Metals*, McGraw-Hill Book Co., New York, 1953, p. 112.)

Structure of Liquids. In a perfect crystal the atoms, ions, or molecules occur at definite distances from any individual atom, ion, or molecule which is taken as the center of a coordinate system. In a gas the molecules have random positions at a given time. Liquids are intermediate between crystals and gases in that the molecules are not arranged in a definite lattice, but there is some order. By a detailed analysis of the intensity of the scattered X-rays it is possible to calculate the distribution of atoms or molecules in the liquid and obtain a plot such as *Fig. 22-15*. The ordinate of this plot gives the probability of finding other atoms at a distance r from a certain atom. This probability is given by $4\pi r^2 \rho$, where ρ is the local density of atoms (number of atoms per unit volume). The area under a plot of the radial distribution function $4\pi r^2 \rho$ against r between two values of r is equal to the number of atoms contained in the corresponding spherical shell. In Fig. 22-15 the smooth parabolic curve represents the purely random distribution of an ideal monatomic gas, and the vertical lines represent the positions and numbers of the atoms in the crystal. As the temperature of a liquid is raised, the maxima and minima in the distribution curve become less pronounced and the distribution function becomes more like that for a gas. The X-ray-diffraction method of investigating liquids is useful for determining the nature of the molecules in the liquid state. Studies of liquid phosphorus show the existence of P_4 molecules.

The theory of liquids is in a much less satisfactory state than the theories of gases and crystals, but important progress is being made in our understanding of the structure of liquids. The thermodynamic properties of a liquid may be expressed in terms of the radial-distribution function.

Electron Diffraction. The structure of gas molecules may be determined by electron diffraction. Electrons which have been accelerated by an electric field have a wavelength associated with them, so that they are diffracted in a manner similar to that described for X rays. In an electron-diffraction apparatus an accelerating potential of about 40,000 volts is used, which gives the electrons a wavelength of 0.06 A. They are shot out of a small pinhole at a photographic plate about 10 cm away in an evacuated apparatus shown in principle in *Fig. 22-16.*

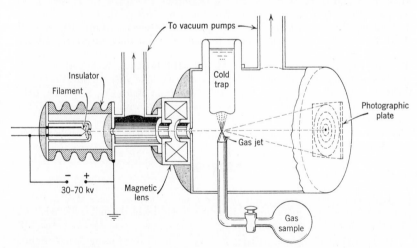

Fig. 22-16. Electron-diffraction apparatus for determining molecular structure. (Courtesy of Prof. L. S. Bartell of Iowa State University.)

A magnetic lens is used to focus the electron beam on the photographic plate so that a sharper pattern will be obtained. A stream of vapor of the substance to be studied is passed at a low pressure (10^{-5} mm) through the beam.

In the gas stream the molecules have all possible orientations. Because of the high velocity of the accelerated electrons the motion of a single molecule is negligible during the time that an electron is traversing the field of the molecule. The distances between all atom pairs in the molecule give rise to electron intensities which are functions of angle, yielding a diffraction pattern of concentric rings. Thus the analysis of the diffraction pattern yields all the possible internuclear distances. In the case of simple molecules, or molecules with considerable symmetry, it is possible to figure out the complete structure and bond lengths and angles. The uncertainty in the bond lengths determined in the best electron-diffraction work is about 0.003 A.

REFERENCES

C. S. Barrett, *Structure of Metals*, McGraw-Hill Book Co., New York, 1952.

M. J. Buerger, *Elementary Crystallography*, John Wiley & Sons, New York, 1956.

C. W. Bunn, *Chemical Crystallography*, Oxford University Press, Oxford, 1946.

B. D. Cullity, *Elements of X-Ray Diffraction*, Addison-Wesley Publishing Co., Reading, Mass., 1956.

W. E. Garner, *Chemistry of the Solid State*, Academic Press, New York, 1955.

C. Kittel, *Introduction to Solid State Physics*, John Wiley & Sons, New York, 1956.

H. P. Klug and L. E. Alexander, *X-Ray Diffraction Procedures for Polycrystalline and Amorphous Materials*, John Wiley & Sons, New York, 1954.

L. Pauling, *The Nature of the Chemical Bond*, Cornell University Press, Ithaca, 1960.

J. M. Robertson, *Organic Crystals and Molecules*, Cornell University Press, Ithaca, 1953.

F. Seitz, *The Modern Theory of Solids*, McGraw-Hill Book Co., New York, 1940.

A. Taylor, *X-ray Metallography*, John Wiley & Sons, New York (in press).

R. W. G. Wyckoff, *The Structure of Crystals*, Chemical Catalog Co., New York, 1931.

R. W. G. Wyckoff, *Crystal Structures* (in five sections with supplements), Interscience Publishers, New York, 1959.

C. Zwikker, *Physical Properties of Solid Materials*, Interscience Publishers, New York, 1954.

PROBLEMS

1. A certain crystal face intercepts the x axis at $\frac{1}{2}a$, the y axis at b, and the z axis at $\frac{1}{2}c$, where a, b, and c are the lengths of the sides of the unit cell. What are the Miller indices of this face? *Ans.* 212.

2. The X-ray-diffraction pattern of a crystal is obtained using X rays from a copper target, and a certain reflection is found at $10°27'$. With a molybdenum target the same reflection was found at $4°48'$. Given the wavelength of the X rays from the copper target (λ = 1.540 A), calculate the wavelength of the X rays from the molybdenum target. $Ans.$ 0.710 A.

3. When an X-ray powder pattern of crystalline copper is taken using X rays from a copper target (the wavelength of the $K\alpha$ line is 1.5405 A), reflections are found at θ = 21.65°, 25.21°, 37.06°, 44.96°, 47.58°, and other larger angles. (a) What type of cubic crystal is formed by copper? (b) What is the length of a side of the unit cell at this temperature? (c) What is the density of copper?
         $Ans.$ (a) Face-centered. (b) 3.616 A. (c) 8.93 g cm^{-3}.

4. Cesium chloride, bromide, and iodide form interpenetrating simple cubic crystals rather than interpenetrating face-centered cubic crystals like the other alkali halides. The length of the side of the unit cell of CsCl is 4.121 ± 0.003 A. (a) What is the density? (b) Calculate the ion radius of Cs$^+$, assuming that the ions touch along a diagonal through the unit cell and that the ion radius of Cl$^-$ is 1.81 A.
         $Ans.$ (a) 3.99 g cm^{-3}. (b) 1.77 A.

5. The density of potassium chloride at 18° is 1.9893 g cm^{-3}, and the length of a side of the unit cell is 6.29082 A, as determined by X-ray diffraction. Calculate Avogadro's number, using the values of the atomic weights. $Ans.$ 6.020 $\times$ 10^{23}.

6. The crystal unit cell of magnesium oxide is a cube 4.20 A on an edge. Each cell contains the equivalent of 4 atoms of magnesium and 4 of oxygen. What is the density of crystalline MgO? $Ans.$ 3.62 g cm^{-3}.

7. Tungsten forms body-centered cubic crystals. From the fact that the density of tungsten is 19.3 g cm^{-3} calculate (a) the length of the side of this unit cell and (b) d_{200}, d_{110}, and d_{222}.
         $Ans.$ (a) 3.16 A. (b) d_{200} = 1.58, d_{110} = 2.23, d_{222} = 0.912 A.

8. From the data of Table II and the ion radii of Cl$^-$, Br$^-$, and I$^-$ from Table III, calculate the maximum radius which Li$^+$ may have. $Ans.$ 0.76 A.

9. What are the Miller indices for a plane in a crystal which intercepts the x axis at a, the y axis at $\frac{1}{3}b$, and the z axis at $\frac{1}{2}c$?

10. Calculate the angles at which reflections would be obtained in problem 3 if an iron target was used in the X-ray tube rather than copper. Given: λ for the $K\alpha$ line of iron is 1.937 A.

11. What is the number of nearest neighbors in atomic crystals of the (a) primitive, (b) body-centered, and (c) face-centered types?

12. The X-ray powder pattern for molybdenum has reflections at θ = 20.25°, 29.30°, 36.82°, 43.81°, 50.69°, 58.00°, 66.30°, and other larger angles when Cu $K\alpha$ X rays are used (λ = 1.5405 A). (a) What type of cubic crystal is formed by molybdenum? (b) What is the length of a side of the unit cell at this temperature? (c) What is the density of molybdenum?

13. Using X rays with a wavelength of 1.54 A from a copper target, it is found that the first reflection from a face of a crystal of potassium chloride at 25° is at θ = 14°12'. Calculate (a) the length of the side of the unit cell for this interpenetrating face-centered lattice and (b) the density of the crystal.

14. The density of platinum is 21.45 g cm^{-3} at 20°. Given the fact that the crystal is face-centered cubic, calculate the length of the side of the unit cell.

15. A substance crystallizes in a form like that of sodium chloride. Its density is 1.984 g cm^{-3}, and the length of the edge of the unit is 6.30 A. Calculate the molecular weight.

16. The density of calcium oxide is 3.32 g cm^{-3}. If the length of a side of the cubic unit cell is 4.81 A, how many molecules of CaO are there per unit cell?

17. From the fact that the length of the side of the unit cell for lithium is 3.51 A calculate the atomic radius of Li. Lithium forms body-centered cubic crystals.

---

18. A face of a cubic crystal intercepts the x, y, and z axes at relative distances of 1, $\frac{1}{2}$, and ∞. What are the Miller indices?

19. Calculate the angles at which the first-, second-, and third-order reflections are obtained from planes 5 A apart, using X rays with a wavelength of 1 A.

20. The diamond has a face-centered cubic crystal lattice, and there are eight atoms in a unit cell. Its density is 3.51 g cm^{-3}. Calculate the first six angles at which reflections would be obtained using an X-ray beam of wavelength 0.712 A.

21. (a) Metallic iron at 20° is studied by the Bragg method, in which the crystal is oriented so that a reflection is obtained from the planes parallel to the sides of the cubic crystal, then from planes cutting diagonally through opposite edges, and finally from planes cutting diagonally through opposite corners. Reflections are obtained at $\theta = 11°36'$, $8°3'$, and $20°26'$, respectively. What type of cubic lattice does iron have at 20°? (b) Metallic iron also forms cubic crystals at 1100°, but the reflections determined as described in (a) occur at $\theta = 9°8'$, $12°57'$, and $7°55'$, respectively. What type of cubic lattice does iron have at 1100°? (c) The density of iron at 20° is 7.86 g cm^{-3}. What is the length of a side of the unit cell at 20°? (d) What is the wavelength of the X rays used? (e) What is the density of iron at 1100°?

22. By means of the Bragg method, a cubic crystal may be oriented in different directions to obtain d_{100}, d_{110}, and d_{111}. Show that the ratios of the distances between the three different sets of planes are:

$$\text{Primitive cubic} \qquad d_{100}:d_{110}:d_{111} = 1:0.707:0.578$$

$$\text{Face-centered cubic} \qquad d_{200}:d_{220}:d_{111} = 1:0.707:1.155$$

$$\text{Body-centered cubic} \qquad d_{200}:d_{110}:d_{222} = 1:1.414:0.578$$

23. Potassium bromide has a face-centered cubic lattice, and the edge of the unit cell is 6.54 A. What is the density of the crystal?

24. Insulin forms crystals of the orthorhombic type with unit-cell dimensions of $130 \times 74.8 \times 30.9$ A. If the density of the crystal is 1.315 g cm^{-3} and there are 6 insulin molecules per unit cell, what is the molecular weight of the protein insulin?

25. Aluminum forms face-centered cubic crystals, and the length of the side of the unit cell is 4.050 A at 25°. Calculate (a) the density of aluminum at this temperature and (b) the distances between 200, 220, and 111 planes.

26. Tantalum crystallizes with a body-centered cubic lattice. Its density is 17.00 g cm^{-3}. (a) How many atoms of tantalum are there in a unit cell? (b) What is the length of a unit cell? (c) What is the distance between 200 planes? (d) What is the distance between 110 planes? (e) What is the distance between 222 planes?

27. Calculate the length of the side of the unit cell of potassium iodide (face-centered cubic) from the ionic radii in Table III and compare it with the value in Table II. Calculate the density of the crystal.

28. Aluminum forms face-centered cubic crystals, and at 20° the closest interatomic distance is 2.862 A. Calculate the density of the crystal.

THEORY OF KINETICS,
PHOTOCHEMISTRY, AND
RADIATION CHEMISTRY

23

Now that we have discussed the quantum theory and the structure of molecules we are in a position to reconsider what happens in a chemical reaction and what factors determine the rate. This is a very difficult theoretical problem, but modern theories have given increased insight into this and other irreversible processes. Photochemistry comprises the study of chemical reactions produced directly or indirectly by the absorption of light and is closely related to chemical kinetics. Radiation chemistry is concerned with the chemical effects of high-energy radiation, such as X rays, alpha, beta, and gamma rays (p. 684), and this field has become of increased interest with the development of nuclear reactors.

Chemical Reactions and Potential-Energy Surfaces. First we will consider how the potential energy of the system of nuclei and electrons varies as the reacting species come together and then the product species separate from each other.

The simplest type of reaction to discuss from a quantitative standpoint is one in which an atom reacts with a diatomic molecule to form another diatomic molecule and an atom. For example, a deuterium atom may react with a hydrogen molecule,

$$D + H_a H_b \rightarrow DH_a + H_b$$

The potential energy of the system depends upon the three internuclear distances r_{DH_a}, $r_{H_a H_b}$, r_{DH_b}, and so a four-dimensional graph would be required to represent the potential energy of the system as a function of the three independent internuclear distances. If the approach is along the line of the two nuclei of the hydrogen molecule, or any other particular angle, the magnitude of potential energy may be represented by a surface above a plane with coordinates r_{DH_a}, $r_{H_aH_b}$. Such surfaces may be approximated theoretically, and the surface for the

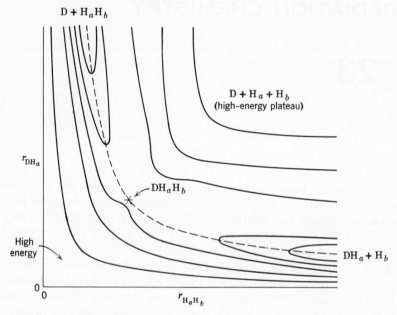

Fig. 23-1. Potential energy as a function of internuclear distance for the three nuclei D, H_a, and H_b when the atoms remain in a line. The lowest energy path from $D + H_aH_b$ to $DH_a + H_b$ is shown by the dashed line, and the transition state is marked by *. The solid lines represent contours of constant energy.

above reaction when the nuclei remain in a line is illustrated in *Fig. 23-1*. At large and constant r_{DH_a} a cross section through the surface gives the potential energy for an H_2 molecule. The intersection of a plane at large and constant $r_{H_aH_b}$ with the potential-energy surface is the potential-energy curve for a DH molecule, which is assumed to be the same as for an HH molecule because the electronic-energy levels are the same for H and D. A given linear configuration of the three atoms is represented by a point in the surface. In the upper right-hand part of the figure the three atoms are all far apart from each other. In the lower left-hand part of the figure the atoms are all so close together that the potential energy of the system is high. In calculating this potential-energy surface it is considered that the electrons remain in equilibrium with the instantaneous nuclear configuration, since they move so much faster than the nuclei.

As a D atom approaches a stationary H_2 molecule, the potential energy rises and the translational energy of the D atom decreases correspondingly. If the translational energy of the D atom is great enough (greater than 14 kcal mole^{-1}), it may reach the point labeled by *, which represents the high point in the pass between the two valleys. Point * represents the transition state, also called the activated complex. When the system reaches this point, DH_aH_b can decompose to $DH_a + H_b$ by moving down the valley to the right or to $D + H_aH_b$ by returning up the valley to the left. Thus not all systems of three atoms which reach * yield products. The rate of reaction can be calculated if the number of complexes passing over the top of the barrier per second can be calculated.†

The dashed line in Fig. 23-1 is the lowest energy path from reactants to products, and this path is the *reaction coordinate* which was referred to on p. 319. The reaction coordinate is more difficult to visualize for reactions involving more than three atoms, but the term is still used in the same sense. A group of atoms in the transition state has no stability in the direction of the reaction coordinate, since the potential-energy surface is concave downward. However, such a group of atoms can vibrate in the direction perpendicular to the reaction coordinate. An ordinary molecule, in contrast with a molecule in the transition state, can vibrate in all directions without flying apart because it is surrounded on all sides by a potential-energy barrier.

Absolute Reaction-Rate Theory. ‡ The Eyring theory for the calculation of the absolute rate of a reaction assumes that the activated complex is in thermodynamic equilibrium with the reactants. However, as shown in the Appendix, the equilibrium constant is not the same as an ordinary equilibrium constant because the activated complex is in the process of flying apart in one direction. Because of this equilibrium constant the terminology of thermodynamics enters absolute-rate theory. The equilibrium constant may be expressed in terms of the standard Gibbs free-energy change $\Delta G^{\circ\ddagger}$ for the activation process, since $\Delta G^{\circ\ddagger} = -RT \ln K$,

$$K = e^{-\Delta G^{\circ\ddagger}/RT} = e^{\Delta S^{\ddagger}/R}e^{-\Delta H^{\ddagger}/RT} \tag{1}$$

† F. T. Wall, L. A. Hiller, Jr., and J. Mazur, *J. Chem. Phys.*, *29*, 255 (1958).
‡ H. Eyring, *J. Chem. Phys.*, *3*, 107 (1935); S. Glasstone, K. J. Laidler, and H. Eyring, *The Theory of Rate Processes*, McGraw-Hill Book Co., New York, 1941.

where the last form of the equation is obtained by introducing

$$\Delta G^{\circ\ddagger} = \Delta H^{\ddagger} - T \Delta S^{\ddagger} \tag{2}$$

The reaction rate is obtained by multiplying the concentration of activated complexes by the average velocity with which complexes move across the barrier, becoming products. The details of this theory are given in the Appendix (p. 726), and the final result is that

$$k = \frac{\kappa R T}{N_0 h} e^{\Delta S^{\ddagger}/R} e^{-\Delta H^{\ddagger}/RT} \tag{3}$$

where κ is the transmission coefficient, the fraction of the times that an activated molecule proceeds to products instead of reverting to reactants, $\Delta S^{\ddagger}$ is the entropy of activation, and $\Delta H^{\ddagger}$ is the enthalpy of activation. The transmission coefficient κ is generally taken to be unity.

Calculation of Enthalpies of Activation and Entropies of Activation. Because of the T in the frequency factor of the Eyring equation the activation enthalpy $\Delta H^{\ddagger}$ is not to be identified with the Arrhenius activation energy E_a. The relationship between $\Delta H^{\ddagger}$ and E_a may be obtained by calculating the slope of a plot of $\ln k$ versus $1/T$ according to equation 3.

$$\frac{d \ln k}{dT} = \frac{1}{T} + \frac{\Delta H^{\ddagger}}{RT^2} \tag{4}$$

$$\frac{d(1/T)}{dT} = -\frac{1}{T^2} \tag{5}$$

$$\frac{d \ln k}{d(1/T)} = \frac{d \ln k}{dT} \frac{dT}{d(1/T)} = \frac{-(\Delta H^{\ddagger} + RT)}{R} \tag{6}$$

As shown earlier, the slope of such a plot is $-E_a/R$ according to the Arrhenius equation. Thus

$$E_a = \Delta H^{\ddagger} + RT \tag{7}$$

Substitution of $\Delta H^{\ddagger} = E_a - RT$ into equation 3 and comparison with the empirical Arrhenius equation

$$k = s e^{-E_a/RT}$$

shows that the frequency factor s in the Arrhenius equation has the following significance when the transmission coefficient is taken as unity:

$$s = e \frac{RT}{N_0 h} e^{\Delta S^{\ddagger}/R} \tag{8}$$

Thus the entropy of activation $\Delta S^{\ddagger}$ may be calculated from the Arrhenius frequency factor. Alternatively, the value of $(RT/N_0 h)e^{\Delta S^{\ddagger}/R}$ in equation 3 may simply be calculated using the value of $\Delta H^{\ddagger}$ and the rate constant at one temperature.

Example 1. For the rearrangement of 1-ethyl propenyl allyl malonitrile to 1-ethyl-2-methyl-4-pentenylidene malonitrile the Arrhenius activation energy in the neighborhood of $130°$ is 25,900 cal mole^{-1}, so that $\Delta H^{\ddagger} = 25,900 - (1.987)(403) = 25,100$ cal mole^{-1}. The first-order rate constant at $130°$ is 9.12×10^{-4} sec^{-1}. The entropy of activation is calculated as follows:

$$9.12 \times 10^{-4} = \frac{RT}{N_0 h} e^{\Delta S^{\ddagger}/R} e^{-25,100/(1.987)(403)}$$

$$\frac{RT}{N_0 h} e^{\Delta S^{\ddagger}/R} = 4.08 \times 10^{10}$$

$$\Delta S^{\ddagger} = 2.303 R \log \frac{N_0 h (4.08 \times 10^{10})}{RT}$$

$$= -10.6 \text{ cal deg}^{-1} \text{ mole}^{-1}$$

For many unimolecular, bond-breaking gas reactions $\Delta S^{\ddagger} = 0$ because the activated complex is so much like the original reactants and there is very little change in shape in going from the reactants to the activated complex. In this case $e^{\Delta S^{\ddagger}/R} = 1$, and at room temperatures

$$s = e \frac{RT}{N_0 h} = (2.718)(8.3 \times 10^7)(300)/(6.02 \times 10^{23})(6.6 \times 10^{-27})$$

$$= 1.7 \times 10^{13} \text{ sec}^{-1}$$

This is the order of magnitude of vibration frequencies in molecules. If the activation of the molecule involves a rearrangement of atoms or a change in configuration, there will be a change in entropy and $e^{\Delta S^{\ddagger}/R}$ is not unity, as in a bond-breaking unimolecular reaction. The values of $\Delta S^{\ddagger}$ are rarely large enough to give a value of more than 10^2 or less than 10^{-2} to the term $e^{\Delta S^{\ddagger}/R}$, and so frequency factors $e(RT/N_0 h)e^{\Delta S^{\ddagger}/R}$ may range from about 10^{11} to 10^{15}. If the spatial arrangements in the activated molecule are more probable than in the unactivated molecule, $\Delta S^{\ddagger}$ will have a positive sign. If there is a loss in rotational and translational freedom, $\Delta S^{\ddagger}$ will have a negative value; this is generally the case. If the frequency factor is very large (over 10^{15} or so), a chain reaction is indicated (p. 328).

The Eyring theory actually includes the collision theory discussed on p. 321 as a special case. This may be shown by calculating the equilibrium constant for the formation of the activated complex, using the partition functions for rigid spherical molecules. The fact that many reactions are slower than the rate of sufficiently energetic collisions is explained by the collision theory as being due to the requirement of a certain orientation. In the modern theory of reaction kinetics the probability of forming an activated complex is reduced because translational and rotational degrees of freedom are lost when the activated complex is formed, and these statistical factors are discussed in thermodynamic language in terms of the entropy of activation.

Salt Effects on Ionic Reactions in Solution. The rate of a reaction between ions of the same sign increases with increasing ionic strength, whereas the rate of a reaction between ions of opposite sign decreases with increasing ionic strength. These effects are referred to as primary salt effects. In both cases the effect can be visualized as resulting from the increasing shielding of the electrostatic repulsion or attraction of the ions by the ion atmosphere as the concentration of electrolyte is increased. For dilute electrolyte solutions these effects can be interpreted quantitively. As discussed in connection with the Debye-Hückel theory (p. 392), the activity coefficient of an ion at low ionic-strength values depends upon its charge. The basic ideas of the following theory by Brönsted and Bjerrum preceded the Debye-Hückel and Eyring theories, but it is convenient to discuss the Brönsted theory in terms of these more recent developments.

For the reaction of A^{z_A} with B^{z_B}, z_A and z_B being the ionic charges, the activated complex $AB^{*(z_A + z_B)}$ has a charge of $z_A + z_B$.

$$A^{z_A} + B^{z_B} \rightleftharpoons AB^{*(z_A + z_B)} \rightleftharpoons \text{products}$$

It is assumed that the activated complex AB^* is in equilibrium with the reactants. The equilibrium constant for this reaction is

$$K = \frac{(AB^*)}{(A)(B)} \frac{\gamma_{AB^*}}{\gamma_A \gamma_B} \tag{9}$$

It is assumed that the rate of the reaction is proportional to the concentration of the activated complex AB^*.

$$-\frac{d(A)}{dt} = k'(AB^*) \tag{10}$$

The second-order rate constant for the reaction is defined by

$$-\frac{d(A)}{dt} = k(A)(B) \tag{11}$$

Combining equations 10 and 11 yields $k = k'(AB^*)/(A)(B)$. Solving equation 9 for (AB^*) and substituting into this expression yields

$$k = \frac{k' K \gamma_A \gamma_B}{\gamma_{AB^*}} = \frac{k_0 \gamma_A \gamma_B}{\gamma_{AB^*}} \tag{12}$$

where $k_0 = k'K$ is the value the second-order rate constant would have at zero ionic strength where $\gamma_A = \gamma_B = \gamma_{AB}{}^* = 1$. For dilute solutions the dependence of the activity coefficient on the ionic strength is given by the Debye-Hückel theory (p. 392). For aqueous solutions at 25°,

$$\log \gamma_i = -0.509z_i^2 I^{\frac{1}{2}} \tag{13}$$

where I is the ionic strength. Taking the logarithm of equation 12 and substituting equation 13 for the three ion species, we obtain

$$\log k = \log k_0 - 0.509 I^{\frac{1}{2}}[z_A^2 + z_B^2 - (z_A + z_B)^2] \tag{14}$$

$$\log k = \log k_0 + 1.018 z_A z_B I^{\frac{1}{2}} \tag{15}$$

According to this equation, a plot of $\log k$ versus $I^{\frac{1}{2}}$ should be linear, the slope depending upon $z_A z_B$ for low ionic-strength values, where the Debye-Hückel theory applies. This prediction is borne out quite well and is illustrated by *Fig. 23-2*. At low ionic-strength values the effects of different salts depend simply on their contributions to the ionic strength, but at higher ionic-strength values more complicated results are obtained.

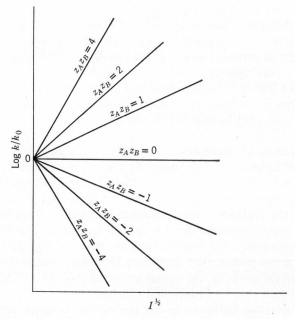

Fig. 23-2.   Dependence of rates of reactions of ions on ionic strength.

Photochemistry. A large number of chemical reactions can be made to occur by irradiating the sample. Only radiation which is absorbed can produce a change. Some of the changes which result from the absorption of light are summarized as follows:

1. The energy of the light may be transformed into *heat* with the result that the temperature of the system is raised. This is the most common result of the absorption of light.

2. A molecule may be *dissociated* into atoms or radicals. One of the fragments may be in an excited state.

3. A molecule may be *excited* to a higher energy level. Such an excited molecule is generally quite reactive. The excited molecule may transfer its energy by collision to a molecule of a different chemical compound, which then undergoes a chemical reaction.

4. A molecule which has been excited by the absorption of light may *fluoresce* at a longer wavelength and lose energy. If a long time delay is involved, as is true for many solids, the process is referred to as phosphorescence.

5. A molecule may become *ionized* by loss of an electron.

The activation energies of chemical reactions are generally in the range 10–100 kcal, and so visible or ultraviolet light, or X rays, are required to produce chemical changes. As discussed in Chapter 17, the absorption of infrared and microwave radiation leads to changes in vibrational and rotational levels and such changes do not lead to chemical reactions. The absorption of visible and ultraviolet radiation occurs only in certain regions of the spectrum, depending upon the structure of the molecule. When absorption occurs, the molecule is excited to a higher electronic state and a chemical reaction may occur if the energy is not lost too quickly by fluorescence or by transformation into heat, that is, into kinetic energy.

Photoexcitation of Molecules. The excitation of molecules upon absorption of light may be discussed by use of potential-energy curves (p. 536), such as those shown in *Fig. 23-3*. In each diagram the potential-energy curve for the ground state is represented by g. When a photon in the visible or ultraviolet range is absorbed, there is a transition to a higher electronic level indicated by e or u. The transitions may be represented by vertical lines as shown in Fig. 23-3 because electrons move so fast that during an electronic change the relative positions of the nuclei do not change appreciably (p. 541). This general principle was stated by Franck and Condon.

In the situation indicated in (a) the excited molecule retains this energy and remains stable until it loses its energy by chemical reaction

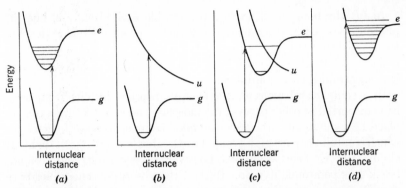

Fig. 23-3. Types of photoexcitation. (a) Excitation to stable excited state; no dissociation; discontinuous spectrum. (b) Excitation to unstable excited state; immediate dissociation; continuous spectrum. (c) Excitation to stable excited state which shifts to unstable excited state; predissociation spectrum. (d) Excitation to a stable excited state but to an energy level above the dissociation energy; continuous spectrum.

or a molecular collision. Only certain quantities of energy can be stored in this excited molecule, as governed by the quantum-number restrictions. Accordingly there are discrete spectral lines, and the absorption spectrum is discontinuous.

In the situation shown at (b) the molecule is excited to an unstable excited state u which does not have any minimum in the potential-energy plot. As soon as the photon raises the molecule to this unstable state, the valence bond ruptures immediately and the molecule dissociates. The fragments are thrown out with varying degrees of kinetic energy, and since kinetic energy is not quantized many different amounts of energy are utilized. The absorption spectrum is continuous, without discrete lines.

As shown at (c), the molecule in its ground state g may be raised to a higher energy state e, which is stable, but in this state there is an opportunity to shift over to an unstable state u. At low vibrational levels in excited state e the molecule cannot shift over to the unstable state, and the spectrum is discontinuous with discrete lines. When a larger quantum of energy is absorbed, the molecule may be in a sufficiently high vibrational level that a transition may occur to a state u which is unstable and leads to dissociation. Since the fragments are sent out with various amounts of kinetic energy which is not appreciably quantized, the spectral lines are not sharp. This type of spectrum, which shows a broadening and fuzziness of the spectral lines in certain regions, is called a predissociation spectrum, and the excitation followed a little later by dissociation is called predissociation.

In (d) the molecule is excited to a stable excited state e, but the photon absorbed has so much energy that it raises the energy level of the excited molecule above the level of stability, and the molecule dissociates into fragments which have varying amounts of kinetic energy. The spectrum then is continuous as in (b).

In a complicated molecule the energy absorbed by one group may be transported to other parts of the molecule and cause reaction to take place in a different part. For example, acetone, like most molecules which contain a carbonyl group $C{=}O$, absorbs ultraviolet light at about 3100 A. The $C{=}O$ bond, however, is very strong and does not break to give atomic oxygen. Rather, the absorption energy leads to the cleavage of an adjacent $C{-}C$ bond which is weaker, thus:

$$\begin{array}{c} CH_3 \\ \diagdown \\ C{=}O + h\nu \to CH_3\cdot + CH_3\dot{C}{=}O \\ \diagup \\ CH_3 \end{array}$$

giving a methyl radical and an acetyl radical.

Quantum Yield. Einstein postulated that in *the primary photochemical process each molecule is activated by the absorption of one photon.* In this simple primary process, then, we should find that the number of molecules activated is exactly equal to the number of photons or quanta absorbed; in order to activate a mole of a substance 6.02×10^{23} photons would have to be absorbed. Avogadro's number of photons is called an "einstein," just as a gram equivalent of electrons (6.02×10^{23} electrons or 96,500 coulombs) is called a "faraday."

It must be strongly emphasized that the Einstein law is usually masked by secondary reactions and complicating circumstances which prevent a simple 1-to-1 relationship between the number of photons absorbed and the number of molecules of *final* products in the reaction. The law is accepted as applicable to the primary process, and then the complicating circumstances which may cause the yield to differ from that calculated from Einstein's law are investigated. They are peculiar to each reaction. Sometimes the activation process is followed by a simple stoichiometric reaction which gives some integer number or fraction of moles of product, such as two molecules per photon, or by a series of repeated reactions giving rise to a chain reaction. On the other hand, the activated molecules may be partially deactivated by collisions, by fluorescence, or by internal rearrangements. Again, dissociated fragments resulting from the absorption of light may recombine so as to give low apparent yields.

The quantum yield Φ is given by the expression

$$\Phi = \frac{\text{Number of molecules reacting chemically}}{\text{Number of photons absorbed}} \qquad (16)$$

It provides a very convenient means for describing the experimental facts and offers valuable information for drawing conclusions regarding the mechanism of the reaction.

Example 2. In the photobromination of cinnamic acid to dibromocinnamic acid, using blue light of 4358 A at 30.6°, an intensity of 14,000 ergs $\sec^{-1}$ produced a decrease of 0.075 millimole of Br_2 during an exposure of 1105 sec. The solution absorbed 80.1 per cent of the light passing through it. Calculate the quantum yield.

$$E = hc/\lambda = (6.62 \times 10^{-27})(3 \times 10^{10})/(4.358 \times 10^{-5})$$

$$= 4.54 \times 10^{-12} \text{ erg per quantum}$$

Number of quanta absorbed $= \dfrac{(14,000)(0.801)(1105)}{4.54 \times 10^{-12}} = 2.74 \times 10^{18}$

Number of molecules of Br_2 reacting $= (7.5 \times 10^{-5})(6.02 \times 10^{23}) = 45.2 \times 10^{18}$

$$\Phi = \frac{45.2 \times 10^{18}}{2.74 \times 10^{18}} = 16.5$$

The quantum yields of a few photochemical reactions are summarized in Table I.

Reaction 1 is one of the most exact photochemical reactions, and it has the same value of Φ from 2800 to 3000 A, at low pressures and high pressures, in the liquid state or in solution in hexane. The primary process $HI + h\nu = H + I$ is followed by the thermal reactions $H + HI = H_2 + I$ and $I + I = I_2$, thus giving two molecules of HI decomposed for each photon absorbed. Reaction 2 has a quantum yield of unity. Reaction 3 has a quantum yield of unity initially, but the reverse thermal reaction reduces it as the product accumulates. In reaction 4 at 3660 A the quantum yield is 2 if correction is made for internal screening by the accompanying N_2O_4, which absorbs some light at 3660 A. The reactions are $NO_2 + h\nu = NO_2^*$, $NO_2^* + NO_2 = 2NO + O_2$, where the asterisk indicates an activated molecule. At longer wavelengths the spectrum is of a different type, and at 4350 A and longer wavelengths no reaction occurs when the radiation is absorbed.

Reaction 5 likewise shows a greater quantum yield at shorter wavelengths. This reaction is interesting because at 300° Φ has a value of more than 300, indicating that the free radicals which are first produced by the absorption of light are able to propagate a chain reaction at the higher temperatures. At room temperature the reactions in-

Table I.[1]   Quantum Yields in Photochemical Reactions
at Room Temperature

Reaction	Approximate Wavelength Region, A	Approximate Φ
1. $2HI \rightarrow H_2 + I_2$	3000–2800	2
2. $S_2O_8^{2-} + H_2O \rightarrow 2SO_4^{2-} + 2H^+ + \frac{1}{2}O_2$	3000–2500	1
3. $C_{14}H_{10} \rightleftharpoons \frac{1}{2}(C_{14}H_{10})_2$	<3600	1–0
4. $2NO_2 \rightarrow 2NO + O_2$	>4350	0
	3660	2
5. $CH_3CHO \rightarrow CO + CH_4 (+ C_2H_6 + H_2)$	3100	0.5
	2537	1
6. $(CH_3)_2CO \rightarrow CO + C_2H_6 (+ CH_4)$	<3300	0.2
7. $NH_3 \rightarrow \frac{1}{2}N_2 + \frac{3}{2}H_2$	2100	0.2
8. $H_2C_2O_4 (+ UO_2^{2+}) \rightarrow CO + CO_2 + H_2O (+ UO_2^{2+})$	4300–2500	0.5–0.6
9. $2NO_3^- \rightarrow 2NO_2^- + O_2$	3000–2500	0.01–0.3
10. $Cl_2 + H_2 \rightarrow 2HCl$	4000	10^5
11. $Br_2 + C_6H_5CH{=}CHCOOH \rightarrow$ $C_6H_5CHBrCHBrCOOH$	<5500	1–100
12. $C_2H_2 \rightarrow \frac{1}{n}(C_2H_2)_n$	2000	7
13. $CO + Cl_2 \rightarrow COCl_2$	4000–4360	1000

[1] W. A. Noyes, Jr., and P. A. Leighton, *Photochemistry of Gases*, Reinhold Publishing Corp., New York, 1941, Appendixes, pp. 415–465; F. Daniels, *J. Phys. Chem.*, 41, 713 (1938).

volved in the chain do not go fast enough to be detected. The products given in parentheses are present also but in small amounts.

In reaction 6 the primary reaction is probably $CH_3COCH_3 + h\nu = CH_3 \cdot + \cdot COCH_3$. The acetyl radical can then decompose into CO and $CH_3 \cdot$, or it can react with $CH_3 \cdot$ to give back acetone. At room temperature it forms biacetyl $(COCH_3)_2$.

In the photolysis of ammonia, reaction 7, hydrogen atoms are split off, and the low yield is probably due to partial recombination of the fragments. The quantum yield varies with pressure and reaches a maximum at 80–90 mm.

Reaction 8 illustrates a photosensitized reaction (p. 662). Reaction 9 is complicated and depends on the pH of the solution. The quantum yield is higher at the shorter wavelengths. Reaction 10 is the best-known example of a chain reaction and is one of the longest chains.

Oxygen and certain other substances act as inhibitors by combining with the chlorine or hydrogen atoms, thus stopping the propagation of the chain and reducing the quantum yield.

The addition of bromine to cinnamic acid, reaction 11, is a chain reaction, the length of the chains depending on the temperature, the concentration of bromine, and the amount of dissolved oxygen. The reaction can be split up into the primary photoprocess, which is not affected by temperature, and the subsequent thermal reaction, which has a large temperature coefficient. When oxygen is removed, the breaking of chains is less frequent, and the quantum yield is of the order of hundreds and more.

The polymerization of acetylene, reaction 12, to give an insoluble substance called cuprene, is effected by short ultraviolet light with a quantum yield of about 7, showing that the primary process is followed by a short chain reaction.

The quantum yield of reaction 13 varies with the pressures of carbon monoxide and chlorine and, like all chain reactions, is sensitive to impurities.

In order to determine a quantum yield it is necessary to measure the intensity of the light. This may be done by use of a thermopile, which is a series of thermocouples with one set of junctions blackened to absorb all the radiation, which is then converted into heat. The other set of junctions is protected from radiation. The temperature difference between the two sets of junctions is measured by the galvanometer deflection. The galvanometer readings may be converted into ergs of radiation per second per square millimeter striking the thermopile, by calibrating with a standard carbon-filament lamp from the National Bureau of Standards.

The amount of radiation may also be measured with an *actinometer*, in which the amount of chemical change is determined. The yield of the photochemical reaction in the actinometer was determined originally by use of a thermopile.

The uranyl oxalate actinometer, studied with great accuracy by Leighton and Forbes,* is the best for most purposes. Although the quantum yield changes slightly with the wavelength, it may be taken that, in a solution 0.01 M in uranyl sulfate and 0.05 M in oxalic acid, 0.57 molecule of the oxalic acid is decomposed for each photon of light absorbed between the wavelengths 2540 and 4350 A. In other words, each mole of oxalic acid decomposed is equivalent to 1.75 einsteins, or to 166,000 cal, if an average wavelength of 3000 A is assumed. The uranyl ion undergoes no chemical change.

* W. G. Leighton and G. S. Forbes, *J. Am. Chem. Soc.*, *52*, 3139 (1930).

In quantitative work, where a knowledge of the reaction mechanism and rate is needed, it is not sufficient merely to place the reaction cell in front of a source of monochromatic light. The reaction may slow down as the material is consumed, not only on account of the decreased reaction rate due to a decrease in concentration but also on account of the lessened absorption of light. If the reaction cell is short or the transmittancy of the material high, the absorption of light is slight, so that practically all parts of the reacting system have about the same illumination. Then stirring is unimportant. If, on the other hand, the light is largely absorbed in the outer layer of the reacting system, the extent of the reaction will vary with the depth, and vigorous stirring may be necessary to give reproducible results. The number of calories of radiation or, better, the number of photons actually absorbed is the significant factor.

Photochemical Kinetics. A photochemical reaction may be accompanied by a thermal reaction, identical with the photochemical reaction, or opposite to it, or entirely different in character. A photochemical reaction may produce a catalyst which then causes a thermal reaction to proceed at a measurable rate. Sometimes an *induction period* occurs while a sufficient quantity of catalyst is being accumulated to make the reaction proceed with a measurable velocity. Again, a thermal reaction once started may continue after the illumination is stopped, giving an *aftereffect*.

If light causes a reaction in one direction, giving a zero-order reaction, and a thermal reaction occurs in the opposite direction with a rate proportional to the concentration of the photochemical product, a steady state will be produced in which the two rates are exactly equal. The situation is described mathematically by the following equation:

$$\frac{dx}{dt} = k_{photo}I - k_{thermal}x \tag{17}$$

where I is the intensity of light, k_{photo} and $k_{thermal}$ are the rate constants of the photochemical and thermal reactions, and x is the concentration of the product of the photochemical reaction. When a steady state is reached,

$$k_{photo}I = k_{thermal}x, \quad \text{and} \quad x = \frac{k_{photo}I}{k_{thermal}} \tag{18}$$

The concentration of product in the steady state is directly proportional to the intensity of the light. An example of this type of reaction is the photopolymerization of anthracene dissolved in xylene. In the presence of ultraviolet light this substance forms dianthracene, which has twice the molecular weight of anthracene, but in the dark the dianthracene depolymerizes, giving the original anthracene.

The experimental determination of the quantum yield constitutes an excellent method for detecting *chain reactions* (p. 328). If several molecules of products are formed for each photon of light absorbed, the reaction is obviously a chain reaction in which the products of the reaction are able to activate additional molecules of reactants.

The photocombination of hydrogen and chlorine is a classical example of such a reaction, about a million molecules reacting for each quantum absorbed. The molecules of hydrogen chloride formed undergo further reaction with the hydrogen and chlorine atoms produced (p. 329). The measurement of the number of molecules per photon gives a measure of the average number of molecules involved in the chain.

It is desirable also to determine the influence of temperature and thus ascertain whether or not thermal reactions are playing an important part. The primary process of photoactivation has a very low temperature coefficient, in contradistinction to the large temperature coefficient of thermal reactions. If the over-all photochemical reaction has a large temperature coefficient, it may be concluded that an ordinary thermal reaction rather than the photoactivation process is the rate-determining step.

Example 3. The following reactions describe the photochemical decomposition of hydrogen bromide with light of 2530 A at 25°. The primary process disrupts the molecule into atoms of hydrogen and bromine, which can then undergo further reactions. The quantum yield for the primary process is sometimes designated by ϕ; the quantum yield for the over-all reaction is designated by Φ. The intensity of light absorbed is designated by I.

(1) $HBr + h\nu \rightarrow H + Br$ Rate $= \phi I$
(2) $H + HBr \rightarrow H_2 + Br$ Rate $= k_2 c_H c_{HBr}$
(3) $Br + Br + M \rightarrow Br_2 + M$ Rate $= k_3 c_{Br}^2 c_M$
(4) $H + Br_2 \rightarrow HBr + Br$ Rate $= k_4 c_H c_{Br_2}$
(5) $H + H + M \rightarrow H_2 + M$ Rate $= k_5 c_H^2 c_M$ (negligible)

The sum of the first three reactions is

$$2HBr \rightarrow H_2 + Br_2$$

Reaction 3, describing the recombination of bromine atoms, requires a collision with a wall or a third molecule M in order to dissipate the energy evolved in the recombination of the two atoms.

Other reactions might be written on paper, such as $Br + HBr = Br_2 + H$ and $Br + H_2 = HBr + H$, but they involve breaking bonds which require so much energy for activation that they do not proceed at room temperature and may be neglected.

As the bromine accumulates, reaction 4 becomes important and reduces the quantum yield.

These facts can be summarized by the expression for the disappearance of hydrogen bromide:

$$\Phi = \phi + \phi \frac{1 - (k_4 c_{Br_2}/k_2 c_{HBr})}{1 + (k_4 c_{Br_2}/k_2 c_{HBr})}$$

When the concentration of bromine is zero at the beginning of the illumination or when mercury or other "acceptor" is added capable of removing the bromine chemically,

$$\Phi = 2\phi \cong 2$$

Photosensitization. Very often the molecules that absorb the light take part in the photochemical reaction only in an indirect manner and act merely as carriers of energy. One of the outstanding examples is mercury vapor activated by the absorption of ultraviolet light of 2536.7 A which is emitted by a mercury-vapor lamp. The energy corresponding to this radiation is very large (112,000 cal mole^{-1}), and it is more than the 102,400 calories necessary to dissociate hydrogen molecules into atoms. When mercury vapor is mixed with hydrogen and exposed to light from a mercury-vapor lamp, the chief reactions may be represented by the following equations, where Hg* represents an activated mercury atom:

$$Hg + h\nu \rightarrow Hg^* \tag{19}$$

$$Hg^* + H_2 \rightarrow Hg + 2H \tag{20}$$

The hydrogen is transparent to this radiation. The mercury acts as a photosensitizer. The hydrogen atoms readily reduce metallic oxides, nitrous oxide, ethylene, carbon monoxide, and other materials. The excited mercury atoms decompose not only hydrogen but also ammonia and various organic compounds.

The photodecomposition of oxalic acid, sensitized by uranyl ion, has already been referred to as a reproducible reaction suitable for use as an actinometer. The light is absorbed by the colored uranyl ion, and the energy is transferred to the colorless oxalic acid, which then decomposes. The uranyl ion remains unchanged and can be used indefinitely as a sensitizer. The fact that the absorbancy index of uranyl nitrate is increased by the addition of colorless oxalic acid indicates that a complex is formed.

Flash Photolysis.† The unstable intermediates in a photochemical reaction are usually present at such low concentrations that they cannot be studied directly. One way to increase their concentrations is to use a very powerful flash of light. The high-energy flash of short dura-

† R. G. Norrish and G. Porter, *Discussions Faraday Soc.*, *17*, 40 (1954); N. Davidson, *J. Chem. Educ.*, *34*, 126 (1957).

tion is obtained by discharging a bank of condensers through a gas-discharge tube. The flashes are so intense that in some cases practically all the molecules in the reaction tube are dissociated into free radicals and atoms. By this technique it has been possible to determine the absorption spectra of radicals such as NH_2, ClO, and CH_3.

In addition the flash-photolysis method is useful for studying the kinetics of the unstable intermediates. Another method for obtaining unstable intermediates of photochemical reactions at a concentration at which they can be studied spectroscopically is to form them in a rigid, unreactive medium such as a frozen rare gas at a sufficiently low temperature that they have a long lifetime.

Fluorescence. When an electron is excited to a higher level, it may return to the original level with the emission of light having the same frequency (referred to as resonance radiation), or it may lose some energy and then return to the original level emitting light of longer wavelength. The half-life of the excited molecules is usually of the order of $10^{-9}-10^{-7}$ sec, but it may be considerably longer.

Among the numerous substances known to exhibit fluorescence may be mentioned fluorite, CaF_2 (from which the phenomenon got its name), solutions of certain organic dyestuffs, eosin, fluorescein, quinine sulfate, chlorophyll, and the vapors of sodium, mercury, iodine, and acetone. Measurements of the intensity of fluorescent light are useful in identification and analysis. Fluorescent dyes have been developed which will emit visible light when activated with the light in the near ultraviolet or short visible range present in daylight, and this fluorescent light added to the light reflected from the colored paint or cloth gives an appearance of unusual brightness.

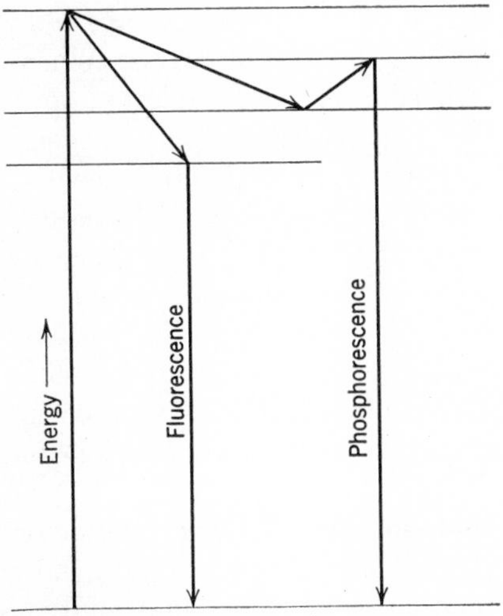

Phosphorescence is distinguished from fluorescence on the basis of the mechanism of emission of the light. This difference is indicated in *Fig. 23-4*. The excited electron may fall to an energy level from

Fig. 23-4. Fluorescence and phosphorescence.

which it cannot undergo a direct transition to the ground state. In quantum mechanics this is called a forbidden transition. If the electron is excited to a higher level by receiving a certain activation energy, it can now return to the ground state with the emission of a photon. In general, then, phosphorescence has a longer time constant than fluorescence. Solids are more likely to exhibit phosphorescence than liquids or gases. The sulfides of the alkaline earths may be mentioned as examples of such substances. Often impurities are necessary for phosphorescence. Many different colors are now available among phosphorescent and fluorescent compounds.

Chemiluminescence is the emission of light resulting from certain chemical reactions. For example, the oxidation of ether solutions of magnesium *p*-bromophenyl bromide gives rise to marked chemiluminescence, the greenish blue glow which accompanies the exposure of the solution to air being visible in daylight. The oxidations of decaying wood containing certain forms of bacteria, of luciferin in fireflies, and of yellow phosphorus are further examples.

The effect of radiation on crystals is interesting. X rays give rise to characteristic colors when passed through alkali halides and other crystals. Sodium chloride becomes yellow and potassium chloride blue, the coloration being due to the absorption of light by electrons which have been released by X rays and are trapped in negative-ion "vacancies" in the crystal lattice. When an irradiated crystal is heated, the trapped electrons are released, and in returning to a lower energy level they give off light, a phenomenon known as *thermoluminescence.*

If the crystal is heated slowly, a series of light emissions occurs at definite temperatures. The nature of these curves, in which the intensity of light emitted is plotted against the temperature, depends on the extent of the radiation exposure, the impurities present, and other factors. Certain minerals, such as limestones and fluorites, exhibit thermoluminescence even without laboratory exposure to radiation, because they contain traces of uranium in parts per million which have been giving off radioactive radiations for geological ages.

Photography. If silver chloride or bromide is mixed with gelatin and exposed very briefly to light, no change is observed; but, when this emulsion is immersed in a solution of a mild reducing agent, such as, for example, pyrogallic acid, the parts that have been exposed to light are reduced to metallic silver much more rapidly than the unexposed parts. The photographic plate consists of a large number of minute grains of crystalline silver halide; some of these grains are completely reduced by the developer to black metallic silver, and others are unaffected. The unaffected grains are dissolved out with sodium thiosulfate ("hypo").

It is necessary for a quantum of energy to strike a sensitive spot in the crystal lattice in order that the silver halide may be reduced to give a nucleus of silver, which then spreads, on further reduction, to include the whole grain. These sensitive spots seem to be identified with minute traces of silver sulfide in the crystal lattice which are particularly responsive to the action of light. By increasing the number of these sensitive spots and by other means, the speed of photographic films and plates has been greatly increased.

The silver halides respond only to the ultraviolet and to the shorter wavelengths of the visible spectrum; but, if certain red dyes, such as dicyanin, are mixed in the emulsion, the plate becomes sensitive also to red. Such red-sensitive plates, called panchromatic plates, give much better tone values to colored objects. This phenomenon constitutes another example of photosensitization.

Biological Applications of Photochemistry. The most important photochemical reaction in the world is the union of carbon dioxide and water in plants through the agency of sunlight and chlorophyll. Chlorophyll, which gives plants their green color, is a complex organic compound containing magnesium. It absorbs red, blue, and, to a lesser extent, green light, as shown in Fig. 18-2. The activated chlorophyll thus formed is responsible for the production from carbon dioxide and water of the starting material of all plant growth.

The important primary reaction involved in the growth of plants may be represented by the equation

$$CO_2 + H_2O + \text{light} + \text{chlorophyll} \rightarrow$$

$$(1/n)(CH_2O)_n + O_2 + \text{chlorophyll}$$

where $(CH_2O)_n$ represents a carbohydrate such as cellulose or sugar.

When cellulose is burned, the reaction is

$$(1/n)(CH_2O)_n + O_2 \rightarrow CO_2 + H_2O \qquad \Delta H = -112,000 \text{ cal mole}^{-1}$$

The endothermic formation of carbohydrates from carbon dioxide and water must require therefore the absorption of 112,000 cal mole^{-1}, and the activation energy must be at least as great as this, as pointed out on p. 320. This activation energy is equivalent to radiation of 2300 A or less. There is no radiation this short in the sunlight that reaches the earth's surface. Chlorophyll, however, acts as a photosensitizer, absorbing visible light and making it available for photosynthesis in the plant. But there is something unique about the reaction. Red light will cause photosynthesis, but red light corresponds to only 40,000 cal $mole^{-1}$; and more than 112,000 cal $mole^{-1}$ are required to cause the reaction. Apparently the reaction takes place in steps. Laboratory experiments with algae have shown that normally about eight photons are required for each carbon dioxide molecule utilized and each oxygen molecule evolved in photosynthesis under favorable conditions with low light intensity.

Exercise I. Show that, in photosynthesis, if eight photons of absorbed light at 6000 A produce one molecule of a product which has a heat of combusion of 112 kcal $mole^{-1}$, the efficiency of conversion of absorbed light into stored chemical energy is 30 per cent.

Example 4. If a good agricultural crop yields about 2 tons $acre^{-1}$ of dry organic material per year with a heat of combustion of about 4000 cal g^{-1}, what fraction of a year's solar energy is stored in an agricultural crop if the solar energy is about 1000 cal $min^{-1} ft^{-2}$ and the sun is shining about 500 min day^{-1} on the average? 1 acre $= 43,560 ft^2$, and 1 ton $= 907,000$ grams.

Solar heat $= (43,560 ft^2 acre^{-1})(500$ min $day^{-1})(1000$ cal $min^{-1} ft^{-2})$

$$\times (365.25 \text{ day year}^{-1})$$

$$= 7.96 \times 10^{12} \text{ cal acre}^{-1} \text{ year}^{-1}$$

Heat stored $= (2 \text{ ton acre}^{-1} \text{ year}^{-1})(9.07 \times 10^5 \text{ gram ton}^{-1})(4000 \text{ cal gram}^{-1})$

$$= 7.26 \times 10^9 \text{ cal acre}^{-1} \text{ year}^{-1}$$

$$\frac{\text{Heat stored}}{\text{Solar heat}} \cong 0.001$$

This 0.001 storage of average agriculture cannot be compared with the 0.300 storage of the laboratory, because in the open field the plants grow only during a third of the year and then the absorption of light is not complete. Half the solar energy is in the infrared, which is not absorbed by chlorophyll; the concentration of carbon dioxide in the air is 0.03 per cent instead of the 3 per cent used in the laboratory experiments; and the sunlight is much too bright for efficient photosynthesis.

Another photochemical reaction of biological importance is the production of vitamin D, which prevents rickets and brings about the normal deposition of calcium in growing bones. Steenbock found that rickets could be prevented by subjecting the food as well as the patient to ultraviolet light below 3100 A. Later the substance which is converted into vitamin D was traced to ergosterol and cholesterol.

Example 5. When ergosterol is irradiated with ultraviolet light below 3100 A, vitamin D, the antirachitic vitamin, is produced in proportion to the number of quanta absorbed. When irradiated ergosterol was included in a diet otherwise devoid of vitamin D, it was found that absorbed radiant energy of about 750 ergs was necessary to prevent rickets in a rat when fed over a period of 2 weeks. The light used had a wavelength of 2650 A.

(a) How many quanta are necessary to give 750 ergs?

$$\epsilon = h\nu = \frac{(6.62 \times 10^{-27})(3.0 \times 10^{10})}{2.65 \times 10^{-5}} = 7.5 \times 10^{-12}\,erg$$

$$\text{Number of quanta} = \frac{750}{7.5 \times 10^{-12}} = 1.00 \times 10^{14}$$

(b) If we assume that the primary photoprocess is the only chemical reaction, how many molecules of vitamin D per day are necessary to prevent rickets in a rat?

$$\text{Molecules per day} = 1.00 \times 10^{14}/14 = 7.14 \times 10^{12}$$

(c) If vitamin D has a molecular weight of the same order of magnitude as ergosterol (382), how many grams of vitamin D per day are necessary to prevent rickets in a rat?

$$\text{Grams per day} = \frac{(7.14 \times 10^{12})(382)}{6.02 \times 10^{23}} = 4.53 \times 10^{-9}$$

The first measurements of this type were made before vitamin D had been isolated. After the vitamin was isolated in nearly pure form, it was found that 5×10^{-8} g day^{-1} was the minimum dosage required to prevent rickets in a rat. This value is in fair agreement with the quantity estimated from theoretical photochemistry at a time when the nature of the vitamin was still unknown.

Radiation Chemistry.* High-energy photons (X rays and gamma rays) and high-speed particles (electrons, protons, alpha particles, and fission fragments) produce excited species as they pass through matter which lead to a variety of chemical reactions. The energies of these types of radiation are much greater than chemical-bond energies. When a high-speed particle, like an alpha particle or electron, moves through matter, energy is dissipated by electrostatic coulomb interaction between the high-speed particle and the electrons of the medium. The energy imparted to individual electrons is large compared to the energy with which they are bound in molecules, and so ionization is produced. The rate of energy loss of a charged particle is proportional to the electron density of the medium. The rate of energy loss increases as the speed of the high-speed particle decreases. If we compare two particles of equal energy but different mass, the heavier one has a smaller velocity and therefore loses energy at a higher rate. Thus the density of ions produced along an alpha-particle track is several thousand times larger than along the track of an electron of the same energy.

* The papers of a symposium on this subject are collected in the *Journal of Chemical Education, 36,* 262 (1959).

Ionizing radiations produce a variety of excited species, such as electronically excited molecules and ions which may be in their ground state or in excited states. Most of the excess energy of excited ions and molecules is dissipated quickly (in 10^{-12} sec or less) by bond rupture, luminescence, and transfer to neighboring molecules, with the result that a number of free radicals remain. The free radicals produced in this way are not uniformly distributed in the medium. Along the path of a high-speed electron there are spurs containing about six free radicals each, which are separated from each other by such large distances that the ensuing chemical reactions are essentially complete before a radical can diffuse from one spur to another. Along alpha-particle tracks the spurs are so close together that there is a continuous cylindrical column of free radicals.

Various chemical dosimeters are used to measure the quantity of radiation. For example, an air-saturated solution containing 0.001 N ferrous sulfate, and 0.001 N sodium chloride in 0.8 N sulfuric acid may be exposed to the ionizing radiation. The amount of ferric ion formed is proportional to the total quantity of radiation. It has been found that 15.6 ± 0.3 ferric ions are formed per 100 electron volts of ionizing radiation absorbed.

The yields in radiation chemistry are generally stated in terms of G values, defined by

$$G = \frac{\text{Number of molecules reacting}}{100 \text{ electron volts of energy introduced}} \tag{21}$$

Thus the G value of the ferrous sulfate dosimeter is 15.6 ± 0.3.

The G value for the radiolysis of water to hydrogen and oxygen is 1.7 moles of hydrogen per 100 ev. The reaction is

$$H_2O = H\cdot + OH\cdot$$

$$H\cdot + H\cdot = H_2$$

$$OH\cdot + OH\cdot = H_2O + \tfrac{1}{2}O_2$$

This reaction is a practical problem in homogeneous nuclear reactors (p. 702) utilizing aqueous solutions. It may be shown that, according to this G value, 10 cu ft of hydrogen is produced by a 1000-kw reactor per min. It has been found that the H_2 and O_2 will recombine at a rapid rate to form H_2O if $CuSO_4$ is added as a catalyst.

REFERENCES

S. Glasstone, K. J. Laidler, and H. Eyring, *The Theory of Rate Processes*, McGraw-Hill Book Co., New York, 1941.

L. J. Heidt, R. S. Livingston, E. I. Rabinowitch, and F. Daniels, ed., *Photochemistry in the Liquid and Solid States*, John Wiley & Sons, New York, 1960.

A. Hollaender, *Radiation Biology*, Vols. I, II, III, McGraw-Hill Book Co., New York, 1954, 1955.

W. A. Noyes, Jr., and P. A. Leighton, *The Photochemistry of Gases*, Reinhold Publishing Corp., New York, 1941.

E. I. Rabinowitch, *Photosynthesis and Related Processes*, Interscience Publishers, New York, 1945.

G. K. Rollefson and M. Burton, *Photochemistry and the Mechanism of Reactions*, Prentice-Hall, Englewood Cliffs, N. J., 1939.

E. W. R. Steacie, *Atomic and Free Radical Reactions*, Reinhold Publishing Corp., New York, 1954.

PROBLEMS

1. F. W. Schuler and G. W. Murphy [*J. Am. Chem. Soc.*, *72*, 3155 (1950)] studied the thermal rearrangement of vinyl allyl ether to allyl acetaldehyde in the range 150–200° and found that

$$k = 5 \times 10^{11} e^{-30,600/RT}$$

Calculate (a) the enthalpy of activation and (b) the entropy of activation, and (c) give an interpretation of the latter.

$Ans.$ (a) 29.7 kcal mole^{-1}. (b) -7.7 cal deg^{-1} mole^{-1}.

(c) The activated complex may be an improbable ring structure.

2. A certain photochemical reaction requires an activation energy of 30,000 cal mole^{-1}. To what values does this correspond in the following units: (a) ergs per molecule, (b) frequency of light, (c) wave number, (d) wavelength in angstroms, (e) electron volts? $Ans.$ (a) 2.08×10^{-12} erg molecule^{-1}. (b) 3.14×10^{14} sec^{-1}. (c) 10,500 cm^{-1}. (d) 9520 A. (e) 1.30 ev.

3. The following calculations are made on a uranyl oxalate actinometer, on the assumption that the energy of all wavelengths between 2540 and 4350 A is completely absorbed. The actinometer contains 20 ml of 0.05 M oxalic acid, which also is 0.01 M with respect to uranyl sulfate. After 2 hr of exposure to ultraviolet light, the solution required 34 ml of potassium permanganate, KMnO$_4$, solution to titrate the undecomposed oxalic acid. The same volume, 20 ml, of unilluminated solution required 40 ml of the KMnO$_4$ solution. If the average energy of the quanta in this range may be taken as corresponding to a wavelength of 3500 A, how many ergs were absorbed per second in this experiment? $Ans.$ 124,000 ergs.

4. A sample of gaseous acetone is irradiated with monochromatic light having a wavelength of 3130 A. Light of this wavelength decomposes the acetone according to the equation

$$(CH_3)_2CO \rightarrow C_2H_6 + CO$$

The reaction cell used has a volume of 59 ml. The acetone vapor absorbs 91.5 per cent of the incident energy. During the experiment the following data are obtained:

Temperature of reaction = $56.7°$
Initial pressure = 766.3 mm
Final pressure = 783.2 mm
Time of radiation = 7 hr
Incident energy = 48,100 ergs sec^{-1}

What is the quantum yield?   *Ans.* 0.17 molecule quantum^{-1}.

5. A 100-ml vessel containing hydrogen and chlorine was irradiated with light of 4000 A. Measurements with a thermopile showed that 11 ergs of light energy was absorbed by the chlorine per second. During an irradiation of 1 min the partial pressure of chlorine, as determined by the absorption of light and the application of Beer's law, decreased from 205 to 156 mm (corrected to $0°$). What is the quantum yield?   *Ans.* 2.6×10^6 moles HCl einstein^{-1}.

6. Discuss the economic possibilities of using photochemical reactions to produce valuable products with electricity at 1 cent per kilowatt-hour. Assume that 5 per cent of the electric energy consumed by a quartz-mercury-vapor lamp goes into light, and 30 per cent of this is photochemically effective. (*a*) How much will it cost to produce 1 lb (453.6 grams) of an organic compound having a molecular weight of 100, if the average effective wavelength is assumed to be 4000 A and the reaction has a quantum yield of 0.8 molecule per photon? (*b*) How much will it cost if the reaction involves a chain reaction with a quantum yield of 100?
                    Ans. (*a*) 13.4 cents. (*b*) 0.107 cent.

7. Calculate the volume of hydrogen at standard conditions produced each minute by the radiolysis of water in a 1000-kw homogeneous nuclear reactor. The G value for this reaction is 1.7.   *Ans.* 280 l.

---

8. According to the Hirschfelder rule [*J. Chem. Phys.*, *9*, 645 (1941)], the activation energy for a bimolecular reaction is approximately 28 per cent of the sum of the dissociation energies of the bonds broken. Estimate the activation energy for the reaction:

$$2ICl(g) + H_2(g) \rightarrow 2HCl(g) + I_2(g)$$

For ICl $\rightarrow$ I + Cl, ΔH = 49,600 cal. The H—H bond energy is given on p. 73.

9. The first-order rate constant for the thermal decomposition of $C_2H_6Br(g)$ is given by

$$k = 3.8 \times 10^{-14} e^{-55,000/RT}$$

where k is in seconds^{-1}. Calculate (*a*) $\Delta H^{\ddagger}$ and (*b*) $\Delta S^{\ddagger}$ at $500°$.

10. A uranyl oxalate actinometer is exposed to light of wavelength 3900 A for 1980 sec, and it is found that 24.6 ml of 0.00430 M potassium permanganate is required to titrate an aliquot of the uranyl oxalate solution after illumination, in comparison with 41.8 ml before illumination. Using the known quantum yield of 0.57, calculate the number of ergs absorbed per second. The chemical reaction for the titration is $2MnO_4^- + 5H_2C_2O_4 + 6H^+ = 2Mn^{2+} + 10CO_2 + 8H_2O$.

11. Assuming a hypothetical photochemical reaction in which one-tenth of the solar radiation is absorbed and utilized with a quantum efficiency of unity (one molecule produced per photon absorbed), how many tons of product can be produced per acre per day, if the molecular weight of the product is 100, the average effective light is 5100 A, and the solar radiation is 1 cal min^{-1} cm^{-2} for 500 min during the day?

12. The oxidation of rubrene, $C_{42}H_{28}$, is effected by oxygen at a wavelength of 4360 A with a quantum yield of unity. How many calories of this light will be required to photooxidize 1 gram of $C_{42}H_{28}$?

13. Sunlight between 2900 and 3130 A can produce sunburn (erythema) in 30 min. The intensity of radiation between these wavelengths in summer and at 45° latitude is about 50 microwatts cm^{-2}. Assuming that 1 photon produces chemical change in 1 molecule, how many molecules in a square centimeter of human skin must be photochemically affected in order to produce evidence of sunburn?

14. Nitrogen dioxide is decomposed photochemically by light of 3660 A with a quantum yield of 2.0 molecules per photon, according to the reaction

$$2NO_2 \rightarrow 2NO + O_2$$

The thermal reaction runs in the reverse direction. When an enclosed sample of nitrogen dioxide is illuminated for a long period of time, the quantum yield decreases and approaches zero. Suggest a mechanism to explain these facts, and write the chemical equations.

15. Calculate the maximum possible theoretical yield in tons of carbohydrate material $(H_2CO)_n$ that can be produced on an acre of land by green plants or trees during a 100-day growing season. Similar calculations apply to algae growing in a square mile of lake or ocean. Assume that the sun's radiation averages 1.0 cal cm^{-2} min^{-1} for 8 hr day^{-1} and that one-half the area is covered by green leaves. Assume that one-third of the radiation lies between 4000 and 6500 A, which is the range of the light absorbed by chlorophyll, and that the average wavelength is 5500 A. Assume that the leaves are thick enough to absorb practically all the light that strikes them. Assume that the quantum yield is 0.12 molecule per photon; that is, 8 photons with chlorophyll can produce 1 H_2CO unit from 1 molecule of CO_2 and 1 molecule of H_2O. Criticize these several assumptions.

16. When CH_3I molecules in the vapor state absorb 2537 A light, they dissociate into methyl radicals and iodine atoms. Assuming that the energy required to rupture the C—I bond is 50 kcal $mole^{-1}$, what is the kinetic energy of each of the fragments if they are produced in their ground states?

---

17. The vapor-phase decomposition of di-t-butyl peroxide is first order in the range 110–280° and follows the equation

$$k = 3.2 \times 10^{16} e^{-39,100/RT}$$

where k is in $seconds^{-1}$. Calculate (a) $\Delta H^{\ddagger}$ and (b) $\Delta S^{\ddagger}$.

18. For the first-order gaseous decomposition of propylene oxide $\Delta H^{\ddagger} = 56.9$ kcal and $\Delta S^{\ddagger} = 6$ cal deg^{-1} $mole^{-1}$ in the neighborhood of 285°. Calculate (a) the frequency factor s and (b) the first-order rate constant at 285°.

19. If a reaction responds to both red and violet light, 7000 and 4000 A, with an equal quantum efficiency, will there be more photochemical reaction per 100 cal of light in the red or in the blue? How much more?

20. For 900 sec, light of 4360 A was passed into a carbon tetrachloride solution containing bromine and cinnamic acid. The average energy absorbed was 19,190 ergs $\sec^{-1}$. Some of the bromine reacted to give cinnamic acid dibromide, and in this experiment the total bromine content decreased by 3.83×10^{19} molecules. (a) What was the quantum yield? (b) State whether or not a chain reaction was involved. (c) If a chain mechanism was involved, suggest suitable reactions which might explain the observed quantum yield.

21. Ammonia is decomposed by ultraviolet light of 2000 A with a quantum yield of 0.14 molecule per photon absorbed. (a) How many calories of this light would be necessary to decompose 1 gram of ammonia? (b) Offer a suggestion to explain this comparatively low quantum yield.

22. Chloroform is often kept in dark bottles to prevent photooxidation by air, giving phosgene, which is poisonous. The quantum yield of the photooxidation has been reported to be about 100 molecules per photon with light of 4360 A. How many calories of this light will be required to oxidize 1 mg of chloroform when the chloroform containing dissolved air is placed in a transparent bottle?

23. A cold high-voltage mercury lamp is to be used for a certain photochemical reaction which responds to ultraviolet light of 2537 A. The chemical analysis of the product is sensitive to only 10^{-4} mole. The lamp consumes 150 watts and converts 5 per cent of the electric energy into radiation of which 80 per cent is at 2537 A. The amount of the light which gets into the monochromator and passes out the exit slit is only 5 per cent of the total radiation of the lamp. Fifty per cent of this 2537 A radiation from the monochromator is absorbed in the reacting system. The quantum yield is 0.4 molecule of product per quantum of light absorbed. How long an exposure must be given in this experiment if it is desired to measure the photochemical change with an accuracy of 1 per cent?

24. The photochemical oxidation of phosgene, sensitized by chlorine, has been studied by G. K. Rollefson and C. W. Montgomery [*J. Am. Chem. Soc.*, **55**, 142, 4025 (1932)]. The over-all reaction is

$$2COCl_2 + O_2 = 2CO_2 + 2Cl_2$$

and the rate expression which gives the effect of the several variables is

$$\frac{dc_{CO_2}}{dt} = \frac{kI_0 c_{COCl_2}}{1 + k'c_{Cl_2}/c_{O_2}}$$

where I_0 is the intensity of the light. The quantum yield is about 2 molecules per quantum. Devise a series of chemical equations involving the existence of the free radicals ClO and COCl which will give a mechanism consistent with the rate expression.

25. The photopolymerization of anthracene reaches a stationary state, owing to the thermal decomposition of the dianthracene. For the photoreaction the temperature coefficient r is 1.1, and for the thermal reaction r is 2.8, where r is defined as k_{t+10}/k_t. Calculate the effect of a 5° rise in temperature on the amount of dianthracene formed when the photostationary state is reached.

26. In the ethyl chlorophyllide actinometer developed by Warburg and Shocken, and by Gaffron, ethyl chlorophyllide and thiourea are dissolved in pyridine and shaken vigorously in an atmosphere containing oxygen. The oxygen is taken up in the photooxidation of thiourea activated by the ethyl chlorophyllide, which has absorbed light. One photon causes the consumption of practically 1 molecule of oxygen. The reduction in volume of oxygen is measured with a capillary gas buret, and the same vessel and buret are used in the measurement of photosynthesis and respiration. All are measured directly in cubic millimeters of oxygen absorbed or evolved. With the actinometer an exposure of 15 min gave a decrease in oxygen of 81 mm^3 when exposed to red light between 6200 and 6500 A. When the vessel was filled with algae under the same conditions, there was an evolution of oxygen amounting to 10.7 mm^3 in 15 min, after correcting for the absorption of oxygen in respiration as determined by measurements taken in the dark. (a) What is the quantum yield of photosynthesis, that is, the number of molecules of oxygen evolved per photon absorbed? (b) How many calories of light were absorbed during the 15-min exposure? (c) The cross section of the vessel with its flat window is 8 cm^2. Assuming that sunlight has about 0.4 cal cm^{-2} min^{-1} of photosynthetically active light, how intense was the light of this experiment, expressed in per cent of sunlight intensity?

NUCLEAR CHEMISTRY

24

Natural radioactivity was discovered by Becquerel in 1896 just shortly after Roentgen's discovery of X rays. The investigation of natural radioactivity was greatly advanced by Professor and Madame Curie, who discovered radium in 1902. In 1932, Irene Curie, daughter of the discoverers of radium, with her husband, F. Joliot, discovered that other elements can be made radioactive by bombarding them with alpha particles (doubly charged helium nuclei emitted by unstable nuclei). In the same year the neutron was discovered by Chadwick. The bombardment of many nuclei with neutrons produces new radioactive nuclei. The demonstration, by Hahn and Strassman in 1939, that a neutron may cause the fission of a uranium nucleus led to development of the nuclear reactor by Fermi, Szilard, Wigner, and others at the University of Chicago in 1942. The dramatic demonstration that the fission of uranium could be used to obtain a controlled, self-sustaining chain reaction introduced a new era. Besides making available nuclear power, the nuclear reactor provides a copious supply of neutrons which may be used to produce further radioactive elements.

Mass Spectrometry. The existence of isotopes was discovered as a result of the study of radioactivity. In the series of radioactive elements it was found that elements were formed which had atomic weights different from those of the naturally occurring elements. The existence of isotopes among even the stable elements was proved by J. J. Thomson in 1913 in his studies of the deflection of positive rays. Positive rays are beams of positively charged particles which were first observed in a gas-discharge tube when the cathode was pierced with small holes so that the positive ions could pass through. The ratio of charge to mass

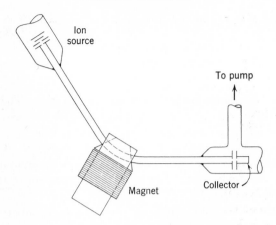

Fig. 24-1. Mass spectrometer.

for positive ions may be determined by the deflection caused by electric and magnetic fields, as in the case of electron beams.

A mass spectrometer* (*Fig. 24-1*) is an instrument that sorts out ions of the same mass-to-charge ratio from an ion beam and makes it possible to determine the relative abundances of the various species. A gas which is to be studied must first be ionized. Solids may be used if they are vaporized first with a hot filament. Ionization is accomplished by allowing the gas to leak at a very low pressure into a chamber where it is bombarded by electrons accelerated by a potential of 50–100 volts. The positive ions produced are accelerated into the analyzer section of the mass spectrometer by means of an electric field of several thousand volts. A narrow beam is collimated by means of slits. The velocity of a charged particle is determined by the electrostatic potential difference E, used to accelerate it according to

$$\tfrac{1}{2}mv^2 = eE \tag{1}$$

where m, v, and e are the mass, velocity, and charge on the particle. If the rest mass is used, this equation applies only if the velocity is much less than that of light. If the particle is sent into a magnetic field of strength H in a direction at right angles to the lines of force, the radius of the circular path followed will be that for which the force of the field Hev is equal to the centrifugal force mv^2/r (p. 583).

$$\frac{mv^2}{r} = Hev \quad \text{or} \quad r = \frac{mv}{eH} \tag{2}$$

* A. J. B. Robertson, *Mass Spectrometry*, John Wiley & Sons, New York, 1954.

Combining with equation 1 to eliminate v^2 yields

$$\frac{m}{e} = \frac{r^2 H^2}{2E} \tag{3}$$

which is the basic equation for the mass spectrometer. The value of r is fixed by the construction of the mass spectrometer, and so ions of different m/e are passed through the slit of the ion collector by changing either the accelerating voltage E or the magnetic field H. The accelerating voltage may be changed continuously, and the ion current may be recorded continuously to obtain the mass spectrum of the sample, such as shown in *Fig. 24-2*.

The nature of the ions which are produced by bombardment of a substance with electrons in the gas phase depends upon the energy of the electrons. Determination of the electron-accelerating potentials required to produce certain fragments yields information as to the energy required to break certain bonds in the molecule.

The mass spectrometer is also useful for analyzing mixtures of organic compounds. In addition to being ionized by the accelerated electrons, the organic molecule is also fragmented, so that a number of ions are produced. This is illustrated by the mass spectrum of butene-1 ($CH_2{=}CHCH_2CH_3$) in Fig. 24-2b.

By means of mass spectrometry it is possible to determine atomic weights to 3 parts in 10^7. Thus chemical atomic weights may be calculated from mass-spectrometric studies more accurately than they can be measured directly. These accurate values are of great importance because they yield useful data on the binding energies of various nuclei.

Isotopic Weights and Abundances. The atomic weights and abundances of isotopes may be determined to a high degree of accuracy with the mass spectrometer. The reference standard for chemical atomic weights is ordinary oxygen taken as 16, but the reference standard for physical atomic weights is the most abundant isotope of oxygen taken as 16 (cf. footnote, p. 12). Atmospheric oxygen is 99.758 per cent O^{16}, 0.0373 per cent O^{17}, and 0.2039 per cent O^{18}. The weighted mean of these values is 16.004462, and so atomic weights on the physical scale are larger by a factor of 1.000272 than those on the chemical scale.

The atomic weights of a number of isotopes on the physical scale are shown in Table I, together with the chemical atomic weights. This table includes only a few of the naturally occurring isotopes. In all chemical and physical-chemical calculations except those concerned with nuclear changes and spectroscopy the chemical atomic weights

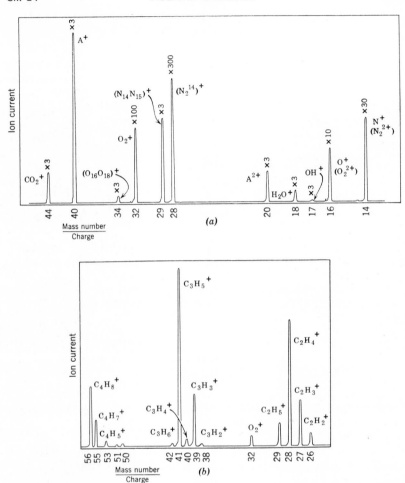

Fig. 24-2. (a) Mass spectrum of air. The heights of the peaks are to be multiplied by the indicated scale factors. (b) Upper part of the mass spectrum of butene-1. (Courtesy Prof. I. Shain of the University of Wisconsin.)

are used. It is likely that a new scale based on C^{12} will be adopted to replace both the chemical and physical scales (p. 12).

The O^{16}/O^{18} ratio in nature has a spread of about 4 per cent, there being a smaller fraction of O^{18} in water and limestone than in air. As a result there is a limit to the accuracy with which it is possible to state chemical atomic weights. Urey and coworkers have found that the isotopic composition of oxygen in calcium carbonate depends upon the temperature at which it was crystallized from solution. Thus a

Table I.¹   Isotopic Weights

Symbol	Number of Protons	Number of Neutrons	Abundance, per cent	Atomic Weight	
				Physical Scale	Chemical Scale
$_1\mathrm{H}^1$	1	0	99.9851	1.00814 ⎫	1.008
$_1\mathrm{H}^2$	1	1	0.0149	2.01474 ⎭	
$_2\mathrm{He}^3$	2	1	1.3×10^{-4}	3.01698 ⎫	4.003
$_2\mathrm{He}^4$	2	2	99.9999	4.00387 ⎭	
$_3\mathrm{Li}^6$	3	3	7.52	6.01702 ⎫	6.940
$_3\mathrm{Li}^7$	3	4	92.47	7.01822 ⎭	
$_6\mathrm{C}^{12}$	6	6	98.892	12.00380 ⎫	12.011
$_6\mathrm{C}^{13}$	6	7	1.108	13.00747 ⎭	
$_7\mathrm{N}^{14}$	7	7	99.635	14.00752 ⎫	14.008
$_7\mathrm{N}^{15}$	7	8	0.365	15.00486 ⎭	
$_8\mathrm{O}^{16}$	8	8	99.758	16.00000 ⎫	
$_8\mathrm{O}^{17}$	8	9	0.0373	17.00453 ⎬	16.00000
$_8\mathrm{O}^{18}$	8	10	0.2039	18.00487 ⎭	
$_{17}\mathrm{Cl}^{35}$	17	18	75.4	34.98018 ⎫	35.457
$_{17}\mathrm{Cl}^{37}$	17	20	24.6	36.97762 ⎭	
$_{82}\mathrm{Pb}^{204}$	82	122	1.48	204.03612 ⎫	
$_{82}\mathrm{Pb}^{206}$	82	124	23.6	206.03859 ⎪	207.21
$_{82}\mathrm{Pb}^{207}$	82	125	22.6	207.04034 ⎪	
$_{82}\mathrm{Pb}^{208}$	82	126	52.3	208.04140 ⎭	
$_{92}\mathrm{U}^{234}$	92	142	0.0058	234.11379 ⎫	
$_{92}\mathrm{U}^{235}$	92	143	0.715	235.11704 ⎬	238.07
$_{92}\mathrm{U}^{238}$	92	146	99.28	238.12493 ⎭	

¹ K. T. Bainbridge in *Experimental Nuclear Physics*, Vol. 1, ed. by E. Segrè, John Wiley & Sons, New York, 1953.

measurement of the atom per cent of O^{18} in a fossil shell makes it possible to calculate the temperature at which it was formed.

Isotope Separation.   The easiest isotope separation is that of deuterium from hydrogen. When an aqueous solution is electrolyzed, the lighter isotope of hydrogen is evolved more readily than the heavier one.* This is an example of the separation of isotopes by competitive reactions. The electrolytic method is expensive and has now been replaced in actual use by the exchange reactions

$$HD(g) + H_2O(g) = H_2(g) + HDO(g)$$

or

$$HDS(g) + H_2O(l) = H_2S(g) + HDO(l)$$

For example, the equilibrium constant of the first reaction is 3.4 at 25° and 2.6 at 100°. Thus deuterium is concentrated in the water mole-

* H. C. Urey and G. K. Teal, *Revs. Modern Phys.*, **7**, 34 (1935).

cules and may be "scrubbed" out of the vapor phase with water. A mixture of hydrogen gas and steam is passed upward through a tower containing a catalyst, which accelerates the exchange, with water flowing down. The water flowing out at the bottom of the tower is enriched in deuterium. Hydrogen gas is obtained from the water by electrolysis, and the process is repeated by using a number of towers in cascade. Heavy water, which is 99.5 per cent D_2O, is available for a few cents per gram. Some of the properties of D_2O and H_2O are compared in Table II.

Table II. Properties of D_2O and H_2O

	Specific Gravity at 20°	Freez- ing Point	Boiling Point	Heat of Vaporiza- tion, cal mole^{-1}	Surface Tension at 20°	Viscosity at 20° $\times 10^3$	Dielec- tric Con- stant	Refrac- tive Index, n_D^{20}	Solubility NaCl, grams per 1000 g
D_2O	1.1059	3.82°	101.42°	9960	67.8	12.6	80.5	1.32844	305
H_2O	0.9982	0.00°	100.00°	9700	72.75	10.09	82.0	1.33300	359

The separation of isotopically different molecules by gaseous diffusion has already been mentioned (p. 281). In order to ensure that the flow through a porous barrier is by diffusion alone, the diameter of the pores should be less than one-tenth of the mean free path of the gas molecules at the pressure used. The rate of diffusion is inversely proportional to the square root of the molecular weight.

During World War II a very large plant was built at Oak Ridge for the concentration of U^{235}, which occurs in natural uranium to the extent of 0.72 per cent. Volatile uranium hexafluoride, UF_6, was used as the process gas, partly because fluorine exists in nature as a single isotope. The ratio of the square roots of the molecular weights of $U^{238}F_6$ and $U^{235}F_6$ is only 1.0043, and therefore many, many diffusion cells in cascade must be used. The principle of a cascade is illustrated in *Fig. 24-3*. If diffusion is allowed to proceed for a long time, the composition of the gas will become the same on both sides of the barrier; but, if only half the gas is allowed to diffuse through the barrier, there will be an enrichment of lighter isotopes in the gas which has passed through the barrier. Half the gas which enters a diffusion cell is allowed to diffuse through the barrier and is pumped on to the next stage. The half which does not pass through the barrier is pumped back to the preceding stage. The area of barrier required is less in the higher stages. Calculations showed that about 4000 diffusion stages would be required to increase the abundance of U^{235} from its normal

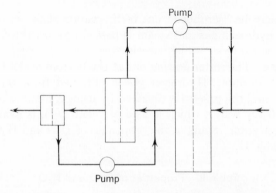

Fig. 24-3. A cascade of gaseous diffusion units.

value to 99 per cent. Consequently, a very large plant was required for this process.

In the thermal-diffusion method the enrichment occurs in a vertical tube containing a central wire or tube maintained at a temperature 200° or 300° above that of the walls of the containing tube. A difference in concentration develops between the hot and cold parts of the fluid, and the material in the cooler region is carried to the bottom reservoir by convection.* Bromine and air in a glass tube can be seen to separate within a few minutes. In such a tube 60 ft high, filled with methane, the methane at the bottom of the tube becomes enriched with C^{13} in a few weeks from 1 per cent to several per cent, and by flowing a fresh supply of methane through slowly at the top it is possible to draw off at the bottom over 100 ml per day of the methane enriched with C^{13}.†

Another method for separating isotopes utilizes the principle of the mass spectrometer. Although only very minute amounts of isotopes can be separated by use of an ordinary mass spectrometer, high-intensity mass spectrometers have been designed for this purpose. Stable isotopes of many elements have been separated by the electromagnetic method and are available for research throughout the world.‡

The substitution of one isotope for another in a compound alters the chemical properties somewhat. The rates of chemical reactions are altered.§ The activation energy for a reaction is affected in such a way that the species containing the heavier isotope generally reacts more

---

* K. Clusius and G. Dickel, *Naturwiss.*, *26*, 546 (1938); *27*, 149 (1938); A. K. Brewer and A. Bramley, *Phys. Rev.*, *55*, 590 (1939).

† T. I. Taylor and G. Glockler, *J. Chem. Phys.*, *7*, 850 (1939); *8*, 843 (1940).

‡ They can be obtained at a nominal price from the U. S. Atomic Energy Commission at Oak Ridge, Tenn.

§ J. Bigeleisen, *Advances in Chem. Physics*, *1*, 15 (1958).

slowly. Also the equilibrium constants of exchange reactions differ from unity. The equilibrium constants for such reactions can be calculated from statistical mechanics, provided that the fundamental vibration frequencies are known.* If the vibration frequencies are not known from direct measurement, they can be estimated, assuming that the force constants are unaffected by isotopic substitution. The equilibrium constant for the reaction

$$N^{15}H_3(g) + N^{14}H_4{}^+(aq) = N^{14}H_3(g) + N^{15}H_4{}^+(aq)$$

is 1.033. Thode and Urey carried out experimental concentration of N^{15}, using this reaction, in an effective column passing the ammonia gas up against a solution of ammonium nitrate flowing down. Concentration of N^{15} up to 72 per cent was obtained, and the experimentally determined value of K was 1.023. Heavy carbon, C^{13}, has been prepared by use of the reaction

$$HC^{12}N(g) + C^{13}N^-(aq) = HC^{13}N(g) + C^{12}N^-(aq)$$

Nuclear Binding Energy. It was shown by Rutherford (p. 457) that a nucleus is very small (about 10^{-13} cm). There are several types of evidence that nuclei consist of protons and neutrons rather than protons and electrons. Electrons are too big, and nuclear spins cannot be accounted for in terms of protons and electrons. The number of protons is equal to the atomic number Z, and the number of neutrons is equal to $A - Z$, where A is the mass number (the integer nearest the atomic weight). The nature of the forces which bind the protons together in spite of their electrostatic repulsion is at present not understood. The stability of a nucleus with a given number of protons depends upon the number of neutrons. The number of neutrons, $A - Z$, in stable and radioactive nuclei is plotted versus the number of protons, Z, in *Fig. 24-4*. As the atomic number increases, the number of neutrons required for stability becomes greater than the number of protons. All nuclei with 84 or more protons are unstable and disintegrate until a stable configuration of neutrons and protons is attained.

Nuclear masses are not equal to the sum of the masses of the constituent neutrons and protons, and consideration of exact atomic weights shows that mass is not conserved in nuclear reactions. However, taken together, mass and energy are conserved; the relation between change in mass and energy is given by Einstein's equation

$$\Delta E = c^2 \, \Delta m_0 \tag{4}$$

* H. C. Urey and L. J. Greiff, *J. Am. Chem. Soc.*, *57*, 321 (1935).

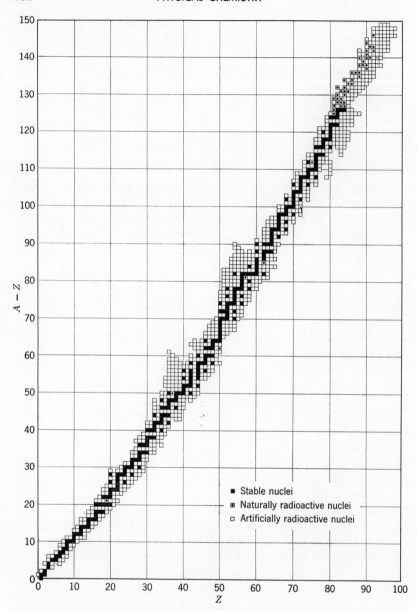

Stable nuclei
Naturally radioactive nuclei
Artificially radioactive nuclei

Fig. 24-4. Chart of the known nuclei. (From Kaplan, *Nuclear Physics*, Addison-Wesley Publishing Co., Reading, Mass., 1955.)

Thus the annihilation of 1 gram of matter produces $(2.9978 \times 10^{10})^2$ or 8.9868×10^{20} ergs of energy.

In discussing nuclear reactions it is convenient to express changes in atomic weight in millions of electron volts (Mev) per atom. Since the charge on the electron is 1.602×10^{-19} coulomb, an electron volt is 1.602×10^{-19} joule, or 1.602×10^{-12} erg, and an Mev is equivalent to 1.602×10^{-6} erg. One atomic mass unit (amu) is $1/6.02 \times 10^{23}$ grams; and so, using equation 4, the corresponding energy in Mev is $(3 \times 10^{10})^2/(6.02 \times 10^{23})(1.602 \times 10^{-6}) = 931$ Mev per atomic mass unit.

The mass of an atom is less than that of the constituent protons, neutrons, and electrons because energy is released when a number of protons, neutrons, and electrons combine to form an atom. If the actual isotopic weight is M, the loss in mass in the formation of the atom, that is, the *mass defect* ΔM, is

$$\Delta M = Zm_{\mathrm{H}} + (A - Z)m_n - M \tag{5}$$

where m_{H} is the mass of a hydrogen atom (that is, one proton plus one electron), and m_n is the mass of one neutron. The binding energy corresponding to the mass defect is calculated using equation 4. This is also the energy required to break the atom into its constituent particles. The binding energy is usually expressed in Mev.

$$\text{Binding energy in Mev} = 931 \, \Delta M = 931[Zm_{\mathrm{H}} + (A - Z)m_n - M] \tag{6}$$

where 931 is the conversion factor between atom mass units and Mev. The masses of the proton and the neutron on the physical scale are given on p. 697.

Example 1. Calculate the mass defect and the binding energy for $_6\mathrm{C}^{12}$, which has an isotopic weight on the physical scale of 12.0038.

$$\text{Mass defect} = (6)(1.00814) + (6)(1.00898) - 12.0038$$
$$= 0.0990 \text{ amu}$$
$$\text{Binding energy} = (931)(0.0990) = 92.3 \text{ Mev}$$

This value, divided by the number of protons and neutrons, gives the binding energy per nuclear particle or nucleon, which is $92.3/12 = 7.69$ Mev.

The binding energy per nucleon for stable nuclides is plotted versus mass number in *Fig. 24-5*. The term *nuclide* refers to a species of atom characterized by the number of protons and neutrons in its nucleus, while the term *isotope* refers to atomic species of the same atomic number. With the exception of He^4, C^{12}, and O^{16}, the values are quite close to the smooth curve shown in the figure.

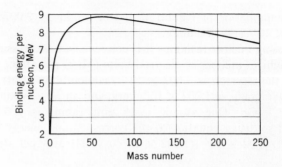

Fig. 24-5. Nuclear binding energy.

Natural Radioactivity. The stabilization or decrease in energy of an unstable nucleus may occur in a number of ways with the emission of high-energy radiation.

If a nucleus has too high a ratio of neutrons to protons for stability, it will emit a negative beta particle (electron) with the result that the number of neutrons is decreased by 1 and the number of protons in the nucleus is increased by 1. If a nucleus has too low a ratio of neutrons to protons, it may capture an orbital electron (K capture) or emit a positive beta particle (positron) with the result that the number of neutrons in the nucleus is increased at the expense of the protons. Sometimes a given nucleus can exist with two or more quantities of energy. When there is a transition from one energy level to another, a gamma ray is emitted. Alpha particles, which are He^{2+} with velocities of the order of one-tenth the velocity of light, may be emitted by a nucleus.

The ranges of gamma rays are in general much greater than those of beta particles, which are in turn much greater than those of alpha particles. The characteristic decreases in intensity of these radiations as they pass through matter are illustrated in *Fig. 24-6*. Because of their large charge and low speed, alpha particles form a high density of ions along their path and lose their energy rather quickly. Thus the

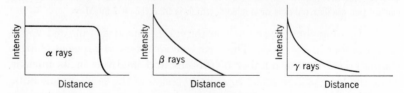

Fig. 24-6. Absorption of alpha, beta, and gamma rays. The three distance scales are very different (roughly 1, 100, 10,000).

range of alpha particles is only a few centimeters of air at atmospheric pressure. The ranges of alpha particles from a given nucleus are all very nearly the same.

Three families of radioactive elements are found in nature. These are the thorium series, uranium series, and actinium series, which are shown in *Fig. 24-7*. In this figure the nature of the radiations and the

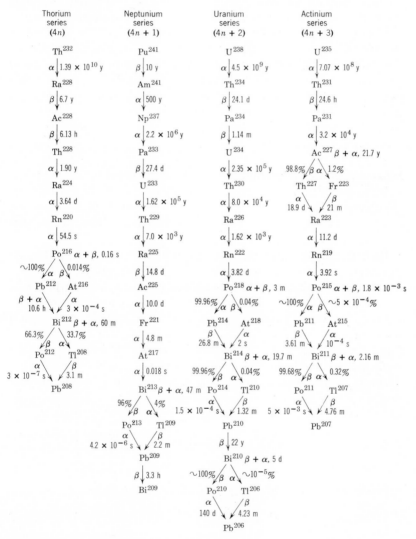

Fig. 24-7. Radioactive series. The half-lives are given in years (y), days (d), minutes (m), or seconds (s).

half-lives are indicated. When an alpha particle is emitted, the mass number of the nucleus is decreased by 4 and the atomic number is decreased by 2. When a beta particle is emitted, the mass number of the nucleus is unchanged because an electron weighs 1/1850 as much as a hydrogen atom, and the atomic number is increased by 1 because 1 negative charge is removed from the nucleus and the total positive charge of the nucleus increases by 1. It will be noted that branching occurs in each series. For example, Po^{216} disintegrates in two ways, but with the same half-life. The mass numbers of all the members of the thorium series are multiples of 4 and may be represented by $4n$. The fact that the uranium series may be represented by $4n + 2$ and the actinium series by $4n + 3$ suggested that a $4n + 1$ series might exist. Although the $4n + 1$ series is not found in nature, the elements in this series have been obtained artificially. This series is called the neptunium series because the laboratory-produced neptunium is the member having the longest half-life.

Measurement of Radioactivity. Action on a photographic plate constitutes one of the simplest tests for the radioactivity of a substance. This method can be used to reveal the distribution of a radioactive substance within an object, such as a mineral, a leaf, or a paper chromatogram.

Radiation from radioactive substances may be detected by the ions produced in a gas. An ionization chamber contains two electrodes across which a sufficient voltage is applied so that all the ions produced by incoming radiations are drawn to the electrodes. The resulting current is measured with a sensitive amplifier (usually a vibrating-reed electrometer).

A Geiger-Müller (GM) counter consists of a cylindrical negative electrode with a central wire as the positive electrode, as shown in *Fig. 24-8*. The tube is filled with an ionizable gas, and a sufficient voltage (about

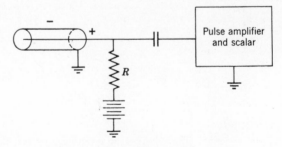

Fig. 24-8. Geiger-Müller (GM) counter.

1000 volts) is applied so that the production of a single ion pair between the electrodes produces an avalanche of ions. The avalanche is due to the fact that in the high electric field ions are accelerated rapidly to a velocity at which they can produce ionization of gas molecules in the tube; the additional ions and electrons are accelerated, resulting in a geometric increase in the number of ions. The pulse of current actuates an electronic relay and is counted. The pulse is terminated when the current through resistor R becomes large enough to reduce the potential difference between the electrodes in the GM tube to the point that no further ionization is obtained. In a GM tube the pulse size is independent of the number of ions formed in the initial ionizing event. The radioactivity of a solution or gas may be determined using a special GM tube, with a jacket which holds the solution or gas. Geiger-Müller counters are quite insensitive to gamma rays because these are so penetrating that few ions are produced.

The construction of a proportional counter is similar to that of a GM counter, but a voltage below that of the GM region is used. Under these conditions the maximum voltage of the pulse of current through the tube resulting from an ionizing particle is *proportional* to the energy of the ionizing particle. The numbers of pulses in certain voltage ranges may be recorded separately, using a pulse-height analyzer. Thus it is possible to determine the number of ionizing particles of different energy.

A scintillation counter contains a volume of liquid or solid which produces flashes of light upon absorption of gamma rays. A photomultiplier tube is used to count the flashes, and the pulse heights are proportional to the gamma-ray, beta-ray, or X-ray energies. The flashes of light are due to the fact that, when a gamma ray interacts with matter, its energy is transferred to an electron as kinetic energy. This energetic electron loses its excess energy in a series of interactions with atoms in which an orbital electron is raised to a higher energy level. When an electron falls into the vacant level, a photon of visible radiation is produced. Different crystals and liquids have different efficiencies, and thallium-activated sodium iodide is often used. Since the pulses produced by gamma rays from various isotopes have characteristic voltages, the radioactivities of different isotopes in a mixture may be determined separately. Thin scintillation counters are also available for counting alpha particles without background interference from gamma rays and cosmic rays.

The Wilson cloud chamber provides an important means for studying ionizing radiations. Air saturated with water vapor is cooled suddenly by an adiabatic expansion. The ions produced by an alpha or beta ray serve as nuclei for condensation. Thus condensation of water vapor in fine droplets occurs along the path, which may be photographed with suitable illumination.

Alpha Decay. As an alpha particle passes through matter, ion pairs are produced by the removal of electrons from molecules. An alpha particle with an energy of 7 Mev produces about 2×10^5 ion pairs in air at 15° and 1 atm pressure before being stopped. A larger number of ion pairs is produced per unit length of path near the end where the alpha particle moves more slowly and spends more time in the vicinity of the molecules it encounters.

Example 2. Rutherford and Geiger discovered that radium emits 3.4×10^{10} alpha particles g^{-1} sec^{-1}. Rutherford and Boltwood found that radium produces helium at the rate of 1.07×10^{-4} ml g^{-1} day^{-1}, measured under standard conditions. Since each alpha particle is transformed into a helium atom, what is the value of Avogadro's number?

$$\frac{(22,400)}{(1.07 \times 10^{-4})}(3.4 \times 10^{10})(24)(60)(60) = 6.15 \times 10^{23}$$

With the exception of alpha particles coming from excited nuclei, the ranges of alpha particles in air at atmospheric pressure lie between 2.5 and 8.6 cm. The velocities, and hence the energies, of alpha particles may be calculated from the deflection of their paths in a magnetic field in a vacuum. The velocities of alpha particles fall in the range 1.6×10^9 cm sec^{-1} to 2.2×10^9 cm sec^{-1}, corresponding to energies of 3–10 Mev. The kinetic energy of the alpha particle is not the total energy of the disintegration, since the product nucleus also recoils with kinetic energy.

The half-lives and disintegration energies of alpha emitters are related, the short-lived nuclides emitting the most energetic alpha particles. The nuclides emitting the most energetic alpha particles have half-lives of the order of 10^{-7} sec. The nuclides emitting the least energetic particles have half-lives of the order of 10^{10} years. Thus a small range in energy corresponds to a very great range in half-life.

The alpha particles from a given nucleus may have different discrete energies; if this is the case, gamma rays are also emitted by nuclei which have been left in an excited state after the emission of an alpha particle. Thus the sum of the energies of the gamma ray and the alpha particle of lower energy is equal to the disintegration energy for the emission of the alpha particle of higher energy. This indicates that there are two energy levels for the product nucleus separated by an energy equal to that of the gamma ray.

Beta Decay. The energies of beta particles are almost always smaller than those of alpha particles, but the beta particles move much faster because of their smaller mass. The relativistic effect on the mass must be taken into account for beta particles, since they may have velocities up to about 0.99 that of light.

Beta particles are much more penetrating than alpha particles of the same energy. A 3-Mev alpha particle will penetrate 2.8 cm of air and produce about 40,000 ion pairs per cm. A 3-Mev beta particle will penetrate 1000 cm of air and produce about 40 ion pairs per cm. Because of the long range in air the absorption of beta particles is studied using metal foils. If the amount of absorber is expressed as the product of the density and thickness, the range of beta particles is nearly independent of the material.

In contrast with alpha particles, beta particles from the decay of a single nuclear species are emitted with a continuous distribution of energy up to some maximum value. The finding that beta particles have a range of energy created a serious theoretical problem. When beta emission occurs, it can be shown that the energy of the nucleus decreases by an amount equal to the *maximum* energy of the beta particles. The principle of conservation of energy requires that another particle be emitted simultaneously with the remaining energy. According to Fermi's theory of beta decay, a neutrino, which is a neutral particle of very small mass, is emitted with the remaining energy. Although neutrinos interact very weakly with matter, they have been detected directly. Because of the distribution of energies the intensity of beta radiation falls off with distance, as illustrated in Fig. 24-3. The intensity of a monoenergetic electron beam decreases linearly with the thickness of the absorber because of scattering.

There are often discrete lines superimposed on the continuous beta-particle spectrum. These lines are due to the ejection of extranuclear electrons; the process is called *internal conversion.* Somehow there is a direct interaction between the nucleus and electrons in the K and L shells, in which the nucleus passes from a higher energy state to a lower energy state and the orbital electron is emitted from the atom with an energy equal to the difference in energy between the two nuclear states minus the binding energy of the electron in the K or L shell.

Gamma Decay. Gamma rays are electromagnetic radiation like X rays. If they are monoenergetic, they follow Beer's law (p. 520), and the penetrating power may conveniently be expressed as the thickness of the absorber required to reduce the intensity to half. Since no absorber thickness reduces the intensity to zero (cf. Fig. 24-6), it can be seen that shielding against gamma radiation is difficult. The processes which are responsible for the absorption of gamma rays are ejection of electrons by the photoelectric effect, Compton scattering (p. 461), and the production of electron-positron pairs. The positron is like an electron but has a positive charge. Gamma rays are much more penetrating than alpha or beta rays. The thickness of lead required to reduce the intensity of 1-Mev gamma rays to half is 1 cm.

Gamma emission often accompanies the emission of alpha or beta particles. When the emission of the gamma ray is delayed considerably, the process is called an *isomeric transition*. Such processes are conveniently represented by energy diagrams, such as *Fig. 24-9*. Figure 24-9a

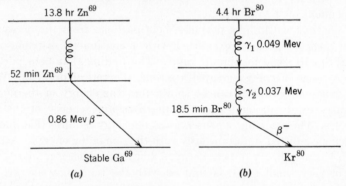

Fig. 24-9. Nuclear energy-level diagrams showing isomeric transitions with the accompanying emission of gamma rays.

shows two nuclear isomers (that is, nuclei with the same number of neutrons and protons but different energy) of Zn^{69}. The one of higher energy decays by the emission of a gamma ray, and the half-life is 13.8 hr. The lower-energy isomer of Zn^{69} decays to Ga^{69} by emission of a beta particle with a half-life of 52 min.

A further example of an isomeric transition is provided by Br^{80}, which emits two gamma rays with a half-life of 4.4 hr, as shown by Fig. 24-9b. The two gamma transitions are in instantaneous cascade.

The deactivation of an excited nucleus may be accomplished by the emission of a gamma ray or by the emission of an extranuclear electron. The emission of an orbital electron in this way is referred to as internal conversion. A line spectrum of the internal conversion electrons is obtained with an electron spectrograph, and the energies of the lines correspond to the difference in nuclear-energy levels minus the binding energy of the shell in which conversion occurs. The latter process occurs in the decay of Br^{80} described in Fig. 24-9b. The vacancy produced in an inner electron shell is filled by another electron, usually from the next higher shell. Usually an X-ray photon is produced, and in some cases addition extranuclear electrons (called *Auger electrons*) are emitted, the sum of their energies being the difference between their binding energies and the energy the X-ray photon would have had.

The Laws of Radioactive Transformation. All the elements with atomic numbers greater than that of bismuth, 83, are unstable and undergo radioactive disintegration into lighter elements. Since the nuclei are not affected by the thermal motions of molecules, no detectable change in the rate of radioactive disintegrations has been observed in studies extending from liquid-helium temperatures to 1000°. The rate of radioactive disintegration is affected by chemical combination only in the case of isomeric transitions, and even here the effect is very small.

In all radioactive disintegrations the number of atoms disintegrating in a short interval of time is proportional to the number present, within statistical variations; and so radioactive decay always follows the first-order equation

$$-\frac{dN}{dt} = \lambda N \tag{7}$$

where λ is the rate constant which has the dimensions of reciprocal time, and the number N of atoms (or gram atoms) remaining unchanged after time t is given by the integrated rate equation

$$\lambda = \frac{2.303}{t} \log \frac{N_i}{N} \tag{8}$$

or

$$N = N_i e^{-\lambda t} \tag{9}$$

where N_i is the number initially present. Since the rate of disintegration dN/dt is proportional to N, according to equation 7, equations 8 and 9 may also be written in terms of the disintegration rates

$$\lambda = \frac{2.303}{t} \log \frac{(dN/dt)_i}{(dN/dt)} \tag{10}$$

$$\left(\frac{dN}{dt}\right) = \left(\frac{dN}{dt}\right)_i e^{-\lambda t} \tag{11}$$

The exponential nature of the decay law is due to the fact that the probability of disintegration of a nucleus of a radioactive element in an interval of time Δt is independent of the past history of the nucleus and is the same for all nuclei of the same type. For sufficiently short time intervals the probability p of disintegration is proportional to Δt.

$$p = \lambda \, \Delta t \tag{12}$$

where λ is the proportionality constant characteristic of the nucleus. The probability that a given nucleus will not disintegrate in an interval Δt is $1 - p = 1 - \lambda \, \Delta t$. The probability that the nucleus will survive a second interval Δt is also $1 - \lambda \, \Delta t$, and the probability that it will survive both intervals is $(1 - \lambda \, \Delta t)^2$. The probability that it will survive n such intervals is $(1 - \lambda \, \Delta t)^n$. This probability is expressed in terms of the total time t by substituting $t = n \, \Delta t$ to obtain $(1 - \lambda t/n)^n$.

To obtain an accurate value for the probability that a given nucleus will not disintegrate in time t, we let Δt become very small or n become very large. Using equations 48 and 52 for series in the Appendix, it may be shown that

$$\lim_{n \to \infty} \left(1 - \frac{\lambda t}{n} \right)^n = e^{-\lambda t} \tag{13}$$

Thus the probability that a given nucleus will survive for a time t is $e^{-\lambda t}$. If there are initially a large number of nuclei, then the fraction N/N_i remaining at time t is equal to $e^{-\lambda t}$, and this yields equation 9.

Successive Radioactive Transformations. The product of a radioactive disintegration may itself be radioactive, and this series of radioactive transformations continues until a stable end product is reached. Such a series of first-order reactions may be treated mathematically by the methods described on p. 309.

In a radioactive series

$$A \xrightarrow{\lambda_A} B \xrightarrow{\lambda_B} C \xrightarrow{\lambda_C} \cdots Z \tag{14}$$

the rate of formation of any member, other than the first or last, is equal to the rate with which it is formed from the preceding member minus the rate with which it disintegrates. For example, for B

$$\frac{dN_B}{dt} = \lambda_A N_A - \lambda_B N_B \tag{15}$$

If only A is present initially, the number of atoms of B will increase rapidly at first and then more slowly, since the number of B atoms disintegrating per unit time is proportional to N_B. As the number of atoms of A decreases, the rate of formation of B decreases, and hence N_B decreases.

If we consider the case in which B has a much shorter half-life than A and the period within which N_A remains nearly constant, a *steady state* is approached in which B disintegrates at the same rate it is formed, and $dN_B/dt = 0$. When this is the case, we can see from equation 15 that

$$\frac{N_B}{N_A} = \frac{\lambda_A}{\lambda_B} \tag{16}$$

Then,

$$\frac{N_B}{N_A} = \frac{t_{\frac{1}{2},B}}{t_{\frac{1}{2},A}} \tag{17}$$

where $t_{\frac{1}{2}}$ is the half-life (p. 299). Thus, if the half-life of the parent element is very long compared with the half-life of the daughters, and if sufficient time is allowed for a steady state to be attained, the ratio of the number of atoms of successive radioelements is the same as the ratio of their half-lives. It is evident that the short-lived elements cannot accumulate in large quantities, because the number of atoms disintegrating per minute must be the same as for the parent element.

Example 3. Radium emits an alpha particle and leaves a gaseous element, radon. For the disintegration of radium, $t_{\frac{1}{2}} = 1620$ years, and for radon $t_{\frac{1}{2}} = 3.82$ days. How many milliliters of radon at $25°$ and 1 atm are present in a steady state with 1 gram of radium?

$$1 \text{ g radium} = \tfrac{1}{226} = 0.00442 \text{ g-atom}$$

$$\frac{N_{Rn}}{N_{Ra}} = \frac{t_{\frac{1}{2},Rn}}{t_{\frac{1}{2},Ra}}$$

$$\frac{N_{Rn}}{0.00442} = \frac{3.82}{(1620)(365.25)}$$

$$N_{Rn} = 2.86 \times 10^{-8} \text{ g-atom}$$

$$\text{Volume of radon} = (2.86 \times 10^{-8})(0.08205)(298)(1000)/1$$

$$= 6.99 \times 10^{-4} \text{ ml}$$

In general the number of atoms (or gram atoms) of B present *at any time* may be calculated as shown on p. 310 for two consecutive first-order reactions.

$$N_B = \frac{\lambda_A N_i}{\lambda_B - \lambda_A} (e^{-\lambda_A t} - e^{-\lambda_B t}) \tag{18}$$

where N_i is the initial number of A atoms (or gram atoms of A). This equation is simplified if the half-life of the parent is much longer than the half-life of the daughter ($\lambda_A \ll \lambda_B$). For this case equation 18 becomes

$$N_B = \frac{\lambda_A N_i}{\lambda_B} (1 - e^{-\lambda_B t}) \qquad (19)$$

The number of atoms of B, N_B, approaches its steady-state value, $\lambda_A N_i/\lambda_B$ (cf. equation 16), asymptotically. It is evident from equation 19 that the time required to reach half this number of atoms is equal to the half-life of B, *not that of the parent isotope* A.

As an example, consider the production of radon from radium, $t = 0$ being taken as the time at which the previously accumulated radon has just been pumped off. Since the half-life of radium is 1620 years and that of radon is 3.82 days, $\lambda_A \ll \lambda_B$. Thus the volume of radon present after 3.82 days would be half the steady-state volume calculated in example 3.

Nuclear Reactions. The existence of spontaneous disintegration led to speculation about causing the disintegration of stable nuclei in the laboratory. In 1919 Rutherford bombarded nitrogen with alpha particles and obtained flashes of light on a screen at distances much greater than the range of the alpha particles. Deflections in a magnetic field indicated that the particles causing these scintillations were protons. Thus the reaction is

$$_2\text{He}^4 + {_7}\text{N}^{14} \rightarrow [_9\text{F}^{18}] \rightarrow {_1}\text{H}^1 + {_8}\text{O}^{17}$$

The proton has a larger energy than the alpha particle, and the experiments indicate that the alpha particle is captured by the nucleus it hits and that the compound nucleus which is formed, $[_9\text{F}^{18}]$, emits a proton. There is a decrease in mass in the reaction, and therefore the products have a greater kinetic energy than the reactants. Rutherford and Chadwick found that alpha particles caused the transmutation of all the light elements from boron to potassium, with the exception of carbon and oxygen.

Nuclear reactions obey several conservation laws. The total mass counted as energy, according to $\Delta E = c^2 \Delta m_0$, and the kinetic energies of all the particles involved are conserved. Thus it is possible, from measurements of kinetic energies of the particles involved, to calculate the change in mass, or vice versa. In addition the momentum of the entire system must remain constant throughout the reaction. The momentum of a photon is $h\nu/c$. The momentum of a particle is simply mv, where m is the mass and v is velocity. For reactions where angular relationships are observed, as in nuclear reactions in the cloud chamber or a photographic emulsion, the principle of conservation of momentum makes it possible to calculate masses and velocities. Furthermore, the total electrical charge and spin of all the reacting particles are also conserved. Thus the spin of a new particle may be determined if the spins of its disintegration products are known.

Example 4. Crockcroft and Walton found that, when Li^7 is bombarded with protons having energies up to 0.7 Mev, two alpha particles emerge at $180°$, each having an energy of 8.66 Mev. Show that the total energy of this reaction, 17.32 Mev, is in agreement with the change in mass in the reaction.

$$_3Li^7 + {}_1H^1 \rightarrow {}_2{}_2He^4$$

$$7.01822 \quad 1.00814 \quad 2(4.00387)$$

$$\Delta M = 0.01862 \text{ amu (atomic mass units)}$$

$$\Delta E = (931)(0.01862) = 17.32 \text{ Mev}$$

In such calculations the masses of the orbital electrons are not subtracted from the atomic weights, since the numbers of electrons on the two sides of the equation are the same.

Example 5. Some nuclear reactions are endothermic and therefore do not occur unless the colliding particles have sufficient energy. Show how the threshold for the photodisintegration of the deuteron may be used to calculate the mass of the neutron, which of course cannot be determined by mass spectrometry. In order to disintegrate deuterons the gamma-ray photon has to have an energy of 2.21 Mev, which by equation 4 is equivalent to 0.00237 mass unit.

$$\gamma \quad + \quad {}_1H^2 \quad \rightarrow \quad {}_1H^1 \quad + {}_0n^1$$
$$0.00237 \quad 2.01474 \quad 1.00814 \quad m_n$$

$$m_n = 2.01474 + 0.00237 - 1.00814 = 1.00897 \text{ amu}$$

This value is given in Table IV.

Artificial Radioactivity. In 1932, Irene Curie and F. Joliot discovered that light elements can be made radioactive by nuclear reaction with alpha particles. The reaction with magnesium is

$$_{12}Mg^{24} + {}_2He^4 \rightarrow [{}_{14}Si^{28}] \rightarrow {}_{14}Si^{27} + {}_0n^1$$

The silicon isotope produced is radioactive with a half-life of 4 sec and emits a positron β^+, described on p. 696.

$$_{14}Si^{27} \rightarrow {}_{13}Al^{27} + \beta^+$$

The study of the nucleus received a great impetus when projectiles other than alpha particles were used for bombardment and when ion beams of high intensity were obtained from various accelerators. Protons or deuterons, accelerated to enormous velocities, are effective in disintegrating nuclei. Several different types of accelerators are used to accelerate ions or electrons to energies up to several billion electron volts. By means of these accelerators, which may be of a circular type or linear, many artificially radioactive isotopes have been produced. A few examples of the many types of nuclear reactions are listed in Table III.

Table III. Typical Nuclear Reactions

General Reactions	Example	Notation
$_zX^M + _0n^1 \rightarrow _zY^{M+1} + _0\gamma^0$	$_{25}Mn^{55} + _0n^1 \rightarrow _{25}Mn^{56} + _0\gamma^0$	$Mn^{55}(n, \gamma)Mn^{56}$
$_zX^M + _1p^1 \rightarrow _{z+1}Y^M + _0n^1$	$_3Li^7 + _1p^1 \rightarrow _4Be^7 + _0n^1$	$Li^7(p, n)Be^7$
$_zX^M + _2\alpha^4 \rightarrow _{z+1}Y^{M+3} + _1p^1$	$_{20}Ca^{43} + _2\alpha^4 \rightarrow _{21}Sc^{46} + _1p^1$	$Ca^{43}(\alpha, p)Sc^{46}$
$_zX^M + _1d^2 \rightarrow _{z+1}Y^M + 2_0n^1$	$_{52}Te^{130} + _1d^2 \rightarrow _{53}I^{130} + 2_0n^1$	$Te^{130}(d, 2n)I^{130}$
$_zX^M + _0n^1 \rightarrow _{z-2}Y^{M-3} + _2\alpha^4$	$_{27}Co^{59} + _0n^1 \rightarrow _{25}Mn^{56} + _2\alpha^4$	$Co^{59}(n, \alpha)Mn^{56}$

Other Particles. In 1930 Dirac presented theoretical arguments that the positive electron, or *positron*, should exist. The positron was discovered in 1932 by Anderson, in the course of an examination in a cloud chamber of particles emitted during the bombardment of a gas by cosmic rays. A powerful magnetic field of known strength was placed across the chamber, and cloud tracks were obtained with such a large curvature that the particle producing the track would have a mass of only 0.000549 on the atomic-weight scale, that is, the mass of an electron. But the surprising observation was that the particle was deflected in the magnetic field in the direction which showed that it was not negatively charged, but positively charged.

Mesons were predicted in 1935 by Yukawa from his theory of nuclear forces which required particles having masses about 300 times that of the electron. Mesons of various charges (positive, negative, and neutral) and masses have been found in cosmic rays and may be produced with high-energy particle accelerators. Information on the mu and pi mesons is given in Table IV. The decay schemes for the mu and pi mesons are:

$$\mu^\pm \xrightarrow{2.2 \times 10^{-6}s} e^\pm + 2\nu + 105 \text{ Mev}$$

$$\pi^\pm \xrightarrow{2.5 \times 10^{-8}s} \mu^\pm + \nu + 33 \text{ Mev}$$

$$\pi^0 \xrightarrow{5 \times 10^{-14}s} 2h\nu + 133 \text{ Mev}$$

where ν represents the neutrino.

Several types of heavier mesons have been observed in cosmic rays. Particles with masses between those of the proton and the deuteron

Table IV.   Masses and Spins of Particles

Particle	Symbol	Charge	Mass Relative to Electron	Mass Physical Scale	Spin
Photon	$h\nu$	0	0		1
Electron	e^-	$-$	1	0.000549	$\frac{1}{2}$
Positron	e^+	$+$	1	0.000549	$\frac{1}{2}$
Neutrino	ν	0	<0.01		$\frac{1}{2}$
Proton	p	$+$	1836	1.00759 [1]	$\frac{1}{2}$
Neutron	n	0	1836	1.00897	$\frac{1}{2}$
Mu meson	$\mu^\pm$	$\pm$	206		$\frac{1}{2}$
Pi meson	$\pi^\pm$	$\pm$	273		0
Pi meson	π^0	0	264		0

[1] The mass of the hydrogen atom on the physical scale is $1.00759 + 0.00549 = 1.00814$.

have been observed in cosmic rays and have been produced in the largest accelerators. These particles, which are called hyperons, are also unstable.

The Neutron. The existence of the neutron was predicted by Rutherford and Harkins. Bothe and Becker reported that if certain light elements were bombarded with alpha particles a very penetrating radiation was obtained. Irene Joliot-Curie and F. Joliot found that, when a sheet of paraffin was placed in the path of this new radiation, protons were ejected with a considerable velocity. In 1932 Chadwick pointed out that the various experimental observations could be explained "if it were supposed that the radiation consisted of particles of mass nearly equal to that of the proton and with no net charge." For example, neutrons are formed by the reaction

$$_2\text{He}^4 + {}_4\text{Be}^9 \rightarrow [{}_6\text{C}^{13}] \rightarrow {}_6\text{C}^{12} + {}_0n^1$$

where $_0n^1$ is the neutron and $[{}_6\text{C}^{13}]$ is an excited carbon nucleus having a mass of 13. Since the neutron has no charge but has approximately the same mass as a hydrogen atom, it is sometimes considered to be the element of atomic number zero.

Since neutrons are uncharged, they are not repelled by nuclei, as are positively charged particles. Thus neutrons can penetrate nuclei and cause nuclear reactions when they have little kinetic energy.

The development of nuclear-fission reactors has made available high fluxes of neutrons for chemical experiments. Neutrons ejected from atomic nuclei in the process of fission usually have energies of the order of 1–10 Mev. Such neutrons are called *fast neutrons*. Neutrons are slowed down, and also absorbed, during passage through matter. Collisions of neutrons with nuclei which do not result in absorption are called *elastic*. The transfer of energy from the neutron is greater, the smaller the mass of the scattering nucleus, i.e., the more nearly equal are the two masses.

Neutrons with energies below 1 ev are referred to as *slow* neutrons. At room temperature the kinetic energy of a thermal neutron is 0.025 ev. The kinetic energies of thermal neutrons are given by the Maxwell distribution law, the same as for gas molecules (p. 274).

The nuclear cross section σ is the apparent cross-sectional area of a nucleus for some nuclear reaction. Nuclear cross sections are usually given in units of 10^{-24} cm^2, which are referred to as "barns." The cross section depends upon the nature of the target nucleus and the velocity of the particle. Cadmium 113 has a very high absorption cross section for thermal neutrons, so great, in fact, that cadmium is used in the control rods of nuclear reactors.

When a slow neutron enters a nucleus, a compound nucleus in a high-energy state is formed. The excess energy is then dissipated by the emission of a gamma ray, an alpha particle, or a proton. The high-energy compound nucleus is indicated by brackets, as shown by

$$_1H^1 + _0n^1 \rightarrow [_1H^2] \rightarrow _1H^2 + \gamma$$

$$_{48}Cd^{113} + _0n^1 \rightarrow [_{48}Cd^{114}] \rightarrow _{48}Cd^{114} + \gamma$$

$$_3Li^6 + _0n^1 \rightarrow [_3Li^7] \rightarrow _1H^3 + _2He^4$$

$$_5B^{10} + _0n^1 \rightarrow [_5B^{11}] \rightarrow _3Li^7 + _2He^4$$

Neutrons can be detected by the ionizing particles which are produced when they are absorbed by the nuclei of certain atoms, such as B^{10}. The reaction is the last one given above. The products have a total energy of 2.5 Mev and cause ionization. An ionization chamber filled with a volatile boron compound can be used as a neutron detector even in the presence of gamma radiation. Also, slow neutrons may be detected by their ability to cause fission of U^{235}. Ionization is produced by the fission fragments.

Neutrons can be produced by mixing radium compounds with beryllium compounds, but they may be obtained at much higher fluxes

Table V.　Radioisotopes Produced by Irradiation with Neutrons [1]

Isotope	Reaction	Radiation	Half-Life [2]
Ba^{131}	$Ba^{130}(n, \gamma)Ba^{131}$	γ	12.0 d
Br^{82}	$Br^{81}(n, \gamma)Br^{82}$	β, γ	35.5 h
C^{14}	$N^{14}(n, p)C^{14}$	β (0.15 Mev)	5570　y
H^3	$Li^6(n, \alpha)H^3$	β (0.0189 Mev)	12.5 y
I^{131}	$Te^{130}(n, \gamma)Te^{131}$ $\rightarrow \beta + I^{131}$	β, γ	8　d
Fe^{59}	$Fe^{58}(n, \gamma)Fe^{59}$	β, γ	46.3 d
P^{32}	$S^{32}(n, p)P^{32}$	β (1.7 Mev)	14.3 d
Na^{24}	$Na^{23}(n, \gamma)Na^{24}$	β, γ	14.9 h
S^{35}	$Cl^{35}(n, p)S^{35}$	β (0.16 Mev)	87.1 d

[1] Catalog of isotopes is procurable from the Atomic Energy Commission at the Oak Ridge National Laboratory.

[2] h, hour; d, day; y, year.

from nuclear reactors. A few of the radioisotopes which may be produced by the absorption of neutrons are indicated in Table V, along with the reaction by which each is formed and its radiation and half-life. The number of isotopes now known is so great that it is not possible to give a complete table here.

The quantity of radioisotope which must be present to supply 3.7×10^{10} disintegrations per second is termed a "curie." Thus a microcurie of radon or C^{14} or Na^{24} will each give 3.7×10^4 disintegrations per second, although the number of atoms in a curie will be very different for these elements.

Example 6. From the fact that the half-life of radium is 1600 years and the atomic weight is 226, show that 1 gram of radium produces 3.7×10^{10} disintegrations per second.

$$\lambda = \frac{0.693}{(1600)(365)(24)(60)(60)} = 1.38 \times 10^{-11} \text{ sec}^{-1}$$

$$-\frac{dN}{dt} = \lambda N = \frac{(1.38 \times 10^{-11})(6.02 \times 10^{23})}{(226)}$$

$$= 3.7 \times 10^{10} \text{ disintegrations per second}$$

Nuclear Fission. In 1939 Hahn and Strassman exposed uranium to neutrons and obtained unexpected products which were identified as barium and other elements of the middle of the periodic table. Meitner pointed out that a large amount of energy would be released in the breakdown of the uranium atom into two elements each having approximately half the atomic weight of uranium. It was soon found that it is the isotope U^{235} that undergoes fission when it absorbs slow neutrons.

The fission reaction is not a single reaction because the nucleus can break up in several ways to produce different pairs of nuclei. According to one model of the nucleus, the absorption of a neutron sets the nucleus into oscillations like a liquid drop. The energy introduced by the neutron is equal to the binding energy of the neutron plus its kinetic energy. If this energy is large enough, the oscillations in the nucleus result in its splitting into two droplets.

The abundances of isotopes of various mass numbers among the fission products of U^{235} are given in *Fig. 24-10*. Since the percentages vary over such a wide range, it is convenient to use a semilogarithmic plot. It can be seen that the most probable type of fission, representing approximately 6 per cent of the total, gives products with mass numbers of 95 and 139. The probability that the uranium nucleus will be split into equal halves is very small. One of the possible modes of fission is represented by

$$_{92}U^{235} + {}_0n^1 \rightarrow 2{}_0n^1 + \gamma + {}_{60}Nd^{147} + {}_{32}Ge^{87}$$

Many other fission reactions with $_{92}U^{235}$ are possible, all of which produce either 2 or 3 new neutrons.

As discussed in connection with Fig. 24-4, the ratio of neutrons to protons is greater in the heavy elements than in the elements in the middle of the periodic table. Therefore the fission fragments are unstable and reduce their neutron-proton ratios by emitting beta particles, or in a few cases neutrons. For example, $_{60}Nd^{147}$ starts the decay chain

$$_{60}Nd^{147} \xrightarrow[11\,d]{\beta^-} {}_{61}Pm^{147} \xrightarrow[4\,y]{\beta^-} {}_{62}Sm^{147}$$

This example is given because the element with atomic number 61 (now named promethium) had not been isolated before.*

Example 7. Calculate the energy for the fission of U^{235} into approximate halves, using data from Fig. 24-5. The binding energy per nucleon is about 7.5 Mev for

* An issue of the *Journal of Chemical Education* is devoted to the new elements [Vol. 36, pp. 3–44 (1959)].

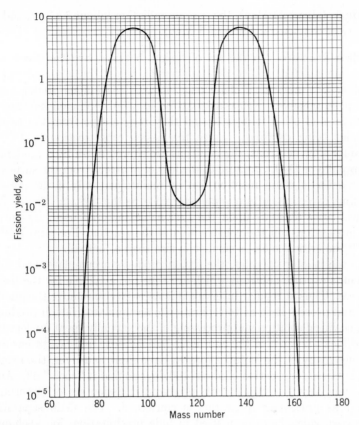

Fig. 24-10. Distribution of fission products for the fission of U^{235} by thermal neutrons.

U^{235}, and about 8.4 Mev for elements of half this mass number. Thus

$$92p + 143n \rightarrow U^{235} + (235)(7.5) \text{ Mev}$$

$$92p + 143n \rightarrow \text{fission products} + (235)(8.4) \text{ Mev}$$

Subtracting the first equation from the second,

$$U^{235} \rightarrow \text{fission products} + (235)(8.4 - 7.5) \quad \text{or} \quad 200 \text{ Mev}$$

Thus the fission of U^{235} releases about $(23 \times 10^3)(200 \times 10^6) = 4.6 \times 10^{12}$ cal g-atom^{-1} or 2×10^{10} cal g^{-1}; in contrast, in chemical reactions, the combustion of 1 gram of carbon evolves 7827 cal of heat. One pound of U^{235} will generate as much heat on fission as the burning of 1250 tons of coal, which is equivalent to 11 million kw-hr of heat.

The fission energy is distributed between the kinetic energies of the fission fragments (about 170 Mev), the decay energy of the fission products (about 20 Mev), the gamma radiation (about 5 Mev), and the energy of the neutrons (about 5 Mev).

Nuclear Reactors. In the act of fission, between two and three neutrons are emitted; and if, on the average, one of these is captured by another U^{235} nucleus, a chain reaction with continuous production of energy is possible. Neutrons may be lost by nonfission capture by uranium and other materials, and they may escape from the reactor without being captured. Since the fission cross section of U^{235} is large for slow neutrons, the neutrons are slowed down by a moderator of graphite or D_2O. Because of the loss of neutrons from the surface of the reactor, a chain reaction can be maintained only if the mass of uranium exceeds a certain value referred to as the "critical" mass. The critical mass depends upon the fissionable material used, its purity, the moderator, and the construction of the reactor. For pure U^{235} or Pu^{239} the critical mass is smaller in size than a football.

As the reactor operates, the fission products accumulate, and these elements capture neutrons which are thus not available for the fission process. Thus at regular intervals it is necessary to remove the nuclear fuel and process it so as to separate the accumulated fission products. The chemical solution and processing of the partially spent nuclear fuel are difficult because of the enormous radioactivity and health hazards.

Since many of the isotopes formed have short half-lives, the reactor fuel is stored for a period of about 100 days so that it "cools" off. After this time only 9 or 10 elements produced in fission are of importance as far as processing spent fuel is concerned. The main separation processes which have been used include precipitation, ion exchange, solvent extraction, and volatilization. Solvent-extraction columns may be used, since $UO_2(NO_3)_2$ may be extracted into an organic solvent. In order to remove a small amount of a desired substance from a large volume by precipitation, it is advantageous to use a "carrier." A carrier is a substance added in appreciable amount to a solution of a trace element and forming a precipitate which carries down the trace element.

The only naturally occurring isotope which undergoes fission by thermal neutrons is U^{235}. However, two other nuclei with this property can be produced in the nuclear reactor. The first is Pu^{239},

$$_{92}U^{238} + {}_0n^1 \rightarrow {}_{92}U^{239} \xrightarrow[23.5\,\text{m}]{\beta^-} {}_{93}Np^{239} \xrightarrow[2.33\,\text{d}]{\beta^-} {}_{94}Pu^{239} \xrightarrow[2.4 \times 10^4\,\text{y}]{\alpha} {}_{92}U^{235}$$

and the second is U^{233}, which is formed from Th^{232} by

$$_{90}Th^{232} + {}_0n^1 \rightarrow {}_{90}Th^{233} \xrightarrow[23.5\,\text{m}]{\beta^-} {}_{91}Pa^{233} \xrightarrow[27.4\,\text{d}]{\beta^-} {}_{92}U^{233} \xrightarrow[16 \times 10^5\,\text{y}]{\alpha} {}_{90}Th^{229}$$

In a nuclear reactor containing U^{238} some of the neutrons are used in the production of $_{94}Pu^{239}$ by the reactions given above. About 2.5 neutrons are produced on the average for each thermal neutron absorbed in U^{235}, and one is required to maintain the chain reaction. Thus there is the possibility that, if the loss of neutrons through the surface of the reactor and by absorption by impurities is sufficiently low, more fissionable material may be produced than is consumed in the operation of the reactor. If more fissionable nuclei are produced than are used up, the process is called *breeding*.

Fusion. Nuclear reactions in which light nuclei fuse to form heavier nuclei are called *fusion* reactions. It can be seen from Fig. 24-5 that these reactions will also yield energy. Fusion reactions occur in the interior of stars, where temperatures are so high that the velocities of nuclei are great enough to initiate such reactions. The following reactions are believed to provide most of the energy radiated by the sun.

$$_1H^1 + {_1H^1} \rightarrow {_1H^2} + e^+ + \nu$$

$$_1H^2 + {_1H^1} \rightarrow {_2He^3} + \gamma$$

$$_2He^3 + {_2He^3} \rightarrow {_2He^4} + 2{_1H^1}$$

The first reaction is the slowest. The net result of this sequence is the transformation of four protons into one helium nucleus.

Fusion reactions can be made to occur by utilizing a fission bomb to produce very high temperatures; this is the basis of the hydrogen bomb. Such reactions are called thermonuclear reactions. Several of these thermonuclear reactions are

$$_1H^2 + {_1H^2} \rightarrow {_1H^3} + {_1H^1} + 4 \text{ Mev}$$

$$_1H^2 + {_1H^2} \rightarrow {_2He^3} + {_0n^1} + 4 \text{ Mev}$$

$$_1H^3 + {_1H^3} \rightarrow {_2He^4} + 2{_0n^1} + 11 \text{ Mev}$$

$$_1H^3 + {_1H^2} \rightarrow {_2He^4} + {_0n^1} + 18 \text{ Mev}$$

If methods could be developed for carrying out these reactions in a controlled way, large amounts of energy would be made available. Intensive research is being directed toward this objective.

Isotopic Tracers. The composition of a mixture of isotopes of a single element remains essentially unchanged * in the course of physical,

* Because of the large isotope rate effect for reactions involving hydrogen the possibility of change in relative abundance must be considered in experiments involving $_1H^2$ or $_1H^3$.

chemical, and biological processes. Thus by determining the radio-activity due to one of the isotopes the concentration of an element may be determined, even though it is present at very low concentration.

The use of isotopes as tracers is furnishing an important means for studying the mechanisms of chemical reactions. For example, radio-active iodine and bromine have been employed to follow the course of the halogen in organic reactions, and radioactive manganese to show that there is no interchange of manganese between the ions of different valence, as, for example, between MnO_4^- and Mn^{2+}, but that there is a rapid exchange between manganous ion and manganic oxalate ion.

Radioactive carbon C^{14} with a half-life of 5570 years is being widely used as a tracer in many biochemical, chemical, and industrial labora-tories. One of the most important applications of C^{14} is in the study of photosynthesis. In this way the first products can be identified as shown by Calvin.*

By determination of the radioactivity of carbon Libby † has shown that it is possible to establish accurately the date at which a plant or animal died. This method is based upon the fact that long-lived C^{14} is formed in the upper atmosphere by the $N^{14}(n, p)C^{14}$ reaction between nitrogen and neutrons produced by cosmic rays. Since the radiocarbon is converted into carbon dioxide and mixed through the atmosphere, it is taken up by growing plants and also becomes a part of the bodies of animals, since they eat plants. It is found that samples of new wood uniformly give 12.5 counts per min per gram of carbon due to their content of C^{14}. When a tree is cut down, the incorporation of C^{14} ceases and the C^{14} present decays with a half-life of 5720 years. This makes it possible to establish the age of various carbon products in the range of about 1000–30,000 years by determination of their radio-activity due to C^{14}. Libby received a Nobel prize for this work.

The stable isotopes, as well as the radioactive isotopes, are useful as tracers. Deuterium, C^{13}, and O^{18} serve in chemical and biochemical investigations. The positions in a molecule or an organism taken by these tagged atoms can be ascertained by degrading the compound or fractionating the organism and determining the isotopic ratios of the reactants and products with the mass spectrometer.

In one of the first tracer experiments ordinary sugar was dissolved in heavy water and the water distilled off. The density of this water was less than before, showing that some of the deuterium of the water had exchanged with hydrogen of the sugar. Quantitative measure-

---

* M. Calvin, *The Path of Carbon in Photosynthesis*, University of Notre Dame, Notre Dame, Ind. (1949).

† W. F. Libby, *Radiocarbon Dating*, University of Chicago Press, Chicago (1952).

ments showed that half the hydrogen atoms of the sugar had exchanged with deuterium. It is known from the structure of sugar that half the hydrogens are bonded to carbon and half to oxygen. It is concluded that the weakly acidic hydrogen atoms attached to oxygen exchange with the deuterium ions of the water, but that the hydrogen atoms attached directly to carbon do not.

Several applications of radioactivity have been made to geology.* One of the earliest was the determination of the age of the earth. The rates of radioactive disintegration are well established, and the age of a given radioactive mineral is obtained by simply dividing the amount of disintegration product by the rate at which the product is generated. If the life of the parent element is very long, the calculations are simplified. The amount of lead found in a uranium mineral is a measure of the amount of uranium which has undergone radioactive disintegration, provided that no lead has been brought from other places and none has been leached out. A determination of the atomic weight or a measurement of the relative amounts of isotopes can be used to correct for any ordinary lead present which did not come from the uranium or thorium in the sample of mineral. The earth must be at least as old as the oldest mineral which is found, and several have been established to be about a billion years old.†

Example 8. A sample of pitchblende was found to contain 51.16 per cent uranium and 2.492 per cent lead, giving a lead-uranium ratio of 0.0487. An atomic-weight determination showed that, whereas most of the lead came from uranium and had an atomic weight of 206, some ordinary lead was present, requiring a correction of Pb^{206}/U^{238} to 0.0453. The disintegration constant for uranium is 1.52×10^{-10} year^{-1}. How old must the pitchblende have been in order to accumulate this much lead?

The mole ratio of Pb^{206}/U^{238} is $0.0453(238/206) = 0.0523$. Therefore, 0.0523 g-atom of Pb^{206} has been formed from 1.0523 g-atom of U^{238}.

$$-dN/dt = \lambda N$$

$$0.0523/dt = (1.52 \times 10^{-10})(1.0523)$$

$$dt = 326 \text{ million years}$$

This is an approximate calculation, assuming that for this problem 326 million years are infinitesimal! The exact calculation is

$$1.52 \times 10^{-10} = \frac{2.303}{t} \log \frac{1.0523}{1.0523 - 0.0523}$$

$$t = 335 \text{ million years}$$

* H. Faul, ed., *Nuclear Geology*, John Wiley & Sons, New York, 1954.

† V. J. Linnenbom, "Radioactivity and the Age of the Earth," *J. Chem. Educ.*, *32*, 58 (1955).

Hot-Atom Chemistry. In an (n, γ) reaction the target nucleus recoils with considerable kinetic energy because momentum is conserved in the gamma-ray emission process. The kinetic energy of the recoiling nucleus is generally much greater than bond energies so that the recoiling nucleus leaves the molecule and breaks bonds in other molecules as it expends its excess energy. The recoil particle may be multiply ionized as a result of internal conversion and Auger processes. Such an atom, with energy far in excess of thermal energies, is called a "hot atom." Since the chemical state of the nuclei which have absorbed neutrons is changed, they may be separated by chemical methods from the target material. For example, when ethyl iodide is irradiated with slow neutrons, the (n, γ) reaction on I^{127} in the ethyl iodide produces I^{128}. The energy of recoil of the atom of I^{128} is sufficient to break the C—I bond. The I^{128} atom, or ion, has a high energy, compared to chemical-bond energies, and is therefore separated from the ethyl iodide molecule. Such a hot atom may suffer one of several possible fates. It may lose its kinetic energy in several encounters without reacting with another ethyl iodide molecule. If it forms II^{128} or HI^{128}, it may be separated from the ethyl iodide by extraction with sodium hydroxide; this method for obtaining nearly pure radioactive isotopes is known as the Szilard-Chalmers process. The hot I^{128} atom, or ion, may react with an ethyl iodide molecule to replace a hydrogen or to cause the molecule to be broken into fragments. If molecular iodine is added before irradiation, the probability of I^{128} returning to organic combination is greatly reduced; in this connection molecular iodine is referred to as a "scavanger."

Exchange Reactions. An exchange reaction is one in which an isotopic label is transferred from one substance to another. Such reactions are often called "virtual" reactions because there is no chemical change. However, the rate of approach to the equilibrium distribution of the isotope between the two species can be determined by isolating one of the species at a series of times and determining its content of the isotope (usually radioactive). An early reaction to be studied quantitatively was †

$$\text{CuChelate} + \text{Cu}^{2+}* = \text{Cu}*\text{Chelate} + \text{Cu}^{2+} \qquad (20)$$

where $*$ designates the radioactive species.

By use of tracers it is possible to determine whether an exchange such as that represented in equation 20 is occurring. The rate of this exchange may be determined by separating the species (in this case Cu^{2+}

† R. B. Duffield and M. Calvin, *J. Am. Chem. Soc.*, *68*, 557 (1946).

and CuChelate) and determining the radioactivity of one of them. Such an exchange reaction is first order because it is always going on at a constant rate, independent of the extent of transfer of the radioactive atoms. In other words, the rate of transfer of radioactive atoms from one form to another is directly proportional to the concentration of labeled species in excess of the equilibrium distribution.

It may be shown † that for a reaction

$$AX + BX^* = AX^* + BX$$

the rate of reaction R between AX and BX in the dynamic equilibrium may be calculated from

$$R = \frac{ab}{(a + b)t} \ln\left(1 - \frac{x}{x_\infty}\right) \tag{21}$$

where $a = (AX) + (AX^*)$, $b = (BX) + (BX^*)$, $x = (AX^*)$, and x_∞ is the concentration of AX^* at infinite time. The dependence of the rate R upon the concentrations of reactants or other substances present may be determined to find the mechanism of the exchange reaction. Equation 21 is obeyed independently of the mechanism of the process.

Biological Effects of Radioactivity. Serious damage can be done to living things by excessive exposure to ionizing radiations. As a rough approximation, the effect of X rays, gamma rays, beta rays, alpha particles, and neutrons is proportional to the amount of ionization which these various radiations produce in the living object. Considerable study has been devoted to establishing a safe limit for exposure to X rays and radioactivity. Even though no immediate effect is evident, genetic defects may appear in later generations. In more severe cases of radioactive poisoning the concentration of red blood cells is reduced through destructive action on the bone marrow; therefore counting red blood corpuscles is a standard procedure in checking for overexposure.

Those who work with radioactive materials must guard themselves against damage from exposure to radioactivity. Safety precautions include the use of special shielding, ventilation, and waste disposal, and frequently lead to the requirement of remote control for laboratory experiments. Since the techniques have been fully worked out, there need be no danger if proper precautions are followed and the laboratory is adequately equipped with sensitive instruments for detecting radioactivity.

† G. Friedlander and J. W. Kennedy, *Nuclear and Radiochemistry*, John Wiley & Sons, New York, 1955, p. 315.

The *roentgen* is the unit of radiation used for X rays or gamma rays; it is defined in terms of the ionization produced in air. One roentgen will produce 1 *electrostatic* unit of charge per cubic centimeter of air at standard conditions. It produces 2.083×10^9 pairs of gaseous ions in air per cubic centimeter under standard conditions and generates 83.3 ergs per gram of air. For laboratory work the exposure of the body to 0.1 roentgen per week is regarded as the maximum dosage which should be permitted.

REFERENCES

M. Calvin, C. Heidelberger, J. C. Reid, B. M. Tolbert, and P. E. Yankwich, *Isotopic Carbon*, John Wiley & Sons, New York, 1949.

W. D. Claus, *Radiation Biology and Medicine*, Addison-Wesley Publishing Co., Reading, Mass., 1958.

G. Friedlander and J. W. Kennedy, *Nuclear and Radiochemistry*, John Wiley & Sons, New York, 1955.

S. Glasstone, *Sourcebook on Atomic Energy*, D. Van Nostrand Co., Princeton, N. J., 1950.

I. Kaplan, *Nuclear Physics*, Addison-Wesley Publishing Co., Reading, Mass., 1955.

E. C. Pollard and W. L. Davidson, *Applied Nuclear Physics*, John Wiley & Sons, New York, 1951.

G. T. Seaborg, *The Transuranium Elements*, Yale University Press, New Haven, 1958.

A. C. Wahl and N. A. Bonner, *Radioactivity Applied to Chemistry*, John Wiley & Sons, New York, 1951.

W. J. Whitehouse and J. L. Putnam, *Radioactive Isotopes*, Oxford University Press, Oxford, 1953.

PROBLEMS

1. The mass spectrum of a mixture of carbon dioxide and methane gave lines which corresponded to the following ratios of mass to number of charges:

$$6, \quad 8, \quad 12, \quad 13, \quad 14, \quad 15, \quad 16, \quad 28, \quad 32, \quad 44$$

Suggest positive ions which may be responsible for each of these lines.

Ans.	6	8	12	13	14	15	16	28	32	44
	C^{2+}	O^{2+}	C^+	CH^+	CO^{2+}	CH_3^+	O_2^{2+}	CO^+	O_2^+	CO_2^+
					CH_4^{2+}		CH_2^+		CH_4^+	

2. Calculate the velocity of 5.48-Mev alpha particles.

Ans. 1.625×10^9 cm sec^{-1}.

3. Calculate the energy of a beta particle having half the velocity of light in (*a*) ergs and (*b*) electron volts. *Ans.* (*a*) 1.265×10^{-7} erg. (*b*) 79.0 kv.

4. How many grams of Ra^{226} will be required to give as much radioactivity for luminous paint as 1 gram of Po^{210}? These isotopes are found in the uranium series.

Ans. 4.5 kg.

5. A sample of radioactive sodium, with a half-life of 14.8 hr, is injected into an animal. How many days will it take for the radioactivity to fall to one-tenth of its original intensity?　　　　　　　　　　　　　　　　*Ans.* 2.05 days.

6. The following measurements of the radioactivity of a sample of Ag^{111} were obtained with a Geiger-Müller counter. The background counting rate in the absence of radioactive material is 25 counts per min.

Time, days	0	5	10	15	20
Counts per min	2157	1373	850	557	359

Calculate graphically the half-life which best fits these data.　　　　*Ans.* 7.5 days.

7. Calculate the weight of Pb^{210} in a steady state with 1 gram of Bi^{210} in the uranium series.　　　　　　　　　　　　　　　　　　　　　*Ans.* 1606 g.

8. All radioactive daughters are separated from U^{238}. How many grams of Th^{234} are there per gram of U^{238} (a) after 1 week, (b) in the steady state?
$$Ans.\ (a)\ 1.12 \times 10^{-14},\ (b)\ 6.18 \times 10^{-14}\ g.$$

9. What is the weight of a curie of (a) C^{14} ($t_{1/2}$ = 5570 years) and (b) Na^{24} ($t_{1/2}$ = 14.8 hr)?　　　　　　　　　　*Ans.* (a) 0.218, (b) 1.14×10^{-7} g.

10. In the reaction
$$_1H^1 + _3Li^7 \rightarrow 2\,_2He^4$$

the range of the alpha particles in air (8.3 cm) shows that their energy is 8.6 Mev. Calculate the energy of the alpha particles expected from the mass change in the reaction.　　　　　　　　　　　　*Ans.* 8.7 Mev per alpha particle.

11. The beryllium isotope with an atomic weight of 7.01916 emits gamma rays of 0.48 million electron volts. (a) What is the product of this radioactive decay, and (b) what is its atomic weight?　　　　*Ans.* (a) Be^7.　(b) 7.01864.

12. One atom of U^{235} evolves about 200 Mev when it undergoes fission. (a) Compare this heat of fission with the heat evolved in the combustion of 1 gram of carbon. Carbon has the highest heat of combustion per gram of any organic material. (b) How many tons (2000 lb) of coke will it take to give as much heat on oxidation as 1 lb (454 grams) of U^{235} evolves on fission? (Coke is assumed to be pure graphite.) (c) If it is assumed that one-fourth of the heat of fission is converted into electricity with standard steam boilers, turbines, and dynamos, how many kilowatts of electricity can be generated by the consumption of 1 lb of U^{235} per day?　　*Ans.* (a) 2.50×10^6 times greater. (b) 1250 tons. (c) 108,000 kw.

13. Radioactive carbon is obtained from the Atomic Energy Commission at Oak Ridge as barium carbonate. (a) If the carbon contains 3 atomic per cent radioactive C^{14}, 1 atomic per cent C^{13}, and 96 atomic per cent C^{12}, how many grams of the barium carbonate does it take to give 1 millicurie? (b) The radioactivity can be measured with sufficient accuracy for a given experiment if there are 100 disintegrations per min, using the equivalent of 50 ml of carbon dioxide gas measured at standard conditions. How much can this material be diluted; that is, how many grams of ordinary carbon can be added to 1 gram of carbon from the sample of radioactive barium carbonate, if the same accuracy of counting is to be maintained (100 counts per min in a 50-ml sample of gas at 0°)?
$$Ans.\ (a)\ 0.102\ g.\quad (b)\ 8.79 \times 10^7.$$

14. Thorium B is an isotope of lead and therefore has nearly the same chemical properties. A given quantity of thorium B was mixed with a lead salt containing 10 mg of lead, taken into solution, and precipitated as the chromate. Ten milli-

710 PHYSICAL CHEMISTRY

liters of the supernatant solution, when evaporated, gave a residue which was 1/24,000 as active as the original quantity of thorium B. What is the solubility of lead chromate in moles per liter? $Ans.\ 2 \times 10^{-7}$ mole l^{-1}.

15. Radioactive carbon C^{14} with a half-life of 5570 years is formed in the upper atmosphere by the following reaction of neutrons produced by cosmic rays.

$$_0n^1 + {_7}N^{14} \rightarrow {_1}H^1 + {_6}C^{14}$$

This radioactive carbon has been distributed over the earth wherever carbon compounds occur as $C^{14}O_2$ in air and $HC^{14}O_3{}^-$ in the sea. As a consequence, growing plants incorporate C^{14}, but once they are dead this process stops and the radioactive carbon decays with the above half-life. A sample of new wood has a radioactivity of 15.3 counts per min when determined in a special way. If a sample of wood from an old Egyptian mummy case gives 9.4 counts per min for the same weight of wood under the same conditions, how old is the Egyptian wood?

$Ans.$ 3930 years.

---

16. Using the data in Table I, calculate the atomic weight of lead on the chemical scale.

17. What is the root-mean-square velocity of a thermal neutron at 25°?

18. Calculate the energy of recoil in kilocalories per mole of a tritium nucleus which emits an 18.9-Kev electron in radioactive disintegration.

19. (a) To how many beta particles per second does an electron current of 2 ma correspond? (b) To how many grams of Pb^{214}, which has a half-life of 26.8 min, would this be equivalent?

20. The radioactivity of radioactive manganese is measured with a Geiger counter with the following results:

Time, hr	0	0.28	0.75	2.13	7.13	10.03	12.82	17.45	∞
Counts per min	20,862	19,197	17,129	11,602	3,159	1,451	690	246	27

The background rate is 27 counts per min. What is the half-life of this radioactive manganese?

21. A radioactive substance has a half-life of 5 hr. (a) How many atoms are there in a sample which has a total disintegration rate of 10^3 per min? (b) What will be the total disintegration rate after 24 hr?

22. Pa^{234} in a steady state with 1 gram of U^{238} gives off 740,000 particles per min. Calculate the half-life of U^{238}.

23. A hospital maintained a solution containing 0.200 gram of radium as a source of radon for therapeutic purposes. The radon was pumped off under reduced pressure once a week. (a) How many grams of radon were obtained each week? (b) What volume would it occupy at 25° and 740 mm pressure?

24. (a) How many grams are there in a millicurie of $_{53}I^{131}$, which has a half-life of 8.0 days? (b) After 30 days, how many disintegrations will there be in a sample of $_{53}I^{131}$ which originally weighed 1 microgram?

25. For the nuclear reaction

$$2{_1}H^1 + 2{_0}n^1 \rightarrow {_2}He^4$$

calculate the energy evolved in (a) Mev and (b) calories.

26. An element gives off beta rays having a maximum energy of 1.5 million electron volts. How much less per gram atom will the new element, which is formed by the radioactive decay, weigh?

27. If the products of a nuclear reaction weigh 0.001 gram more per gram atom than the reactants, what is the minimum energy which must be supplied to effect the reaction: (a) expressed in kilogram-calories per gram atom; (b) expressed in electron volts?

28. Assuming that 200 Mev of energy is released per nucleus undergoing fission, calculate (a) the number of calories and (b) the number of kilowatt-hours of heat liberated by the fission of 1 gram of U^{235}.

29. How many disintegrations per second are produced in a microgram of P^{32} ($t_{\frac{1}{2}}$ = 14.3 days)? What weight of KH_2PO_4 containing a mole fraction of 10^{-9} of $KH_2P^{32}O_4$ would be needed in an experiment requiring a sample in which there are 2000 disintegrations per sec?

30. Suppose that a radioactive nuclide is formed at a rate A by bombardment with a neutron source. Derive the equation for calculating the number N of radioactive nuclei from A, the time of bombardment, and the decay constant for the radioactive nuclide.

31. A sample of zircon contains 392 micrograms of Pb^{206} per gram and 29.5 micrograms of Pb^{207} per gram. Calculate the age of the mineral, assuming that these isotopes arise solely from U^{238} and U^{235}.

$$N_{Pb^{206}} = N_{U^{238}} (e^{\lambda_{238}t} - 1)$$

$$N_{Pb^{207}} = N_{U^{235}} (e^{\lambda_{235}t} - 1)$$

Since a trial solution is needed, an approximate answer of 10^9 years is given [V. J. Linnenbom, *J. Chem. Educ.*, *32*, 58 (1955)].

---

32. The mass spectrum of propane has peaks at m/e of 44(8), 43(6), 42(2), 41(3), 40(1), 39(4), 38(2), 37(1), 30(1), 29(26), 28(14), 27(10), 26(2), 15(2), and 14(1). The relative intensities are given by the numbers in parentheses. Suggest positive ions that may be responsible for each of these lines.

33. Calculate the energy in Mev of an alpha particle which has a velocity of 2.20×10^9 cm sec^{-1}. The relativity correction of the mass may be neglected as being barely significant.

34. Calculate the velocity and wavelength of a proton that has been accelerated through a potential difference of 10^9 volts (1 Bev). (The relativistic correction on the mass must be taken into account.)

35. One gram of U^{238} gives off 7.4×10^5 alpha particles per min. What is the half-life of U^{238}?

36. (a) After how many years will 1 gram of Po^{210} decay to such a point that it is equivalent in radioactivity to 1 gram of Ra^{226}? (b) After 10 years what will be the relative intensities of radioactivity of equal weights of Ra^{226} and Po^{210}?

37. What weight of Pa^{234} is in a radioactive steady state with 1 gram of U^{238}?

38. (a) Radon is removed from a sample of radium with which it was in a steady state and is allowed to decay. What percentage of the radon will be left after 2, 4, 8, and 16 days? (b) The sample of radium immediately starts regenerating radon. What percentage of the maximum amount of radon will be present after

2, 4, 8, and 16 days? (c) Plot the data of (a) and (b) against time, and draw two curves through the points.

39. (a) How many grams of radioactive Br^{82} with a half-life of 35.9 hr is required in order to give a millicurie? (b) How many days can one wait before the millicurie of bromine becomes worthless for an experiment which requires 100 disintegrations per min for counting?

40. How large would a proton current have to be in amperes in a cyclotron in order to correspond to 1 microcurie?

41. If the atomic weight of a nucleus can be determined to 3 parts in 10^7, calculate the uncertainty in Mev of the heat evolved for a reaction involving this nucleus if its atomic weight is about 20.

42. Calculate the heat energy in calories evolved in the following nuclear reactions:

$$(a) \quad {}_1H^1 + {}_1H^2 \rightarrow {}_2He^3 + \gamma$$
$$(b) \quad {}_2He^4 + {}_7N^{14} \rightarrow {}_1H^1 + {}_8O^{17}$$

43. An electron and a positron annihilate each other upon reaction, producing two gamma-ray photons.

$$e^+ + e^- \rightarrow h\nu$$

Calculate (a) the energy of this reaction in kilocalories per mole, and (b) the wavelength of the photons produced.

44. (a) How many grams of U^{235} must be consumed per day in driving a large ship at 20 mph with 100,000 kw of power, if it is assumed that 25 per cent of the heat of fission can be converted into useful work through boilers, turbines, and dynamos? (b) How many kilograms of U^{235} would be consumed in traveling 20,000 miles?

45. In a homogeneous nuclear reactor containing water the ionizing radiation causes the liberation of 1.7 molecules of gas (hydrogen plus oxygen) per 100 electron volts of energy. Calculate the number of cubic feet (STP) of the explosive mixture of hydrogen and oxygen produced per minute in a nuclear reactor which produces 1000 kw of heat. It may be assumed that all the energy is liberated in the water as ionizing radiation.

46. The thermal neutron flux in a certain nuclear chain-reacting pile is 10^{12} neutrons per cm^2 per sec, and a 1-gram sample of $MnSO_4$ is exposed to this flux in order to prepare radioactive manganese according to the reaction

$$_{25}Mn^{55} + {}_0n^1 \rightarrow {}_{25}Mn^{56}$$

The $_{25}Mn^{56}$ decays by K capture with a half-life of 2.59 hr. The $MnSO_4$ is placed in the pile for 1 hr. Assuming that the only radioactivity formed in the sample is due to $_{25}Mn^{56}$ and taking the cross section for its formation as 12.8×10^{-24} cm^2, calculate the activity present in the sample expressed in disintegrations per minute 4 hr after removal from the pile.

47. The weight of lead in a sample of uraninite from the Black Hills of South Dakota was found to be 22.8 per cent of the weight of the uranium. Calculate from this fact a minimum age for the earth.

48. An isotope with a disintegration constant of λ is produced by neutron capture in a neutron source. The rate of formation of this isotope by absorption of neutrons is P atoms per second. Derive an equation giving the number of these radioactive atoms at any time t.

APPENDIX

This appendix includes a summary of mathematics used in elementary physical chemistry and the derivations of several equations which are mentioned in the text but not derived there. It contains also advanced material, such as the Debye-Hückel theory.

MATHEMATICS USED IN PHYSICAL CHEMISTRY

The following outline contains the basic equations which are actually used in the first course in physical chemistry.

Algebra. The solution of a quadratic equation

$$ax^2 + bx + c = 0$$

is

$$x = \frac{-b \pm \sqrt{b^2 - 4ac}}{2a} \tag{1}$$

If $b^2 - 4ac$ is positive, the roots are real and unequal, but for a real problem usually only one root is physically possible. If $b^2 - 4ac$ is zero, the roots are real and equal. If $b^2 - 4ac$ is negative, the roots are imaginary and unequal.

Logarithms. The logarithm of a number is the exponent to which the base (usually 10 or $e = 2.71828\cdots$) must be raised to give the number. Base 10 logarithms are represented by $\log x$, and base e logarithms by $\ln x$.

$$x = 10^{\log x} \tag{2}$$

$$x = e^{\ln x} \tag{3}$$

Logarithms to the base e arise in the integration of dx/x, but logarithms to the base 10 are more commonly used in actual computations. The factors for converting from one type of logarithm to the other may be derived by setting expressions 2 and 3 equal and taking the base 10 logarithm.

$$\log x \log 10 = \ln x \log e$$

Since $\log 10 = 1$ and $\log e = \log 2.71828 = 0.4343$,

$$\log x = 0.4343 \ln x \tag{4}$$

$$\ln x = 2.303 \log x \tag{5}$$

Equation 5 is important because it is often necessary to convert equations from $\ln x$ to $\log x$ for numerical calculations. Logarithms are pure numbers, and logarithms can be taken only of pure numbers. When a logarithm is apparently taken of a physical quantity with dimensions, it will actually turn out on closer inspection that the logarithm of a dimensionless ratio is taken.*

Logarithms, in general, consist of an integer, which is called the characteristic, and a decimal part, called the mantissa.

Example 1. (a) What are the values of $\log 102.5$, $\ln 102.5$, $\log 0.0025$, and $\ln 0.0025$?

$$\log 102.5 = 2.0107$$

$$\ln 102.5 = (2.303)(2.0107) = 4.64$$

$$\log 0.0025 = 0.3979 - 3 = -2.6021$$

$$\ln 0.0025 = (2.303)(-2.6021) = -6.00$$

(b) What are the antilogarithms of the following?

$$\log x = 3.570; \; x = 10^{3.570}$$

$$x = 3.72 \times 10^3$$

$$\log x = -1.230 = 0.770 - 2$$

$$x = 10^{0.770} \times 10^{-2} = 5.89 \times 10^{-2}$$

The following equations show some of the properties of logarithms.

$$\log ab = \log a + \log b \tag{6}$$

$$\log (a/b) = \log a - \log b \tag{7}$$

$$\log a^n = n \log a \tag{8}$$

$$\log a^{1/n} = (1/n) \log a \tag{9}$$

Exponentials. Many exponential equations are used in physical chemistry. Logarithmic equations may also be written in exponential form.

$$\ln x = z \tag{10}$$

$$x = e^z \tag{11}$$

* J. E. Boggs, *J. Chem. Educ.*, *35*, 30 (1958).

Some properties of exponents are illustrated by

$$a^x a^y = a^{(x+y)} \tag{12}$$

$$(a^x)^y = a^{xy} \tag{13}$$

$$a^{-x} = 1/a^x \tag{14}$$

$$a^{1/x} = \sqrt[x]{a} \tag{15}$$

$$a^x/a^y = a^{(x-y)} \tag{16}$$

$$(ab)^x = a^x b^x \tag{17}$$

Trigonometry. The simple trigonometric functions which are encountered are

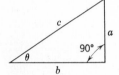

$$\sin \theta = a/c \tag{18}$$

$$\cos \theta = b/c \tag{19}$$

$$\tan \theta = a/b \tag{20}$$

$$a^2 + b^2 = c^2 \tag{21}$$

$$\sin^2 \theta + \cos^2 \theta = 1 \tag{22}$$

Analytical Geometry. The equation for a straight line is

$$y = mx + b \tag{23}$$

where m is the slope when y is plotted versus x, and b is the intercept on the y axis where $x = 0$. The slope may be calculated from any two points (x_1, y_1, and x_2, y_2) on the line.

$$m = \frac{y_2 - y_1}{x_2 - x_1} \tag{24}$$

The magnitude b of the intercept may be obtained by extrapolation to $x = 0$ or by substituting the value of the slope m and any point x_1, y_1 into equation 23 and solving for b.

The equation for a rectangular hyperbola is

$$xy = k \tag{25}$$

The equation for a parabola is

$$y^2 = kx \tag{26}$$

In general, x is taken as the independent variable and plotted horizontally, while y is the dependent variable, which is plotted vertically.

Differential Calculus. Important derivatives and differentials are given in the following table, where c represents a constant, x represents a variable, and u and v represent functions of x.

Derivatives   Differentials

$$\frac{dc}{dx} = 0 \qquad\qquad\qquad dc = 0 \tag{27}$$

$$\frac{d(cu)}{dx} = c\frac{du}{dx} \qquad\qquad d(cu) = c\,du \tag{28}$$

$$\frac{d(u+v)}{dx} = \frac{du}{dx} + \frac{dv}{dx} \qquad\qquad d(u+v) = du + dv \tag{29}$$

$$\frac{d(uv)}{dx} = u\frac{du}{dx} + v\frac{du}{dx} \qquad\qquad d(uv) = u\,dv + v\,du \tag{30}$$

$$\frac{d(u/v)}{dx} = \frac{1}{v}\frac{du}{dx} - \frac{u}{v^2}\frac{dv}{dx} \qquad\qquad d\frac{u}{v} = \frac{1}{v}du - \frac{u}{v^2}dv \tag{31}$$

$$\frac{dx^n}{dx} = nx^{n-1} \qquad\qquad d(x^n) = nx^{n-1}\,dx \tag{32}$$

$$\frac{du^n}{dx} = nu^{n-1}\frac{du}{dx} \qquad\qquad d(u^n) = nu^{n-1}\,du \tag{33}$$

$$\frac{d\ln x}{dx} = \frac{1}{x} \qquad\qquad d(\ln x) = \frac{dx}{x} \tag{34}$$

$$\frac{d\ln u}{dx} = \frac{1}{u}\frac{du}{dx} \qquad\qquad d(\ln u) = \frac{du}{u} \tag{35}$$

$$\frac{de^x}{dx} = e^x \qquad\qquad d(e^x) = e^x\,dx \tag{36}$$

$$\frac{da^x}{dx} = a^x \ln a \qquad\qquad d(a^x) = a^x \ln a\,dx \tag{37}$$

An important use of differentiation is in determining the maxima and minima of functions, since at these points the first derivative of the function is equal to zero. At an inflection point the second derivative is equal to zero.

A general property of derivatives which is useful is

$$\frac{du}{dx}\frac{dx}{dy} = \frac{du}{dy} \tag{38}$$

Partial Derivatives. When a quantity is a function of more than one independent variable, it is necessary to use partial derivatives when discussing differentials or derivatives. For example, if $u = f(x, y)$ the partial derivative of u with respect to x, $(\partial u/\partial x)_y$, is the rate with which u changes with a change in x at a constant value of y. A subscript is used on the partial derivative when it is important to emphasize which variable is held constant. If u is a function of x and y, it may be represented as a surface above the x-y plane, as indicated in *Fig. A-1*. The following expression for the total differential:

$$du = \left(\frac{\partial u}{\partial x}\right)_y dx + \left(\frac{\partial u}{\partial y}\right)_x dy \tag{39}$$

may be derived by considering the surface over an infinitesimal rectangular area with dimensions dx and dy. The increase in the function u when x increases by dx is

$$u_b - u_a = \left(\frac{\partial u}{\partial x}\right) dx$$

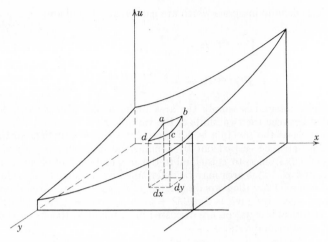

Fig. A-1. Derivation of expression 39 for the total differential.

where $(\partial u/\partial x)_y$ is the slope of line ab. The increase in the function u when y increases by dy is

$$u_c - u_b = \left(\frac{\partial u}{\partial y}\right)_x dy$$

where $(\partial u/\partial y)_x$ is the slope of the line bc. The total increase du in u when x is increased by dx and y is increased by dy is $u_c - u_a = u_b - u_a + (u_c - u_b)$, which is accordingly given by equation 39.

The order of partial differentiation is immaterial so that

$$\left[\frac{\partial}{\partial x}\left(\frac{\partial u}{\partial y}\right)_x\right]_y = \left[\frac{\partial}{\partial y}\left(\frac{\partial u}{\partial x}\right)_y\right]_x \tag{40}$$

Integral Calculus. A number of elementary integrals are required in physical chemistry. A short table of integrals follows, and longer tables are available in handbooks. The five integrals which are most frequently encountered are probably

$$\int dx = x + c \tag{41}$$

$$\int x^n \, dx = \frac{x^{n+1}}{(n+1)} + c \tag{42}$$

$$\int \frac{dx}{x} = \ln x + c \tag{43}$$

$$\int e^x \, dx = e^x + c \tag{44}$$

$$\int a^x \, dx = \frac{a^x}{\ln a} + c \tag{45}$$

A couple of definite integrals which are particularly useful are:

$$\int_0^\infty e^{-a^2 x^4}\, dx = \frac{\sqrt{\pi}}{2a} \tag{46}$$

$$\int_0^\infty x^{2n} e^{-ax^4}\, dx = \frac{1\cdot 3\cdot 5\cdots (\ )(2n-1)}{2^{n+1}a^n}\sqrt{\frac{\pi}{a}} \tag{47}$$

The definite integral is simply the area under a plot of the function being integrated between the two limits of the variable x.

In some cases the function is not given by a simple equation, so that the integration must be carried out by a numerical or graphical method. The integral of $y\, dx$ from x_1 to x_2 is equal to the area under a plot of y versus x between x_1 and x_2. This area may be determined by reading off the values of y at equal values of Δx; these are designated $y_0, y_1, y_2, \cdots, y_n$. According to the "trapezoid rule," the area is $\Delta x(y_0/2 + y_1 + y_2 + \cdots + y_n/2)$. Other methods of numerical integration are discussed in standard textbooks on the treatment of experimental data.

Series. Series expressions of functions are frequently used in physical chemistry. For a certain range of the variable involved only the first one or two terms of the series may be sufficient to represent the function to the required degree of accuracy. An equation may be profitably simplified in this way. Series are valid only for a certain range of values called the range of convergence.

$$(1 \pm x)^n = 1 \pm nx + \frac{n(n-1)x^2}{2!}$$

$$\pm \frac{n(n-1)(n-2)x^3}{3!} + \cdots \qquad (x^2 < 1) \tag{48}$$

where factorial $3! = 1\cdot 2\cdot 3$.

$$(1 \pm x)^{-\frac{1}{2}} = 1 \mp \frac{1}{2}x + \frac{1\cdot 3}{2\cdot 4}x^2 \mp \frac{1\cdot 3\cdot 5}{2\cdot 4\cdot 6}x^3 + \cdots (x^2 < 1) \tag{49}$$

$$(1 + x)^{-1} = 1 - x + x^2 - x^3 + \cdots \qquad (x^2 < 1) \tag{50}$$

$$(1 + x)^{\frac{1}{2}} = 1 + \frac{x}{2} - \frac{x^3}{8} + \frac{x^3}{16} + \cdots \qquad (x^2 < 1) \tag{51}$$

$$e^x = 1 + x + \frac{x^2}{2!} + \frac{x^3}{3!} + \cdots \qquad (x^2 < \infty) \tag{52}$$

$$\ln(1 + x) = x - \tfrac{1}{2}x^2 + \tfrac{1}{3}x^3 - \tfrac{1}{4}x^4 + \cdots \qquad (-1 < x < 1) \tag{53}$$

COMPOSITION OF SOLUTIONS

(p. 147)

The calculations of compositions are illustrated in the following example. A solution of acetic acid containing 80.8 grams of acetic acid ($M = 60.1$) per liter of solution at 20° has a density of 1.0097 g cm^{-3}.

Molar concentration:

$$\frac{80.8 \text{ g liter}^{-1}}{60.1 \text{ g mole}^{-1}} = 1.34 \text{ moles liter}^{-1}$$

Molal concentration:

$$\frac{80.8/60.1}{1009.7 - 80.8} \times 1000 = 1.45 \text{ moles per } 1000 \text{ g } H_2O$$

Mole fraction:

$$\text{Mole fraction acetic acid} = \frac{80.8/60.1}{80.8/60.1 + (1009.7 - 80.8)/18} = 0.025$$

Mole fraction water $= 0.975$

Percentage by weight:

$$\frac{80.8}{1009.7} \times 100 = 8.00\% \text{ acetic acid}$$

$$\frac{1009.7 - 80.8}{1009.7} \times 100 = 92.00\% \text{ water}$$

MAXWELL-BOLTZMANN DISTRIBUTION OF VELOCITIES IN THE x DIRECTION

(p. 273)

According to equation 3 in Chapter 11,

$$f(v_x) \, dv_x = K e^{-mv_x^2/2kT} \, dv_x \tag{1}$$

where K is a constant to be evaluated. Integration of this equation from $v_x = -\infty$ to $+\infty$ must give unity, since this is the probability that a molecule will have any velocity in the x direction.

$$\int_{-\infty}^{+\infty} f(v_x) \, dv_x = K \int_{-\infty}^{+\infty} e^{-mv_x^2/2kT} \, dv_x = 1 \tag{2}$$

Substituting $mv_x^2/2kT = \beta^2$ and $mv_x \, dv_x/2kT = \beta \, d\beta$, so that $dv_x = (2kT/m)^{1/2} \, d\beta$,

$$K \left(\frac{2kT}{m}\right)^{1/2} \int_{-\infty}^{+\infty} e^{-\beta^2} \, d\beta = 1 \tag{3}$$

Since

$$\int_{-\infty}^{+\infty} e^{-\beta^2} \, d\beta = \pi^{1/2} \quad (\text{p. } 718) \tag{4}$$

$$K = \left(\frac{m}{2\pi kT}\right)^{1/2} \tag{5}$$

MOLECULAR VELOCITIES FROM KINETIC THEORY

(p. 275)

1. Most Probable Velocity. The most probable velocity v_p is that given by the maximum of the velocity-distribution curve. The magnitude of the most probable velocity is obtained by differentiating $f(v)$ (equation 7, Chapter 11) with respect to v and setting this derivative equal to zero.

$$\frac{df(v)}{dv} = \left(\frac{m}{2\pi kT}\right)^{3/2} e^{-mv^2/2kT} \left[8\pi v + 4\pi v^2 \left(\frac{-mv}{kT}\right)\right] \tag{1}$$

For $df(v)/dv = 0$,

$$v_p = \left(\frac{2kT}{m}\right)^{1/2} \tag{2}$$

2. Arithmetic Mean Velocity. The arithmetic mean velocity is obtained by multiplying each velocity by the probability $f(v)$ of that velocity and summing over all velocities. Since the velocity varies continuously, an integration is used.

$$\bar{v} = \int_0^\infty v f(v) \, dv \tag{3}$$

Substituting the Maxwell distribution,

$$\bar{v} = 4\pi \left(\frac{m}{2\pi kT}\right)^{3/2} \int_0^\infty e^{-mv^2/2kT} v^3 \, dv \tag{4}$$

Substituting $mv^2/2kT = x^2$ and $dv = 2kTx \, dx/mv$ and using the result

$$\int_0^\infty e^{-x^2} x^3 \, dx = \frac{1}{2} \tag{5}$$

we obtain

$$\bar{v} = \left(\frac{8kT}{\pi m}\right)^{1/2} \tag{6}$$

3. Root-Mean-Square Velocity. The average value of the square of the velocity $\overline{v^2}$ is obtained by multiplying each velocity squared by the probability $f(v)$ of that velocity and integrating over the whole range of velocities.

$$\overline{v^2} = \int_0^\infty f(v) v^2 \, dv \tag{7}$$

The root-mean-square velocity $(\overline{v^2})^{1/2}$ is the square root of this quantity.

$$(\overline{v^2})^{1/2} = \left[\int_0^\infty f(v) v^2 \, dv\right]^{1/2} \tag{8}$$

Substituting the Maxwell distribution,

$$(\overline{v^2})^{1/2} = \left[4\pi \left(\frac{m}{2\pi kT}\right)^{3/2} \int_0^\infty e^{-mv^2/2kT} v^4 \, dv\right]^{1/2} \tag{9}$$

Substituting $mv^2/2kT = x^2$ and $dv = 2kTx\,dx/mv$ and using the relation

$$\int_0^\infty e^{-x^2}x^4\,dx = \tfrac{3}{8}\sqrt{\pi} \tag{10}$$

we obtain

$$(\overline{v^2})^{1/2} = \left(\frac{3kT}{m}\right)^{1/2} \tag{11}$$

RELATIONSHIP BETWEEN THE RATE LAWS OF THE FORWARD AND REVERSE REACTIONS AND THE EQUILIBRIUM CONSTANT *

(p. 311)

The rate laws for the forward and reverse reactions are not independent of each other because at equilibrium the rates of the forward and reverse reactions must be equal. For example, for the reaction

$$A + 2B = C \tag{1}$$

the rate law for the forward reaction might be

$$-\frac{d(A)}{dt} = k(A)(B)^2 \tag{2}$$

The rate law for the reverse reaction might be

$$-\frac{d(C)}{dt} = k'(C) \tag{3}$$

Setting these rates to be equal at equilibrium yields the equilibrium expression for reaction 1, but there are other possibilities. Suppose that the rate law for the forward reaction is found by experiment to be

$$-\frac{d(A)}{dt} = k(A)(B) \tag{4}$$

The rate law for the reverse reaction could be

$$-\frac{d(C)}{dt} = \frac{k'(C)}{(B)} \tag{5}$$

or

$$-\frac{d(C)}{dt} = \frac{k''(C)^2}{(A)(B)^3} \tag{6}$$

Since at equilibrium the rates of the forward and reverse reactions are equal, the right-hand sides of equations 4 and 5 are equated to obtain

$$\frac{k}{k'} = \frac{(C)}{(A)(B)^2} \tag{7}$$

* K. G. Denbigh, *Principles of Chemical Equilibrium*, Cambridge University Press, Cambridge, 1955, p. 442.

which is the correct equilibrium expression for reaction 1 in terms of concentrations rather than activities. Equating the right-hand sides of equations 2 and 6 also yields a valid expression for the equilibrium constant of reaction 1 but with the coefficients multiplied by 2.

$$\frac{k}{k'} = \frac{(C)^2}{(A)^2(B)^4} \tag{8}$$

The rate law for the forward reaction might be considerably more complicated than equation 4. The rate law may consist of a summation of several terms, each corresponding to a particular reaction path. In this case the rate law for the reverse reaction will consist of a summation of the same number of terms, each corresponding to one in the rate law for the forward reaction. This is required by the principle of detailed balancing (p. 313).

In view of the relationship between the rate laws and the equilibrium expression it might be supposed that the rate law should be, more properly, written in terms of activities rather than concentrations. Although it is true that changes in conditions which change activity coefficients do cause changes in the rate constants, the changes are not simply those anticipated from the changes in the activity coefficients of the reactants. The thermodynamic condition can be satisfied equally well if the rate expressions for the forward and reverse reactions written as activities (or concentrations multiplied by activity coefficients) are each multiplied by some factor β which is a function of the concentrations. For reaction 1 the following rate law is consistent with the thermodynamic requirement:

$$\frac{d(A)}{dt} = -k(A)(B)^2 \gamma_A \gamma_B^2 \beta - k'(C)\gamma_C \beta \tag{9}$$

Brönsted has interpreted β as the reciprocal of the activity of the activated complex, as is shown in Chapter 23.

DEBYE-HÜCKEL THEORY

(p. 392)

The density of charge ρ in the vicinity of an ion is

$$\rho = \frac{(dn_+ - dn_-)\epsilon}{dV} = n\epsilon(e^{-\epsilon\psi/kT} - e^{\epsilon\psi/kT}) \tag{1}$$

where n is the total number of positive and negative ions per cubic centimeter, ϵ is the electronic charge, k is the Boltzmann constant, and ψ is the electric potential at a distance r from a particular ion. Expanding the exponential terms into a series and neglecting higher terms, we have, as a close approximation for small potentials,

$$\rho = \frac{-2n\epsilon^2\psi}{kT} \tag{2}$$

The Poisson equation also relates ψ and ρ. Since ψ depends only on r, the equation is

$$\frac{d^2\psi}{dr^2} + \frac{2}{r}\frac{d\psi}{dr} = \frac{-4\pi\rho}{D} \tag{3}$$

In this equation D is the dielectric constant of the medium. Substituting equation 2 into equation 3, we have

$$\frac{d^2\psi}{dr^2} + \frac{2}{r}\frac{d\psi}{dr} = \frac{8\pi n\epsilon^2\psi}{DkT} = \kappa^2\psi \tag{4}$$

where κ is a measure of the ion atmosphere and is defined by

$$\kappa^2 = \frac{8\pi n\epsilon^2}{DkT} \tag{5}$$

It can be verified that a solution of equation 4 is given by

$$\psi = A\frac{e^{-\kappa r}}{r} + B\frac{e^{\kappa r}}{r} \tag{6}$$

and, since there are two independent arbitrary constants A and B, this must be a general solution. The potential must approach zero as the distance r from the selected ion becomes very large, and so B must be zero; otherwise the term $e^{\kappa r}/r$ will make ψ very large at large values of r.

A can be evaluated by making use of the fact that the total charge surrounding the ion (which we will assume to be positive) must be $-\epsilon$, since the solution as a whole is neutral. Comparison of equations 2, 4, and 6 shows that

$$\rho = \frac{-D\kappa^2\psi}{4\pi} = \frac{-D\kappa^2Ae^{-\kappa r}}{4\pi r} \tag{7}$$

Hence, integrating (by parts) from the closest distance of approach of the ions, which we will call a, gives

$$-\epsilon = \int_a^\infty 4\pi r^2\rho\, dr$$

$$= -\int_a^\infty rD\kappa^2Ae^{-\kappa r}\, dr$$

$$= -DAe^{-\kappa a}(1 + \kappa a) \tag{8}$$

Therefore

$$A = \frac{\epsilon e^{\kappa a}}{D(1 + \kappa a)} \tag{9}$$

and

$$\psi = \frac{\epsilon e^{\kappa(a-r)}}{D(1 + \kappa a)r} \tag{10}$$

The potential at the ion is the value of ψ at $r = a$,

$$\psi = \frac{\epsilon}{D(1 + \kappa a)a} \tag{11}$$

In calculating the activity coefficients and other properties of the solution, Debye attributed all the deviation from the behavior of ideal solutions to the electric charges on the ions. Consider the following imaginary process:*

1. Gradually discharge an ion in an extremely dilute solution of the electrolyte.
2. Transfer the discharged ion to a more concentrated solution.
3. Gradually charge the ion again.

The changes in Gibbs free energy in steps 1 and 3 are equal to the electric work done on the system, and the Gibbs free-energy change in step 2 is the same as for ideal solutions.

$$\Delta G_1 = \int_{q=\epsilon}^{q=0} \psi \, dq = \int_{q=\epsilon}^{q=0} \frac{q}{D(1 + \kappa a)a} \, dq$$

$$= -\frac{\epsilon^2}{2Da} \, (\kappa a \ll 1 \text{ here})$$

where q is the electric charge.

For the second step

$$\Delta G_2 = \frac{RT}{N_0} \ln \frac{c}{c_0} = kT \ln \frac{c}{c_0}$$

where c and c_0 are the concentrations of the final and initial solutions, respectively.

$$\Delta G_3 = \int_{q=0}^{q=\epsilon} \frac{q}{D(1 + \kappa a)a} \, dq = \frac{\epsilon^2}{2D(1 + \kappa a)a}$$

$$= \frac{\epsilon^2}{2Da} - \frac{\epsilon^2 \kappa}{2D(1 + \kappa a)}$$

Therefore,

$$\Delta G = \Delta G_1 + \Delta G_2 + \Delta G_3 = kT \ln \frac{c}{c_0} - \frac{\epsilon^2 \kappa}{2D(1 + \kappa a)} \tag{12}$$

The Gibbs free-energy change is also given by the equation

$$\Delta G = \frac{RT}{N_0} \ln \frac{\gamma c}{c_0} = kT \ln \frac{c}{c_0} + kT \ln \gamma \tag{13}$$

where γ is the activity coefficient of the ion in the final solution. $\gamma = 1$ in the initial solution.

Comparing equations 12 and 13, we see that

$$kT \ln \gamma = -\frac{\epsilon^2 \kappa}{2D(1 + \kappa a)} \tag{14}$$

If we use equation 5 and $n = c/1000N_0$, where c is the concentration in moles per liter and N_0 is the Avogadro number, equation 14 may be written

$$\log \gamma = -\frac{\epsilon^2 \sqrt{\dfrac{8\pi c \epsilon^2}{1000 N_0 DkT}}}{2.303 \times 2DkT \left(1 + a \sqrt{\dfrac{8\pi c \epsilon^2}{1000 N_0 DkT}}\right)} \tag{15}$$

* E. Guntelberg, *Z. physik. Chem.*, *123*, 199 (1926).

If c is small, equation 15 becomes

$$\log \gamma = -\Theta \sqrt{c} \tag{16}$$

where

$$\Theta = \frac{\epsilon^3 (2\pi)^{1/2}}{2.303(DkT)^{3/2}(1000N_0)^{1/2}} \tag{17}$$

This equation was derived for a 1–1 electrolyte. The expression for the activity coefficient of other types of electrolytes in solutions containing different electrolytes (p. 353) can be derived in a similar manner.

For water at 25°, $\theta = 0.509$.

RELATION BETWEEN THE DIFFUSION COEFFICIENT AND FRICTIONAL COEFFICIENT

(p. 582)

If a system is not in equilibrium, it will move toward equilibrium and the negative gradient of the chemical potential μ may be considered the driving force of diffusion, just as the negative gradient of the gravitational or electrical potential is the driving force in a gravitational or electrical field.

Let us consider diffusion in a rectangular cell in which there is no convection and there is flow due to diffusion only in the x direction. Here the force F per mole of substance is

$$F = -\frac{d\mu}{dx} = -\frac{d\mu}{dc}\frac{dc}{dx} = -\frac{RT}{c}\frac{dc}{dx} \tag{1}$$

for an ideal solution, since $\mu = \mu^* + RT \ln c$, where c is concentration.

Now, according to hydrodynamics, the velocity of a particle in a continuous medium is directly proportional to the applied force, and, by definition, the frictional coefficient f is the force required to give the particle unit velocity.

$$\frac{F}{N_0} = fv \tag{2}$$

where f is the molecular frictional coefficient and v is the velocity. Therefore,

$$v = \frac{F}{N_0 f} = \frac{-RT}{N_0 fc}\frac{dc}{dx} \tag{3}$$

Fick's first law is

$$J = vc = -D\frac{dc}{dx} \tag{4}$$

where J is the flow and D is the diffusion coefficient.

Substituting equation 3 for v yields

$$J = -\frac{RT}{N_0 f}\frac{dc}{dx} = -D\frac{dc}{dx} \tag{5}$$

Therefore,

$$D = \frac{RT}{N_0 f} \tag{6}$$

which is a relation first obtained by Einstein.

ABSOLUTE RATE THEORY

In the Eyring theory * (p. 649) the rate of reaction is taken to be equal to the product of the concentration of activated molecules and the rate of passage over the barrier. The complex flies apart because one of its vibrations becomes a translation.

The equilibrium constant used in the Eyring theory to calculate the concentration of activated molecules $C^{\ddagger}$ is not of the usual type because the complex is in the process of undergoing decomposition and so has an extra degree of freedom. It may be shown * that

$$\frac{C^{\ddagger}}{C_{\text{reactants}}} = K^{\ddagger} \left(\frac{2\pi MRT}{N_0^2 h^2}\right)^{\frac{1}{2}} l \tag{1}$$

where l is a measure of the width of the activated state on the energy surface. Introducing

$$K^{\ddagger} = e^{\Delta S^{\ddagger}/R} e^{-\Delta H^{\ddagger}/RT} \tag{2}$$

from the equations $\Delta G^{\circ\ddagger} = \Delta H^{\ddagger} - T\,\Delta S^{\ddagger} = -RT \ln K^{\ddagger}$, we obtain

$$C^{\ddagger} = \left(\frac{2\pi MRT}{N_0^2 h^2}\right)^{\frac{1}{2}} l e^{\Delta S^{\ddagger}/R} e^{-\Delta H^{\ddagger}/RT} C_{\text{reactants}} \tag{3}$$

The activated molecules are moving along the top of the energy barrier with a velocity $(RT/2\pi M)^{\frac{1}{2}}$, so that the length of time spent in the activated state is $l/(RT/2\pi M)^{\frac{1}{2}}$. Then the rate of the reaction is given by the expression

$$\text{Rate} = kC_{\text{reactants}} = \frac{\kappa C^{\ddagger}}{l/(RT/2\pi M)^{\frac{1}{2}}} \tag{4}$$

where κ, the transmission coefficient, is the probability that a molecule once fully activated will give the products of the reaction. Equation 3 is now substituted into equation 4. The final equation is obtained by solving for k.

$$k = \frac{\kappa RT}{N_0 h} e^{\Delta S^{\ddagger}/R} e^{-\Delta H^{\ddagger}/RT} \tag{5}$$

In calculations the transmission coefficient κ is generally taken equal to unity.

PHYSICAL-CHEMICAL CONSTANTS

The following tables give the recommended values of the fundamental constants for physical chemistry as of July 1, 1951.† They are based upon the reanalysis and re-evaluation of experimental values by DuMond and Cohen.§

* S. Glasstone, K. J. Laidler, and H. Eyring, *The Theory of Rate Processes*, McGraw-Hill Book Co., New York, 1941.

† F. D. Rossini, F. T. Gucker, H. L. Johnston, L. Pauling, and G. W. Vinal, *J. Am. Chem. Soc.*, *74*, 2699 (1952).

§ J. W. M. DuMond and E. R. Cohen, *Phys. Rev.*, *82*, 555 (1951).

Table I. Values of the Basic Constants

Velocity of light	c	$2.997902 \pm 0.000013 \times 10^{10}$ cm sec^{-1}
Planck constant	h	$6.62377 \pm 0.00027 \times 10^{-27}$ erg sec
Avogadro number		
Chemical scale		
(0 = 16.0000)	N_0	$6.0238 \pm 0.0001 \times 10^{23}$ mole^{-1}
Physical scale		
(0^{16} = 16.0000)	N_0'	$6.0254 \pm 0.0001 \times 10^{23}$ mole^{-1}
Faraday constant	F	$96,493 \pm 1$ coulombs equiv^{-1}
		$23,062.4 \pm 0.3$ cal (volt equiv)$^{-1}$
Absolute temperature of		
the "ice" point, 0°C	$T_{0°C}$	$273.16 \pm 0.01°$K *
Pressure-volume prod-	$(PV)_{T_0°}^{P=0}$	$22,414.6 \pm 0.4$ cm^3 atm mole^{-1}
uct for 1 mole of a gas		22.4140 ± 0.0004 liter-atm mole^{-1}
at 0° and zero pressure		2271.16 ± 0.04 joules mole^{-1}

Table II. Values of the Derived Constants

Electronic charge	$e = \dfrac{F}{N_0}$	1.60186×10^{-19} coulomb
		1.60186×10^{-20} emu
		4.8022×10^{-10} esu
Gas constant	$R = \dfrac{(PV)_{T_0°}^{P=0}}{T_0°}$	1.9872 cal deg^{-1} mole^{-1}
		82.057 cm^3 atm deg^{-1} mole^{-1}
		0.082054 l-atm deg^{-1} mole^{-1}
		8.3144 joules deg^{-1} mole^{-1}
Boltzmann constant	$k = \dfrac{R}{N_0}$	1.38026×10^{-16} erg deg^{-1}

Table III. Values of the Defined Constants

Standard gravity	980.665 cm sec^{-2}
Standard atmosphere	$1,013,250$ dynes cm^{-2}
Standard millimeter of mercury pressure	$\frac{1}{760}$ atm
Calorie (thermochemical)	4.1840 joules
	4.18331 international joules
	41.2929 cm^3 atm
	0.0412917 l-atm

* The temperature of the triple point is now defined as 273.16°K, and therefore the temperature of the ice point becomes 273.15°K (*Temperature: Its Measurement and Control in Science and Industry*, Vol. II, p. 125, Reinhold Publishing Co., New York, 1955).

Conversion Factors for Energy

	Ergs	Joules	Calories	Electron Volts	Kilowatt-Hours
1 erg =	1	10^{-7}	2.389×10^{-8}	6.242×10^{11}	2.778×10^{-14}
1 joule =	10^7	1	2.389×10^{-1}	6.242×10^{18}	2.778×10^{-7}
1 cal =	4.184×10^7	4.184	1	2.612×10^{19}	1.162×10^{-6}
1 ev =	1.602×10^{-12}	1.602×10^{-19}	3.829×10^{-20}	1	4.450×10^{-26}
1 kw-hr =	3.600×10^{13}	3.600×10^6	8.604×10^5	2.247×10^{25}	1

Conversion Factors for Energy per Molecule or per Mole

	Erg Molecule^{-1}	Joules Mole^{-1}	Kcal Mole^{-1}	Electron Volts	Centi-meters^{-1}
1 erg molecule^{-1} =	1	6.024×10^{16}	1.4397×10^{13}	6.243×10^{11}	5.036×10^{15}
1 joule mole^{-1} =	1.660×10^{-17}	1	2.389×10^{-4}	1.036×10^{-5}	8.360×10^{-2}
1 kcal mole^{-1} =	6.946×10^{-14}	4.184×10^3	1	4.336×10^{-2}	3.498×10^2
1 ev =	1.602×10^{-12}	9.649×10^4	23,060	1	8.067×10^3
1 cm^{-1} =	1.986×10^{-16}	1.196×10	2.859×10^{-3}	1.240×10^{-4}	1

GREEK ALPHABET

A	α	Alpha	N	ν	Nu
B	β	Beta	Ξ	ξ	Xi
Γ	γ	Gamma	O	o	Omicron
Δ	δ	Delta	Π	π	Pi
E	ϵ	Epsilon	P	ρ	Rho
Z	ζ	Zeta	Σ	σ	Sigma
H	η	Eta	T	τ	Tau
Θ	θ	Theta	Υ	υ	Upsilon
I	ι	Iota	Φ	ϕ	Phi
K	κ	Kappa	X	χ	Chi
Λ	λ	Lambda	Ψ	ψ	Psi
M	μ	Mu	Ω	ω	Omega

PHYSICAL CHEMISTRY

International Atomic Weights

1956–1957

Journal of the American Chemical Society

	Sym-bol	Atomic Number	Atomic Weight ^{a}		Sym-bol	Atomic Number	Atomic Weight ^{a}
Actinium	Ac	89	...	Mercury	Hg	80	200.61
Aluminum	Al	13	26.98	Molybdenum	Mo	42	95.95
Americium	Am	95	...	Neodymium	Nd	60	144.27
Antimony	Sb	51	121.76	Neon	Ne	10	20.183
Argon	Ar	18	39.944	Neptunium	Np	93	...
Arsenic	As	33	74.91	Nickel	Ni	28	58.71
Astatine	At	85	...	Niobium	Nb	41	92.91
Barium	Ba	56	137.36	Nitrogen	N	7	14.008
Berkelium	Bk	97	...	Nobelium	No	102	
Beryllium	Be	4	9.013	Osmium	Os	76	190.2
Bismuth	Bi	83	209.00	Oxygen	O	8	16
Boron	B	5	10.82	Palladium	Pd	46	106.4
Bromine	Br	35	79.916	Phosphorus	P	15	30.975
Cadmium	Cd	48	112.41	Platinum	Pt	78	195.09
Calcium	Ca	20	40.08	Plutonium	Pu	94	...
Californium	Cf	98	...	Polonium	Po	84	...
Carbon	C	6	12.011	Potassium	K	19	39.100
Cerium	Ce	58	140.13	Praseodymium	Pr	59	140.92
Cesium	Cs	55	132.91	Promethium	Pm	61	...
Chlorine	Cl	17	35.457	Protactinium	Pa	91	...
Chromium	Cr	24	52.01	Radium	Ra	88	...
Cobalt	Co	27	58.94	Radon	Rn	86	...
Copper	Cu	29	63.54	Rhenium	Re	75	186.22
Curium	Cm	96	...	Rhodium	Rh	45	102.91
Dysprosium	Dy	66	162.51	Rubidium	Rb	37	85.48
Einsteinium	Es	99	...	Ruthenium	Ru	44	101.1
Erbium	Er	68	167.27	Samarium	Sm	62	150.35
Europium	Eu	63	152.0	Scandium	Sc	21	44.96
Fermium	Fm	100	...	Selenium	Se	34	78.96
Fluorine	F	9	19.00	Silicon	Si	14	28.09
Francium	Fr	87	...	Silver	Ag	47	107.880
Gadolinium	Gd	64	157.26	Sodium	Na	11	22.991
Gallium	Ga	31	69.72	Strontium	Sr	38	87.63
Germanium	Ge	32	72.60	Sulfur	S	16	32.066 ^{b}
Gold	Au	79	197.0	Tantalum	Ta	73	180.95
Hafnium	Hf	72	178.50	Technetium	Tc	43	...
Helium	He	2	4.003	Tellurium	Te	52	127.61
Holmium	Ho	67	164.94	Terbium	Tb	65	158.93
Hydrogen	H	1	1.0080	Thallium	Tl	81	204.39
Indium	In	49	114.82	Thorium	Th	90	232.05
Iodine	I	53	126.91	Thulium	Tm	69	168.94
Iridium	Ir	77	192.2	Tin	Sn	50	118.70
Iron	Fe	26	55.85	Titanium	Ti	22	47.90
Krypton	Kr	36	83.80	Tungsten	W	74	183.86
Lanthanum	La	57	138.92	Uranium	U	92	238.07
Lead	Pb	82	207.21	Vanadium	V	23	50.95
Lithium	Li	3	6.940	Xenon	Xe	54	131.30
Lutetium	Lu	71	174.99	Ytterbium	Yb	70	173.04
Magnesium	Mg	12	24.32	Yttrium	Y	39	88.92
Manganese	Mn	25	54.94	Zinc	Zn	30	65.38
Mendelevium	Md	101	...	Zirconium	Zr	40	91.22

^{a} Mass numbers for radioactive elements are omitted except for naturally occurring uranium and thorium and for certain other elements that are only very slightly radioactive.

^{b} Because of natural variations in relative abundance of the sulfur isotopes, its atomic weight has a range of ± 0.003.

INDEX

LOGARITHMS

Natural Numbers	0	1	2	3	4	5	6	7	8	9	PROPORTIONAL PARTS								
											1	2	3	4	5	6	7	8	9
10	0000	0043	0086	0128	0170	0212	0253	0294	0334	0374	4	8	12	17	21	25	29	33	37
11	0414	0453	0492	0531	0569	0607	0645	0682	0719	0755	4	8	11	15	19	23	26	30	34
12	0792	0828	0864	0899	0934	0969	1004	1038	1072	1106	3	7	10	14	17	21	24	28	31
13	1139	1173	1206	1239	1271	1303	1335	1367	1399	1430	3	6	10	13	16	19	23	26	29
14	1461	1492	1523	1553	1584	1614	1644	1673	1703	1732	3	6	9	12	15	18	21	24	27
15	1761	1790	1818	1847	1875	1903	1931	1959	1987	2014	3	6	8	11	14	17	20	22	25
16	2041	2068	2095	2122	2148	2175	2201	2227	2253	2279	3	5	8	11	13	16	18	21	24
17	2304	2330	2355	2380	2405	2430	2455	2480	2504	2529	2	5	7	10	12	15	17	20	22
18	2553	2577	2601	2625	2648	2672	2695	2718	2742	2765	2	5	7	9	12	14	16	19	21
19	2788	2810	2833	2856	2878	2900	2923	2945	2967	2989	2	4	7	9	11	13	16	18	20
20	3010	3032	3054	3075	3096	3118	3139	3160	3181	3201	2	4	6	8	11	13	15	17	19
21	3222	3243	3263	3284	3304	3324	3345	3365	3385	3404	2	4	6	8	10	12	14	16	18
22	3424	3444	3464	3483	3502	3522	3541	3560	3579	3598	2	4	6	8	10	12	14	15	17
23	3617	3636	3655	3674	3692	3711	3729	3747	3766	3784	2	4	6	7	9	11	13	15	17
24	3802	3820	3838	3856	3874	3892	3909	3927	3945	3962	2	4	5	7	9	11	12	14	16
25	3979	3997	4014	4031	4048	4065	4082	4099	4116	4133	2	3	5	7	9	10	12	14	15
26	4150	4166	4183	4200	4216	4232	4249	4265	4281	4298	2	3	5	7	8	10	11	13	15
27	4314	4330	4346	4362	4378	4393	4409	4425	4440	4456	2	3	5	6	8	9	11	13	14
28	4472	4487	4502	4518	4533	4548	4564	4579	4594	4609	2	3	5	6	8	9	11	12	14
29	4624	4639	4654	4669	4683	4698	4713	4728	4742	4757	1	3	4	6	7	9	10	12	13
30	4771	4786	4800	4814	4829	4843	4857	4871	4886	4900	1	3	4	6	7	9	10	11	13
31	4914	4928	4942	4955	4969	4983	4997	5011	5024	5038	1	3	4	6	7	8	10	11	12
32	5051	5065	5079	5092	5105	5119	5132	5145	5159	5172	1	3	4	5	7	8	9	11	12
33	5185	5198	5211	5224	5237	5250	5263	5276	5289	5302	1	3	4	5	6	8	9	10	12
34	5315	5328	5340	5353	5366	5378	5391	5403	5416	5428	1	3	4	5	6	8	9	10	11
35	5441	5453	5465	5478	5490	5502	5514	5527	5539	5551	1	2	4	5	6	7	9	10	11
36	5563	5575	5587	5599	5611	5623	5635	5647	5658	5670	1	2	4	5	6	7	8	10	11
37	5682	5694	5705	5717	5729	5740	5752	5763	5775	5786	1	2	3	5	6	7	8	9	10
38	5798	5809	5821	5832	5843	5855	5866	5877	5888	5899	1	2	3	5	6	7	8	9	10
39	5911	5922	5933	5944	5955	5966	5977	5988	5999	6010	1	2	3	4	5	7	8	9	10
40	6021	6031	6042	6053	6064	6075	6085	6096	6107	6117	1	2	3	4	5	6	8	9	10
41	6128	6138	6149	6160	6170	6180	6191	6201	6212	6222	1	2	3	4	5	6	7	8	9
42	6232	6243	6253	6263	6274	6284	6294	6304	6314	6325	1	2	3	4	5	6	7	8	9
43	6335	6345	6355	6365	6375	6385	6395	6405	6415	6425	1	2	3	4	5	6	7	8	9
44	6435	6444	6454	6464	6474	6484	6493	6503	6513	6522	1	2	3	4	5	6	7	8	9
45	6532	6542	6551	6561	6571	6580	6590	6599	6609	6618	1	2	3	4	5	6	7	8	9
46	6628	6637	6646	6656	6665	6675	6684	6693	6702	6712	1	2	3	4	5	6	7	7	8
47	6721	6730	6739	6749	6758	6767	6776	6785	6794	6803	1	2	3	4	5	5	6	7	8
48	6812	6821	6830	6839	6848	6857	6866	6875	6884	6893	1	2	3	4	4	5	6	7	8
49	6902	6911	6920	6928	6937	6946	6955	6964	6972	6981	1	2	3	4	4	5	6	7	8
50	6990	6998	7007	7016	7024	7033	7042	7050	7059	7067	1	2	3	3	4	5	6	7	8
51	7076	7084	7093	7101	7110	7118	7126	7135	7143	7152	1	2	3	3	4	5	6	7	8
52	7160	7168	7177	7185	7193	7202	7210	7218	7226	7235	1	2	2	3	4	5	6	7	7
53	7243	7251	7259	7267	7275	7284	7292	7300	7308	7316	1	2	2	3	4	5	6	6	7
54	7324	7332	7340	7348	7356	7364	7372	7380	7388	7396	1	2	2	3	4	5	6	6	7